Solid State Dosimetry

Solid State Dosimetry

Edited by

S. AMELINCKX

*Institute of Physics, University of Brussels
and S.C.K. — C.E.N., Mol, Belgium*

B. BATZ

Institute of Physics, University of Brussels, Belgium

R. STRUMANE

S.C.K. — C.E.N., Mol, Belgium

*Proceedings of the NATO Summer School held at
Brussels, Belgium, September 4–16, 1967*

GORDON AND BREACH SCIENCE PUBLISHERS
New York   London   Paris

Editorial office for the United Kingdom:
  Gordon and Breach, Science Publishers Ltd.
  12 Bloomsbury Way
  London W.C. 1

Editorial office for France:
  Gordon & Breach
  7–9 rue Emile Dubois
  Paris 14^e

Distributed in Canada by:
  The Ryerson Press
  299 Queen Street West
  Toronto 2B, Ontario

Contents

Introduction

It is well known that in recent years nuclear energy has become competitive as a source of electricity and in certain circumstances, even of drinking water, especially when both are produced simultaneously. A rapid increase in the number of nuclear power stations is therefore to be expected in the near future. In Belgium in particular, all future large power stations will very probably nuclear.

The use of radioisotopes and of other sources of ionizing radiation, such as X-ray generators, has been increasing steadily during the last decade and no decrease in the rate of increase is to be expected in a foreseeable future.

On the other hand, recent advances in our knowledge concerning the effects of radiation on living beings has caused an increased conscientiousness of the hazards that accompany exposure to ionizing radiation or to neutrons. Taking these two statements together it becomes evident that there will be a rapidly growing demand for qualified personnel and for instrumentation allowing an efficient control and adequate monitoring of the radiation levels to which workers are exposed. In a number of countries laws have been passed that regulate strictly all activities that may lead to exposure to radiation of workers and of the population living in the vicinity of radiation sources. For all these reasons we felt that it would be worth while to have competent speakers present the recent advances in the field of radiation dosimetry. We felt that especially the more recent methods based on solid state phenomena would attract attention.

Roughly speaking, two types of radiation measurements can be performed. One can either measure the instantaneous radiation level, for instance by means of a counter that detects individual particles, or one can use integrating methods that measure the amount of radiation received after a known interval of time, e.g. with photographic means.

From the title of our summer school it is clear that we shall be mainly interested in the second type of measurement, which is usually called a *dose* measurement as opposed to a *flux* or *dose-rate* measurement. Our interest will however not be limited to the measurement of small doses of interest in health physics. We shall also hear about methods for the measurement of large doses like those that are of interest in the study of radiation effects on materials.

It is well known that all solid materials undergo changes in almost all their physical and chemical properties after irradiation with high energy particles. I shall enumerate just a few that will certainly be mentioned in the course of this school: the colour of alkali halides changes under even weak X-radiation; the electrical resistivity of metals increases under neutron irradiation whereas the internal friction decreases; the yield strength increases; the changes in magnetic properties can be observed as well by resonance experiments as by studying the changes in the magnetization curve; the lattice parameter usually increases whereas the density usually decreases, etc. (dimension changes: graphite e.g. expands in the *c*-direction and contracts in the direction perpendicular to it). We could go on and enumerate practically every physical property that we can think of; all of them change; some only to a very limited extend, others exhibit large changes under irradiation.

When building a reactor it is of course necessary to know such changes in advance so as to be able to take tham into account in the design of the core.

The study of such changes under irradiation is usually termed radiation damage. Studies of radiation damage are obviously of great technological importance. They are performed in materials testing reactors. Here again we are faced with a problem of dosimetry; one wants to know exactly the dose to which a given material has been exposed. Such dose measurements are at present very often performed by activating foils or wires of a given isotope for which the capture cross section is accurately known. However, the dose detected in this way is not necessarily representative of the dose of interest in the radiation damage experiments because neutrons of different energies may be responsible on the one hand for the inducted radioactivity and on the other hand for the damage caused to the material. It would therefore be desirable to have dosimeters based themselves on radiation damage in solids. One could then in principle measure the change of any easily measurable property as a result of the irradiation and calibrate this measurement in terms of neutron dose.

From what follows one can conclude that radiation damage can be considered in the first place as a study which is of interest for its own sake; in other words, because we want to know the behaviour of materials under and after irradiation. However, conversely radiation damage phenomena can be used to measure radiation doses. It is this last aspect which is of particular interest in the context of this course. In the lectures on radiation damage emphasis shall therefore be put on those phenomena which can potentially be used for dosimetry purposes.

We are obviously faced with two main classes of dosimetry problems in two quite different areas of interest: "health physics" on the one hand, and "radiation damage" on the other hand. Although the doses to be measured may be orders of magnitude different and although the methods used may be different as well, the underlying principles are similar because in all cases the effect of radiation on the solid consists in the creation of some kind of defect, electronic or atomic in structure, or the change in the properties of pre-existing defects. In both cases the macroscopic physical properties of the solid are affected and the magnitude of the changes can be used as a measure for the radiation dose received.

From these considerations it becomes clear why we have included in our program a number of lectures on defects in solids and on their influence on various physical properties such as for instance optical, magnetic and electrical. We have further tried to include the basic theory of these esolid state phenomena on which presently used methods for dosimetry are based or from which possibly new methods could be derived.

Further developments in this field may give rise to surprising and unexpected results. I will quote just one example, only a few years ago thermoluminescence was nothing but an interesting basic solid state phenomenon mainly studied for its own sake. At present several firms sell dosimetry systems for health physics purposes based on this phenomenon. A number of nuclear establishments have already adopted this system, which is still capable of further development and refinement. Also it is worth mentioning that thermoluminescence has been developed into a reliable method for dating objects of archeological interest.

Let me now say a few words about the organisation of the course. We have tried to proceed along the following general scheme for our two week program. During the first week we have scheduled whenever possible the courses which serve as a theoretical basis for the understanding of the practical methods which will mainly be treated during the second week of the

PART I

Introduction

_____

CHAPTER I–1

Introduction to crystal defects

Y. QUÈRÈ

Centre d'études nucléaires de Fontenay-aux-Roses

---

1   THE NATURE OF CRYSTALS

1.1   Crystal structure

A crystal is an agglomerate of atoms—or molecules—characterized by a 3-fold periodicity.

To describe completely a crystal one has to define precisely the positions of atoms—or molecules—inside a *unit cell*, built on 3 vectors $\mathbf{a}_i$ ($i = 1, 2, 3$) of arbitrary origin. All the atoms of the crystal will be obtained from the atoms of the unit cell by all the translations $\mathbf{t}$

$$\mathbf{t} = \sum \alpha_i \mathbf{a}_i \tag{1}$$

the α_i being all the integers positive or negative (see an example of planar crystals in Fig. 1).

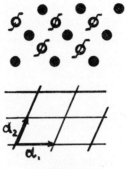

FIGURE 1

Very often the symmetry of the atomic arrangement is high. In these cases, the 3 vectors $\mathbf{a}_i$ are not just any vectors; for instance in cubic crystals $\mathbf{a}_i\mathbf{a}_j = \delta_{ij}$ (Fig. 2). Cubic crystals are generally either face centered (f.c.c.) or body centered (b.c.c.) or have the diamond structure which is made of two interpenetrating f.c.c. structures.

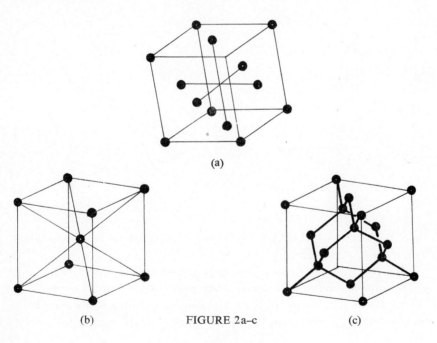

(a)

(b)   FIGURE 2a–c   (c)

There are 7 crystal systems: cubic, rhomboedral, hexagonal, tetragonal, orthorhombic, monoclinic and triclinic.

The points in space defined by the relation (1), applied from an arbitrary origin, constitute the Bravais lattice. The structure of the lattice is obviously made of straight lines and planes. If the origin of the lattice is situated at the center of an atom, these lines and planes are meterialized by *atomic rows* and *atomic planes*.

1.2   Crystal bonding

One generally classifies the solids through the type of chemical bonding between the atoms.

Ionic crystals may be correctly described in classical physics. One (or several) electron(s) is given by an electropositive atom (Na for instance) to a nearby electronegative atom (Cl for instance). The result is the existence of ions of opposite signs (Cl^-: anion. Na^+: cation) and spherical (having their s and p shells complete). Each ion is surrounded by ions of opposite sign, which result in a strong electrostatic attraction. The equilibrium distance between ions results from a compromise between this attraction and the repulsion of internal electronic shells of the ions.

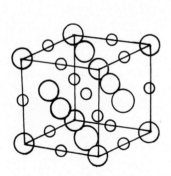 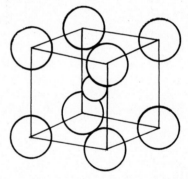

FIGURE 3

One may expect a high symmetry in such a packing. As a matter of fact, the NaCl structure and the CsCl structure are the prototypes of most of the simple ionic crystals (Fig. 3).

The other types of bonding have to be studied with quantum physics.

The *covalent bonding* is due to the decrease of energy of electrons shared by several atoms. The prototype is the H_2 molecule bonding where 2 electrons are shared by 2 atoms with the formation of 2 levels: one of low energy (binding) and one of high energy (anti-binding) (Fig. 4). In case of solide, more than 2 electrons are shared, but the principle is the same. In the case of diamond (or G or Si) 4 electrons of one atom are shared with its four nearest neighbours, each of which shares 4 electrons, etc. This builds a huge covalent molecule of cubic symmetry.

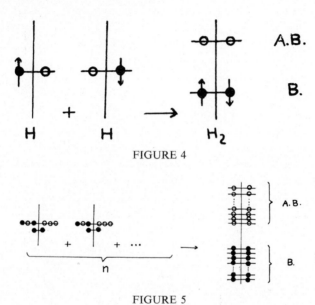

FIGURE 4

FIGURE 5

In the case of the H_2 molecule, the initially unique energy level of the H atom was split during the bonding, in 2 separate levels. For the $4n$ electrons of a crystal of n C (or Ge) atoms, one has a splitting in $4n$ levels of which $2n$ are binding and $2n$ anti-binding. These levels are grouped in 2 distinct bands (Fig. 5). The $4n$ electrons just occupy the $2n$ binding levels (lower or valence band) which explains the binding, and also the insulating properties of diamond: the $4n$ electrons are bound to remain on these levels.

Let us suppose that the two bands overlap: they constitute then a unique band in which now, the electrons are relatively free to move and to change their energy slightly. This is the case of the *metallic bonding* where 1 (Na, Cu...) 2 (Zn...), etc. electrons per atom can be treated as a gas of particles obeying the Pauli principle and which are contained in the "box" made by the positive ions (Cu^+, Zn^{++}...). Here again the equilibrium distance between these ions is a compromise between the "attraction" due to the electrons filling the conduction band thus reducing their energy, and the repulsion between the positive ions. Here again a high symmetry is expected due to the sphericity of ions such as Cu^+ or Zn^{++}: most of the metals have f.c.c. (Cu, Ni, Al, Pt, Au...), c.c. (Mo, Fe α, W...) or hexagonal (Mg, Ti, Zr...) structures.

Some atoms (or molecules) have no electron to give to their neighbour and none even to share with them: it is the case of noble gasses (He, Ne, Ar...) or of covalent molecules (H_2, N_2...). However, these elements have a solid (and crystalline) state though the melting points (related to the bonding) are generally low. The bonding here is due to *Van der Wals–London forces* a purely quantum effect which may be described as due to electrical dipoles induced on each atom (or molecule) by the polarisability of the electronic clouds.

This classification is unfortunately an over-simplification. Some crystals may belong to two classes. The example of graphite is well known: here only three instead of four in diamond) electrons are shared with 3 neighbours in a plane which is then a covalent, tightly bound, plane. But the fourth electron, nearly free between the covalent planes, gives to graphite a metallic character.

Moreover, inside of one class the physical properties may vary strongly. One of the most important examples is the presence among covalent crystals of *insulating* crystals (dielectrics) like diamond but also of *semi conductors*, like Si or Ge. A crystal is a semi conductor if the "gap" of energy ΔE between the top of the valence band and the bottom of the conduction band is low enough to permit some electrons to be thermally excited from one band to the other.

In the same way, if the two bands overlap, but very slightly, ($\Delta E \lesssim 0$) one has a *semi metal* like Bi.

Thus there is a rather smooth continuity between pure dielectrics and pure metals through semi conductors and semi metals. This explains why covalent crystals may have some of the metallic characters (silicium), and why metallic crystals may exhibit some typical covalent bonds (titanium carbide).

Anyway, having said that a correct description of the bonding in ionic crystals may be obtained in classical electrostatics, this should not lead to the idea that these crystals do not present any quantic behaviour. In fact the electrons given by the positive ions to the negative ions just fill, in a perfect crystal a band called the *anion band*. Some of these electrons may be excited in a band of higher energy called the *cation band*, leaving in the anion band as many *holes*, and leading to a conduction of charges. The excitation corresponds to the jumps of an electron from an anion (e.g. Cl^-) to a cation (e.g. Na^+) leaving two neutral (Cl and Na) atoms. The conduction corresponds to the jump both of the electron from cation to cation in the cation band and of the hole from anion to anion in the anion band.

By introducing the density of states in the different bands, that is the number $n(E)$ such that $n(E)\,dE$ is the number of states (occupied or not) between the energies E and $E + dE$, we can summarize on Fig. 6 some of the main types of chemical bondings in crystals.

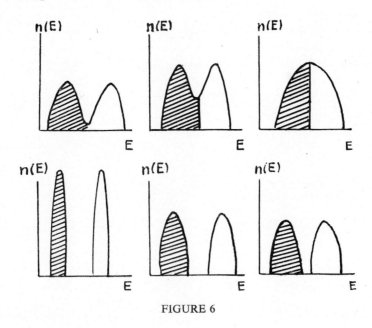

FIGURE 6

2   DEFECTS IN CRYSTALS

2.1   Definitions

There is an obvious reason above all others why perfect periodicity implied by (1) is impossible: the atoms are never at rest. An atom at rest would contradict the Heisenberg relation since one would then know simultaneously its position and its velocity v ($v = 0$). The thermal vibrations then make it impossible to obey (1). We may only speak of an average (or equilibrium) position—which we can call the atomic site—as obeying (1) and hope that the atom is not very far from this site. As a matter of fact the distance Δ a between the atom and the site is such that $\dfrac{\Delta a}{a}$ is small (a being the average nearest neighbouring-distance) and will only reach about 1/10 at its maximum (near the melting point).

There is a second obvious impossibility for (1): luckily the crystals are never infinite. They are limited by free surfaces. These free surfaces are the first and the most unavoidable type of crystal defects. As we shall see, there are many other defects in a real crystal.

The first crystal, defined by (1), is called an *ideal crystal*. The second one, in which only the thermal vibrations disturb the periodicity, is called a *perfect crystal*. The third one which has at least free surfaces, but probably many other disturbances, or *defects*, is a real crystal.

In summarizing, we may write:

Unit cell + relation (1)   → ideal crystal
Ideal crystal + thermal vibration → perfect crystal
Perfect crystal + crystal defects → real crysatl.

2.2   Classification of defects

One generally classifies defects according to their dimension.

1   Dimension: zero. Point defects.

Point defects are essentially concentrated in one, or very few, atomic volumes. We may mention mainly:

Impurities: an atom B in a crystal A. This atom B may have taken the place of an atom A (substitutional impurity) or may be inserted in the crystal in an additional site not belonging to the perfect crystal (interstitial impurity).

Vacancies: a vacancy is the defect obtained if one atom is extracted from its site and not replaced.

Self-interstitials: an atom A inserted in a crystal A in a site not belonging to the perfect crystal. We shall call it more simply: interstitial (Fig. 7).

2   Dimension: one. Dislocations.

Dislocations are lines along which stresses are concentrated in the crystal. They will be defined further (§ 4).

3   Dimension: two. Surface defects.

Let us mention:

Free surfaces

Grain boundaries: the surfaces along which crystallites of different orientations are connected (Fig. 8).

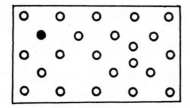

FIGURE 7

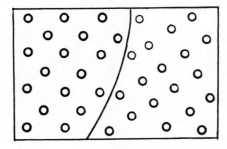

FIGURE 8

Twin boundaries: a spacial case of grain boundary where the 2 parts of the crystal defined by the boundary are deduced from each other by a mirror symmetry.

Stacking faults: a plane along which a part of the crystal has undergone a slight translation relative to the other.

4   Dimension: three. Volume defects.

Let us mention:

Precipitates: clusters (which are generally crystallized) of B atoms in a matrix A.

Bubbles: a special case of precipitates in which the B atoms are gas atoms.

Vacancy (or *interstitial*) *clusters*: agglomerates of point defects.

Amorphous zones: small volumes in which one can no longer speak of crystallinity.

N.B. The distinction between point and volume defects is not always very clear: for instance, when vacancies cluster together to become a cluster, one deals successively with divacancies, trivacancies, etc... Clusters of a few (>5) point defects are still called point defects.

2.3   Existence of defects

2.3.1   *Equilibrium*

The general feature of defects is to create disorder in a normally ordered structure. This means that they increase the configurational entropy of the crystal. It is then normal to expect a thermodynamical equilibrium concentration of defects in any crystal at any temperature $\neq 0$.

For instance, let us consider the case of *impurities*. Let n atoms B be alloyed with $N-n$ atoms A, with a total of N sites. Let us suppose $\dfrac{n}{N} = c \ll 1$.

The presence of n atoms B makes it possible to arrange the atoms A and B in many different ways on the N sites with the associated entropy increase:

$$S = -Nk[c \log c + (1 - c) \log (1 - c)].$$

If ΔE is the energy of one impurity atom in the crystal, the change of free energy is

$$F = N\Delta Ec + NkT[c \log c + (1 - c) \log (1 - c)]$$

which is minimum when

$$\frac{c}{1 - c} = \exp\left(-\frac{\Delta E}{kT}\right). \tag{2}$$

This equation shows that the solubility c cannot be zero and explains why it is so difficult to purify solids.

There is also a change of lattice vibrations around the impurity; so there will be a change of vibrational entropy ΔS_{vib}. If we also take into account the effect of pressure P, we have to write, instead of ΔE

$$\Delta G = \Delta H - T\Delta S_{\text{vib}}$$
$$= \Delta E + P\Delta v - T\Delta S_{\text{vib}},$$

Δv, here, change of volume of the crystal due to one impurity atom, is called the formation volume of the defect. H is the formation enthalpy.

And now:

$$\frac{c}{1-c} = \exp\frac{\Delta S_{\text{vib}}}{k} \cdot \left(-\frac{\Delta H}{kT}\right). \tag{2'}$$

Equation (2') holds for the case of vacancies and more generally, with some changes in the constants, for any type of defect.

But practically, only impurities and vacancies are observed under equilibrium, due to high values of ΔE (and ΔH) for the other defects like interstitials or dislocations.

2.3.2 *Non-equilibrium*

All defects can be observed in metastable equilibrium. Some may be extremely "stable" like grain (or twin) boundaries or dislocations, and exist without any special treatment. But all can be created by out-of-equilibrium—experiments like cold work and irradiation which both displace atoms from their sites.

Most of the defects which will be spoken of during this summer school, will be irradiation defects.

3   POINT DEFECTS

3.1   Impurities

3.1.1   *Electronic structure*

The introduction of an impurity atom in a crystal must not alter the electrical neutrality of the crystal.

In an *ionic crystal* a substitutional cation of valence m different from the valence n of the normal cation has to replace locally $\frac{m}{n}$ initial cations. For example in a NaCl crystal a Ca^{++} cation must take the place of 2 Na^{+} cations. This means that one should expect a substitutional Ca^{++} cation to be adjacent to a Na^{+} vacancy (Fig. 9). Substitution of a homovalent cation leads to no electronic complication (K^{+} in NaCl).

In *covalent crystals* (e.g. valence 4) a substitutional atom B of valence $4 + v$ yields 4 electrons for the covalent bonding (in the valence band) with 4 neighbours A. v electrons are left which are submitted to the attractive potential of the extra v positive charges of the nucleus of B. These v electrons behave roughly like the electrons in an atom of atomic number v and of dieelectric constant K, the one of the crystal. If $v = 1$ (As in a Ge crystal) there is one extra electron rotating on a hydrogenoid orbital (Fig. 10).

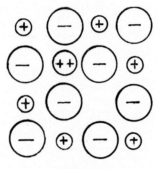

FIGURE 9

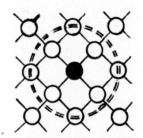

FIGURE 10

The energy levels of these electrons are above the fully occupied bonding levels (valence band) but below the antibonding levels (conduction band). They occupy discrete levels slightly below the conduction band in which they can be rather easily excited.

If v is negative (Ga in Ge: $v = -1$) the B atom is surrounded by-v holes having levels slightly above the valence band. Electrons of this band can be easily excidet on these levels (Fig. 11).

For $v > 0$ the impurity is called donor. The conductivity corresponding to the migration of the n electrons from atom to atom on antibonding orbitals is called n-conductivity.

For $v < 0$ the impurity is called acceptor. The conductivity due to the motion of holes is called *p*-conductivity.

In *metals*—which are conductors—the introduction of an impurity *B* of valence *m* different from the valence *n* of the metal *A* must not introduce

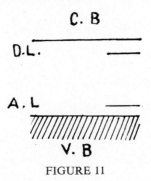

FIGURE 11

any electrostatic field in the limits of classical physics. This implies that the extra charge $-(m-n)e$ situated on the nucleus of *B* should be screened in a volume more or less as small as the atomic volume. The screening could be thought due to the *m–n* electrons bound to the *B* nucleus, but this is no longer possible, the levels of these electrons being now merged in the quasi continuous conduction band of the metal.

This means that the *m–n* electrons are given by the *B* atom to the whole of the quasi free electron gas and that the screening is due to a local deformation of this gas around (and very close to) the impurity. There will be a local increase of electonic density arrund a Zn atom Cu ($m–n=1$), a local decrease of electronic density around a Cu atom in Al ($m-n = -2$).

This deformation is accompanied by a diffraction effect which modulates the variation of charge density around the impurity (Fig. 12).

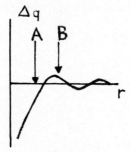

FIGURE 12

3.1.2   *Elastic effect*

Although we said that point defects are concentrated in practically one atomic volume, it should not be concluded that their long range action is negligible. An impurity atom produces a local distortion (change of volume) and this distortion is transmitted to the whole crystal.

The easiest way to study this action is to use the elastic theory in which the crystal is assimilated to a continous medium. In linear elasticity (distortion linear with stresses) and for an isotropic medium the solution of the elasticity equation for a punctual source of distortion leads to

$$\rho = \alpha \frac{\mathbf{r}}{r^3}, \tag{3}$$

ρ is the displacement vector due to the impurity of "force" α (Fig. 13).

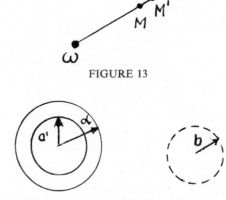

FIGURE 13

FIGURE 14

The elastic equivalent for an impurity is given by the inclusion-in-hole model (Fig. 14) where aspherical inclusion is inserted in a hole of different radius (a and a'). Hole and inclusion are then stuck together at some intermediate equilibrium radius b.

In these conditions and for an infinite medium one finds

$$\mathbf{v} \cdot \alpha = \frac{-v}{12} \frac{1+v}{1-v}, \tag{4}$$

where v is the difference of volume between hole and inclusion and v the Poisson's ratio of the elastic medium $\left(v \simeq \dfrac{1}{3} \right)$.

From (3) and (4) one calculates the stresses due to the point defect and then the elastic energy stored in the medium. ΔE

$$\Delta E = \frac{x}{x+1} 8\pi\mu b^3 \eta^2 ,$$

where $x = \dfrac{1+\nu}{2(1-2\nu)}$; $\eta = \dfrac{a'-a}{b}$ is called size factor of the inclusion. μ is the shear modulus.

If the inclusion has elastic constants different from those of the matrix, one has

$$\Delta E = \frac{x}{x + \dfrac{X'}{X}} 8\pi\mu b^3 \eta^2 , \tag{5}$$

where X and X' are the compressibilities of the matrix and the inclusion.

To apply this model to a substitutional impurity $a =$ the atomic radius in the matrix and $a' =$ the atomic radius of B in a pure B crystal are taken. One also takes for X' the compressibility of a pure B crystal which is a rough approximation.

According to (5), the energy ΔE increases as the square of η. This gives a qualitative explanation of Hume-Rothery's rule according to which the solubility of an element in another one is always very small if the size factor is larger than 0.15.

The elastic theory may be used to calculate the change of volume and of elastic constants due to the impurity atom. One obtains

$$\frac{1}{3} \frac{dV}{V \, dc} = \frac{da}{a \, dc} = \lambda \frac{a'-a}{a}$$

$$\frac{dX}{X \, dc} = \lambda \frac{X'-X}{X} , \tag{6}$$

$\dfrac{dV}{V}, \dfrac{da}{a}, \dfrac{dX}{X}$ are respectively the changes of volume, of lattice parameter, of compressibility, due to a concentration dc of impurities characterized by a lattice parameter a' and a compressibility $X' \cdot \lambda = \dfrac{1+x}{\dfrac{X'}{X}+x}$ where $x = \dfrac{1+\nu}{2(1-2\nu)}$.

2 Amelinckx (1347)

One finds on Fig. 15 and 16 the variations of α and X given by (6). If $X' = X$, there is a linear variations of lattice parameter between the two values a and a'. This is Vegard's law. If $X' \neq X$ one will notice that the variation of a and of X is governed by the harder material.

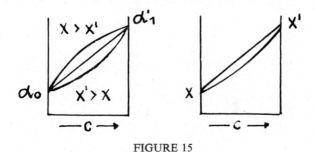

FIGURE 15

3.2 Vacancies and interstitials

3.2.1 *Electronic structure*

Many types of vacancies can be observed in *ionic crystals*. We shall mainly describe them in the simple case of alkali halides A^+B^-.

According to 3.1.1 an anion vacancy is expected to be associated with a cation vacancy. This pair which preserves the neutrality is produced by the extraction of a "molecule" A^+B^- (Fig. 16) and is called a Schottky defect.

In the same way an interstitial cation plus a cation vacancy is called a Frenkel defect. "Negative" Frenkel defects may also exist but with a very high elastic energy due to the size of the anion interstitial.

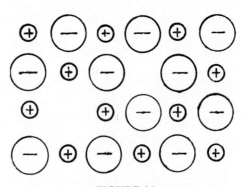

FIGURE 16

An anion (e.g. Cl⁻) vacancy is called an α centre. We expect it to be very electronegative: an α centre $+a$ bound hydrogenoïd electron is called an F centre: F like Farbe because the absorption of light due to the excitation of this electron produces colour (these centres are called colour centres).

"Symmetric"—one says antimorph—of the F centre, the V_F centre consists in a hole bound on a cation (e.g. Na⁺) vacancy. The F' centre consists of 2 electrons trapped on an α center.

The V_K centre is a hole trapped on a halide ion. This centre which does not involve any vacancy or interstitial is in fact distributed on 2 neighbour halides which are pulled slightly together by the resulting interaction.

The vacancies may migrate when an adjacent ion jumps into it. This results in the possibility for vacancies to join and to form clusters.

An α centre migrating to an F centre creates an F_2^+ centre. One shows that a strong vocalent bonding (much stronger than the electrostatic one) exists between the α centre and the F centre as soon as the 2 centre are a few

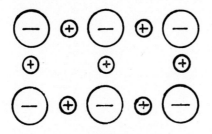

FIGURE 17

atomic distances apart (Fig. 17). The resulting attractive energy favours the encounter of the two vacancies. One may write the equation

$$\alpha + F \rightarrow F_2^+$$

and then

$$\alpha + F_2 \rightarrow F_3^+$$

where the F_2 (or M) centre has been created by capture of an electron:

$$F_2^+ + e \rightarrow F_2.$$

One also observes, in KCl, the reaction

$$F + F \rightarrow F_2$$

also favoured by a covalent link between the two F centers.

2*

Bigger vacancy aggregates are created by similar reactions.

The main interstitial centre are the H centre (an anion interstitial) and the I centre (a cation interstitial). The latter has been observed in irradiated LiF where it is shown to combine with a Li^+ cation to form a Li_2^+ molecule situated on a $\langle 110 \rangle$ direction the two positive ions being bound in a co-valent way.

In *covalent crystals* a vacancy breaks four bonds (in tetravalent crystals). These bonds become strongly electronegative: they accept electrons and then give rise to acceptor levels.

As a rough approximation one may equate the vacancy formation energy E_f to the cohesive energy E_c. By breaking 4 bonds, one creates a vacancy and a vapour atom, whereas one needs to break only 2 bonds per atom to break the crystal into atoms. So that:

$$E_f + E_c = \text{energy of 4 bonds} = 2E_c \rightarrow E_f = E_c.$$

Two adjacent vacancies form a divacancy which most probably has an acceptor character as above.

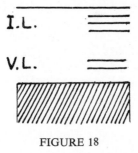

FIGURE 18

One may notice that if the migration of the vacancy is simple (jump of a neighbour atom in the vacancy thanks to a distortion of the covalent bonds) the mechanism of migration of a divacancy must be complex since the 2 vacancies of a divacancy have no common neighbour in the diamond structure. The divacancy must dissociate to migrate, which requires a high energy.

An interstitial atom has very little space in the densely packed diamond structure. It is likely that this atom thus turns into a smaller positive ion surrounded by one or several electrons situated on donor levels (Fig. 18).

In a *metal* of valency p a vacancy may be vizualized as a virtual negative charge $-p|e|$ on the site of the vacancy. The *energy E_f* may then be separated in two parts:

—a positive contribution E_1 due to the influence on all the conduction electrons of the repulsive potential associated with the virtual charge;

—a negative contribution E_2 due to the increase of volume of the crystal when an atom is taken from the inside and put on the surface.

It may be shown that in the free electrons model, $E_1 = \frac{2}{3} pE_F$, $E_2 = -\frac{2}{5} pE_F$ so that

$$E_f = \frac{4}{15} pE_F,$$

where E_F is the Fermi energy of the metal. For Ag ($p = 1$) one finds $E_f = 1.45$ eV; (E_f experim $= 1.06$ eV).

In a monovalent metal, the positive ions (e.g. Ag^+) just around the vacancy are attracted by the virtual negative charge: the *size effect* of the vacancy consists locally in a collapse of the atoms *towards* the vacancy. But in a trivalent metal, the charge oscillations (see Fig. 12) are such that the ions in the position of first neighbour of the vacancy "see" an inversed virtual charge which appears to them as positive: these ions have then probably a slight movement *outwards*.

A divacancy consists of two neighbouring vacancies and here contrary-wise to the case of covalent crystals, the movement of a divacancy is easier than the one of a vacancy, at least for f.c.c. metals.

The electronic configuration of the interstital is poorly known. One may treat this defect as an impurity of supplementary valence $+p$. Most of the energy may probably be evaluated in the elastic model.

3.2.2 *Elastic effects*

The results obtained in 3.1.1 may be directly applied to the case of vacancies and interstitials. The vacancy is taken as a soft impurity ($X' = \infty$) of atomic size a' slightly smaller than that of the matrix (size effects: § 3.2.1). The interstitial is taken as an inclusion identical to the matrix ($X' = X$) forced into a very small hole of the matrix ($a \ll a'$).

The interstitial is then found to have a high energy ($\simeq 5$ eV). In f.c.c. metals its configuration is quite probably split in a $\langle 100 \rangle$ direction: it consists of 2 atoms sharing the site of a vacancy. This configuration gives to the interstitial a cylindrical, rather than a spherical, symmetry. (Fig. 7).

Other configurations, like the crowdion (splitting in a ⟨110⟩ direction), may be metastable at very low temperatures.

The vacancy is found to decrease the density, the lattice parameter (except for trivalent metals), and to increase the compressibility X (Fig. 19).

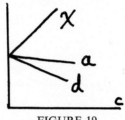

FIGURE 19

For concentrations c_i and c_v of interstitials and vacancies, the following important expression is obtained:

$$c_i - c_v = 3\left(\frac{\Delta L}{L} - \frac{\Delta a}{a}\right),$$

where $\dfrac{\Delta L}{L}$ and $\dfrac{\Delta a}{a}$ are the changes of length and lattice parameter due to the presence of these defects. If there are as many vacancies as interstitials one has

$$\frac{\Delta L}{L} = \frac{\Delta a}{a} \quad \text{(Fig. 20)}.$$

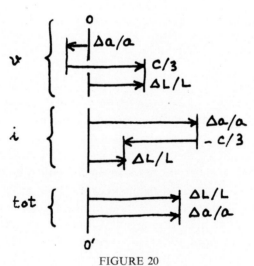

FIGURE 20

4 DISLOCATIONS

4.1 Plasticity

A crystal submitted to external stresses σ (e.g. traction of a wire) is deformed (Fig. 21). At first the deformation ε (e.g. elongation of the wire) is elastic: if the stress is removed, ε comes back to zero. Then the deformation is per-

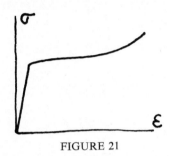

FIGURE 21

manent (except for a slight elastic effect at the removal of the stress): this is the plastic domain which will end at the rupture of the specimen. Some crystals, like pure metals, are well known to present a large plastic domain.

It may be shown experimentally that plastic deformation is mostly due to the glide of dense atomic planes on each other. How does this glide take place?

One can imagine that one half of the perfect crystal glides on the other half, along a dense plane, as a whole (Fig. 22). During the movement, all

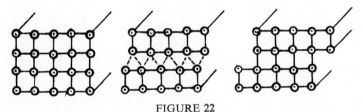

FIGURE 22

the atomic bonds crossing the plane P support at the same time the same distortion. An activation energy ΔE must be given simultaneously to all these N bonds with the result of a displacement of one half of the crystal relative to the other. The resulting effort is prohibitive and by no means comparable to the experimental stresses necessary for the deformation of, say, a metal.

One can then imagine that this effort is broken into many small pieces. It will be the case if the crystal contains a defect such as the one of Fig. 23. A supplementary half plane *S* has been introduced in the upper part of the crystal. There is of course a cylindrical region of imperfect crystal around the

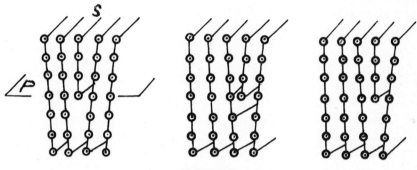

FIGURE 23

straight line *L* limiting this half plane and perpendicular to the plane of the figure. The line *L*, intersection of planes *P* and *S*, is called a line of edge *dislocation* (the half plane *S* having been forced into the crystal like an edge).

Let us come back to plasticity and exert a stress parallel to *P* (as in Fig. 22). Now most of the bonds in plane *P* will "ignore" the stress except for some of the already distorted bonds in the region of the dislocation. We see (Fig. 22a, b, c) that at the expense of some slight atomic rearrangements around the dislocation, the line *L* will have moved by a distance a in the crystal. The applied stress will then produce another jump of the dislocation, etc., till the dislocation arrives on the free surface, which clearly means that a half plane has appeared on this surface, and that a deformation has been produced.

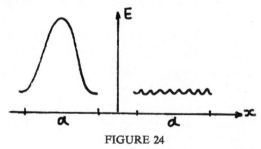

FIGURE 24

The important point is that the effort which had (on Fig. 22) to be applied to provide sumiltaneously N times the elementary energy ΔE is now cut into small pieces which are dispersed in time (Fig. 24).

4.2 Definitions

The use of dislocations to explain plasticity is rather recent ($\simeq 20$ years) though the general description of these defects had been given in elasticity theory at the beginning of this century (mainly by Volterra).

Let us consider, inside of a volume of elastic matter, a surface S limited by a line L (Fig. 25); cut the matter along S and separate the 2 lips of the

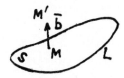

FIGURE 25

cut by a constant vector **b**; fill the empty space (or remove the matter in excess if necessary); stick the lips together and remove the applied stresses.

The stresses induced in the elastic matter are continuous over the whole volume except along the line L. This line is called a dislocation line and **b** its Burgers vector. A segment of L perpendicular to **b**, is said to be an edge dislocation. A segment of L parallel to **b**, is said to be a screw dislocation.

We have already met an edge dislocation on Fig. 23. Here the cut was made along the (plane) surface S; the 2 lips were separated by the vector **b**(**b** $//$ P **b** $\perp$ S $|\mathbf{b}|$ = a) and the hole thus created was filled with the atoms of plane S.

In the case of a straight dislocation, it is easy to calculate the elastic energy stored between 2 cylinders having the line as axis and of radius r_0 and $r_1(r_1 > r_0)$. For a screw dislocation, this energy per unit length (which is also a *line tension* for the dislocation) is

$$F \simeq \frac{\mu b^2}{4\pi} \log \frac{r_1}{r_0}, \tag{6}$$

μ: shear modulus.

One will notice that for a unique dislocation in an infinite crystal ($r_1 \to \infty$) the energy would be infinite.

For real crystals r_1 should be taken either of the order of the dimension of the crystal or as the average distance to the hearest dislocations. r_0, a distance under which linear elasticity cannot be applied, is of the order of the atomic distances. The energy stored in the cylinder of radius r_0 (called the core of the dislocation) is generally small compared to (6). For reasonnable values of r_0 and $r_1(r_0 = 1 \text{ Å}, r_1 = 1\mu)$ one has

$$F \simeq \mu b^2.$$

If b is of the order of atomic distances a (like in Fig. 23) one has $E = \mu a^3 \simeq 5$ eV as energy of dislocation per atomic length of the defect. This shows that the equilibrium concentration of dislocations in a crystal is completely negligible. All the dislocations present in a solid should be considered as metastable.

The energy being proportional to the square of b, dislocations with a high value for b are unlikely to exist. If created, they will tend to dissociate in dislocations $L_1, L_2 \ldots$ such that $\mathbf{b}_1 + \mathbf{b}_2 \ldots = \mathbf{b}$.

4.3   Dislocations in crystals

It is clear, espicially in Fig. 23, that one could not choose just any Burgers vector $\mathbf{b}$ if one wishes to keep the coherence of the crystal outside of the core. For example, on *F*ig. 23, $\mathbf{b}$ is equal in size and direction to a vector of the unit cell (here a square).

More generally, a perfect sticking of the two lips of the cut requires that $\mathbf{b}$ be a period of the Bravais lattice of the crystal. The corresponding dislocations are called *perfect*.

One can also obtain a correct, though not perfect, sticking without $\mathbf{b}$ being a period of the Bravais lattice. It is the case of *imperfect dislocations* which form the boundary of stacking faults (see 5.3).

The movement of a dislocation parallel to its Burgers vector (as in Fig. 23) is generally easy: it is called *glide* of the dislocation and is essential in explaining plasticity. Any obstacle preventing the glide of dislocations (defects, impurities, other dislocations) is a source of *hardening*.

The movement of an edge dislocation perpendicular to its Burgers vector—for instance a movement, up or down of the dislocation of Fig. 23 instead of right or left—is much more difficult. It requires absorption or emission of atoms, more precisely of vacancies. Vacancies must be sent to the dislocation of Fig. 23 for an upward movement. Such a movement is called *climb*.

The absorption (or emission) of vacancies is made easier if the dislocation is not straight, but irregular. Figure 26 shows such an irregularity which is called a *jog*. By preventing a dislocation from being straight, jogs increase the configurational entropy of the dislocation, so that there exists a thermo-

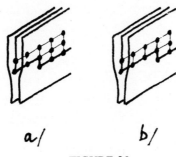

FIGURE 26

dynamical equilibrium of jogs along a dislocation. Jogs are considered as very active sources of point defects and especially of vacancies when a crystal is heated and has to create its equilibrium concentration of vacancies.

4.4 Electrical or electronic effects

In ionic crystals the elastic considerations on the energy (4.2) are not sufficient to describe dislocations properly. We must add the condition that the extra half plane—in case of an edge dislocation—should not disturb the neutrality in the crystal.

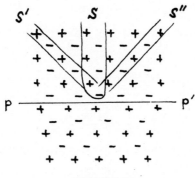

FIGURE 27

In the *NaCl structure*, where the major glide plane is {110}, such a dislocation is obtained if inserting 2{110} planes, perpendicular to the glide plane (Fig. 27). One will notice that the dislocation can be considered as obtained by the insertion either of two {110} planes (*S*), or of two {100} planes (*S′S″*).

The border of the two {110} extra planes consists of a row of ions of alternate sign (Fig. 28). If there is, on this line, a jog corresponding to

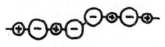

FIGURE 28

2 successive {110} planes, there is no disturbance in the sequence of positive and negative ions along the line. The jog is neutral. If the jog corresponds to only one {110} plane, the two ions on the jog have the same sign. This charged jog is also called an *incipient vacancy* because of the attraction it produces to an ion of the other sign. The effective charge of such a jog is half the ionic charge of the ions of the jog.

In *covalent crystals* a dislocation is a line of broken bonds, sometimes called dangling bonds (Fig. 29). These unpaired bonds can either accept

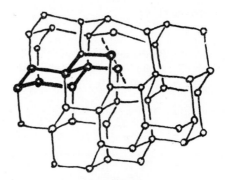

FIGURE 29

electrons to reconstitute a nearly normal 8 electrons environment for the atoms on the dislocation, or give up the remaining electrons to the conduction band. In Ge, dislocations seem to act predominantly as acceptors.

One should not deduce that for an *n* type semi conductor the donor levels will all be emptied to the benefit of the somewhat lower acceptor levels of the dislocations: when some acceptor levels of the dislocation are occupied by electrons, the dislocation becomes negatively charged, which creates around the dislocation a repulsive potential for other electrons. This makes it impossible to describe the occupation of the dislocation levels by Fermi Dirac statistics. Only a small proportion of the levels will in fact be occupied.

The cylinder around the dislocation in which the donor impurities have given their electron to the dangling bonds of the dislocation, is called the *space charge cylinder*. This cylinder has a strong scattering effect on electrons or holes, especially for those not moving parallel to the dislocation. It explains the big influence of dislocations upon the electrical properties of semi conductors especially *n*-type semi conductors.

In *metals*, the displacement of charges due to the local distortion in the core of the dislocation is screened by the conduction electrons. This screening produces a potential around the dislocation. In a normal metal and for an edge dislocation, this potential oscillates (as around point defects: §3.1.1) with a wawe length $\frac{1}{2} \lambda_F$ (λ_F: wawe length of electrons at the Fermi level) and an amplitude decreasing as $r^{-7/2}$, r being the distance to the dislocation.

5 SURFACE DEFECTS

These defects have been less extensively studied than point defects or dislocations.

5.1 Free surface

A free surface is the biggest perturbation in the regularity of a crystal.

As all the defects, a free surface is characterized by an energy called the surface energy, which arises from the bonds broken when one cuts the crystal in two parts.

Let us cut an *ionic crystal* along a surface S and separate the two parts (Fig. 30). The ions on the surface have lost part of their neighbours and the

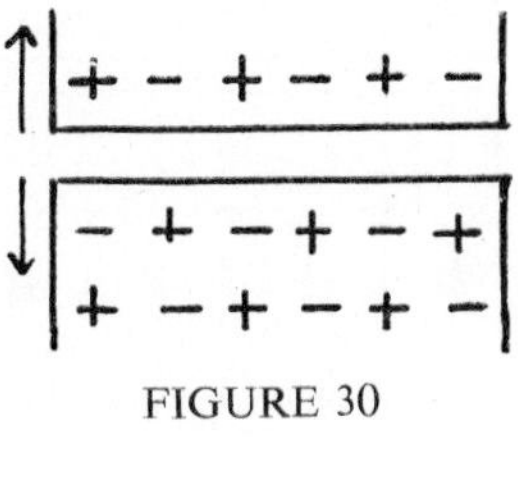

FIGURE 30

electrostatic balance is perturbed. The energy surface comes from the work done, against the electrostatic forces, to separate the two parts.

In *covalent crystals* surface energy comes directly from the bonds broken at the surface. The surface gives rise to acceptor levels which are, in an *n*-type semi conductor, partly filled by the electrons from the donor impurities. In this case the surface has a *p*-character.

In *metals* the energy is again mainly due to conduction electrons. The wave functions—the square of which represents the electronic density—practically vanish at the surface: this creates a region very near the surface, inside of the metal, of reduced electronic density, local repulsion and increase of kinetic energy of electrons. This effect is only partially compensated by the fact that some electrons slightly tunnel out of the metal, so that the wave functions are not exactly zero at the surface.

In all cases one expects a positive *surface entropy* of vibrational nature because atoms on the surface can easily vibrate normally to the surface with frequencies lower than inside of the crystal.

Surface energy is generally strongly anisotropic. It is lower for dense planes because less bonds are broken in that case. To cut along a low density plane is in fact to cut along several dense planes as is shown in Fig. 31.

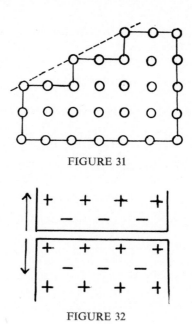

FIGURE 31

FIGURE 32

In ionic crystals the compensation of charges is different according to the chosen surface. The surface of Fig. 30 is obviously more stable than the surface of Fig. 32. The strong anisotropy of energy surface in ionic crystals explains why cristals like NaCl grow preferentially along dense planes.

Anyhow the free surfaces are never perfectly flat. The energy is lower on dense planes but the entropy increases if one introduces defects on a flat surface. A surface is generally covered by atomic-scale steps, themselves often aligned on dense rows and broken by kinks. These kinks are favourable sites for the creation or absorption of vacancies (F. 33).

FIGURE 33

5.2 Grain boundaries

Grain boundaries are the frontiers along which crystals of different orientation (grains) stick together, in non single crystal samples.

5.2.1 *Low angle boundaries*

If the misorientation between the two grains is small the boundary can be analyzed as a net of dislocations. A simple case called a tilt boundary is pictured in Fig. 34 where the net is reduced to a series of parallel equidistant edge dislocations in the plane of the boundary.

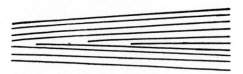

FIGURE 34

5.2.2 *Large angle boundaries*

The structure of these boundaries (Fig. 8) has not been studied in great detail. Their energy, which depends on the relative orientation of the two grains, makes them become as planar as possible when enough energy is supplied—especially by heating. They are sites of enhanced chemical activity and sources (or sinks) of point defects like vacancies.

5.2.3 *Twin boundaries*

A coherent twin boundary joins two crystals symmetrical with respect to
the plane of the boundary (Fig. 35). The energy of such boundaries is generally low especially in close packed crystals. The planes of twin boundaries
are often dense planes, especially {111} planes (f.c.c. metals, Ge...).

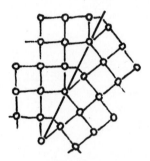

FIGURE 35

5.3 Stacking faults

Crystals can be considered as stacked atomic planes, the order of stacking
not being arbitrary. For instance a f.c.c. crystal is a stacking of dense {111}
planes with an order labelled *ABCABCA*... which means that from a given
plane *A* one must jump 3 planes further to find atoms at vertical position
with respect to the atoms of the plane *A*. The two intermediate planes *B*
and *C* are translated so that the atoms projected on plane *A*, form an equi-
lateral triangle *ABC* (Fig. 36).

Now, there may be a mistake in the stacking order. For instance, instead of *ABCABCA*..., we can have *ABCABABC*... Locally the triangle
ABC has been replaced by the segment *ABA*. The defect which is concentrated along the *B* plane of the sequence *ABA* is called stacking fault.

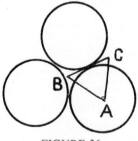

FIGURE 36

It is easy to see that changing the rotation order, that is making a crystal *CBACBAC*... yields an f.c.c. crystal twinned with respect to the first. Then a crystal *ABCABCBACBA* is twinned with a coherent twin boundary on the central *C* plane. It then appears that a stacking fault, here, may be considered as a thin twin with 2 twin boundaries one planar distance apart (Fig. 37).

A
C
A
C
B
A

FIGURE 37

Starting from a perfect crystal it is easy to create a stacking fault along a surface *S*: cut the crystal along *S* (which is supposed to be parallel to a dense plane); translate one part with respect to the other, the translation vector being one of the 3 vectors *AB*, *BC* or *CA*.

This is just the definition of a dislocation created along the line *L* bounding *S* and of Burgers vector the translation vector (*AB*, *BC* or *CA*).

Such dislocations bounding stacking faults and having Burgers vectors which are not periods of the Bravais lattice are called *imperfectdislocations*. From the obvious relation $AA' = BC - AB$, one deduces that a perfect dislocation of Burgers vector AA' can be dissociated in two imperfect dislocations (*BC* and *BA*). The dissociation is energetically favourable, since $BC^2 + BA^2 < AA'^2$ [see (6)] and creates a stacking fault ribbon between the two imperfect dislocations. The energy of the stacking fault will give a limitation to the width of this ribbon.

5.4 Antiphase boundaries

These boundaries separate in an ordered alloy two domains which have undergone a translation with respect to each other (Fig. 38). In an ordered alloy *AB* such boundaries bring into contact atoms of same nature which have a tendency to chemical repulsion since the alloy is ordered.

6 VOLUME DEFECTS

These defects have a big size compared to the atomic volume. We shall only draw up a list of the most important ones.

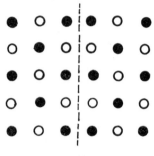

FIGURE 38

When clustering, *impurity atoms* build first *clusters*, then *precipitates*, as in two-phase binary alloys.

A well known case is the clustering of Guinier–Preston zones in Al–Cu alloys. These zones, platelets of Al_2Cu, deeply modify the mechanical properties of the alloy.

There are several types of *vacancy* clusters.

By irradiation with high energy particles one creates vacancy zones (or Seeger zones). These are regions of size about 20 or 40 Å, where a high density of vacancies is concentrated.

When annealing a crystal containing a high concentration of vacancies, these defects cluster but the result of this clustering depends on the material and also on the experimental procedure. For example in aluminium, one may obtain holes or loops. The *holes* are not quite spherical: their borrow dense planes to minimize the surface energy (see 5.1.). The dislocation loops—or *loops*—are due to the gathering of vacancies in one atomic layer, or disc, which collapses to suppress the surface energy. The dislocation thus obtained has an edge character. In gold one observes dislocation loops and also *tetrahedral loops* the "disc" of vacancy having now the shape of a regular tetrahedron of {111} faces. The four faces of the tetrahedron are covered by a stacking fault.

When irradiating materials one often introduces gas (for instance α particles turning to helium). If the solubility of gas in the irradiated crystal is low, which is frequent, the gas atoms cluster. One obtains *bubbles*. These bubbles generally have, like holes, planar rather than spherical faces. The pressure of the gas balances the surface tension of the bubble. In the conditions of equilibrium, a gas atom occupies a much bigger volume in the bubble than in the crystal. Thus, the growth of the bubble, when one gas atom joins it, requires the arrival of N vacancies. Supposing the bubble to be spherical (radius R) one finds:

$$N = \frac{3}{4} \frac{kT}{\gamma v_{at}} R,$$

where γ is the surface energy of the crystal, and v_{at} the atomic volume. For example, if $\gamma = 10^3$ erg cm^{-2}, $T = 500°C$, and $v_{at} = 20 \, A^3$, one gas atom joining a bubble of radius $1 \, \mu$ provokes a flux of $\simeq 400$ vacancies to the bubble.

At last the irradiation with fast particules may produce regions of "bad crystal" where the number and variety of defects are too high to be properly described: for example *fission tracks* which will be spoken of later in this course (see J. Mory's lectures), or *amorphous zones*, regions in which the crystalinity, detected by X ray diffraction, seems to have disappeared.

7   INTERACTIONS BETWEN DEFECTS

The number of defects we have mentioned being of the order of 20, I do not intend to describe the $\frac{1}{2} \times 20 \times 19 = 190$ types of possible interactions.

Let us only mention some among the most important of them.

7.1   Point defect–point defect

The oscillatory potential around an impurity in a metal explains very correctly the interaction between 2 first neighbour metallic impurities B and C in a metal A, if B and C have valences Z_B and Z_C different from Z_A.

If $Z_A = 1$, there is a repulsion $B-C$ if Z_B and Z_C are both <1. It is for instance the case for 2 zinc atoms in copper which tend to keep far from each other (existence of local order in Cu–Zn alloys).

If $Z_A = 3$, there is an attraction $B-C$ if Z_B and Z_C are both $>$ or <3. It is the case for 2 copper atoms in aluminium, which tend to cluster (Guinier-Preston zones in Al–Cu alloys).

Chemical interactions concerning vacancies are often strong but they are not always very well understood, the exact electronic configuration around a vacancy not being well known.

Most of the time, two vacancies are most generally strongly bound and form a divancy. So are 3 vacancies (trivacancies)... So are also 2 interstitials at least in metals (di-interstitials). The stability of these small groups of point defects and also their geometrical configuration is generally studied by means of computer calculations. One introduces analytical forms of

3*

potential between atoms and calculates the total potential energy for the configuration minimizing this energy.

A vacancy and an impurity atom generally attract each other. We have already mentioned the Ca^{++}-vacancy complex in NaCl and also the covalent band between two such defects as the α and the F centres (3.1.1 and 3.2.1). In Si, the oxygen-vacancy complex called A—centre has been extensively studied. This centre, which is aligned on a $\langle 110 \rangle$ direction has a non-spherical symmetry. If a uniaxial stress is applied on a single crystal containing A centres, some of the 6 $\langle 110 \rangle$ directions become more stable than the other. Some of the A centres rotate about their center to become stabilized, as spins in a magnetic field. From this analogy the phenomenon is called *para-elasticity*. It has been also observed and extensively studied for O_2 molecules in alkali halides.

In metals, stable vacancy-impurity complexes are called Johnson molecules. They play an essential role in diffusion phenomena (7.1).

7.2   Point defect—dislocation

To an edge dislocation are associated a region in compression ("above" the dislocation on Fig. 23) and a region in tension (under the dislocation). Thus an impurity of any (positive or negative size factor should find, near such a dislocation, a site reducing its elastic energy. There may also be a chemical interaction. Strong in covalent crystals, this interaction is negligible in metals compared to the elastic interaction. These interactions explain why impurity atoms generally gather around dislocations and form clouds (Cottrell clouds).

Like impurities, vacancies interact with dislocations. If r is the dislocation-vacancy distance, the attractive potential is an r^{-1} or an r^{-2} function: r^{-1} if the interaction is mainly due to the local change of volume of the vacancy; r^{-2} if the interaction is mainly due to the change of elastic constants (vacancy softening). In Al and Au an r^{-2} dependance is experimentally observed but in metals one may have to deal with the interaction between vacancies and split dislocations, rather than perfect dislocations, a problem which has not been studied in detail.

The interaction between point defects and stacking faults associated with split dislocations is generally large. The Suzuki effect is the gathering of impurity atoms around stacking faults. The interaction is strong enough to stabilize dissociation of dislocations which would not otherwise take place (Crussard effect).

7.3 Dislocation–dislocation

The interaction between dislocations is accounted for in the elastic theory. This elastic interaction is pictured in Fig. 39: it is a repulsion if the two Burgers vectors are parallel, an attraction if they are antiparallel. More

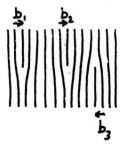

FIGURE 39

generally the repulsion and attraction conditions are respectively $\mathbf{b}_1 \cdot \mathbf{b}_2 > 0$ and $\mathbf{b}_1 \cdot \mathbf{b}_2 < 0$. For parallel straight screw dislocations, at a distance r from each other, there appears between the two dislocations a central force of magnitude:

$$F = \frac{\mu \mathbf{b}_1 \mathbf{b}_2}{2\pi r},$$

$\mathbf{b}_1$ and $\mathbf{b}_2$ being the two Burgers vectors.

A dislocation gliding during plastic deformation, has to cut through the dislocation situated out of the glide plane. These dislocations are the "trees" of the so called "forest". The trees are either repulsive or attractive for the gliding dislocation. This distinction is important in the theory of workhardening (hardening of metals by plastic deformation).

7.4 Dislocation–surfaces

When one creates a *free surface* by cutting a sample in 2 pieces I and II, the suppression of, say, II produces in I new forces called image forces (like in electrostatics) arising from the disappearance of the elastic effect which II induced upon I before cutting.

For a straight screw dislocation parallel (distance r) to a free surface these forces combine to give an attractive force

$$F = \frac{\mu b^2}{4\pi r}.$$

If r is small enough, this force pulls the dislocation to the surface. If the dislocation is not straight, segments of dislocation are more or less attracted to the surface according to their distance to it: the closer they are, the stronger the attraction; so that dislocations end on a free surface perpendicular to it.

This applies in particular to bubbles (Fig. 40).

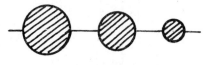

FIGURE 40

As for the surface between 2 phases of different elastic constants μ_I and μ_{II} (e.g. boundaries between a matrix and precipitates) dislocations in phase I are attracted by the boundary if $\mu_I > \mu_{II}$ and repelled if $\mu_I < \mu_{II}$.

8 SOME DEFECT-SENSITIVE PROPERTIES AND PHENOMENA

8.1 Solid state diffusion

Diffusion is the mobility, in crystals, of atoms jumping from site to site. Mobility of atoms A in a crystal A is called self-diffusion. Mobility of atoms B in a crystal A is called hetero-diffusion.

In all the cases which have been experimentally studied, *self-diffusion* is due to the jump of an atom A in a vacancy situated next to it. Self-diffusion is thermally activated with an activation energy E_a. The probability p that an atom A makes a jump is equal to the probability p_1 for A to have a vacancy next to it, multiplied by the probability p_2 for A to jump into the vacancy. If E_m is the energy necessary for the jump (E_m is called migration energy of the vacancy) one has

$$p_1 \propto \exp\left(-\frac{E_f}{kT}\right), \quad p_2 \propto \exp\left(-\frac{E_m}{kT}\right),$$

whereas

$$p \propto \exp\left(-\frac{E_a}{kT}\right).$$

The resulting equation:

$$E_a = E_f + E_m$$

is thus a test of the reality of the jump-in-vacancy mechanism, and has been verified in some f.c.c. metals by independant measurements of E_a, E_f and E_m.

One may induce a similar mechanism for hetero-diffusion, an atom B jumping into a neighbouring vacancy of the A crystal. If there was no inter-action, either chemical or elastic, between B and a vacancy, the hetero-diffusion would be nearly equal to the self-diffusion. Generally hetero-diffusion in A is faster than self-diffusion of A, which is due to a negative binding energy B—vacancy.

In some cases, especially if the B atom is small, diffusion happens inter-stitially, a B atom jumping from interstitial to interstitial site in the A crystal (e.g. C in Fe or Li in Ge).

If in some parts of a crystal the concentration of vacancies is higher than the average, diffusion should be enhanced in these regions. This is the case along dislocations (pipe diffusion), grain boundaries (g.b. diffusion) and, as an extreme case, on free surfaces (surface diffusion). It is also the case under irradiation, point defects being then created out of equilibrium.

8.2 Plastic deformation

We have already mentioned the direct link between platicity and disloca-tions. We shall not enter deeply into this huge subject which is not essential to the theme of the school. Let us only give some definitions.

We emphasized that any defect impeding the glide of dislocations would produce hardening. Hardening is mainly due to solute impurities (*solution hardening*), to precipitates (*precipitation hardening*) to radiation defects (*radiation hardening*; see 8.4) and to defects created by the plastic defor-mation itself and mainly dislocations (*work-hardening*).

Climb of dislocations, which is easy only in the case of non split dislo-cations, implies a transport of matter. That is why it generally happens at about the same temperature as self diffusion. Climb, together with self-diffusion, governs such phenomena as *creep* (plastic deformation under applied stress) *sintering* (stricking of small solid particles and disappearance of the holes (or "porosity") between the particles), or *recrystallisation* (rearrangement of the crystal after a heavy plastic deformation or cold work).

8.3 Electrical properties

It is to explain the electrolytic conductivity in *ionic crystals* that Frenkel proposed in 1926 the existence of defects in these crystals. It was later shown that this conductivity was mainly due to cation vacancies. The Arrhenius plot of the conductivity σ underlines the existence of two temperature domains (Fig. 41). The knee K between I and II depends on the impurity content c_i of the crystal so that conductivity in the high temperature domain *I*

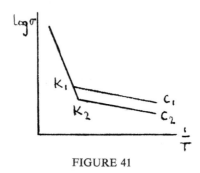

FIGURE 41

is due to thermal equilibrium vacancies (intrinsic conductivity) and conductivity in *II*, proportional to c_i, is due to impurity induced vacancies (see 3.1.1).

Conductivity measurements in region II of crystals containing a well known amount of impurities give the mobility of the cation vacancies. From measurements in region I, one then deduces the equilibrium concentration of cation cavancies at high temperature. This concentration near the melting point is of the order of 10^{-4} in most alkali halides (see Pick's paper).

Another striking effect is the enhancement of electrical conductivity during plastic deformation, moving dislocations creating Schottky defects. This enhancement may be of 2 orders of magnitude in NaCl for a moderate deformation.

We have already emphasized the drastic impact of all types of defects upon the electrical properties of *semi-conductors* (see 3.1.1, 3.2.1, 4.4, 5.1.1, 8.1). The sensitivity is such that as few as 10^{12} Frenkel pairs per cm^3 are easily detected by conductivity of Hall coefficient measurements.

In *metals* the short range potential around defects scatters the conduction electrons with a cross section which is of the order of the "size" of the defect (e.g. $\simeq 1$ atomic volume for a vacancy). There results a contribution $\Delta\varrho$ of the defects to the resistivity of the metal. $\Delta\varrho$ being practically constant with respect to temperature (Matthiesen's rule) the resistivity of defects contributes noticeably to the total resistivity only at low temperature. Contrariwise to the cases of ionic or covalent crystals, the high temperature conductivity is very little affected.

8.4 Irradiation properties

The main result of irradiation is to create defects out of equilibrium. All the under—or after—irradiation properties are due to these defects.

Defects are created either by *Wigner effect* (collisions of particles on atoms or ions thus ejected from their sites) by *ionization* or Varley mechanism (in ionic crystals, a multiply ionized anion becomes unstable and jumps outes ot its former site), or by *nuclear reactions* creating new impurity atoms (e.g. fission of ^{235}U).

The number of defects first increases linearly with the irradiation dose, then tends generally to a saturation value because of the spontaneous recombination of defects when they are numerous and close to each other. Sometimes the irradiation may lead to the destruction of the sample. For instance in the phenomenon of growth (U, Zr, Ti), dislocation loops of identical sign pile up, thus changing the size of the sample, till it is practically destroyed.

The radiation defects alter, sometimes drastically, all the properties of crystals. Let us mention:

1 The *optical properties* of ionic crystals, through the production of colour centres. Irradiation with X rays turns NaCl to yellow, KCl to blue the absorption of light, increasing linearly with dose for low or medium doses.

2 The *electrical properties* of semi conductors, which are extremely sensitive to radiation defects (8.3). This extreme sensitivity makes electrical measurments an ideal tool to study the critical energy of incident particles like electrons above which Frenkel pairs are created (see Baruch's paper).

For high energy particles like fast neutrons, small regions of high concentration of defects are created. These regions have a p-character and in n-type germanium thus appear p–n junctions. A space charge volume, opaque to electrons, bigger than the defect-rich region, is located around each region, decreasing the conductivity and increasing the Hall coefficient.

3 *Plastic properties* which are altered by irradiation defects. In metals, like copper, the critical shear stress is increased by irradiation. This hardening is generally attributed to the friction of dislocations on Seeger zones

(§ 6) for high energy particle irradiations (e.g. fast neutrons) or on split interstitials if the particles cannot create zones (e.g. electrons). If gas is formed by some nuclear reaction it may induce hardening by friction of dislocations either on gas atoms (boron, a frequent impurity in steel, gives helium in a neutron flux) or on gas bubbles.

In steels irradiated with fast neutrons the ductile—fragile transition temperature is increased.

8.5   Other properties

Other defect sensitive properties or phenomena will be described in detail in this book, like *luminescence, photographic process, magnetic properties...*

References

Among the numerous articles or books covering partly or entirely the subject in more detail, let us cite:

H. G. Van Bueren, *Imperfections in crystals*, North Holland Pub. Company Amsterdam (1961).

J. Friedel, Crystalline defects, in *Radiation Damage in Solide*, Academic Press, New York (1962).

A. Seeger, "Recent advances in the theory of defects in crystals," *Physica Status Solidi* **1** 669 (1961).

J. Friedel, *Dislocations*, Pergamon Press, New York (1964).

J. Friedel, "Defauts ponctuels et irradiation," in *Physique des Basses Températures*, Presses Universitaires, Paris (1962).

A. C. Damask et G. J. Dienes, Point defects in metals, Gordon and Breach, New York (1963).

Y. Quere, Défauts ponctuels dans les métaux, Masson, Paris (1967).

Proceedings of the international conference on crystal lattice defects, *J. Phys. Soc. Jap.* **18** Sup. I–III (1963).

Proceedings of the international conference on vacancies and interstitials in metals, *K.F.A.* Jülich (1968).

Units in dosimetry and radioprotection

F. DUHAMEL

C.E.A., Paris, France

INTRODUCTION

In the past some confusion has arisen concerning the definition and the use of parameters and units in dosimetry. The International Commission on Radiological Units and Measurements has brought more clarity in this field since 1925, and particularly since 1955, in collaboration with the World Health Organization. It is therefore rather easy now to define the units in dosimetry and radioprotection. One can indeed always refer to the report of this commission, and especially to the 1962 report published in several languages by the International Atomic Energy Agency.

On the other hand it is sometimes interesting to review the basic ideas upon which the definitions of dosimetric parameters and units are built. By doing this one is able to keep the firmly established scientific attainments better in mind, and also to be aware of the imperfections and inaccuracies which are still left in some fields.

1 PARAMETERS RELATED TO THE NOTION OF DOSE

The term dose itself has originally been taken from therapeutics and although it corresponds well to the needs of therapeutical language, it was not appropriate as such for the requirements of biological science. Nevertheless it has become an established term, by the fact that its definition has been better and better specified.

The notion of dose assumes that equal doses correspond to equal effects. Unfortunately the biological effects depend upon a large number of parameters, only a few of which are actually known. For example the total energy transported by some radiation may be interesting to consider, but it can only give a very unprecise indication of the biological danger caused by the radiation. Even the amount of energy lost by the radiation in the body which is traversed cannot be directly related to the expected effect: e.g. the energy brought about by a lethal dose of gamma radiation from cobalt 60 could only yield a temperature rise of the order of one thousandth of a degree in spite of its complete conversion into heat, whereas the matabolic energy emitted per second in the body is of the same order of magnitude.

The analysis of the phenomena of biological effects is necessary in order to distinguish the essential mechanisms, to find out whether or not the proportionality rules may be applied, to decide if statistical evaluations are allowed, or to eliminate some parameters of which the influence is negligible. Unfortunately the scientific data in this field are still very unsatisfactory, since they are limited to the analysis of the interaction phenomena from the only point of view of fundamental physics. Hence the biological effects are supposed to be almost proportional to the physical parameters describing intensity and time.

The most important physical parameters are the following: the nature of the radiation, its energy or its energy spectrum, its distribution (density, direction) in space and time. On the other hand we insist on the importance of another parameter, namely the irradiation volume.

The International Commission on Radiological Units and Measurements has paid considerable attention to the irradiation volume since its definition remained one of the major difficulties in the field of defining notions and units. An accurate definition of parameters which are inhomogeneous in space, indeed requires to consider infinitesimal elements in theory, and small but finite elements in practice. Generally the continuity conditions are such that the transition from theory to practice does not involve particular problems. But the case of radioprotection dosimetry is peculiar in this sense that the aim of a measurement is to predict an effect which itself is related to the amount of irradiated volume. The radiation fields are generally not uniform, and the parameters have to be defined by considering infinitesimal small volume elements; however these volume elements must contain a large number of interactions. This problem could theoretically be solved by considering the average of a large number of measurements. The investigation concerning the phenomena at the scale of these infinitesimal volumes is called microdosimetry. We will limit ourselves to the study of the units in the field of macroscopic dosimetry.

The International Commission on Radiological Units has clearly expressed its concern with respect to the problem by introducing the general use of the symbol Δ before the definition symbols, in order to emphasize the infinitesimal dimensions. We believe that this method is excellent, but it might be appropriate in practice to omit this notation when it is not essential for the exactness of the reasoning.

2 PHYSICAL DEFINITION OF INCIDENT RADIATION

As is frequently done in theoretical physics, it is convenient to begin with the definition of the phenomena and parameters on a mathematical basis.

The most general situation we have to consider is the case of an inhomogeneous and time dependent space distribution of particle sources. The radiation field may then be described by considering, in a point M, all particles with energy around ε which have crossed a unit surface around M; if these particles are moving in an infinitesimal solid angle $d\Omega$ around the direction Ω perpendicular to this surface, the number of particles at a time t will be

$$n(\varepsilon, \Omega) \, d\varepsilon \, d\Omega$$

and in a time interval Δt, their number will be $(dn/dt) \, \Delta t$.

The flux density is obtained by integrating dn/dt with respect to Ω and ε

$$\varphi = \int d\varepsilon \int \frac{dn}{dt} d\Omega.$$

This is the number of particles which passes through a small sphere around M, per unit time, and per unit surface of a large circle of this sphere.

The radiation intensity is

$$I = \int d\varepsilon \int \frac{dn}{dt} \varepsilon d\Omega.$$

This is the energy which passes through a small sphere around M, per unit time and per unit surface of a large circle of this sphere.

We can put

$$\Phi = \int \varphi \, dt$$

and

$$dN = \Phi \, da$$

where N is the number of particles traversing a sphere around M, and da is the surface of a large circle of this sphere.

These parameters are scalars. In order to describe the field completely one may define the corresponding vector parameters by introducing the unity vector $\mathbf{\Omega}$. With these notations one is able to describe the physical phenomena concerning the mean radiation field if statistical fluctuations are neglected. But in order to apply the field equations to dose calculations, it is necessary to introduce some simplifications concerning the ionization phenomena which give rise to the irradiation*.

The International Commission on Radiological Units and Measurements has given exact definitions concerning the theoretical aspects of radiation description. The parameters which are defined are the following—the surface flux (or flux rate) is the flux density φ defined by

$$\varphi = d\Phi/dt$$

—the particle flux, is the time integral of the surface flux:

$$\Phi = \int \varphi \, dt \quad \text{or} \quad \Phi = dN/da,$$

---

* See HH. Rossi and W.C. Roesch, "Field Equation in Dosimetry," *Radiation Research*, **16**, 783 (1962).

—the energy flux is the time integral of the intensity I:

$$F = \int I \, dt \quad \text{or} \quad D = dE/da$$

where E is the sum of the energies of the N particles.

The intensity (or energy flux per unit surface, or also the energy flux rate):

$$I = dF/dt.$$

The definitions established by the International Commission on Radiological Units and Measurements are given in the appendix of the present paper; as we have mentioned before the notation Δ is used.

All the radiations we have to consider in radioprotection dosimetry are ionizing radiations but they may be directly or indirectly ionizing, or they may consist of a mixture of these two kinds of radiation.

Particles are said to be directly ionizing if they bear any electric charge (electrons, protons, helions, etc.) and if their kinetic energy is high enough to ionize by collision.

On the other hand, particles are said to be indirectly ionizing if, being electrically neutral themselves (photons, neutrons, neutral mesons) they are able to liberate directly ionizing particles from an atom or a nucleus.

These radiations give rise to considerable biological effects, although the energy involved in their interaction with biological species is small as compared to the energies encountered in the physicochemical phenomena.

3 PARAMETERS USED IN RADIOPROTECTION DOSIMETRY

a) Parameters related to the biological effects of radiation

The definitions of parameters which enable a quantitative evaluation of radiation effects, must be such that the interpretation of measurements is as simple as possible, in order to obtain a good evaluation of the damage undergone by an irradiated person. Consequently the interpretation of the radiation effects must be facilitated on one hand, and relations must be established between these effects and the directly measurable physical effects, on the other hand.

Although it has been clearly established that ionization (with its consequent excitation) is the predominant phenomenon in the biological effect of radiation, the different mechanisms by which durable changes in the biological structure are produced by ionization are not yet well known.

It is especially important to know whether the effect is proportional with the ionization density produced in some infinitesimal volume, or with the number of such volumes in which a given number of ionizations have been produced.

The old biological theories suppose that the quantities of energy producing ionization and excitation, are the same in gases, liquids, gels and solids, and that the energy necessary for the formation of a pair of ions is a constant. The average so-called ionization energy is often taken equal to 34 eV in air*.

The International Commission on Radiological Units and Measurements has exactly defined the average energy required for the formation of an ion pair by a charged particle in a gas:

$$W = \varepsilon/N'_\varepsilon$$

where ε is the initial energy of the charged particle, and N'_ε the average number of ion pairs produced after complete slowing down of the particle in the gas.

The Commission specifies the values $W = 33.7$ eV for photons and $W = 35$ eV for neutrons.

In fact the biological effectiveness of different types of radiation does not vary according to the predictions of the older biological theories. But the definition of dosimetric parameters are still based upon the basic ideas of these theories, and progressively improved as a function of the new acquisitions of biological science. It is not yet possible to evaluate rigourously a parameter describing the noxiousness of a complex radiation.

The fundamental parameter in radioprotection dosimetry is the absorbed dose, which is defined with the help of another parameter called the transferred energy, for each point of the irradiated material.

The energy transferred to the material, E_D, is the part of the energy of the incident radiation which is absorbed in a mass m of the material, and which is hence able (starting from this quantity of material) to produce biological actions in the irradiated body. This parameter has also been called the integral teet absorbed dose, since it corresponds to the space integral of the absorbed dose.

The absorbed dose is equal to the ratio E_D/m, where E_D is the transferred energy, and m the mass of material around the considered point.

---

* This energy is not to be confused with the minimum energy required for ionization, nor with the so-called mean ionization and excitation potential, which is obtained by considering the average ionization energy $\bar{I}$ of all the electrons of the atoms ($\bar{I} \approx 13\,Z$ in eV, i.e. 85 eV in air).

These definitions are concerned with point values. Therefore the International Commission on Radiological Units and Measurements prescribes

$$D = \Delta E_D / \Delta m.$$

The absorbed dose rate is then $\Delta D / \Delta t$, i.e. the increase of absorbed dose as a function of time. The accurate definitions by the International Commission on Radiological Units and Measurements are given in the appendix.

The three parameters described above may be expressed in MKSA units, and the usual unit is the rad which is equivalent to $1/100$ of a MKSA unit or 100 CGS units.

$$1 \text{ rad} = 100 \text{ erg/g} = 10^{-2} \text{ joule/kg.}$$

Hence the transferred energy may be expressed in grammes X rad, and the absorbed dose rate is rads per second.

However, the value of absorbed dose in rads has no absolute meaning if it is not accompanied by additional information about the irradiated material and the irradiation conditions.

The energy transferred per charged particle to the neighbouring material is distributed along its path, and this distribution has an influence upon the biological effects of the radiation. Hence it has been useful to define the line energy transfer: it is the average energy E_s transferred to the irradiated material per unit path by a charged particle covering a distance l.

L.E.T $= E_l/l$, usually expressed in keV per micron. This definition can be limited to the energy transferred to the nearest neighbourhood of the particle's path. It can also be extended to more general cases, e.g. for high energy particles.

Since in fact the dose itself is not representative for the biological noxiousness, the biological effectivness of a given dose will vary when the radiation characteristics are changed, particularly when the nature and the spectral distribution of energy change. It is therefore necessary to decompose each radiation into components with each a given biological effectiveness, assuming however that afterwards independent factors can be introduced to add the partial doses corresponding to each component.

In this way the total absorbed dose will be a linear function of the partial absorbed doses D_i corresponding to each component of the total radiation:

$$\text{total dose} = \sum_i k_i D_i,$$

provided one can define a common infinitesimal volume with mass Δm.

For this reason the International Commission on Radiological Units and Measurements has proposed the definition of a parameter called the dose equivalent, representing each of the components $k_i D_i$:

$$D.E = \sum (DE)_i.$$

In the definition of $(DE)_i$ one may introduce all useful factors in order to obtain a weighed summation of the components D_i of the absorbed dose:

$$(DE)_i = D_i (QF)_i \, (DF)_i \dots;$$

QF is the quality factor which is attributed to the biological effectiveness of each type of radiation.

DF is the dose distribution factor, which enables to take into account the non uniformity of the radiation field.

Following the complexity of the cases considered, other additional factors may occur.

The unit of dose equivalent is the rem, which is a peculiar unit related to the rad by the equation

$$(DE)^{\text{rem}} = D^{\text{rad}},$$

if the different factors accounting for the effectiveness, the distribution, etc. are equal to unity.

The term dose, used without epithet, keeps its general meaning and may be used for a qualitative indication of radiation in sentences such as e.g. "to subject a sample to a certain dose of gamma radiation".

b) Parameters related to the physical processes of interactions of radiation with matter

The quantities defined above clearly indicate the moving incertainty in which radioprotection has to operate. On the other hand radiation fields may be described and defined in a rigourous way although the measurement equipments are of course subject to imperfections. They have to be built such that an optimal evaluation of the dosimetric parameters becomes possible; also the phenomena by which the measurements are made must represent as good as possible the processes governing the biological effects of radiation.

Consequently one has to define quantities related to these phenomena, which enable a quick interpretation of the experimental data collected by the apparatus, and which are immediately useful in biology.

It is also possible to estimate the transferred energy and the other connected quantities with the help of some accurately defined quantities which
are themselves calculated from precise physical data describing the radiation.

The basic phenomenon considered for the definitions of practical dosimetric parameters is the liberation of electrical charges in the atmospheric
air.

We first consider the case of electromagnetic radiation:

If Q is the sum of electric charges with the same sign produced by photons
in a mass m of air, the quantity

$$X = Q/m$$

is defined as the exposure. Hence this parameter is the ionization per mass
unit of the air. The value X represents the exposure due to an electromagnetic
radiation only if all the electrons liberated by the photons in the mass of
air are completely stopped in the air. The possible ionization due to Bremsstrahlung is not included in the value of Q.

Hence the exposure is expressed by the ration of a quantity of electricity
to a mass. The unit of exposure, the roentgen, is the exposure obtained in a
mass of 1 cm³ of air (at normal conditions of temperature and pressure),
i.e. 1.293×10^{-3} g of air, when the charge Q amounts to 1 esu.

In terms of the MKSA system, and since 1 esu is $(1/3) 10^{-9}$ Coulomb and
1 cm³ $= 10^{-6}$ m³, one roentgen is the exposure corresponding to the
production of one threethousandth of a Coulomb per cubic meter at normal
temperature and pressure conditions.

When the exposure is expressed in roentgen, one has

$$X^{\text{roentgen}} = 1 \text{ cm}^3/\text{g} \frac{Q^{\text{esu}}}{V^{\text{cm}^3}} ; \quad \text{or}$$

$$X^{\text{roentgen}} = 1.293 \times 10^{-3} \frac{Q^{\text{esu}}}{m^{\text{gramme}}} ; \quad \text{i.e.}$$

$$X^{\text{roentgen}} = 3000 \text{ m}^3/\text{kg} \frac{Q^{\text{Coulomb}}}{V^{\text{m}^3}} , \quad \text{or}$$

$$X^{\text{roentgen}} = 3879 \frac{Q^{\text{Coulomb}}}{m^{\text{kg}}} .$$

Since the elementary electric charge is equal to 4.8×10^{-10} esu, one roentgen corresponds to the formation of 2.082×10^9 ion pairs per cm³ air
(at normal temperature and pressure conditions).

4*

The exposure rate is defined by the ratio dX/dt of the increase of exposure per unit time.

The energy dissipated by the radiation can be estimated from the value of the exposure: assuming that the creation of an ion pair requires 33.7 eV for photons, it is clear that one roentgen corresponds to an energy loss of 0.112 ergs in 1 cm^3 air (at normal conditions) or 86.9 ergs in 1 gramme of air.

We now consider the general case of indirectly ionizing radiation.

The energy dissipated by radiation in the case of indirectly ionizing particles, e.g. neutrons, may be estimated using a peculiar unit called Kerma. This unit is more directly related to the physical characteristics of the radiation than the exposure. The latter assumes indeed that all the liberated charges are completely stopped in the mass of air considered. In the definition of the Kerma one only considers the initial kinetic energies of the charged particles liberated by the effect of indirectly ionicing particles in a volume of mass m. If E_K represents the sum of these energies, the kerma is

$$K = E_K/m.$$

Since this definition is very general, one has to take into account all the charged particles produced by direct or indirect radiation, e.g. the Auger electrons and the charges liberated by Bremsstrahlung.

The kerma is expressed in joules per kilogramme (MKSA) or in ergs per gramme (CGS).

The kerma rate is the ratio dK/dt of the kerma increase with time.

The kerma unit is more general than the exposure which is only defined for air. One might however create or imagine a cavity in a point of a material (air, water, etc.) provided that this cavity does not sensibly perturbate the radiation field. In dosimetry, as in any other field, it is impossible to do a measurement in a given point without, at least theoretically, creating a perturbation of the quantity to be measured; this perturbation has to remain negligible.

4   PARAMETERS RELATED TO THE SUBSTANCES CROSSED BY RADIATION AND TO DOSIMETRIC MEANS

Although the phenomena described above require the presence of biological or other substances crossed by radiation, the definitions of the parameters do not concern the particular characristics of these substances. However, it is necessary to examine if the material used in the actual measuring devices allow reliable estimates of the quantities defined above. On the other hand, the calculation of the interactions by the theoretical means entails the consideration of some basic characteristics of the materials or substances crossed, in order to estimate the quantities described above.

A number of coefficients have formed the subject of accurate recommendations of the International Commission on Radiological Units and Measurements.

a) Definitions of the factors or constants

The attenuation factor of a substance is defined in the case of indirectly ionizing particles. If N is the number of particles penetrating under normal incidence a layer of thickness dl, we have

$$\mu_l = \frac{1}{N} \frac{dN}{dl} \text{ line attenuation factor}$$

$$\mu_s = \frac{\mu_l}{\varrho} = \frac{1}{\varrho N} \frac{dN}{dl} \text{ attenuation factor per surface mass unit,}$$

where ϱ is the specific mass of the substance.

dN is the number of particles undergoing an interaction in the layer dl, and which do not contribute to the emerging beam. A specific attenuation factor is related to each interaction process, and the total attenuation is the sum of the partial attenuation factors (photoelectric effect, Thomson effect, Compton effect, etc.).

The attenuation factors are related to the flux Φ by the equation

$$\mu_l = \frac{dN}{dV} \cdot \frac{1}{\Phi}$$

$$\mu_s = \frac{dN}{dm} \cdot \frac{1}{\Phi}$$

where dV and dm are the volume and the mass of the layer respectively.

The stopping power of the same substance is defined in the case of directly ionizing particles with energy ε which move along an infinitesimal trajectory dl:

$$S_l = \frac{d\varepsilon}{dl} ,$$

the line stopping power,

$$S_s = \frac{S_l}{\varrho} = \frac{1}{\varrho} \frac{d\varepsilon}{dl} \, ,$$

the stopping power per surface mass unit $d\varepsilon$ is the mean energy loss of a particle moving along dl, independently of the interaction process. A stopping power may also be defined for each of the different processes.

The energy transfer factor is described per surface mass unit, by the formula

$$\mu_K = \frac{1}{\varrho_E} \frac{dE_K}{dl} \, ,$$

where dE_K is the sum of the kinetic energies of all the charged particles liberated in the layer, whereas E is the total energy of the indirectly ionizing particles penetrating the layer.

One also has

$$\mu_K = \frac{K}{F} \, ,$$

i.e. the ratio of the kerma to the energy flux.

It should be mentioned that there exists a certain inaccuracy in the use of the term transfer. The energy transfer factor and the kerma are related to the energy liberated by the material, whereas the previously defined line energy transfer is related to the energy transmitted to the material.

Instead of considering the liberated energy dE_K, one might also be interested in the energy dE_D transmitted to a layer with thickness dl, if the difficulties concerning the definition of infinitesimal dimension can be solved. Consequently one defines the energy absorption factor per surface mass unit:

$$\mu_{en} = \frac{1}{\varrho_E} \frac{dE_D}{dl} \, ,$$

$$\mu_{en} = \frac{D}{F}$$

i.e. the ratio absorbed dose to energy flux. The International Commission on Radiological Units and Measurements has given another definition, which is mentioned in the appendix.

When radiation of given nature and energy comes from outside the irradiated substance, it is sufficiently described by the quantities defined above: particle flux and surface flux, energy flux and intensity. On the other hand, when the substance contains radiation sources, it is necessary to use a number of quantities which characterize these sources. The most important one is the activity. It is defined for each radioactive compound, i.e. for each type of atom containing a given number of neutrons and protons. The activity of a compound is defined by

$$A = \frac{dN}{dt},$$

where dN is the increase of the number of nuclear transmutations during an increase dt of time; this definition includes the assumption that it is possible to take the mean value of the statistical fluctuations of dN for a sufficiently large sum of time intervals dt.

The unity, called curie, is defined by

$$1 \text{ Ci} = 3.7 \times 10^{10} \text{ per second.}$$

It is not a material constant.

Even if an emitting source of gamma radiation is external to the irradiated substance, it might be helpful to define the radiation by using the activity of the source. In the case of a point source in vaccum the surface flux in a point is inversely proportional to the square of the distance l of the point to the source; hence the same is true for the exposure rate $\frac{dX}{dt}$, and the product $l^2\frac{dX}{dt}$ is a distance independent characteristic of the exposure rate due to the source. This value per unit activity of the source is called the gamma radiation specific constant:

$$\Gamma = \frac{1}{A} l^2 \frac{dX}{dt}.$$

This quantity is defined for a point source, ad in the absence of diffusion (i.e. in vacuum) although the exposure is defined in air. In practice one has to account for the self-absorption of radiation by the source, and for diffusion by the air. In MKSA-units it is expressed in coulomb $\times$ m² per kg, the exposure being related to the mass of irradiated material. It may also be expressed in roentgen $\times$ m² per Ci per hour or in multiples of this unit.

b)   Use of the factors

In principle the set of definitions given above allow to study all dosimetry problems starting from the radiation-matter interaction laws expressed in terms of cross sections. Although we will not deal with the formulation of these laws, it is necessary to discuss briefly the basic assumptions which are at the origin of some definitions describe aboved.

In the table of appendix 1 we have summarized the different quantities we defined. They have been divided in four classes:

1) Quantities derived from the notion of the number of particles.
These quantities are mathematically defined by considering the particles crossing a small sphere around the point considered, in any direction in the case of the flux and the derived parameters, or in parallel beams in the case of the attenuation and stopping power factors. The approximations adopted in practice are essentially concerned with the energy spectrum of the particles, and its influence upon the value of the factors. The attenuation factors are related to the indirectly ionizing particles, whereas the stopping power is related to the directly ionizing particles (i.e. more generally, the charged particles taking into account the particles with insufficient kinetic energy to cause an ionization).

2) Quantities derived from the notion of transferred energy.
The different modes of energy transfer by primary particles participate in the definition of this energy, independently of the place at which the transfer takes place. Nevertheless, some interactions may be explicitely excluded in order to characterize separately several components of the transferred energy. Obviously, the increase of rest mass which might occur in the considered volume is not included in the value of the transferred energy, since it cannot contribute to the biological effect. In fact the final aim of the measurement of absorbed dose is to learn something about the biological effect.

The difficulties involved with the use of the concept of absorbed dose are especially related to the choice of definitions of infinitesimal volumes such that this parameter remains independent of them. Furthermore the transferred energy cannot be directly measured. Even delicate calorimetry does not yield good measurements. One has to build devices which allow the measurement of other quantities, such as the exposure or the kerma.

Two other remarks should be made about the two factors:

the line energy transfer is often defined with the help of the definitions any infinitesimal volume.

the International Commission on Radiological Units and Measurements relates the energy absorption factor to the liberated energy by the equation

$$\mu_{en} = \mu_K(1 - G),$$

where G is the part of the energy of the secondary particles lest in the form of Bremsstrahlung in the substance. The latter definition avoids the confusion which has occurred between several absorption factors. In fact the two definitions are equivalent.

3) Quantities derived from the notion of liberated energy.
These quantities enable relatively simple theoretical evaluations using the quantities defined in the first group. It is of interest to remark that in some cases of particle equilibrium, the kerma is equal to the absorbed dose.

4) Quantities derived from the notion of liberated charges.
In concerns quantities related to the ionization phenomena. In particular the exposure and the exposure rate are only defined in air and in the case of a purely electromagnetic radiation. These quantities are in fact of interest in the case of ionization chamber measurements. They would not be conveniently useful for the measurement of neutron irradiation. In the latter case one prefers to use the concept of liberated energy and the derived quantities.

CONCLUSION

We may summarize by saying that the defined parameters belong to four different kinds, and that it is necessary to establish the relations between them. The main difficulty is to relate the transferred energy to the liberated energy. The relation can only be simple in the case of a particle equilibrium in the considered volume; then the behaviour of the phenomena at the border of the volume may be examined qualitatively. The particles are said to be in equilibrium in a given volume if in any point the fluxes of the different particles are proportional to each other.

In the case of particle equilibrium the energies may be related to the coefficients of the media considered; the value of the absorbed dose in a material M may be deduced from the value of the exposure measured in a gas*. Indeed, the Bragg-Gray principle, which states that the secondary radiation flux is independent of the density of the medium, in fact means that the absorbed dose is proportional to the stopping power per surface mass unit:

$$\frac{D_M}{(S_s)_M} = \frac{D_G}{(S_s)_G}$$

or

$$D_M = sWJ,$$

where

$$s = \frac{(S_s)_M}{(S_s)_G},$$

W = mean energy for the production of an ion pair in a gas,
J = number of ion pairs produced per mass unit of the gass, deduced from the measurement of the quantity of electricity. For a mass m of gas, one has $J = \frac{1}{e} \frac{Q}{m}$.

But in practice such equations are only applicable as an idealistic picture, since the detector should have the same atomic composition as the irradiated species. If one has to be certain that the evaluated dose is representative for the biological effect, even the molecular composition should be the same.

In fact the use of a detector introduces an additional heterogeneity in the medium. The nature of this heterogeneity and its influence upon the quantities measured, determine the utility of the detector, e.g. either to measure exposures or absorbed doses.

More and more detectors are built such that e.g. the energy transfer factors vary in the same way as the corresponding factors in the biological species considered, or that the line energy transfers permit to include directly the quality factor of the radiation in a total measurement. However, it is not certain that the biological effect can be measured in such simple way, and the futur development of good detectors will be much influenced by the progress in biological science itself.

---

* We recall that the divergence of the primary particle beam must be small in the volume considered, that the energy loss by this particle in the volume must be relatively weak, and that each secondary particle must not loose more than a small fraction of its energy in the same volume.

APPENDIX 1

Table of useful parameters in radioprotection dosimetry

Parameters	Dimensions*	Defined for directly ionizing particles	Defined for indirectly ionizing particles	Special units
1) *Number of particles N (of energy E)*		X	X	
flux $\phi = \dfrac{dN}{da}$	L^{-2}	X	X	
surface flux $\varphi = \dfrac{d\phi}{dt}$	$L^{-2}T^{-2}$	X	X	
energy flux $F = \dfrac{dF}{da}$	EL^{-2}	X	X	
intensity $I = \dfrac{dF}{dt}$	$EL^{-2}T^{-1}$	X	X	
attenuation factors $\mu_l = \dfrac{1}{N}\dfrac{dN}{dl}$	L^{-1}		X	
(parallel beam) $\mu_s = \dfrac{1}{\varrho}\dfrac{dN}{dl}$	$L^2 M^{-1}$		X	
stopping power $S_l = \dfrac{d\varepsilon}{dl}$	EL^{-1}	X		
(for a particle with energy ε) $S_s = \dfrac{1}{\varrho}\dfrac{d\varepsilon}{dl}$	$EL^2 M^{-1}$	X		
2) *Transferred energy E_D*	E	X	X	g x rad
Absorbed dose $D = \dfrac{E_D}{m}$	EM^{-1}	X	X	rad
Absorbed dose rate $\dfrac{dD}{dt}$	$EM^{-1}T^{-1}$	X	X	rad x s^{-1}
Line energy transfer $L = \dfrac{E_l}{l}$	EL^{-1}	X		keV $(\mu m)^{-1}$
Energy absorption factor (parallel beams) $\mu_{en} = \dfrac{1}{\varrho E}\dfrac{dE_D}{dl}$ $[\mu_{en} = \mu_K(1 - G)]$	$L^2 M^{-1}$		X	

* For better clarity of this table we have taken as fundamental quantities M, L and T on one side, and energy E (i.e. ML^2T^{-2}) or charge Q (IT in the (MKSA system and $M^{1/2}L^{3/2}T^{-1}$ in the electrostatic CGS system) on the other hand.

Parameters	Dimensions *	Defined for di-rectly ionizing particles	Defined for indi-rectly ionizing particles	Special units
3) *Liberated energy E_K*	E		$\times$	
kerma $K = \dfrac{E_K}{m}$	EM^{-1}		$\times$	
kerma rate $\dfrac{dK}{dt}$	$EM^{-1}T^{-1}$		$\times$	
energy transfer factor (parallel beams) $\mu_K = \dfrac{1}{\varrho E}\dfrac{dE_k}{dl}$	L^2M^{-1}		$\times$	
4) *Liberated charge Q*	Q	(photons in air)		
Exposure $X = \dfrac{Q}{m}$	QM^{-1}		$\times$	R
Exposure rate $\dfrac{dX}{dt}$	$QM^{-1}T^{-1}$		$\times$	$R \times s^{-1}$
Mean ionization energy (charged particles, in a gas) $W = \dfrac{\varepsilon}{N'_\varepsilon}$	E	$\times$		eV†
specific gamma radiation constant $\Gamma = \dfrac{l^2}{A}\dfrac{dX}{dt}$	QL^2M^{-1}		$\times$	Rm² h⁻¹ Ci
Activity A	T^{-1}			Ci
Dose equivalent (DE)	—			rem

* For better clarity of this table we have taken as fundamental quantities M, L and T on one side, and energy E (i.e. ML^2T^{-2}) or charge Q (IT in the (MKSA system and $M^{1/2}L^{3/2}T^{-1}$ in the electrostatic CGS system) on the other hand.

† 1 eV $= 1.6 \times 10^{-19}$ joules $= 1.6 \times 10^{-12}$ ergs.

APPENDIX 2

The following parameters have been presented differently in the text. However, we believe that it is useful to mention exactly the definitions given by the International Commission on Radiological Units and Measurements.

Physical definition on incident radiation (section 2 of the text)

The particle flux (Φ) is the ration of ΔN to Δa, where ΔN is the number of particles penetrating a sphere, and Δa the surface of a large circle of this sphere

$$\Phi = \frac{\Delta N}{\Delta a}.$$

The surface particle flux (φ) is the ratio of $\Delta \Phi$ to Δt, where $\Delta \Phi$ is the particle flux during a time Δt.

$$\varphi = \frac{\Delta \Phi}{\Delta t}.$$

This quantity is also called the particle flux rate.

The energy flux (F) of particles is the ratio of ΔE_F to Δa, where ΔE_F is the sum of the energies, except the rest energy, of all the particles penetrating a sphere, and Δa the surface of a large circle of this sphere

$$F = \frac{\Delta E_F}{\Delta a}.$$

The energy flux per surface unit, or intensity (I) is the ratio of ΔF to Δt, where ΔF is the energy flux during a time Δt

$$I = \frac{\Delta F}{\Delta t}.$$

This quantity is also called the energy flux rate.

Parameters used in radioprotection (section 3 of the text)

a) The energy transferred by ionizing radiation to a given volume of a material, is the difference between the sum of the energies of all the directly or indirectly ionizing particles entering the volume, and the sum of the energies of all the particles leaving, less the energy-equivalent of all increases of rest mass resulting from nuclear reactions or reactions between elementary particles in the volume.

The absorbed dose (D) is the ratio of ΔE_D to Δm, where ΔE_D is the energy transferred by ionizing radiation to the material in a volume element, and Δm the mass of material in the volume element,

$$D = \frac{\Delta E_D}{\Delta m}.$$

The rad is the special unit for the absorbed dose:

$$1 \text{ rad} = 100 \text{ erg/g} = \frac{1}{100} \text{ J/kg},$$

where J is the Joule.

The absorbet dose rate is the ratio of ΔD to Δt, where ΔD is the increase of absorbed dose during a time Δt.

Absorbed dose rate $= \dfrac{\Delta D}{\Delta t}$.

As a special unit for the absorbed dose rate one can use the ratio of a rad to any convenient time unit (rad/s, rad/min, rad/h, etc.)

The line energy transfer (L) of charged particles in a medium is the ratio of dE_L to dl, where dE_L is the mean energy locally transferred to the medium by a charged particle with given energy moving by a distance dl.

$$L = \frac{dE_L}{dl}.$$

b) The exposure (X) is the ration of ΔQ to Δm, where ΔQ is the sum of electric charges of all ions of the same sign produced in air when all the (positive and negative) electrons liberated by the photons in a volume element of air with mass Δm, are completely stopped in the air

$$X = \frac{\Delta Q}{\Delta m}.$$

The roentgen (R) is the special unit for the exposure

$$1 \text{ R} = 2.58 \times 10^{-4} \text{ C/kg}.$$

The exposure rate is the ratio of ΔX to Δt, where ΔX is the increase of exposure during a time Δt.

Exposure rate $= \dfrac{\Delta X}{\Delta t}$.

As special unit for the exposure rate one can use the ratio of roentgen to any convenient time unit (R/s, R/min, R/h, etc.).

The kerma (K) is the ratio of ΔE_K to Δm, where ΔE_K is the sum of the initial kinetic energies of all the charged particles liberated by indirecly ionizing radiation in a volume element of a given substance, and Δm the mass of the material in this volume element

$$K = \frac{\Delta E_K}{\Delta m} \, .$$

The kerma rate is the ratio of ΔK to Δt, where ΔK is the increase of kerma during a time interval Δt.

Parameters related to the substances crossed by radiation. (section 4 of the text)

a) the energy absorption factor (per surface mass unit) $\left(\dfrac{\mu_{en}}{\varrho} \right)$ of a substance, for indirectly ionizing particles, is

$$\frac{\mu_K}{\varrho} (1 - G)$$

where G is the fraction of energy of the secondary charged particles lost by Bremsstrahlung in the substance.

In the case of air, $\dfrac{\mu_{en}}{\varrho}$ is proportional to the ratio of exposure to energy flux.

b) The International Commission on Radiological Units and Measurements indicates how it is possible to calculate μ_K from the components of the attenuation factor for X- or γ-rays. These components are τ (photo-electric effect), σ (Compton effect) and $\varkappa$ (pair production), whereas the coherent scattering does not take part in these relationships. For a given incident energy $h\nu$, one has furthermore to known the mean energies emitted per incident photon by the fluorescence photons and by the Compton electrons.

Radiation injuries, diagnosis and treatment

J. R. MAISIN

Département de Radiobiologie
Centre d'Etude de l'Energie Nucléaire
MOL (Belgique)

INTRODUCTION

Man has always looked for means of prolonging his lifespan and thanks to the discoveries of science and medicine has succeded in diminishing the incidence of many diseases causing early death. Paradoxically, the scientific and technological progress achieved in the twentieth century has created new environmental conditions which may have unfavourable influence on human lifespan; one of these is exposure to ionizing radiations.

During his life, everybody is exposed to a dose of about 250 millirads per year: the half of this dose originates from man made sources of radiations.

In this lecture, we intend to summarize our present knowledge on:

1. The acute and late effects of short- and long-term exposure to internal or external sources of radiations.

2. The diagnosis of radiation damages (biological indicators).

3. The treatment of radiation injuries. First of all the duration of the exposure to an internal or external source of radiation over a short- or long-term must be considered

Short-term exposure in human include:

a) exposure to radiation of the total-body or of substantial part over a short time in nuclear reactor or accelerator accidents;

b) exposure of limited areas of the body applicated as a single dose or fractionated over a few days or weeks as in therapeutic radiation or diagnostic radiology. Usually, an acute exposure of 25 *R* is concidered not to have severe consequences.

Long-term exposure can be continued repeated exposure to radiation over months or years. *X*-ray examinations repeated frequently over long time, exposure to cosmic radiation naturally occuring, radioactive isotopes and fallout, are cases of long-term exposures. Usually, one considers a dose od radiation as negligible when it does not exceed 100 *mR* per week; 100 to 1000 *mR* as a low dose and more than 1000 *mR* per week as a high dose.

Although, it is not possible to make a principal distinction between early and late effects—effects observed soon after radiation may persist for a long time—it is convenient for practical purposes to define effects which arise within 60 days after begin of the exposure as early and these occuring after 60 days as late.

The organs can be arranged in order of decreasing sensitivity[1]:

1) *Differentiating tissues* (lymphatic and hematopoietic tissues).

2) *Rapidly dividing tissues*, reproductive organs, intestinal tract, skin and air follicules.

3) *Slowly dividing tissues*: cartilage, growing skeleton, liver, adrenals, pancreas, lung, nervous system, muscle, connective tissues and bones.

I   RADIATION INJURIES

A   External radiation

a   *Short-term exposure*

  1. *Acute effects*

Whole-body radiation—The mode of death after acute total-body or regional exposure depends on dose level, time after exposure, types of radiations and species.

Our sources of informations on acute effects of radiations after whole-body radiation of men are derived from: the Japanese survivors at Hiroshima and Nagasaki; the accidents at atomic explosions (Marshallese and Japanese fisher men 1954); the exposure of a few people to reactor or radiation accidents; the exposure of patients to therapeutic radiation. Nevertheless, we still ignore the exact value for the LD 50 in men. If the data for large animals apply also to men, the acute LD 50 for men is well below 450 rads in air, and may be in the neighbourhood of 250 rads[2,3] 90% mortality would then occur after about 500 rads (Fig. 1).

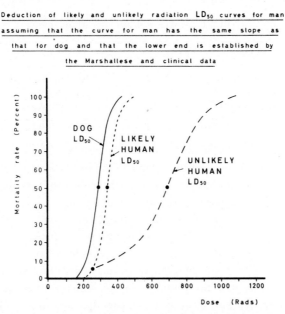

FIGURE 1 Deduction of likely and unlikely radiation LD 50 curves for man assuming that the curve for man has the same slope as that for dog and that the lower end is established by this marshallese and clinical data (from E. P. Cronkite and V. P. Bond, *U.S. Armed Forces—Med. J.* **11** 249–260, 1960).

After a single whole-body dose 50 R and more, certain symptoms may depending on the dose appear within one to two hours[4]. There are:

i) *General*: headache, vertigo, abnormal sensation of taste, or smell, increased irritability, insomnia and fear, etc...

5*

ii) *Gastrointestinal*: anorexia, nausea, vomiting, diarrhea, etc...

iii) *Cardiovascular*: tachycardia, fall of blood pressure, shortness of breath, etc...

iv) *Hematological*: leukocytosis, lymphopenia, and increase sedimentation rate, etc...

These initial symptoms are followed dependent on the dose level and the species by one of the three common syndromes of whole-body irradiation, i.e. the central nervous, the gastrointestinal and the hematological syndrome (Table I).

TABLE I   Modes of death after irradiation

Modes	Doses (R)	Time
Central nervous	>10.000	a few hours and less
Gastrointestinal	1000–10.000	a few days
Hematopoietic	300–1000	two to six weeks

Very high doses of radiation (10000 to 100000 rads) cause death in a few hours or less. This syndrome depends on exposure of the *brain*. After the initial phase of radiation sickness, there is rapid progression from drowsiness to severe apathy, prostration and lethargy [5−10].

The *gastrointestinal* death predominates from 1000 to 10000 R[11,12]. It is characterized by early symptoms of anorexia, nausea, vomiting within 30 minutes to a few hours. Later, diarrhea develops caused by the denudation of the intestinal epithelium. Anorexia, nausea and vomiting prevent normal food and fluid intake. Simultaneously, high fever persists and bloody stools may appear. The abdomen is distended and intestinal peristalsis is absent. Rapidly the state of the patient deteriorates. Severe paralytic ileus, dehydratation and concentration of the blood develop. Then, the circulation fails and the patient becomes comatose and dies, a few days after exposure, from collapse[13].

The hematopoietic form of the death occurs after lower doses of radiation (300 to 1000 rads)[14,15]. As in gastrointestinal death, anorexia, apathy, nausea, vomiting and some diarrhea develop to a maximum 6 to 12 hours after exposure. These symptoms may subside and from 24 to 36 hours, the individual may feel well while the atrophy of his lympho and hematopoietic tissues progress. During the third day the patient develops malaise, headache, fatigue, anorexia, dyspnea on exertion, skin petechies and infection of the gingiva and the tonsil. At this time, partial or complete loss of hair is usually seen. The 5th to 6th weeks are the critical time because of anemia and infection. This increased susceptibility to infection is caused by the impairment of the cellular and humoral defence mechanism (decrease of granulocytes, lymphocytes) decreased antibody production) and by the bacterial invasion from ulcerations in gingiva, tonsils, skin and gut. Convalescence may begin at the end of the second month after exposure, or the patient will die between the 2*d* to the 6th week.

Prognosis—The early symptoms appearing after irradiation are important for diagnosis of the damage[16,17]. A subject presenting marked nausea, vomiting and diarrhea usually dies. Patients where nausea and vomiting are brief (one or two days) and are followed by a period of well being have a good chance to survive (Table II). In general, most people irradiated with doses lower than 200 R survive; many patients recover after irradiation with doses from 200 to 500 R, but only a few after doses from 500 to 1000 R. Survival after more than 1000 R is impossible.

Local radiation—Two weeks after irradiation of the *head*, jaw or tongue of a mouse with doses of 1500 R of *X*-rays or higher, oral death occurs. This mode of death is essentially caused by lesions of the mucosa of the oral cavity, followed by inanition[18,19].

TABLE II Prognostic, doses and symptoms after total body irradiation

Prognostic	Doses (rad)	Symptoms
Recovery probable	<200	nausea
Recovery possible	200–500	granulocytopenia in-
Recovery improbable	500–1000	fection hemorrhages
Recovery impossible	>1000	gasrointestinal central nervous

Irradiation of the *thorax* of mice or rat, with doses of 1500 to 3000 R, is responsible for death from radiation pneumonities one to twelve months after exposure[20]. In rats and mice, this pneumonitis is characterized by a congestion and an oedema of the alveolar wall developing from 1 and 6 months after *X*-ray exposure. Later, thickening of alveolar septa by reticulum fibers, infiltration with macrophage, deposition of blood pigment, edema, congestion and hermorrhages in the alveolar spaces become predominant.

Effect of radiation on the *reproductive organs* is especially important because of the possibility that genetic defects may be transmitted to the progeny. Doses of radiation causing only marginal changes in gut or blood forming tissues may cause hormonal disfunction and complete sterility. In men it is difficult, with high acute doses of radiation, to cause permanent sterility[21,22]. Temporary sterility of 12 months duration usually follows after 250 R. Even 30 R to the human testes may be detrimental. Repeated doses of radiation appear more efficient than single ones in causing permanent sterility. Irradiation can lead to atrophy of the mammalian ovaries with temporary or permanent sterility depending the doses. Changes in ovaries may be followed by secondary endocrine disturbances and atrophy of secondary genital organs in most mammals. There are marked differences in radiosensibility between species. In female mice, 100 R may produce complete sterility in a few months. In woman, an acute dose of 100 R is able to produce permanent sterility, in some cases, usually doses around 600 R are, however, needed[21,22].

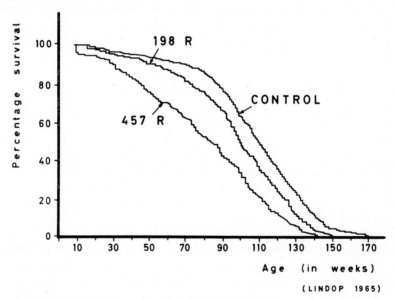

(LINDOP 1965)

FIGURE 2   Influence of acute radiation exposures on the survival of mice.

Late effects—Substantial doses to the whole or to large parts of the body shorten the lifespan of mammals. If one plots the percentage of surviving mice versus age, one obtains a curve which rises slowly at first and then more rapidly (Fig. 2) The age at which 50% of the population survives is defined as median lifespan. If mice are exposed to a single dose of radiation at a certain age, the survival curve is shifted to the left (Fig. 2). From this shift in the curve the lifeshortening produced by a given dose can be determined and the percentage reduction of the median lifespan per unit dose can be calculated[23].

The lifeshortening effect in mice and in other mammals depends on several factors such as *physical* ones (radiation quality, dose-rate, dose, etc...) and *biological* ones (age, strain, sex, etc...).

Physical parameters

1) *Radiation quality*: The radiation quality may influence the lifeshortening effect through the difference in relative biological effectiveness. X-rays of high energy are about 20% more efficient than X-rays of low energy and fast neutrons are about 2 to 3 times more efficient than X-rays[23].

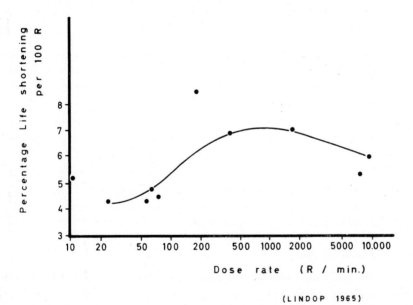

(LINDOP 1965)

FIGURE 3 Variation of specific lifeshortening with dose rate for single radiation exposure in mice.

2) *Dose-rate*: Irradiation given at a low dose-rate is less effective than one given at a high dose-rate (Fig. 3)[23]. Between 20 to 50 R/min, the effect on lifeshortening does not change, but for a dose-rate of more than 50 R/nim, it increases and is maximal between 500 to 1000 R/min where the effect is 60% larger than a dose-rate of 20 R/min. At higher dose-rates, the efficiency of X-rays does not increase any further. The lower efficiency of irradiation given at a low dose-rate is similar to that observed for acute effects and is probable due to a partial repair of the injury.

3) *Dose*: The shortening of lifespan for doses from 100 to 400 R is proportional to the dose absorbed if the γ-rays are given in a short time. After higher doses, the effect on lifespan apparently increases more rapidly. Thus, an X-ray dose of 400 R decreases the lifespan by about 10% whereas a dose of 800 R decreases it by about 45%. After doses below 100 R, no significant difference between the lifespan of the irradiated and that of the non-irradiated animals appears to occur. Thus, most likely a *treshold dose* of radiation exist below which irradiation is without effect on lifespan[24]. If a treshold dose would exist, the exposition of human at very low doses would not be dangerous. It must be added, however, that some workers have observed in mice a linear relationship between doses and lifespan[25,26].

Biological parameters—Among the biological factors, age is most important. The following figure[23] (Fig. 4) shows that mice have a lifeshortening of about 5% for 100 rads if whole-body irradiated at young age, and about 1.3% for 100 rads if irradiated at old age, i.e. at an age 70% of their normal lifespan. The conditions of irradiation were 250 kV and a doserate of 50 R/min. A comparison of the curve of Fig. 4 with that of the life expectation as function of age shows that both have the same slope[23]. This means that if lifeshortening is expressed not as a percentage of the total lifespan of the controls, but as a percentage of the remaining lifespan of the controls or of the survival time from the age at exposure: the specific lifeshortening remains constant throughout most of life[23].

b *Long-term exposure*

In chronic radiation, animals are exposed continually or for a large proportion of time to radiation at a certain dose-rate. From the known dose-rate and the total time of exposure, the cumulative dose received can be calculated. One must consider, however, that some radiation is "wasted"

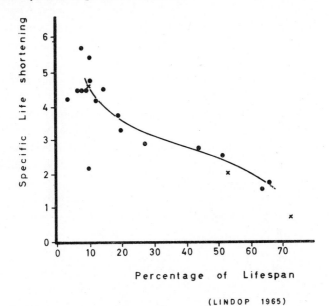

(LINDOP 1965)

FIGURE 4   Specific lifeshortening as a function of age for mice exposed to single doses of radiations.

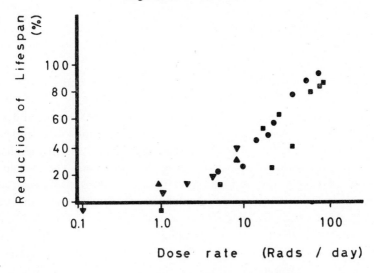

(UPTON 1960)

FIGURE 5   Variations of percentage lifeshortening with dose rate for chronic radiation exposures in mice.

in this way since radiation is delivered until deaths, but the animals would have died from the accumulated damage if the irradiation had been terminated somewhat earlier[23].

The following figure summarizes some of the results published in the litterature on lifeshortening of mice chronically exposed to X- and γ-rays as a function of dose-rate. A high dose-rate is about equally effective with respect to lifeshortening as a single exposure at a young age (5% per 100 rads of accumulated doses), but at a lower dose-rate (1 rad/day), the effect decreases to 0.5% per 100 rads. In this region, the percentage of lifeshortening is proportional to the dose-rate (Fig. 5)[27].

Lifeshortening in man—In 1963, a study on three groups of American medical professions was carried and indicated for the first time that lifeshortening from irradiation exists in man[28] (Table III). The first group con-

TABLE III   Median age of death of Radiobiologists, Internists and Medical Doctors not using X-rays

Period	Radiologists	Internists	Doctors not using X-rays
1935–44	71,4	73,4	76,2
1945–54	72	74,8	76
1955–58	73,5	76	76,4

sisted of 3700 radiologists which received irradiation often. The second group consisted of 7000 internists who received probably somewhat less radiations than the radiologists; the third group were 8000 medical doctors who did not use irradiation in their practice. Table III shows a considerable higher rate of mortality in internists and still higher one in radiologists than in other medical doctors not exposed to radiations. The median age at death is 5 years earlier in radiologists than in medical doctors not using radiations. In the younger generation of radiologists, the lifeshortening is smaller (about 3 years) because of better procedures of protection.

Unfortunately, the total dose of radiation received and other essential data are unknown. Thus, it is difficult to exploit these studies in a quantitive manner. It may be assumed, however, that the lifeshortening effect in man is probably not higher than in the most sensitive animals.

Causes of lifeshortening—The observations in man and mammals indicate that lifeshortening by radiation is not produced by specific causes of death but rather that the causes of death are the same but appear at an earlier age in the irradiated subject than in non irradiated ones. Most frequently, cancers, degenerative lesions and infection produce death.

Ionizing radiation is capable of inducing all type of cancers. The frequency of appearance of the different types of cancers depends of several factors, e.g.: the constitution of the host and the conditions of irradiation. The incidence of leukemia increases mostly after small doses of radiation, whereas other types of cancers prevail after high doses. Thus, the incidence of leukemia is about 5 to 10% higher among the survivors of Hiroshima and Nagasaki than in the rest of the Japanese population[29,30]. A similar observation was made in Great Britain among patients irradiated on their spine for ankylosing spondylitis[31,32].

Embryonal and young tissues are more radiosensitive to induction of leukemia than adult ones[33-37], thus, children irradiated in utero for radiological examination of the mother (which implies exposure to very small doses of radiations) present a significantly higher incidence of leukemia than the normal controls[38].

Other chronic manifestations were already observed by the pioneers of radiation therapy as late sequences of irradiation. Induction of *cataracts* after irradiation of the eyes is well documented[39,40]. *Nephrosclerosis* is found after exposure of the kidneys in radiotherapy[41]. Atrophic and fibrotic changes are observed in human hematopoietic organs long after local irradiation and occlusion of blood vessels is observed in heavily irradiated areas. *Radiation osteitis* is an important degenerative effect of intense radiation exposure. Infections are also frequent after irradiation such as: abcesses of the brain, bronchopneumonia, septicemia, etc...

Principal theories concerning the action of radiation on lifeshortening— Various theories have been advanced to explain ageing and lifeshortening after irradiation. Lifeshortening could be due to a progressive loss of the ability to repair damages[42]; a modification of the physiological equilibrium[43] or to an increase of the number of somatic mutations[44,45]. All these factors could explain natural ageing as well as acceleration by irradiation.

It is assumed that irreparable lesions produced by irradiation add to those from normal ageing of the body and together bring about the early death of the irradiated animals. The following figure (Fig. 6) shows a scheme of these processes. The ordinate represents the amount of radiation damages; the abscissa, the age of the animals. In animals irradiated at 150 days of age, a certain number of lesions remain unrepaired and add up to the lesions resposible of normal ageing bringing about earlier death at a certain level of lesions[46].

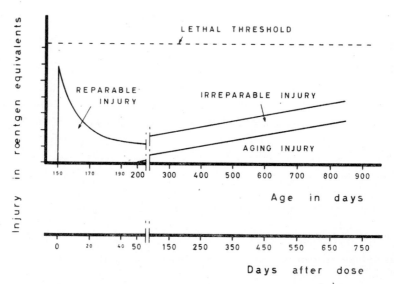

FIGURE 6   Diagrammatic summary of radiation injury, recovery, accumulation of irreparable injury following a single exposure to radiation of rats.

B   Internal radiation

The increasing use of radioisotopes in medicine, agronomy and industries and the possible accidental discharge of radioactive material from reaktors in nuclear detonation increase the risk of internal or cutaneous contamination with various radioactive products. The deleterious effects of a radionuclide depends on its quantity; its biological and physical half time and the nature of the contaminated tissue.

The most frequent routes of contamination of the body are *ingestion*, *inhalation* and *skin-absorption*.

Ingestion is important only when the isotope is soluble. Inhalation is the most important route of entry for potentially hazardous materials in the industry and may lead to:

1) Absorption into the blood circulation and subsequent deposition at a critical tissue or organ:

2) Irradiation of the lungs themselves from material deposited on respiratory surfaces and picked up by bronchial lymphnodes.

Absorption of radioisotopes through the *skin* is not yet sufficiently studied. Although, substances especially inorganic ones are usually not taken up by the skin, absorption through the skin may be important under certain conditions even for substances such as tritiumwater $(H_2{}^3O)$[47,48].

Our experience on long-term effects of internal emitters in man is essentially confined to radium used therapeutically and in the dial painting industry; to thorium used as a contrast medium for roentgen-graphic diagnosis and to the elements from the decay chains of radium and uranium to which miners have been exposed[49]. Cancer has occured frequently in these exposed groups.

More recently, radiophosphorus[50], radioiodine and other nuclides (Ru–106)[50] have been often used in experiments, treatment and diagnosis, but the reports of tumor induction by these isotopes require verification. Radiostrontium which becomes localized in bones, induces osteosarcomas and epidermoid carcinoma of the oral and nasal mucosa in mice. Pulmonary tumors occur often in mice inhaling radon and the incidence of cancers of the lung after inhalation of plutonium-239, strontium-90 and cobalt-60, etc...., is significantly higher than in the normal controls[51–54].

II DIAGNOSIS

After a nuclear accident, the extent of damage to the irradiated subject is often unknown since the dose measured by the badge film is not at all representative of the dose received by other parts of the body. Then, the accident must be reconstructed; this may take a few weeks and by then the patient is died or has recovered. Clearly, while physical dosimetry is very important, particularly in the prevention of accidents, it is only limited value for an accurate estimate of radiation damage. But, even if physical dosimetry could give us an accurate determination of the dose received by the different parts of the body we would still be left with the question how to translate these dose values into terms of damage implicated of the particular individual. The idea of using biological indicators is of course not new: remember the skin erythema dosis and many other reactions, for example blood status, which are still used as monitors of radiation damages in an irradiated population. An ideal biological indicator should[55]:

1) *Be sufficiently sensitive* to distinguish between clinically important stages of radiation damage and allow recognition of damage not immediately evident on clinical inspection.

2) *Respond early* so that the answer can be of use in guiding therapy.

3) *Not be influenced* by disorders other than those caused by irradiation. and

4) *Be simple* to execute even in moderately well equiped laboratories and should not burden the patient with an additional injury.

Most probably, the ideal biological indicator will never be found; we will have to content ourselves with a number of tests from which we estimate

TABLE IV   Selected biochemical indicators of radiation damage (from Gerber, *Belgicatom* 1965)

Substance studied	Spezies	Time	Dose depen-dency	Deter-mination	Mechanism related to
Urine					
β Aminoisobutyric acid	rat man	1–5 days	?	more complicated	DNA metabolism
Creatine	rat man	1–3 days	+	easy	Muscie membrane
Deoxycytidine	rat man	1st day	+	more complicated	DNA metabolism
5 Hydroxyindol acetic acid	rat	1st day	+	more complicated	Tryptophan Serotonin metabolism
Indoxyl sulfate	rat man	1–2 days	+	easy	Metabolism of intestinal bacteria?
Pseudouridine	rat	1 day	+	more complicated	Nucleic acid metabolism?
Taurine	rat man	1st day	+	more complicated	Destruction organs
Blood					
Serum proteins	rat man	3–5 days	?	easy	increased catabolism
Serum transaminase	rat man	1–3 days	?	easy	release from organe
Lactic acid dehydrogenase	rat man	1–3 days	?	easy	

radiation damage. In a similar manner we are limited by the type of samples which we can take from a living subject and which at the same time should be representative of the damage to the total body. Thus, samples from blood or urine become most important, two types of biological indicators may be using: the biochemical and the cytological indicators.

Biochemical indicators

Table IV lists letabolic substnaces the concentration of which in the urine and in the blood is changed after irradiation[55,56]. It should be pointed out that some of the biological indicators have been studied in more details (creatine, taurine, deoxycytidine) whereas other have just been found by one investigator at one dose level[55].

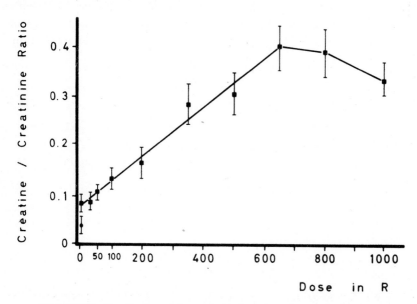

FIGURE 7   Creatine/creatinine ratio in the urine of rats after treatment with different *X*-ray doses (from Altman, *Belgicatom* 1965).

The following figure shows the creatine/creatinine ratio in the urine of rats as function of the *X*-ray dose (Fig. 7)[57]. For *X*-ray doses below 700 R, a certain correlation exists between the amount of creatine in the urine and the doses of radiation. It is of interest that in many cases a biphasic curve for the excretion of metabolites is found: a peak shortly after irradiation probably representing the immediate damage or the reaction of the body and a second peak which coincides with the secondary disease of the irradiated organism.

Cytological indicators

Chromosome alterations in cells from the circulating blood or from the skin may also aid the diagnosis of radiation damages. These chromosome lesions can be detected shortly after irradiation, but persist, in part, for a long time thereafter. The method is not simple to execute, but very sensitive; the percentage of chromosome fragments in cells produced by one roentgen is approximately 0.0025 per cell[22]. This technique has already been applied in several cases; for example, at an accident at Oak Ridge, 8 individuals were exposed to doses from 22-350 R consisting of gamma rays and $\frac{1}{4}$ neutrons. Twenty-nine months later, Bender and Gooch[58] observed abnormal chromosome number in 7–23% of the examined cells and a percentage of 2 to 10% chromosome aberrations. Fourty-two months after irradiation, many chromosome alterations were still present.

III   TREATMENT

A   External radiation

If there are reasons to suspect that radiation dose given to patients may be in the lethal range, the following should be considered in addition to the usual principles of good medical care[59].

1. Isolation precautions should be used and special nurses should be assigned to irradiated patients thus reducing the possibility of cross infection from other areas in the hospital.
2. Antibiotics should not be used prophylactically but only for treatment of infection.
3. Severe bleeding present as a consequence of thrombocytopenia may be treated by platelet transfusions either of gresh whole-blood or of fresh platelet rich plasma.
4. Blood transfusions are reserved for the treatment of severe anemia.
5. Bone-marrow therapy must be reserved for those situations where the clinical and laboratory findings suggest that a fatal outcome is likely.

Chemical protectors given before X-ray exposure protect mammals against radiation damage, but the toxicity of these substances and the need to apply then before exposure, limit their utilization in human[60]. The best protectors are certain sulfhydryl compounds and 5-hydroxytryptamine, which yield a dose reduction factor of about 1.7. If 99% of the mice are killed by a dose of 750 R within 30 days, a dose of 1350 R is needed for the same effect after protection with mercaptoethylamine or 2-β-aminoethyl-isothiouronium. Administration of a mixture of chemical protectors increases the protective effect further and at same time decreases also the toxicity. Thus, a mixture of mercaptoethylamine, 2-β-aminoethylisothio-uronium, glutathione, cysteine and 5-hydroxytryptamine gives a dose reduction factor about 3 (yet the 99% lethal dose for mice is increased for 750 to 2300 R)[61,62].

B Internal radiation

Recent efforts to promote the excretion of deposited radioisotopes such as plutonium, thorium, yttrium and the rare earths, have been encouraging[63]. Since the *chelating* agent diethyl-thiamine-penta-acetate (DTPA) has proved to be superior to the ethylenediaminetetraacetate (EDTA) used generaly, DPTA should be useful in the prompt treatment of accidental exposure to these radionuclides[63]. Prolonged treatment with DTPA is even effective in removing substantial fractions of firmly deposited plutonium from the bone[64]. The removal of strontium or radium seems less efficient and no use-ful treatment is presently available for incorporation with these radio-isotopes. Recently, however, uptake of strontium has been shown to be diminished by treatment with *sodium alginate* which, in swine, decreases the uptake of strontium-85 in relation to that of calcium-47 and caesium-134[65]. Application of large quantities of calcium by the diet may also retard the deposition of strontium and may even hasten its excretion, but this effect seems to be too small to justify the risks entailed in the con-sumption of such large amounts of calcium.

CONCLUSIONS

This lecture attempted to summarize the present knowledge on short- and long-term effects of radiation in mammals and the diagnosis and treatment of radiation lesions. Much progress has been realized in these fields during recent years, but more remains to be done to protect the population from radiation risks. Thus, effective non toxic radioprotectors or radiorestaurators and adequate biological indicators must be found. Moreover, the long-term effects of very low doses of radiation in the irradiated population and on their progeny must be studied in more details.

This work was done through grants from the "Fonds de la Recherche scientifique fondamentale collective".

References

1. C. J. Clemedson and A. Nelson, In *Mechanisms in Radiobiology*, M. Errera and A. Forssberg, ed. Academic Press, New York, (1960).
2. E. P. Cronkite, V. P. Bond, and C. L. Dunham, U.S. Atomic Energy Commission, Report No YID-5358, (1956).
3. V. P. Bond, E. P. Cronkite, C. A. Soudhaus, G. Imirie, J. S. Robertson, and D. C. Borg *Radiat. Res.*, **6**, 554, (1957).
4. F. Ellinger, Medical radiation biology. Charles C. Thomas, Springfield, Ill., (1957).
5. A. Arnold, P. Bailey, R. A. Harvey, L. L. Haas, and J. S. Laughlin, Radiology, **62**, 37, (1954).
6. V. P. Bond, T. Fliedner, and J. O. Archambeau, In Mammalian Radiation lethality, Academic Press, New York, (1965).
7. C. D. Clemente and E. A. Holst, *Arch. Neurol. Psychiat.*, **71**, 66, (1954).
8. W. Haymaker, F. S. Vogel, J. Cammermeyer, G. L. Laqueur, and W. J. Nauta, *Amer. J. Clin. Pathol.*, **24**, Suppl. **70**, 70, (Abstract) (1954).
9. H. B. Gerstner and S. P. Kent, *Radiat. Res.*, **6**, 626, (1957).
10. S. P. Hicks, K. A. Wright, and C. J. D'Amato, *Arch. Pathol.*, **66**, 394, (1958).
12. R. Hasterlik, "Clinic Report of four individuals accidentally exposed in gamma radiation and neutrons", U.S. Atomic Energy Commission, Argonne National Laboratory, Lemont, Illinois, (1953).
13. L. J. Cole, P. C. Nowell, and E. M. Ellis, *J. Nat. Cancer Inst.*, **17**, 435, (1957).
14. G. Mathe, In *Nuclear Hematology*, ed. E. Szirmai, Academic Press, New York, p. 275, (1965).
15. S. Watanabe, In *Nuclear Hematology*, ed. E. Szirmai, Academic Press, New York, p. 485, (1965).
16. E. P. Cronkite, *Radiology*, **56**, 661, (1951).
17. C. F. Behrens, in *Atomic Medicine*, Williams and Wilkins Co. Batimore, Maryland 3 d edition. Chap. 9, 10, 11, 13. (1959).
18. A. Dunjic, J. R. Maisin, P. Maldague, and H. Maisin, *C. R. Soc. Biol.*, **150**, 587, 1956.
19. A. C. Upton, R. F. Buffett, J. Furth, and D. C. Doherty, *Radiat. Res.*, **8**, 475, (1958).
20. A. Dunjic, H. Maisin, and P. Maldague, *Arch. Intern. Physiol. Biochem.*, **66**, 22, (1958).
21. A. Leonard, *J. Belge Radiol.*, (in press).
22. A. Leonard, *J. Belge Radiol.*, (in press).

23. P. J. Lindop, In *Scientific basis of Medicine*, p. 91, The Athlone Press, (1965).
24. A. C. Upton, A. W. Kimball, J. Furth, K. W. Christenberry, and W. M. Benedict, *Cancer Res.*, **20**, 1, (1960).
25. J. B. Storer and P. C. Sanders, *Radiat. Res.*, **8**, 64, (1958).
26. P. J. Lindop and J. Rotblat, *Proc. Roy. Soc. B*, **154**, 332, (1961).
27. A. C. Upton, *Gerontologia*, **4**, 162, (1960).
28. R. Seltser and P. E. Sartwell, *Amer. J. Epidemiol.*, **81**, 2, (1965).
29. R. Heyssel, A. B. Brill, L. A. Woodbury, E. T. Nishimura, T. Ghose, T. Hoshino, and M. Yamasaki, *Blood*, **15**, 313, (1960).
30. L. H. Hempelmann, Cancer Res., **20**, 18, (1960).
31. W. M. Court-Brown and R. Doll, Medical Research Council Report No 295.
32. W. M. Court-Brown, *Brit. Med. Bull.*, **14**, 168, (1958).
33. C. L. Simpson, L. H. Empelmann, and L. M. Fuller, *Radiology*, **64**, 840, (1955).
34. C. L. Simpson and L. H. Hempelmann, Cancer, **10**, 42, (1957).
35. C. L. Simpson, In *Radiation Biology and Cancer*, U. Texas Press, Austin, Texas, (1959).
36. H. B. Latourette and F. J. Hodges, *Amer. J. Roentgenol.*, **82**, 667, (1959).
37. L. S. Snegireff, *Radiology*, **72**, 508, (1959).
38. A. Stewart, J. Webb, and D. Hewitt, *Brit. Med. J.*, **I**, 1495, (1958).
39. D. G. Cogan and K. K. Dreisler, *A. M. A. Arch. Ophtal.* **5P**, 30–34, (1953).
40. F. R. Merriam, Jr. and E. F. Focht, *Am. J. Roentgenol.* **71**, 357–369, (1958).
41. R. W. Luxton, *Quart. J. Med.*, **22**, 215, (1953).
42. J. B. Storer, *Radiat. Res.* **10**, 180, (1959).
43. G. A. Sacher, *Radiology*, **67**, 250, (1956).
44. L. Szillard, *Proc. Nat. Acad. Sci.*, **45**, 30, (1959).
45. G. Failla, *Proc. Nat. Acad. Sci.*, **45**, 30, (1959).
46. G. W. Casarett, In *Advances in gerontological Research*, Vol. 1, p. 109. Academic Press, New York, (1964).
47. C. W. Delong, R. C. Thompson, and H. A. Kornberg, *Amer. J. Roentgenol.*, **71**, 1038, (1954).
48. E. A. Pinson and W. H. Langham, *J. Appl. Physiol.*, **10**, 108, (1957).
49. G. Saccomanno, V. E. Archer, R. P. Saunders, L. A. James, and P. A. Beckler, *Health Physics*, **10**, 1195, (1964).
50. S. Laskin, M. Kuschner, B. Altshuler, and N. Nelson, *Health Physics*, **10**, 1229, (1964).
51. H. Cember and J. A. Watson, *Amer. Ind. Hygiene*, **19**, 36, (1958).
52. S. Warren and O. Gates, (personal communication).
53. H. Kjeldsberg, *Tidsskr. Norske Laegeforen*, **77**, 1052, (1957).
54. W. J. Clarke, J. F. Park, J. L. Palotay, and W. J. Bair, *Amer. Rev. of Respiratory Diseases*, **90**, 1964.
55. G. B. Gerber, *Belgicatom*, **10**, 3, (1965).
56. G. B. Gerber, *Symp. über unfallbedingte Bestrahlung am Arbeitsplatz*, Nizza, (1966).
57. K. I. Altmann, *Belgicatom*, **10**, 13, (1965).
58. M. A. Bender and P. C. Gooch, *Radiat. Res.*, **18**, 389, (1963).

59. United Nations General Assembly Scientific Committee on the Effects of Atomic Radiation—Draft of Annex D of the 1962 comprehensive Report "Somatic Effects of Radiation".
60. Z. M. Bacq, *Chemical protection against Ionizing Radiation*, Charles Thomas, Publ., Springfield, Illinois, U.S.A., (1965).
61. J. R. Maisin and G. Mattelin, *Nature*, **214**, 207, (1967).
62. J. R. Maisin, G. Mattelin, A. Manduzzio-Fridman, and J. van der Parren, *Radiation Research*, (in press).
63. E. G. Tombropoulos, *Health Physics*, **10**, 1251, (1964).
64. M. W. Rosenthal, J. F. Markley, A. Lindenbaum, and J. Schubert, *Health Physics*, **8**, 741, (1962).
65. O. van der Borght, J. Colard, S. van Puymbroeck, and R. Kirchmann, Proc. Intern. Symp. "Radioecological Concentration Processes" Stockholm, p. 589, (1966).

PART II

Basic topics

Radiation effects in solids— theory of semiconductors

P. BARUCH

Groupe de Physique des Solides
Faculté des Sciences et Ecole Normale Supérieure
Paris, France

It is quite remarkable to see that the advent of the "nuclear age" almost coincides with the "age of semiconductor electronics" (the first reactor in 1943, the first transistor in 1948). Semiconductor physics has very rapidly taken an important place in the disclosure of a new and revolutionary technology. But from the very first investigations on these materials, it became clear that it is necessary to know the influence of nuclear radiations on their properties. Not only fundamental imperatives, but also practical reasons play a role, and especially the question up to which degree of reliability transistorized electronic equipment can be used in a radiation field.

The first studies were performed about 20 years ago at Oak Ridge and at Purdue University, where it was shown that germanium (the first semi-conductor investigated) is extremely sensitive to radiation. Fluences of 10^{13}–10^{14} fission neutrons, or 1 MeV electrons are sufficient to alter appreciably the electrical properties of germanium. Such a sensitivity is somewhat 10^3 to 10^4 times as high as in the case of usual metals. Only the ionic crystals are still more sensitive, and especially the silver halides, by the photographic process.

However, this phenomenon was not too surprising for the semiconductor physicists. They had indeed found that the presence of impurities and im-perfections are very intimately related to the peculiar properties which made the semiconductors so interesting. In research and applications since radiation was a new tool for influencing purity and perfection, the pheno-menon was obvious.

One should nevertheless be careful by the fact that the radiation-induced changes are essentially caused by *nuclear* interactions, which yield atomic displacements by momentum exchange. The electronic ionization processes, which play a predominant role in ionic crystals, glasses and organic ma-terials, generally only give rise to a transient effect in semiconductors. Hence the creation of permanent changes (or at least stable ones at the temperature at which they are formed) will depend upon the energy and the nature of radiation, in a completely different way as compared to the phenomena related to ionization. Applications in dosimetry should take into account this fact. For a better understanding of the nature of irradiation effects, we will summarize briefly the different possible interactions between a semi-conducting crystal and nuclear radiations (neutrons, gamma-rays, elec-trons, protons and high energy ions).

I INTERACTIONS BETWEEN RADIATION AND CRYSTALS

Although this subject may seem extremely vast, covering a large part of physics, we will limit ourselves for the present purpose to high energy radiation (above 100 keV) or, more precisely, to radiation carrying per particle a momentum above some 100 keV/c. This precision will enable us to include the description of the effects of ionic bombardment with slow but heavy ions. We will classify these interactions, and we will show particular interest for the ones which are able to create persistent changes in the properties of the crystal. We will discuss successively the thermal, the electronic, the non-elastic nuclear and the elastic nuclear effects.

1 Thermal effects

When a particle penetrates a solid it looses energy, first by ionization, and at the end of its path the type of energy transfer is abruptly changed giving rise to an energy exchange by interaction with the atoms. Since these interactions take place along a very short length, a large quantity of energy is lost within a very limited region. This region may be heated up to a high temperature, which is shown by calculation to be above the melting temperature of the material. This yields a localized collective disorder, the so-called thermal spike. These localized effects seem to play an important role in the bombardment by fission fragments or by fast neutrons, where these particles act either directly or through secondary displacement cascades[2-4].

2 Electronic effects : ionization

The interaction of ionizing radiation with the electron shells of the atoms leads to charge separation or ionization. In covalent semiconductors this ionization gives rise to the creation of free carriers, electrons and positive holes, in quantities which are proportional to the energy injected into the crystal if the created carriers are not trapped. This is the case in germanium or silicon and it is the reason which makes these materials so appropriate for the manufacture of radiation detectors[1]. The excess number of free carriers will show up as transient variations of physical properties: conductivity increase, light emission, etc. More particularly, the carriers created inside the space charge region of a *p–n* junction are entirely collected, giving rise externally to a current pulse. The junction thus operates like an ionization chamber, yielding for each detected particle a pulse which is proportional to the energy loss (or to the energy, depending on the counter's thickness).

The energies involved with the creation of excess electrons by ionization in metals or semiconductors are insufficient to disrupt the bonds. Hence ionizing radiation is not able to create defects. On the contrary the rupture of the electrostatic equilibrium in ionic crystals (or in crystals with a pronounced ionic binding, such as some semiconductors like InSb) may, through complex mechanisms, give rise to structural changes; a very weak energy (a few electron volts) may be sufficient contrarily to displacement phenomena which will be described later. One may conclude that there will be no essential difference between low energy photons (visible light) and high energy photons (X or γ) with respect to their action upon alkali halides (colour centers) or silver halides (photographic process).

However, secondary effects due to ionization may influence the appearance of permanent changes, even in covalent semiconductors.

First of all the ionization-induced increase of the conductivity during a "nuclear flash" can be such that the equipment is really short-circuited, and the operating electrical equipment destroyed.

The surface ionization phenomena may create "chemical" changes in the surface: adsorption or desorption of foreign molecules. Since most of the semiconductor devices, and especially the field effect transistor, are very sensitive to the surface properties, deterioration of characteristics is possible.

Finally, as will be shown later, properties of radiation-induced defects in covalent crystals depend upon their charge. Since the ionization effects change the electronic density they will influence, by a secondary mechanism, the structure and the properties of the defects created by the primary interactions.

3 Inelastic nuclear effects

Without going into detail, it can be said that the capture of a slow neutron may give rise to a transmutation, i.e. to a change of the chemical nature and the chemical properties of the material. Doping of silicon with phosphorus by transmutation has been proposed for manufacturing certain types of diodes. However these phenomena are finally related to the variation of chemical properties. Therefore they will not be treated within the scope of the present paper.

In the same way the introduction of the impurities by means of an ion beam sufficiently energetic to penetrate deeply into the crystals, has recently been used in order to change the doping of semiconductors, to produce junctions, etc.[11-13].

4 Elastic processes [2-6]

With these processes one enters into the field of elastic interactions between a projectile with mass M_1 and energy E_1, and an atom at rest with mass M_2. The recoil energy of the nucleus is then

$$T = T_m \sin^2 (\Theta/2),$$

where Θ is the scattering angle in the center of mass system, and T_m is the maximum kinetic energy transferred.

In the non-relativistic case T_m is equal to

$$T_m = \frac{4M_1 M_2}{(M_1 + M_2)^2} E_1.$$

For neutrons and protons $T_m = (4/A) E_1$; for electrons, $T_m = \frac{4m}{M_2}$ $\times E\left(1 + \dfrac{E}{2mc^2}\right)$, where $\dfrac{E}{2mc^2}$ is a relativistic correction.

An energy transfer takes place during such an elastic interaction. In a crystal which is in thermodynamic equilibrium, 1 to 2 eV is required to bring an atom from its lattice site to the surface; this is also the energy required to create a vacancy. In the case of a process out of equilibrium, e.g. under irradiation, a much larger energy will be required to pull out an atom by a collision.

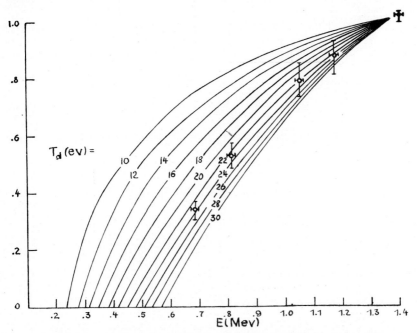

FIGURE 1 Determination of the displacement energy E_D for copper. The full drawn curves are calculated for the indicated values of E_D and are normalized at 1.3 MeV. The experimental data are situated on the curve $E_D = 23$ eV (after Corbett *et al.*, *Phys. Rev.* **108**, 954 (1957))

Wigner has been the first to estimate the energy E_D required to removing an atom out of its crystalline position; it is of the order of $4E_S$, where E_S is the sublimation energy.

This reasoning is in accordance with experiment in the case of copper, where the experimental displacement energy is $E_D \approx 22$ eV (Fig. 1). In fact the observed energies vary in a range of 10 to 100 eV. If an energy larger than E_D is supplied an ejected atom 'may be obtained with a certain kinetic energy, sufficient to create further a number of secondary effects. This phenomenon is described by a displacement probability which is a function of the transferred energy T. This probablity varies continuously from 0 to 1 (Fig. 2), but may be represented schematically by a step function.

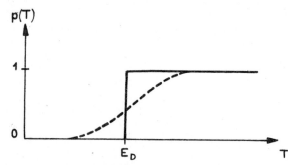

FIGURE 2   Displacement probability of an atom as a function of the transferred energy T. The full drawn curve represents the usual approximation

In the following discussion it will be assumed that a well determined displacement energy exists.

Table I shows the bombardment energies needed to transfer respectively 25 eV and 50 keV to a copper atom.

TABLE I

Cu	$T_m = 25$ eV	$T_m = 50$ keV
protons	410 eV	820 keV
neutrons		
electrons	492 keV	38 MeV

It is clear that if one wants to reach these threshold energies, the simplest way will be to use electrons which are easily obtained from an electrostatic accelator.

Other useful data are summarized in table II.

TABLE II

	Threshold energy in eV	Electron energy in keV
Si	12.9	145
Ge	15.1	360
InP	8.7	274
	9	111
GaAs	9	233
	9.4	256
InSb	5.7	240
	6.6	285

For germanium an energy between 10 and 15 eV is found by different authors; in fact the really important value to know is the mean energy interval within which the phenomenon of defect creation starts.

The displacement energies depend upon the nature of the bonds and crystal structure. The compounds such as InP, GaAs, and InSb exhibit two threshold energies related to each kind of the displaced atoms. In InSb a rather peculiar effect is observed[7]. The crystallographic directions [111] and [$\bar{1}\bar{1}\bar{1}$] are not equivalent with respect to the displacement of In and Sb atoms. The displacement energies will also be different for different irradiation directions. Indium is more easily displaced along [$\bar{1}\bar{1}\bar{1}$] than along [111]; the inverse happens for antimony (Fig. 3).

The calculation of the number of defects which can be created is performed using collision theory.

Only two types of collisions will be considered here:

1) hard sphere collisions, due to fast neutrons or heavy atoms;
2) Coulomb collisions, due to charged particles (protons, deuterons, alpha's, electrons, and gamma's through the effect of photoelectrons).

It is useful to calculate in each of these cases the differential and total cross sections for these interactions, as far as they give rise to displacements. The total displacement cross section σ_D enables one to calculate the number of defects created. If the number of sites per unit volume is denoted by M, the defect density is

$$n = M\sigma_D\Phi,$$

where Φ is the integrated flux.

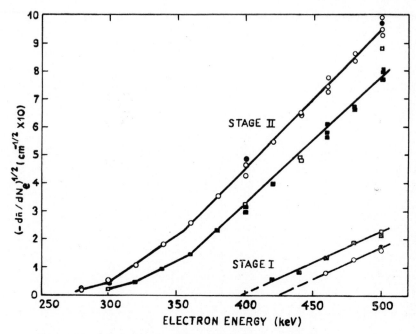

FIGURE 3 Determination of E_D in InSb. Curves I correspond with the displacement of Sb, and the curves II with the displacement of In. The symbols □ and ○ refer to irradiation along [$\overline{111}$] (Sb side) the symbols ■ • to irradiation along [111] (In side). (after Eisen, ref. 7)

The individual collisions may be described by the differential cross section $d\sigma$. σ_D and $d\sigma$ are related by the equation

$$\sigma_D(E) = \int_0^{T_m} p(T)\, d\sigma\,(E, T),$$

where E is the incoming energy and T the transmitted energy.

In the case of an abrupt energy threshold, this formula is simplified to

$$\sigma_D(E) = \int_{E_D}^{T_m} d\sigma.$$

The mean value of transmitted energy is then defined by

$$\langle T \rangle = \frac{\int T\, d\sigma}{\int d\sigma}.$$

These three parameters σ_D, $d\sigma$ and T give a complete description of the primary event of the collision.

We will summarize now the calculations in the case of hard sphere collisions. Since the differential cross section $d\sigma$ is a constant, all recoil directions have the same probability (in the center of mass system), and so are energy transfers from 0 to T_m.

In the case of neutrons where the displacement energy is negligible compared to the maximum transmitted energy, one has $\bar{T} = (1/2)T_m$; however a fast neutron of 1.26 MeV will not supply more than 100 keV to a copper atom (50 keV as an average). The total displacement cross section is almost equal to the collision cross section; it has values between 1 and 10 barns for fast neutrons.

In Coulomb collisions one deals with small angle collisions which are always very important. In this case the (non relativistic) differential cross section is:

$$d\sigma = \frac{\pi R^2}{4} T_m \frac{dT}{T^2} ;$$

with

$$R = \frac{Z_1 Z_2 e^2}{(1/2)\, \mu v^2} ;$$

μ = reduced mass and v = incoming velocity measured in the center of the mass system.

This mechanism is favourable to low energy transfers, and the mean value of transferred energy is always smaller than in the case of neutrons:

$$\langle T \rangle = E_D \log (T_m/E_D).$$

The cross sections are of the order of 1000 barns for protons and deuterons, and 50 barns for electrons (Fig. 4).

5 Secondary collisions

If the transferred energy is large enough the atom displaced during a primary knock on, may also play the role of projectile, and create a cascade of new displacements.

If the collisions are described by the hard sphere model, each step of the cascade will, on the average, transfer equally the energy between the displaced atoms. The cascade is stopped when the transmitted energy becomes smaller than the displacement energy (Table III). Hence the average number

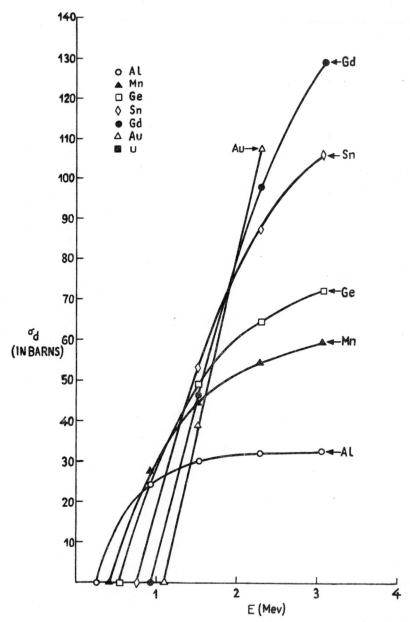

FIGURE 4 Displacement cross sections in different metals irradiated with electrons (theoretical curves calculated for $E_D = 25$ eV) (after Walker, ref. 4)

$\bar{\nu}$ of displaced atoms per primary collision transmitting E will have the following asymptotic value

$$\bar{\nu} = E/2E_D \quad \text{(for } E \gg E_D\text{)}.$$

TABLE III

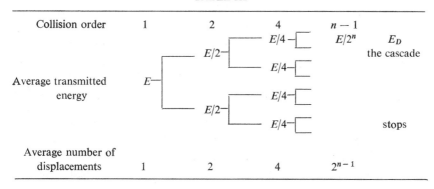

Collision order	1	2	4	$n-1$	
Average transmitted energy	E	$E/2$, $E/2$	$E/4$, $E/4$, $E/4$, $E/4$	$E/2^n$	E_D the cascade, stops
Average number of displacements	1	2	4	2^{n-1}	

More exact calculations yield a similar picture which depends weakly on the assumptions made concerning the collisions process (Fig. 5).

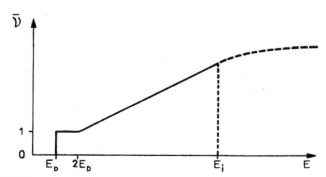

FIGURE 5   Average number of displacements per primary collision, as a function of primary energy. Above E_i the ionization losses have to be taken into account

Hence the average number of displacements per primary collision may be determined. This should enable one to obtain the total number of defects created by the irradiation, and their spatial distribution. Without going into details of the calculations, it results that for equal energy transfer, according to the cross section laws described above, charged particles will create less displacements than fast neutrons. Moreover, the neutron-induced defects will be much more clustered together, giving rise to strongly disordered regions which seem to have been observed in some cases.

Nevertheless the theoretical calculations have not been confirmed by experiment. In the few cases where one has been able to compare the observed defect creation rate with the calculated values, it was shown that the number of defects are over-estimated by theory by a factor of 2 (influence of fast electrons) to 10 (fast neutrons). This is true even if it is taken into account that the experimentally observed defects are not single but generally complexes which are due to migration and partial recovery of the originally created defects.

These discrepancies between theory and experiment may be explained as follows:

Above a certain limit, the displacement of an atom in a lattice does no longer create damage, since the atom looses its energy by ionization. Hence there is a cut-off at a certain energy which depends on the velocity and the energy of the atom (Fig. 5).

In the preceding calculations the crystal was considered as disordered. If the lattice order is taken into account, the phenomenon of focused collisions arises. This phenomenon occurs in the neighbourhood of the threshold energy. It consists of chains of consecutive replacement collisions propagating along an atom row, transporting energy without creating defects[3-5].

At higher energies the phenomenon of particle channeling occurs: if a particle has a small angle of incidence with respect to a crystallographic direction, it is channeled and is no longer subject to collisions (Fig. 6).

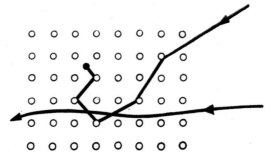

FIGURE 6   Schematic   trajectories   of   channeled   and   non-channeled
particles

The values of the cross sections will consequently strongly depend on the crystallographic orientation. This effect, which has only been discovered relatively recently[5,6,13] plays an important part both in the creation of defects and in the efficiency of nuclear reactions.

As a conclusion it may be stated that it is difficult to define a relation of equivalence between the different types of radiation, since both the nature and the number of the created defects can be different.

II RADIATION EFFECTS IN SEMICONDUCTORS

The aim of the physicist is to recognize and to classify the macroscopic radiation effects, in order to obtain information concerning the microscopic structure of the created defects. On the other hand the aim of the engineer is to attempt to predict the radiation effects in a given semiconductor device.

We will not be able, within the scope of the present paper, to treat in detail these viewpoints, and both of them will be discussed very briefly.

1 Macroscopic effects

We shall limit ourselves to electrical effects; the radiation induced defects consist generally of "localized centres" which are able to exhibit different charge conditions and where free carriers can be trapped. Consequently these defects may be characterized by energy levels in the forbidden band, and by capture cross sections for electrons and holes. In this respect the defects behave in a way analogous with chemical impurities, donors and acceptors.

Hence the free carrier concentration, the mobility and the life time may vary under irradiation. Consequently variations of conductivity and life time are observed. In the case of conductivity it is difficult to give a general law for the direction of the variation. On the other hand the life time decreases in almost all of the cases.

The latter parameter is the most important one for the working of the majority of semiconductor devices[9]. It can easily be shown that the recombination probability for electron–hole pairs is proportional to the defect concentration. Hence

$$1/\tau = 1/\tau_0 + K\Phi,$$

where τ is the life time after irradiation at a flux Φ, and τ_0 the initial life time; K is a coefficient which depends on temperature, nature of irradiation, and nature of the semiconductor involved. This equation is valid for low fluences, i.e. as long as the free carriers concentration has not much changed.

From this equation one may conclude that the gain of a transistor or the efficiency of a solar battery will vary according to the law indicated, at least as a first approximation which is not valid for weak fluences (predominance of surface effects) nor for high fluences (predominance of resistivity changes). For example, the efficiency of a solar battery will drop to half its value for approximately 10^{15} electrons of 2 MeV per cm², or for the same number of fission neutrons. The main technical problem is to determine the coefficients K. They are hardly predictable as we will see that in a given semiconductor, the nature of the defects (and hence their efficiency) strongly depend on the type and quantity of the impurities, and on the type of radiation. It has nevertheless been possible to establish "correspondance tables" between radiation, which are valid (at operating temperature) for a given type of device; e.g. solar battery with n/p Si, or HF Si-transistor, etc.

2 Microscopic structure of radiation defects

The physicist will attempt to explain the observed macroscopic effects (the electrical effects described above; the optical effects: infrared absorption, photoconductivity; the magnetic effects: electron spin resonance, etc.) by the existence of a certain number of defects, maybe of different types: vacancies, interstitials, divacancies, several complexes, etc.

Such theoretical interpretations of experiments yield valuable information. On the other hand data concerning e.g. migration energy annihilation proces (reaction kinetics) are obtained by annealing experiments (recovery of defects by heating the sample). The latter data allow one to precise the identification, particularly in comparison with the properties of defects observed in other conditions than irradiation (heating and quenching, deformation, etc.).

In the first part of this paper we have described the way in which radiation may create defects, and we have also indicated the calculation principles. From these calculations it becomes clear that the defects will almost consist of vacancies or interstitials, in isolated position or bunched together in clusters of variable size, depending on the nature of irradiation. In particular, 1 to 3 MeV electrons create vacancy-interstitial pairs. Hence the first investigations were performed in order to verify the existence of these simple defects, and to build up a theoretical model for their properties.

Such a model seemed to be satisfactory up to 1958, but afterwards several experimental observations were shown to be in flagrant contradiction with the model.

At the present time the interpretation of the radiation effects (at least for germanium and silicon) is ruled by the following three basic principles[7-10]:

a) the simple defects (vacancies, interstitials) are stable only at low temperature (below 100°K or less); as soon as temperature increases, these defects migrate in the lattice and are annihilated or transformed into more stable structures.

b) strong interactions exist between the defects, or between defects and impurities. Hence one generally observes only associations of defects, particularly in the form of impurity—simple defect complexes.

c) the stability and the mobility of the defects depend on their charge behaviour (whether or not they are electron or hole traps). This charge behaviour itself is determined by the free electron density in the crystal in its equilibrium state, or by the number of charge carriers created by external influences (ionizing radiation, illumination, injection by a junction).

The conclusion is that the behaviour of a semiconducting crystal under irradiation depends on the type and the quantity of impurities (doping), history (pre-existing defects) and also on the experimental conditions.

We shall discuss these ideas in the case of germanium and silicon. The other semiconductors will not be discussed since it seems to be difficult to give a general view as yet. On the other hand we shall limit ourselves to the radiation effects of electrons and gamma-rays with a medium energy (between the threshold energy—see Table II—and 10 or 20 times this value). In this way the complication due to secondary cascades are avoided. Consequently we exclude for the time being the case of neutrons, although it is very important.

2.1 *Silicon*

The structure of the defects in silicon has been established with a rather good precision, by means of electron paramagnetic resonance, which technique allows one to determine the spatial configuration of the defects.

A number of relatively stable defects are observed after irradiation at room temperature, which anneal above 150°C. Nevertheless the structure of the defects depends on the impurity content of the crystal. In n-type silicon e.g. associations of vacancy – oxygen and vacancy – phosphorus are formed. Silicon pulled from the melt using a quartz crucible will have a large oxygen content and hence the first defect will be predominant, otherwise the second defect will be predominant in a crystal with a low oxygen content, such as obtained by the floating zone method. Another important defect is the double vacancy, created directly (by secondary collisions) or by the association of simple vacancies. The role of the impurities becomes even more significant in the case of lithium-doped silicon. The presence of lithium gives rise to a pronounced decrease of the effects of the life-time change, by a "spontaneous recovery": it is believed that the creation of defects is not suppressed, but that the defects are "complexed" by lithium, making them inoperative. Some investigators have proposed to use this remarkable phenomenon to obtain radiation-insensitive solar batteries.

Low temperature investigations have led to the explanation of this influence of impurities. It has indeed been possible to prove that simple vacancies are effectively created by irradiation, but that this defect is very mobile. It is able to move in the crystal lattice already at 90°K in n-type silicon and at 130°K in p-type silicon, and it is trapped by impurities to form more stable complexes. In this case the importance of the charge of the defect with respect to its stability becomes clear. This point also plays a part in a number of different experiments: e.g. the minority carrier injection by a junction may in certain circumstances[10] reduce the damage by irradiation (p/n solar batteries, 1 Ω cm, irradiated at 100°K).

The behaviour of interstitials is still not accurately known. According to one hypothesis, it would be mobile up from 4°K, but would interact very rapidly with substitutional impurities such as boron, "pushing" them into interstitial positions[10].

2.2   *Germanium*

Although this semiconductor is very similar to silicon, the structure of its defects is not so well known. Indeed paramagnetic resonance has not yet produced important results, and the optical experiments give rise to some difficulties.

As in the case of silicon, the associations with impurities seem to be predominant at room temperature. The defects are less stable (annealing at about 80–100°C) and exhibit recovery kinetics depending on the type of predominant impurities (arsenic, antimony, etc.) Nevertheless the exact structure is not yet known. In any case it does not seem that simple isolated defects exist at room temperature. It has indeed been possible to observe migration of simple defects at lower temperatures (90–130°K), giving rise to association with impurities in the same way as in silicon: vacancy-oxygen complex, or displacement of a substitutional antimony by a germanium interstitial.

Many experiments have been performed in the very low temperature range (4 to 80°K). It has been shown that in electron irradiated *n*-type germanium, a defect is formed which is stable up to 650°K; it is believed that it consists of a weakly bound vacancy – interstitial pair. This would confirm the existence of the primary defect predicted by theory. Nevertheless the observed creation rate does not correspond to the calculated value; it depends in fact strongly on the free electron concentration in the crystal: the existence of the vacancy–interstitial pair seems to be stabilized by the capture of an electron. This assumption partly accounts for the fact that this defect is not found in *p*-type germanium, irradiated in the same conditions. It is also compatible with the influence of the ionization intensity (e.g. due to irradiation) on the creation rate of the defects. Finally the creation of electron–hole pairs by illumination yields a decrease of the annealing temperature from 65° to 20°K. Recent experiments seem to indicate that a coherent model will soon be built up in order to account for the properties of this primary defect.

2.3 *Effect of fast neutrons*

In the detailed description of the models of defects we have omitted the defects created by neutrons. As we have seen above these particles give rise to secondary displacement cascades, and to localized thermal effects. A description of radiation damage may be given by assuming very strongly disordered regions (with a diameter of 100 to 1000 Å) distributed in a less perturbed matrix, but containing more simple defects like the ones described above.

The disordered regions, in semiconductors, will behave like small islands giving rise to strong perturbations of the electrical properties. It has been possible to prove their existence by the study of these electrical properties, by the study of thermal conductivity and even by direct microscopic observations.

The effect of heavy charged particles will, depending on their energy, be intermediate between the effects of electrons and neutrons.

CONCLUSION

Notwithstanding the complexity of the effects described above, it has been possible to establish certain general rules. For a given semiconductor the exact type of radiation defects depends on its purity, its crystallographic perfection, temperature, the type of radiation used, and finally on the electronic conditions (ionization, injection). Further investigations will probably allow a better definition of these factors and a unified description in the near future. At the same time semiconductors with better known composition will probably be obtained in a reproducible way, owing to progress of manufacturing technology.

From the point of view of dosimetry, the great radiation sensitivity of semiconductors may be made profitable in two different ways; the semiconductor counters are very accurate instruments which have already partly superseded the proportional and the scintillation counters in the nuclear physics branch. They permit to count and to measure the energy of ionizing particles at low intensity.

The deterioration of semiconductors by irradiation seems in particular to be a problem for the use of electronic devices. By their behaviour under weak fluxes the semiconductors may be used for certain dosimetric purposes. Nevertheless a few conditions should be taken into account: one has to be sure about the manufacturing reproducibility of the device used (e.g. the changes of the efficiency of a solar battery will be measured, or the forward current of a p–i–n diode). One should also be aware that not the total energy deposited in the dosimeter will be measured (like in usual dosimetry) but a quantity of a different type, such as the number of incident particles with energy larger than a given energy.

References

A   *Ionization effects and semiconductor counters*
 1. Dearnaley, Northrop, Semiconductor counters for nuclear radiation, Spon. (1963).

B   *Radiation defects in solids*
 2. G. J. Dienes and G. H. Vineyard, *Radiation Effects in Solids*, Interscience Publ., New York (1957).
 3. D. S. Billington and J. Crawford, *Radiation Damage in Solids*, Princeton University Press (1961).
 4. D. S. Billington (editor) *Radiation Damage in Solids* (Ispra 1960) Academic Press (1961).

5. R. Strumane, R. Gevers, J. Nihoul, and S. Amelinckx, (editors) "Interaction of radiation with solids" (*Mol Summer School 1963*), North Holland Publishing Cy, Amsterdam (1964).
6. T. L. Chadderton, *Radiation damage in crystals*, Methuen London (1965).

C   *Irradiation of semiconductors*

7. P. Baruch (editor) "Effects des rayonnements sur les semiconducteurs" (*Colloque de Royaumont, 1964*) Dunod Paris (1965).
8. J. W. Corbett, Electron radiation damage in semiconductors and metals, Academic Press, New York (1966).
9. Bielle *et al.* (editors) "Effects des rayonnements sur les dispositifs à semiconducteurs" *Journées d'Electronique*, Toulouse (1967).
10. F. L. Vook (editor) "Radiation effect in semiconductors" (*Colloque de Santa Fe, 1967*) Plenum Press, New York (1968).

D   *Channeling and implantation effects*

See particularly ref. 5, 6, 10 and
11. Mac Caldin *Progress in solid state chemistry* **2**, 9–25, (1965) Pergamon Press, NewYork.
12. *Conference on atomic collisions and penetration studies with energetic ion beams* (*Chalk River Conference*, 1967) to be published in *Can. J. Phys.*
13. Ph. Glotin (editor) *Conférence sur les applications des faisceaux ionique à la technologie des semiconducteurs*, Grenoble (1967).

Theory of luminescence

JAMES H. SCHULMAN

U.S. Naval Research Laboratory
Washington, D.C.

I INTRODUCTION

It is almost two decades since the introduction of the first practical dosimetry method based on luminescence changes in solids, the radiophotoluminescence method.[1] Other luminescence-based methods were proposed shortly thereafter in rather quick succession—thermoluminescence,[2] infrared-stimulated luminescence,[3] and luminescence degradation.[4] The lion's share of effort has been devoted to development of solid-state materials and devices to exploit radiophotoluminescence[5-8] and thermoluminescence.[9-13]

Major advances along these lines have made in the past decade, resulting in dosimeters of truly remarkable sensitivity, range, simplicity, ruggedness, and small size—attributes which have excited intense interest in the use of luminescence-based devices in health physics, radiobiology, and clinical radiology.[14-18]

In this paper we will review the principles involved in the operation of various types of luminescence dosimeters. In addition to the obviously relevant topic of luminescence itself, we shall discuss the defects and radio-chemical changes produced in solids by ionizing radiations. The underlying principles will be illustrated by descriptions of practical dosimetry systems of historical or current importance.

II GENERAL ASPECTS OF LUMINESCENCE

A Terminology of Luminescence

For our purposes it will be adequate to define luminescence as the emission of light that is not attributable to incandescence. For most of the applications of interest to dosimetry the emitted light lies in the visible region, but in general the luminescent radiation may lie anywhere in the spectrum, either of the ultraviolet or the infrared side of the visible region.

Since the energy radiated by a system must be provided in some way, various types of luminescence are often distinguished by a prefix denoting the nature of the energy source. Thus, luminescence excited by bombardment with cathode rays is called cathodoluminescence; by application of an electric field, electroluminescence; by conversion of the chemical energy of a system, chemiluminescence; by absorption of light, photoluminescence. Very often this labelling is carried to extremes, and it can even be misleading. Thus, the rather ill-chosen term "thermoluminescence", on the face of it, implies a contradiction of our rough definition of luminescence. "Radio-photoluminescence" does not describe a mode of excitation but, as we shall see later, a sequence of processes which includes the creation of lumi-nescence response in a nonluminescent material. Although they are part of the vocabulary of luminescence, excessive significance should therefore not be attached to terms like the foregoing. The features common to all forms of luminescence are (a) the occurrence of some process whereby an atom, molecule, or "center" (an aggregate of atoms or defects in a crystal) is excited to a higher energy state; and (b) its radiative de-excitation to the ground state, i.e., via the emission of a photon of appropriate energy, after the lapse of some period of time.

A further distinction between various types of luminescence is also frequently made based on the time-dependence of emission. Initially the term "fluorescence" was applied to luminescence which persisted only as long as the excitation was continued; if luminescence was observable after removal of the exciting source, the phenomenon was called "phosphorescence." Clearly, a distinction on this basis is not very meaningful, because with instrumental techniques one can readily observe a luminescent "afterglow" ("persistence", "decay time") of the order of 10^{-8}–10^{-9} seconds. Systems that would have to be classed as "fluorescent" using a visual criterion of persistence, would therefore have to be called "phosphorescent" based on the instrumental measurement of afterglow.

A more meaningful distinction between fluorescence and phosphorescence is based on the temperature-dependence of the luminescence decay time, τ_{lum}, rather than on its absolute magnitude*. Thus, if the emission is due to a spontaneous transition of the system from an excited energy level E^* to the ground energy level E^0, (Fig. 1), the luminescence will decay exponentially with a decay time determined by the probability of the transition between these states. If this is an allowed electric dipole transition, with emission of a photon in the visible region of the spectrum, the decay time will be in the range 10^{-8}–10^{-9} seconds. If the transition $E^* \rightarrow E^0$ is of a different type (electric quadrupole, magnetic dipole, etc.), the transition probability is many orders of magnitude lower, with a corresponding increase in decay time. However, the transition probability in all cases is an intrinsic characteristic of the luminescent center; the luminescence decays exponentially with time, and the decay time is independent of temperature (in the range of temperature where the luminescence efficiency remains high †. All the

---

* The terminology described here conforms to usage in the field of inorganic luminescent materials. The terminology used in research on organic systems does not conform to this.

† When a system in the excited state E^* can also return to E^0 via a *radiationless* or dissipative transition of time constant τ_{diss}, the observed decay time $\tau_{observed} + \tau_{lum}$. Since E^* can be depopulated by two parallel paths, $\dfrac{1}{\tau_{observed}} = \dfrac{1}{\tau_{lum}} + \dfrac{1}{\tau_{diss}}$ and $\tau_{observed}$ is therefore less than τ_{lum}. Increase in temperature of a system ultimately establishes parallel radiationless de-excitation paths. The resulting temperature-dependent decay is accompanied by an observable decrease in luminescence efficiency, however; which is why the above parenthetic restriction is cited.

above cases are properly characterized as fluorescence, the "allowed" transition producing a "fast" fluorescence while the relatively "forbidden" transitions produce "slow" fluorescences.

The term "phosphorescence" is most properly applied when the luminescence decay time depends on the temperature even in the temperature range where the luminescence efficiency is high (cf. * and **). On an atomic scale this situation can arise (Fig. 1) when the atom, molecule, or center

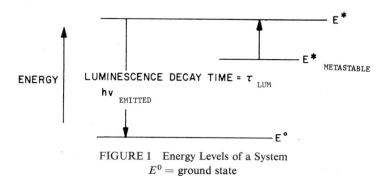

FIGURE 1   Energy Levels of a System
E^0 = ground state
E^* = an excited state from which a spontaneous radiative transition can occur with high probability
$E^*_{\text{metastable}}$ = an excited state from which a radiative transition is "forbidden"

is somehow excited to an energy level, $E^*_{\text{metastable}}$, from which it cannot return to the ground level with emission of a photon; i.e., the transition $E^*_{\text{metastable}} \rightarrow E^0$ is completely or largely forbidden by the selection rules. Let us suppose that a higher excited level, E^*, exists to which the system can be raised by absorption of the energy $\Delta E = (E^* - E^*_{\text{metastable}})$, and that the radiative transition $E^* \rightarrow E^0$ is an allowed one (Fig. 1). Under these circumstances light of the energy $\Delta E_{\text{emitted}} = (E^* - E^0)$ will be emitted if energy $\Delta E_{\text{absorbed}} = (E^* - E^*_{\text{metastable}})$ is provided to the center. If $\Delta E_{\text{absorbed}}$ can be provided by thermal means at room temperature, e.g. by absorption of phonons from the lattice in the case of a crystalline system, a continuing luminescence emission (phosphorescence) can be observed even after the excitation source is removed. This emission will continue with dimishing intensity until there are no longer any centers in the metastable state. If the system is raised to a higher temperature, the energy $\Delta E_{\text{absorbed}} = (E^* - E_{\text{metastable}})$ will be provided at a more rapid rate; consequently, the phosphorescence will brighter and the decay time will be shorter due to the faster depopulation of the metastable state via the path: $E^*_{\text{metastable}}$ + heat $\rightarrow E^* \rightarrow E^0 + h\gamma_{\text{emitted}}$. Conversely, lowering of the temperature will produce the opposite effects—a decrease in phosphorescence brightness and in an increase in the decaytime. Thus the temperature-dependence of the decay time is the important difference between phosphorescence and fluorescence.

From the foregoing description it will be clear that so-called "thermoluminescence"—temperature-stimulated light emission following removal of excitation—is merely a case of phosphorescence observed under conditions of steadily increasing temperature. In the usual thermoluminescence experiment the system is excited at a temperature at which the phosphorescence intensity is low (long decay time), and then heated through a temperature range where the phosphorescence is bright (very short decay time), until a temperature is reached at which all the centers have been thermally excited out of their metastable levels and the luminescence completely disappears.

It will also be apparent that the energy $\Delta E_{\text{absorbed}} = (E^* - E^*_{\text{metastable}})$ can sometimes be provided by light absorption, for example by infrared light. In this case the system exhibits the phenomenon of "optically stimulated" luminescence. This terminology is not to be confused with the stimulated emission involved in laser action. In the optically stimulated emission referred to here the stimulating light is of different frequency $\left(\nu_{\text{stim}} = \dfrac{(E^* - E^*_{\text{metastable}})}{h} \right.$ from that of the emitted light $\left(\nu_{\text{emitted}} = \dfrac{(E^* - E^0)}{h} \right)$, and the emission is incoherent.

B Luminescent materials

Luminescence of interest to dosimetry applications occurs in both inorganic and organic materials in a variety of states—crystalline, glassy, and solution. The principal applications involve inorganic insulating materials such as alkali and alkaline earth fluorides, phosphates, borates, and sulfates. An important class of inorganic materials, mainly for other applications, are semiconducting crystals such as the zinc-cadmium sulfides and selenides. Organic materials of high luminescence efficiency are generally aromatic compounds with multiple benzene rings, such as naphthalene, anthracene, and terphenyl.

We shall devote our discussion primarily to solid inorganic insulating materials. The vast majority of these owe their luminescence ability to small concentrations of selected chemical impurities, structural defects, or combinations of the two; these entities are called "activators." Among the most widely employed impurity activators in inorganic solids are manganese, the rare earths, thallium, lead, tin, antimony, copper, and silver. They are generally incorporated in the host matrix by firing 10^{-5}–10^{-2} mole fraction of the impurity compound with the host. The luminescent materials themselves are commonly referred to as "phosphors" whether or not they exhibit phosphorescence.

C   Temperature-dependence of phosphor spectra and efficiency; configuration coordinate diagrams

In contrast to the absorption and luminescence spectra of dilute gaseous atomic systems, which consist of sharp lines, the corresponding spectra in solid phosphors generally consist of rather broad bands having widths of a few tenths of an electron volt. In the photoluminescence of solid systems the emitted light generally is of longer wavelength (lower energy) than the exciting light, a condition first experimentally noted in 1851 by G. Stokes and known as Stokes' Law. These spectral characteristics, as well as other properties connected with the temperature-dependence of the luminescence efficiency of phosphors, may be understood by consideration of so-called "configuration coordinate" diagrams which are generally used to summarize the characteristics of luminescent centers.

These diagrams are attempts to represent the potential energy of the various electronic states of the center in terms of a single coordinate that characterizes the center. If the center were a vibrating diatomic molecule, for example, the configuration-coordinate diagram would be identical with the ordinary potential energy diagram, in which the potential energy of the molecule in the ground state and in the various electronically excited states is plotted as a function of the internuclear distance. In this case the internuclear distance would be the "configuration coordinate". In a more complex center, consisting of a central positively charged impurity ion and its nearest shell of anion neighbors in a solid, there are several modes of vibration of the center (Fig. 2). If it is assumed that one of these modes, i.e., the radial or "breathing" mode (Fig. 2a), is the one which has the greatest influence on the energy of the center, the configuration coordinate can be taken as the distance between the central ion and any one of its equidistant anion neighbors.

Figure 3 shows the configuration-coordinate diagram of such a center. The minimum in the lower curve, which describes the potential energy of the

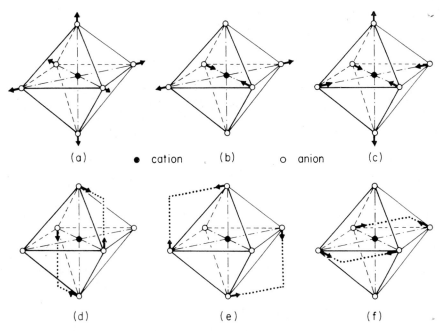

(a)   • cation   (b)   o anion   (c)

(d)   (e)   (f)

FIGURE 2   Vibrational modes of a luminescent center, a central cation
octrahedrally surrounded by anions

system in its electronic ground state, occurs at the equilibrium separation
between the central ion and its neighbors. At all temperatures above absolute
zero, thermal vibrations will cause displacements of the order of kT from
the equilibrium positions. The upper curve shows the potential energy of the
first electronically excited state of the center. Because the interatomic forces
in the excited state are generally weaker than those in the ground state, the
top curve has correspondingly less curvature; its minimum is also generally
displaced with respect to the minimum of the ground-state curve.

   To describe the luminescence process with the aid of this diagram, we
must recall the Franck-Condon principle, which states that an electronic
transition involving absorption or emission of a photon takes place in a
time interval much shorter than that of nuclear motions. Such absorptive
or emissive transitions are therefore represented by vertical lines on the
diagram. The process of photoluminescence in the center is then as follows:
Absorption of a photon, $h\nu_{\text{abs}}$, excites the system from a point such as A
on the ground-state curve to a point A' on the excited-state curve. Since the

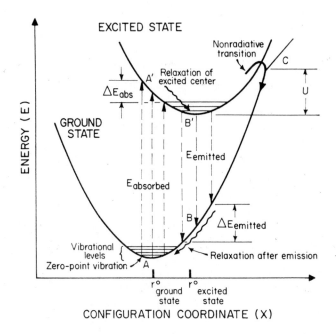

FIGURE 3   Schematic configuration-coordinate diagram of a luminescent center

system at A' is not in its equilibrium configuration, it will dissipate its excess vibrational energy nonradiatively to neighboring molecules, thereby arriving at the point B' on the curve. Here it will remain for a time that depends on the probability of the optical transition $B'B$. When this transition occurs, a photon $h\nu_{lum}$ is emitted. The system is now back in the ground electronic state, but with an excess of vibrational energy. This excess energy is also dissipated to the surroundings, and the system returns to its original condition.

From this representation it is clear that the energy of the emitted photon is less than that of the absorbed photon, the difference being due to the energy dissipated as heat in the relaxations of the center from $A' \rightarrow B'$ and $B \rightarrow A$. The corresponding relationship between the wavelengths of the emitted light and the absorbed light gives the basis for Stokes' Law.

The diagram also shows how a radiationless transition can take place from the excited state to the ground state by an "internal conversion" process.

The curves for these two states approach very closely (or "cross") at point C. If the activation energy $U(= B'C)$ is provided, the center can make this transition without emitting radiation, after which it relaxes to the minimum of the ground-state curve by giving its excess vibrational energy to the surroundings. All of the absorbed energy is thus dissipated nonradiatively. The probability of such a radiationless transition, P_{diss}, is proportional to $\varepsilon^{-U/kT}$, while the radiative transition probability, P_{lum}, is independent of temperature. The quantum efficiency of luminescence is thus

$$\eta_{lum} = (1 + \text{const } \varepsilon^{-U/kT})^{-1}.$$

The dissipative transition is therefore favored by an increase and the radiative transition by a decrease of temperature. This general result is confirmed by experiment; a great many system that are nonluminescent at room temperature luminesce quite efficiently at liquid-nitrogen or liquid-helium temperature.

From measurements of the quantum efficiency as a function of temperature one can obtain the activation energy U. A good activator has a high value of U. When the doping agent or defect has a low value of the activation energy, the absorbed energy is easily degraded as heat, and the center is called a "killer" center or "poison".

From the configuration-coordinate curves some general ideas can be obtained about the shape and temperature dependence of the absorption and emission bands of a center. From Fig. 3 it can be seen that the spread of energies in an optical transition increases with the amplitude of oscillation of the center. On a purely classical picture, for an assumption that the center can be represented by a harmonic oscillator, it follows rather simply that the bandwidth in absorption and emission is proportional to $T^{1/2}$. This predicts that all absorption and emission spectra should narrow to sharp lines at very low temperature. Experimentally the $T^{1/2}$ law is approached at higher temperatures but is seriously in error at low temperatures. Experiment shows that the bands do not narrow at fast as this law would predict at low temperatures, and that the width remains as high as a few tenths of an electron volt even when the temperature is lowered to near absolute zero. This behavior has been explained on the basis of a quantum-mechanical description of the center. Because of the zero-point energy of a quantized oscillator, the system accupies the lowest vibrational level $1/2hv_{vib}$ above the minimum of the classical curve rather than being *at* the minimum (cf. Fig. 3).

8*

III   RADIATION-INDUCED IMPERFECTIONS IN SOLIDS: COLOR CENTERS[29]

Luminescence methods of dosimetry depend upon radiation-induced changes in the optical properties of solids, these changes arising from the alteration of existing imperfections or the production of new imperfections by the high energy radiation. Imperfections in the alkali halides have long been the objects of intensive study by optical absorption, luminescence, and electron paramagnetic resonance methods, hence they are particularly suitable compounds to illustrate the concepts underlying luminescence dosimetry. The structure of these salts consists of two interpenetrating cubic lattices of alkali ions and halide ions. A two-dimensional representation of this simple type of structure is shown in Fig. 4. The ideal crystal consists of an uninterrupted alternation of alkali ions and halide ions as illustrated in Fig. 4a. Extensive studies have shown, however, that real crystals do not attain the ideal structure pictured in that figure; instead they have a great many structural imperfections, of the types illustrated in Figs. 4b, 4c, and 4d. The imperfections (Schottky defects) found in the alkali halides are generally those shown in Fig. 4b, wherein occasional positive and negative ions are missing at random throughout the crystal. In a pure crystal the number of missing alkali ions (alkali-ion "vacancies") must equal the number of halide-ion vacancies in order that the crystal as a whole be electrically neutral. Other imperfections (Frenkel defects) are possible, in principle, as shown in Figs. 4c and 4d. Here alkali ions or halide-ions respectively have been displaced from normal lattice positions into interstitial positions, leaving behind corresponding vacancies.

The existence of these imperfections has important consequences when the crystal is exposed to ionizing radiation. Thus, for example, the halide-ion vacancies shown in Figs. 4b and 4d are regions of localized positive charge, because the negative ion which normally occupies the lattice site is missing and the positive charges of the surrounding alkali ions are not fully neutralized. If an electron is made free in the crystal by the action of an x-ray photon and wanders near the halide-ion vacancy, it is attracted by a Coulomb force to the localized positive charge and it can be "trapped" in the vacancy, as shown in Fig. 4e. Similarly, an interstitial halide ion shown in Fig. 4d represents a region of localized excess negative charge. When an x-ray strips an electron from one of the normal lattice ions, the deficiency of electronic charge (called a "positive hole" or just "hole") can migrate through the crystal, and can be attracted and bound coulombically as shown

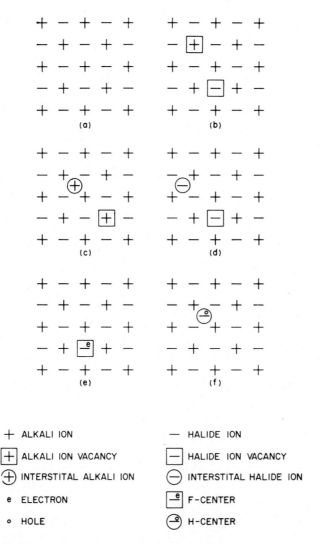

FIGURE 4 Schematic representation of some structural imperfections, as well as trapped-electron and trapped-hole centers, in alkali halides

in Fig. 4f. It should be noted that the ionizing radiation can also *produce* vacancies and interstitials in structurally perfect regions of the crystals, in addition to liberating free electronic charges which interact with these structural imperfections in the manner just described.

The system (or "center") comprising an electron trapped at a halogen-ion vacancy, Fig. 4e, roughly resembles a hydrogen atom, in which an electron is bound by the positive charge of a proton. Like a hydrogen atom the electron-vacancy system has discrete allowed energy levels, and it can make transitions between these levels by absorption or emission of the proper quanta of energy. The absorption of a light photon of the proper frequency can raise the electron from the ground state of the system to one of its higher excited states, and a sufficiently energetic photon can even expel it from its vacancy "trap" altogether. The possibility of absorbing light makes the crystal colored, and the imperfections which give rise to these absorptions are therefore called "color centers". The particular center consisting of an electron trapped at a halide-ion vacancy shown in Fig. 4e is called an "*F*" center (after the German word for color center: "Farbzentrum"). The specific trapped-hole center shown in Fig. 4f is the so-called "*H*" center, which is formed when alkali halides are irradiated at very low temperatures. For most alkali halides the principal *F*-center absorption band lies in the visible region of the spectrum; the *H*-band absorption lies in the near ultraviolet.

IV   RADIOPHOTOLUMINESCENCE

As we have mentioned earlier, the return of a center from an excited state to its ground state can take place either by radiationless dissipation of its excess energy, by emission of this energy as a photon of light (luminescence), or more generally by a combination of these processes. Thus, if stable color centers are created by high-energy radiation, they may also act as luminescent centers when they are subsequently excited by appropriate optical-frequency radiation. This is the situation described by the term "radiophotoluminescence": the radiation-induced creation of new centers that are photoluminescent.

Figure 5 schematically illustrates the properties of the *F* center in an alkali halide. The far ultraviolet absorption bands intrinsic to the pure unirradiated crystal occur at the shortest wavelengths shown in the figure. The various absorptions due to the *F* center are shown by the solid curve. (The nomenclature of the shorter wavelength absorption bands—"*K*", "L_1". etc.—has grown up in a purely arbitrary fashion). The luminescent emission which results when the excited *F* center returns to the ground state is shown by the dashed curve. The processes corresponding to these optical phenomena

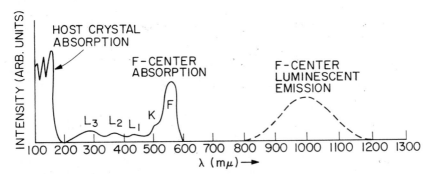

FIGURE 5   Schematic representation of absorption and luminescence
spectra of an alkali halide containing *F* centers

are shown in Fig. 6, which represents the energy-level diagram of an alkali-
halide crystal containing both alkali-ion and halide-ion vacancies. The
absorption of a far-ultraviolet photon by the pure crystal ejects an electron
from the uppermost filled band of allowed energies ("valence band") into
the higher-lying empty band of allowed energies ("conduction band"). The
electron thus becomes free to wander through the crystal in the conduction
band; the positive hole in the valence band can also migrate through the
crystal by an analogous process. The result of the absorption act may be
pictured as an electron transfer from a halide ion to an alkali ion, converting
both species to neutral atoms, with the electron and positive hole both
moving around at random thereafter, rather than residing on any particular
alkali or halogen. Free electrons and holes can, of course, be produced also
by absorption of more energetic radiation, such as the x-rays or γ-rays of
interest in dosimetry.

   Located in the band of energies between the valence band and the conduction band, i.e., in an energy gap forbidden to electrons in an ideal
crystal, there are localized energy levels that arise from crystal defects. In
Fig. 6 the discrete, unoccupied localized energy level created by a negative-
ion vacancy is shown as a short line above the schematic picture of the
vacancy. When an electron from the conduction band is trapped by the
vacancy and occupies this energy level, the empty vacancy is converted into
an *F* center, as also shown schematically in the figure. The ground and excited states of the *F* center are indicated as localized energy levels above the
schematic picture of the *F* center; optical transitions from the ground state
nto the various excited states give rise to the "*F*", "*K*", "*L$_1$*", etc. ab-

Solid state dosimetry

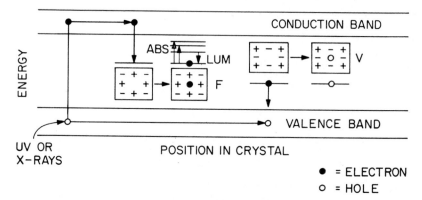

FIGURE 6 Representation of *F*-center and *V*-center formation during irradiation of an alkali halide in terms of simplified energy-level diagram

sorption bands. After excitation to these states, the *F* center can emit luminescence which is shown in Fig. 6 also.

To complete the picture one should ask about the fate of the positive hole created by the original ionizing absorption event (ultraviolet or x-ray absorption). Figure 6 shows a possible process wherein the hole migrates through the valence band and is trapped at a positive-ion vacancy to give a center which is the antimorph of the *F* center.

In principle, then, a system of dosimetry could be based upon the production of *F* centers by radiation. The concentration of centers—and hence the radiation exposure or dose—could be determined by measuring either their absorption or their photoluminescence. In practice, however, this is not feasible; neither the efficiency nor reproducibility of *F*-center formation in the "pure" salts is adequate for most dosimetric applications, and the act of measuring the absorption of these centers "bleaches" them out at normal temperatures. Furthermore, *F* centers luminesce efficiently only at very low temperatures, hence their photoluminescence is not observable or usable at normal temperatures. Radiation-induced centers having the requisite reproducibility of yield, stability to measuring light, and useful luminescence are found only in alkali halides "activated" by selected chemical additives in solid solution—in particular the Ag^+-ion.

Figure 7 depicts some of the centers which have been shown to exist in Ag^+-doped alkali halides before and after x-irradiation.[30,31] The figure caption also lists the peak wavelengths of the absorption and luminescence

	IONIC Ag$^+$	"E" CENTER	"B" CENTER
25°C ABSORPTION PEAK λ	< 2500A	4400A	2800A
25°C EMISSION PEAK λ	2750A	NONE	4350A

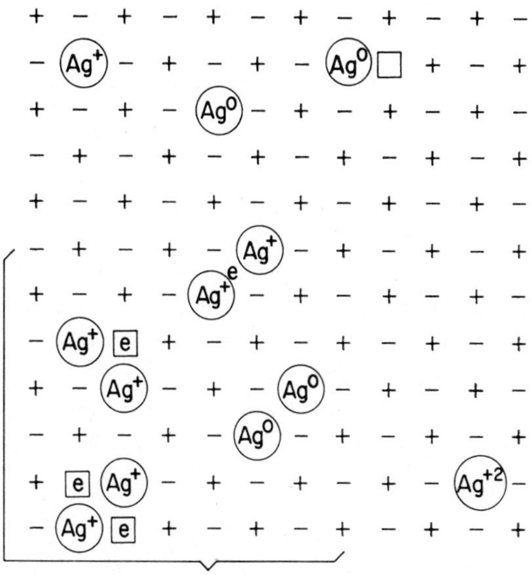

	VARIOUS POSSIBLE "C" CENTERS	"D" CENTER
25°C ABSORPTION PEAK λ	3100A	3400A
25°C EMISSION PEAK λ	5560A	5670A

FIGURE 7   Models of various silver-bearing centers formed by irradiation of Ag$^+$-doped potassium chloride

bands associated with these centers. Before irradiation, the Ag$^+$-doped alkali halides are essentially transparent to near-ultraviolet light, hence they do not luminesce under this type of illumination. Absorption bands in the near ultraviolet are produced by x-irradiation, corresponding to the radiation-induced centers labelled *B*, *C*, *D* and *E* in Fig. 7,* and illumination with near-ultraviolet light then produces visible luminescence. Originally,[1,5] the

---

* W. Kleemann has recently shown (Nachr. Gött. Akad. Wissen. II Kl. No. 13, Nov., 1967) that the "*B*" center is a Ag^{-1} ion substituting for a halide ion, rather than the configuration shown in Fig. 7, which was proposed earlier[30].

radiophotoluminescence of Ag^+-doped alkali halides was ascribed either to neutral silver "atoms" (Ag^0 centers, or "E" centers) or to Ag^+-modified F centers. Further studies[30,31] have shown, however, that the centers in question are probably more complex: the "C" centers and "D" centers, the latter being trapped-hole centers rather than trapped-electron centers.

V RADIOPHOTOLUMINESCENT DOSIMETERS

For practical dosimetric application of the silver radiophotoluminescence, a glass matrix is preferable to an alkali halide matrix because of economic and other factors. Phosphate glasses containing Ag^+-ion as constituent were found to exhibit useful radiophotoluminescence[1,5] properties similar to those of the Ag^+-doped alkali halides, and most of the practical radiophoto-luminescence systems use silver-activated alumino-phosphate glasses as the sensitive element. These materials are made by melting together the meta-phosphates of aluminium, silver, and other cationic constituents, which may be combinations of $Ba^{+2} + K^+$ metaphosphates ("high Z" glasses)[1,5] or $Mg^{+2} + Li^{+1}$ metaphosphates ("low Z" glasses).[7] Typical weight per cent compositions of these glasses are given in Table I.

TABLE I   Compositions of Typical Radiophotoluminescent Glasses (wt. %)

	Ag	K	Li	Ba	Mg	Ag	P	O
"High Z"	4.3	7.7	—	10.8	—	4.3	28.4	44.1
"Low Z"	4.3	—	1.9	—	3.1	4.3	33.7	52.3

The optical properties of silver-activated phosphates glasses are shown in Fig. 8. Radiation exposure produces new optical absorption in the near ultraviolet due to the formation of new color centers involving the silver atoms. Optical excitation into this new absorption provokes an orange luminescence, whose intensity is used as a measure of radiation exposure. With increasing radiation dose the near-ultraviolet absorption increases and its long wavelength extension into the visible spectrum overlaps the emission wavelengths. Ultraviolet exciting light is thus absorbed in a thinner and thinner layer of the glass, and some of the luminescent light is re-absorbed by the radiation-induced centers. The radiophotoluminescence response therefore first increases linearly, then saturates, and finally decreases as a function of dose (Fig. 9).

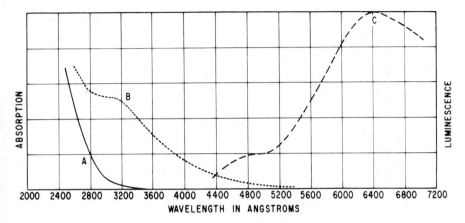

FIGURE 8   Absorption and luminescence of silver-activated phosphate
glass
A. Absorption of unirradiated glass
B. New absorption band produced by radiation exposure
C. Luminescence emission provoked by illumination into band *B*

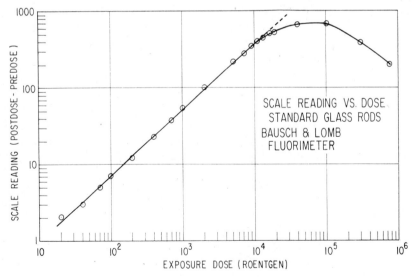

FIGURE 9   Radiophotoluminescence of silver-activated phosphate glass
versus dose

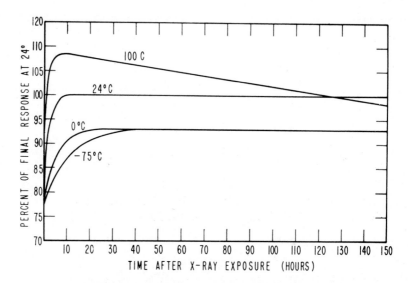

FIGURE 10   Growth and fading of radiophotoluminescence of silver-
activated phosphate glass at various temperatures

After a short radiation exposure the full radiophotoluminescence response
is not achieved immediately; the response builds up to its ultimate value after
a period of time which depends on the temperature and on the composition
of the particular glass. The higher the temperature and the higher the silver
concentration, the faster is the build-up. For the "high Z" glass composition
used in the U.S. Navy personnel dosimeter,[5] the build-up is shown as a
function of temperature in Fig. 10. It will be seen that higher temperatures
accelerate the build-up of response, but also induce thermal destruction of
the radiophotoluminescent centers. At still higher temperatures than those
shown in the Figure the thermal destruction of the centers is very rapid;
a 0.5–1 hour heating at 300–400°C "bleaches" the glass virtually to its
initial non-luminescent state. At normal ambient temperatures, however,
exposed dosimeters maintain their readings for more than a year with only a
few per cent loss.

The earliest application of the radiophotoluminescent glass was to a
personnel casualty dosimeter for military purposes. Figure 11 shows a model
of the U.S. Navy personnel dosimeter, which consists of a rectangular
parallelopiped of the glass approximately 2 cm square and 6 mm thick
enclosed in a plastic locket. In order to make a reading of dose, the locket

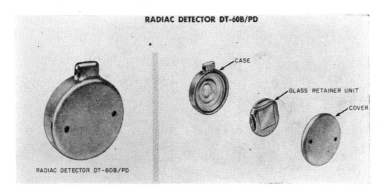

FIGURE 11 United States Navy radiophotoluminescent personnel casualty
dosimeter

is unscrewed and the portion containing the glass block is placed into a
fluorimeter or "reader", which contains an ultraviolet lamp to excite the
luminescence and a photomultiplier tube to measure its intensity. The photomultiplier output is directly interpreted as an exposure reading (in R) on the
meter. The lowest detectable exposure using these devices is of the order of
the few roentgens; in practice it is limited to about 10 roentgens because of
the "pre-dose" light signal, which arises from the fluorescence of impurities
or from scattered, light. The phosphate glass dosimeter provides a rugged,
inexpensive, device needing no preparation for use; one which can be read
many times to confirm the dose indication, and which can accumulate and
add successive readings.

In order to counteract the severe energy-dependence of the glass, a new
method of selective shielding was devised[32] which kept the energy-dependence of the dosimeter constant within $\pm 20\%$ between 80 KeV and
1.2 MeV (Fig. 12). This method involved the use of a perforated shield. The
shielding material and its thickness were chosen to cut down the escess
response of the glass over the moderately high energy part of the above range,
while perforations of the appropriate size were incorporated to permit
penetration of a certain proportion of the low-energy radiation which
otherwise would have been completely filtered out by the shield. This method
of shielding has since been extensively used in many types of dosimeters
in which the volume-averaged radiation effect is used as a measure of dose.

Figure 13 shows miniature "needle" dosimeters which were developed in
1953 for application to *in vivo* dosimetry.[6] The principle of operation is

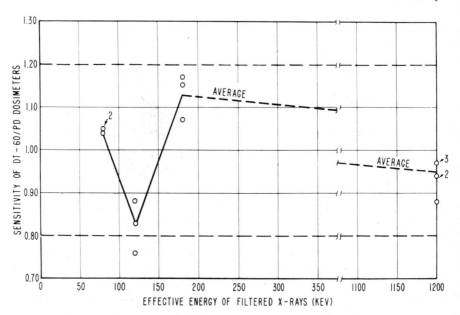

FIGURE 12   Energy-dependence of United States Navy dosimeter after correction by perforated lead shield. (Direction of incidence of radiation normal to shield)

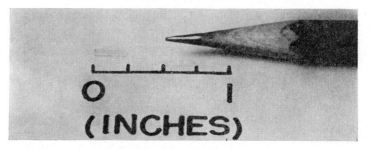

FIGURE 13   Miniature "needle" dosimeters of silver-activated phosphate glass

identical with that of the larger personnel dosimeter, and its range is also roughly the same.

During the past few years careful attention to chemical purity and optical perfection in the synthesis of the silver activated phosphate glass has greatly reduced the fluorescence from impurities and scattered light. Improvement in fluorimeter design have also decreased the "pre-dose" luminescence. Both these developments[8] have combined to extend the sensitivity of the radio-photoluminescence method down to the 10–50 milliroentgen range, making its use in health-physics monitoring quite attractive.

VI THERMOLUMINESCENCE

Thermoluminescence (and infrared-stimulable luminescence) can also be illustrated in terms of the properties of defects in the alkali halides. Figure 14 once again shows trapped-electron centers (F centers) and trapped-hole centers (H or V centers) formed by irradiation of a pure salt. (The previously

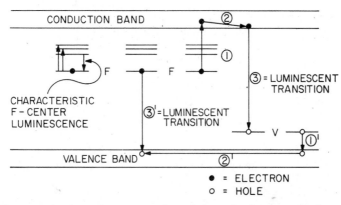

FIGURE 14 Schematic representation of thermoluminescence (and optically stimulated luminescence) processes in an alkali halide containing color centers

discussed absorption and radiophotoluminescence of the F center are indicated in the energy level diagram farthest to the left). We now focus our attention on the process whereby an electron may be completely ejected from the F center into the conduction band (step 1) by absorption of a sufficiently energetic light quantum or by acquiring the necessary energy from the thermal vibrations of the surrounding crystal ions. The ejected electron can wander through the crystal (step 2) and recombine with a trapped hole (step 3), giving out the energy of recombination in the form of a light quantum, i.e., luminescence. As noted in Section II, if step 1 is provoked by light absorption, (generally infrared light), the phenomenon is "optically (infrared) stimulated luminescence"; if it is provoked by heat, it is called "phosphorescence". When the phosphorescence is accelerated by raising the temperature, the phenomenon is called "thermoluminescence". A symmetrical series of processes can also take place (shown as 1', 2', and 3') wherein a hole is optically or thermally liberated from its trap, and migrates via the valence band; the luminescent process 3' is the recombination of the free hole with a trapped electron.

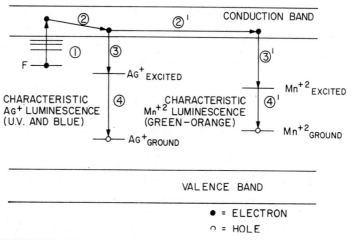

FIGURE 15   Thermoluminescence processes in an impurity-activated alkali halide, leading to luminescence characteristic of the impurity (Mn^{+2}, or Ag^+ impurities as examples)

To insure that step 3 (or 3') is indeed a luminescent process and to control the luminescence emission spectrum, we can "dope" the salt with known luminescent ions or "activators". Figure 15 illustrates how Ag^+ or Mn^{+2} can serve as activators. On irradiation of the doped salt, electron trapping leads to F-center formation as before, but the hole is trapped by the Ag^+-ion or Mn^{+2}-ion. When the electron is subsequently ejected from the F center, it recombines with the hole at the Ag^+ or Mn^{+2} ion. After this recombination the activator ion is in an excited state and quickly emits its characteristic luminescence (Ag^+-ion = ultraviolet-blue and Mn^{+2} ion = green-orange). The thermoluminescent phosphors $CaF_2 : Mn^{11}$ and $CaSO_4 : Mn^{10}$ are examples of manganese activation and the optically-stimulable $NaCl : Ag$ and $KCl : Ag$ phosphors[33] are examples of silver activation.

The concentration of electron (and hole) traps can also be influenced by doping with impurities. Figure 16 shows how a divalent positive-ion impurity, substituting for an alkali ion in an alkali halide, affects the concentration of vacancies. In order to compensate for the excess positive charge of the impurity an alkali ion must be omitted from the structure, i.e., each substitutional divalent impurity ion creates a positive-ion vacancy. The concentration of negative-ion vacancies is correspondingly decreased. Furthermore, since the divalent cation impurity is a local positive charge and the cation vacancy is a local negative charge, the two attract each other and can form "complexes" as shown in the figure. The concentration and nature of electron and hole traps is thus profoundly affected by the impurity. Besides the changes it makes in the numbers and relative proportions of positive and negative ion vacancies, the divalent impurity cation is itself a

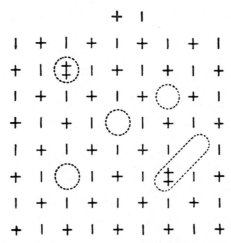

FIGURE 16   Schematic representation of vacancies, substitutional divalent cation impurity, and vacancy-impurity "complexes" in an alkali halide crystal

possible electron trap by virtue of its excess positive charge, and the "complexes" it forms also are sites where radiation-induced changes can take place more easily than at the normal lattice sites. The foregoing effects are undoubtedly involved in "dosimetry grade" LiF, whose useful trapping properties are known to be connected with the presence of Mg^{+2} as an impurity.

The distinctions between the radiophotoluminescence and thermoluminescence (or optically stimulated luminescence) processes will be quite evident by comparing the different processes in the same phosphors—the silver-activated alkali halides. First, there is the difference in emission spectrum. The *radiophotoluminescence* emission spectrum is due to the silver centers generated by the radiation, presumably $(Ag_2)^0$, $(Ag_2)^+$ or $(Ag)^{+2}$; by contrast, the *thermoluminescence* emission spectrum of these salts is characteristic of the Ag^+ originally incorporated into the crystal. Secondly, in radiophotoluminescence the radiation-induced centers are not destroyed by the operation of counting them; the measuring light merely provokes the centers to luminesce, and this operation can be performed continuously or repeatedly. In thermoluminescence the radiation-induced centers are destroyed by the measuring operation; each center that is counted is "discharged" or "erased". Thus, the experimentally measured quantity in radiophotoluminescence is the constant level of luminescence brightness provoked by a fixed intensity of exciting light, while the fundamental measured quantity in thermoluminescence is the total integrated light output (the so-called "light sum") as the stored energy in the phosphor is excelled by heating. The luminescence brightness during this treatment will vary with time depending on the schedule of heating adopted. The curve of brightness versus temperature obtained when the phosphor temperature is continuously raised is called the "glow-curve".

The theory of glow curves[19,24] has been studied very intensively by phosphor researchers with the aim of deducing the "depths" and other

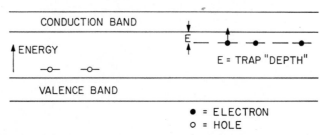

FIGURE 17 Energy level diagram for thermoluminescence from single type of trap

properties of electron or hole traps from these curves. Since we are interested primarily in the use of these curves for thermoluminescence dosimetry, an elementary discussion of their characteristics will be sufficient for our purpose.

We consider the case where: there is only one kind of electron trap, having a depth E below the conduction band Fig. 17; an electron freed from a trap is not re-trapped, but undergoes a luminescent recombination with a positive hole; the rate-determining process for the luminescence is the rate of escape of the electron from the trap; and the phosphor is heated at a constant rate $\beta°/$sec. If is the mean lifetime of an electron in the trap, the probability per unit time of ejection of the electron from the trap is

$$P = \tau^{-1} = s \exp\left(-\frac{E}{kT}\right),$$

where T is the absolute temperature, k is Boltzmann's constant, and s is a factor having the dimensions of frequency, related to (but generally much less) than the frequency of atomic vibrations in the solid. The luminescence intensity is determined by the rate of emptying of electrons from traps,

$$I = -\frac{dn}{dt} = np = ns \exp\left(-\frac{E}{kT}\right).$$

If the phosphor is heated at a constant rate $dT/dt = \beta$,

$$-\frac{dn}{dt} = -\beta\frac{dn}{dT} = ns \exp\left(-\frac{E}{kT}\right),$$

where

$$n_T = n_0 \exp \int_{T_0}^{T} -\frac{s}{\beta} \exp\left(-\frac{E}{kT}\right) dT$$

and

$$I_T = n_0 s \exp\left(-\frac{E}{kT}\right) \exp \int_{T_0}^{T} -\frac{s}{\beta} \exp\left(-\frac{E}{kT}\right) dT.$$

The graphical form of the last equation is shown in Fig. 18 for various values of the parameters E and s, for a constant heating rate (2.5°/sec.)[24] The luminescence increases as electrons are ejected from the traps by the increasing temperature, reaches a maximum at some temperature T^*, and then decreases as the store of trapped electrons is depleted. T^* moves to higher temperatures as E or β increase or as s decreases. The area under each curve is proportional to n_0, the number of electrons that were initially trapped (which, in the dosimetric use of phosphors is determined by the radiation exposure or dose). For a particular type of trap (E and s fixed) and a fixed arbitrary heating rate β, one can of course also use the glow-peak height (luminescence intensity at T^*) as a measure of n_0. If a phosphor contains several different types of traps, each trap characterized by its own values E and s, the glow curve will contain several glow peaks. Those having low values of E and high values of s will not store energy well; traps having $E \leqq 0.8$ eV along with $s \geqq 10^9$/sec suffer severe depopulation in one day or less (mean life ~ 1 day) at room temperature.

A major problem for phosphor researchers has been to determine the trap parameters from the experimental glow curves. This is rather complicated and laborious, and therefore several methods have been suggested for deducing E from the value of T^*. At T^*, $dI/dT = 0$, giving:

$$\beta \frac{E}{T^{*2}} = s \exp\left(-\frac{E}{kT^*}\right),$$

whence E is an implicit function of T^* defined by the parameter $\theta = \beta/s$. For $\theta = 10^{-9}$ ("normal" values of $\beta = 1°$K/sec and $s = 10^9$/sec) an empirical relation given by Urbach[19] holds approximately: E (in electron volts) $= \dfrac{T^*}{500}$. For higher values of θ (faster heating rates or lower s-factors), the denominator increases considerably; for example, a trap of 1 eV depth at a

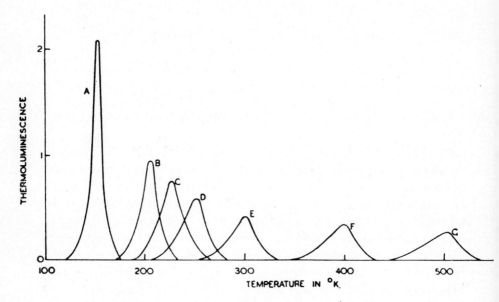

FIGURE 18   Theoretical glow curves for phosphors with single trap depth and no retrapping

hundredfold faster heating rate ($\theta = 10^{-7}$) would give a glow peak near 600°K rather than 500°K.

By combining the above ideas with other operational considerations we can list the following general properties that phosphors should have if they are to be useful for thermoluminescence dosimetry:

1) A high concentration of electron or hole traps.

2) A high efficiency of luminescence when the electrons (or holes) are thermally released and recombine.

3) Long storage of trapped electrons or holes at normal working temperatures ($=$ large E and low s).

4) A simple trap distribution, preferably a single type of trap for greatest simplicity of operation and interpretation of readings.

5) A spectral distribution of luminescence which matches the detector, generally a blue-sensitive photomultiplier tube, and is separated as far as possible from the incandescent emission of the heating source. (Near-ultraviolet, blue, or green emission preferred; orange or red emissions are disadvantageous.)

6) Stability of traps, activators, and host lattice to radiation, i.e., radiation should fill the traps but not create new traps or new activators, nor destroy traps or activators.

7) Depending on the purpose in hand one may add still other requirements, such as energy-independence, and sensitivity or insensitivity to neutrons.

The thermoluminescent output may be measured in two ways, either as the integrated light output (the "light sum") or as the glow-peak height. The former measurement has the advantage, in principle, of being independent of the heating rate, so that this rate need not be accurately reproducible between one reading and the next. It has the disadvantage that a certain degree of arbitrariness is introduced in deciding when the integration should be cut off, particularly when one is dealing with a small signal (i.e., resulting from a low dose) which runs into the incandescence signal from the heater (see Fig. 19). The peak-height method of measurement requires that the heating schedule be accurately reproducible from run to run and from dosimeter to dosimeter, because the peak height is a very sensitive function of the heating rate as Fig. 19 shows. Practical advantage is taken of this dependence to increase the light signal from small exposures by heating the phosphor very rapidly, (of the order of 20°C/sec.). Reproducibility of heating schedule is not hard to achieve in practice.

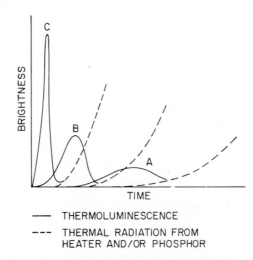

FIGURE 19 Thermoluminescence brightness versus time at different rates
of heating, $\beta_C > \beta_B > \beta_A$

VII THERMOLUMINESCENT DOSIMETERS

The earliest attempts to use thermoluminescence for dosimetry centered on lithium fluoride as the sensitive material.[2] The complexity of its behavior led to the abandonment of this salt in favour of Al_2O_3[9] and $CaSO_4 : Mn$[10]. The former suffered from insufficient sensitivity for most purposes, and the latter from a too shallow trap depth, so that the thermoluminescence method of dosimetry remained for years in a state of suspended animation, more or less as a laboratory curiosity. The situation was suddenly changed with the development of a manganese-activated calcium fluoride phosphor, which had high radiation sensitivity and a relatively simple distribution of stable trapping centers.[11] With the employment of this phosphor in an appropriately designed dosimeter configuration[12] most of the tremendous potential of thermoluminescent dosimetry was achieved, and interest in this method was abruptly revived. In this revival, attempts were again made to exploit the thermoluminescence of lithium fluoride,[13] and studies of the rather complex behavior of this salt proliferated.[16] Because of these complexities the practical performance of a thermoluminescence system will be illustrated in this paper principally by a description of the relatively simple CaF_2 : Mn-based dosimeter referred to above. Although CaF_2 : Mn can be used as a loose powder[11] or encapulated in a high melting glass matrix,[34] spurious luminescence effects from friction between phosphor grains (triboluminescence) or interaction with atmospheric gases are avoided if the phosphor is sealed in a vacuum or other inert environment.[12] This arrangement permits the detection of very low exposures, of the order of milliroentgens or less.

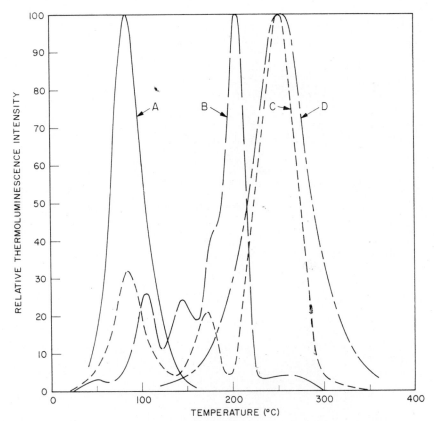

FIGURE 20 Glow curves of phosphors used in thermoluminescence
dosimetry

A. Manganese-activated $CaSO_4$

B. LiF

C. Natural CaF_2 from M.B.L.E.

D. Synthetic manganese-activated CaF_2

The glow curve of synthetic manganese-activated CaF_2 phosphor is shown in Fig. 20 along with the glow curves of other phosphors of interest. The relatively high temperature of the glow peak in $CaF_2 : Mn$ (curve *D*) implies the existence of deep stable traps. The luminescence emission of the phosphor is blue-green in color.

The construction of an early prototype dosimeter[21] is shown in Fig. 21. In principle, the dosimeter resembles an ordinary incandescent electric lamp bulb or radio tube, the filament of which is coated with a thin layer of the

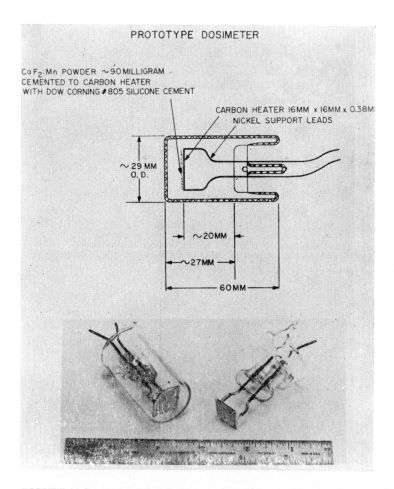

FIGURE 21 Prototype sealed-dosimeter tube with internal heating element

phosphor. In the prototype device the "filament" was actually a thin square graphite plate. The volume of the dosimeter tube was evacuated or filled with a suitable inert gas. Such a dosimeter is read by electrical heating of the filament to bring the phosphor rapidly well above its highest glow temperature. The heater current is switched off as soon as the stored energy is expelled from the phosphor in order to minimize thermal glow from the filament, which otherwise would be heated to incandescence. The construction of this dosimeter makes the heating curve quite reproducible on repeated runs with the same heating current. The thermoluminescent light is registered by a photosensitive device such as a photomultiplier tube, whose output can be recorded as a function of time on a chart recorder. The total time for making a reading is approximately thirty seconds. When the discharged dosimeter has cooled to room temperature, it is ready for re-use. In our laboratory, dosimeters of this type using calcium fluoride have survived as many as a hundred cycles of exposure and reading.

SCHEMATIC DIAGRAM OF READER

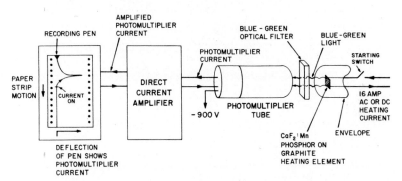

FIGURE 22   Schematic diagram of apparatus for reading thermoluminescent dosimeters

Figure 22 shows a schematic diagram of the apparatus for reading the dosimeters. The filter interposed between the dosimeter and the phototube transmits the blue-green light from the phosphor and discriminates against the small amount of thermal emission from the hot support plate. Figure 23 shows the typical chart records obtained.

The remarkable sensitivity and range of the dosimeter is shown in curves A and A' of Fig. 24. Curve A refers to a dosimeter with a "non-browning"

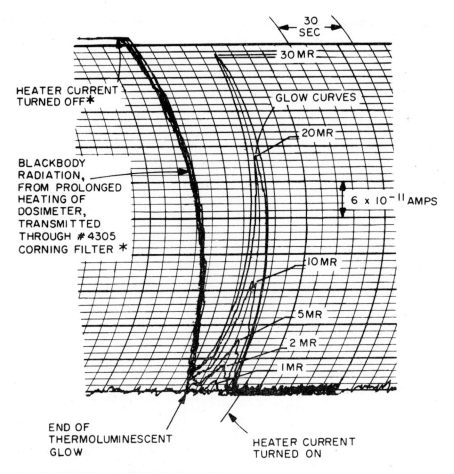

FIGURE 23 Chart records of response from thermoluminescent CaF_2 : Mn
dosimeters

glass window, while A' refers to a dosimeter bulb made entirely of Pyrex,
which darkens at high doses. Exposures of 1 mR Co^{60} γ-rays can clearly be
measured, and the response is linear over more than eight decades up to
approximately 3×10^5 R when a "non-browning" window is employed.
The device is useful over a range which extends well below and well above
the range encompassed by the photographic film badge normally employed

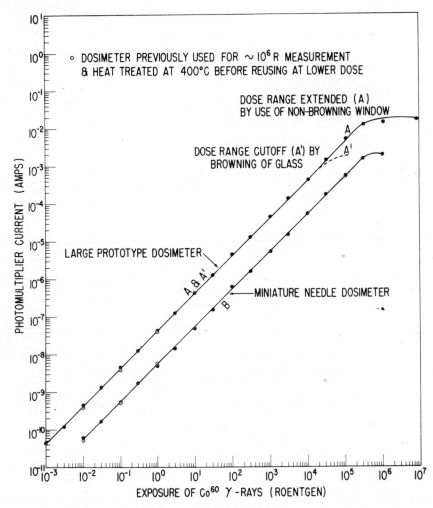

FIGURE 24   Thermoluminescence peak height versus dose for CaF$_2$: Mn
dosimeters

in personnel monitoring. Interpretable results can thus be obtained even
in the event of severe accidental over-exposures of personnel.

It has been found that the short heating period used in the reading
operation does not completely expel all the stored energy from dosimeters
that have received large doses. Thus, if a dosimeter has been exposed
to 100 R and read by the foregoing procedure, it is not immediately useful

for registering exposures in the *mR* range. To exhaust the stored energy completely it must be held at elevated temperature for longer period of time. A heat treatment at 400°C for fifteen minutes was found sufficient for this purpose. The open circles on curves *A* and *A'* in Figure 24 refer to measurements made after large exposures followed by this bake-out procedure. It will be seen that this treatment leaves the dosimeter sensitivity unchanged.

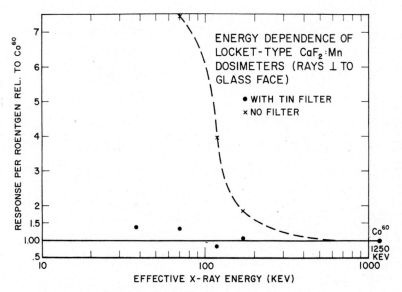

FIGURE 25   Energy dependence of CaF_2 : Mn and its correction by a perforated tin shield

As with most solid detectors, calcium fluoride shows considerable energy dependence of response per roentgen, as shown in the dashed curve of Fig. 25. The solid curve of the figure shows the energy dependence of the dosimeter when fitted witha perforated 2.8 mm thick tin shield to filter the incident radiation.

Other modifications of the thermoluminescent calcium fluoride dosimeter have been investigated at the U.S. Naval Research Laboratory,[14] with particular reference to the miniaturization of the device. Figure 26 shows three such versions. The first consists merely of a needle-shaped sealed glass tube filled with phosphor under an argon atmosphere; the second is identical in construction except for a coaxial platinum filament which is sealed

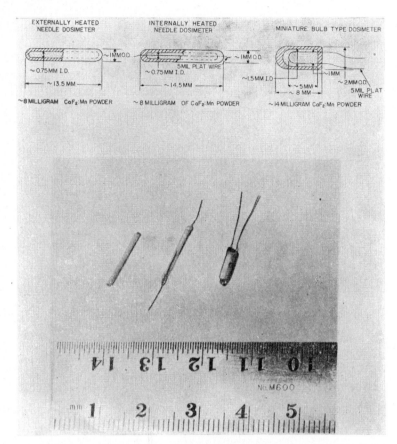

FIGURE 26   Miniature thermoluminescent dosimeters using CaF$_2$: Mn

through both ends of the tube; the third modification, shaped like a small bulb, is about twice the diameter of the other two, and contains a filament bent in a V shape, the two ends of the filament emerging from the same end of the dosimeter where they terminate in a contacting base. Reading of the first type of miniature dosimeter is accomplished by placing it in a nichrome strip holder which is electrically heated. Except for this external heating scheme, its operation is identical with the other miniature dosimeters. The power supplied to the internally-heated dosimeters if of the order of 1–2 watts, and the measurement time is thirty seconds. As shown in curve B of Fig. 24, the minimum detectable exposure with all three miniature modifications is of the order of 10 mR, using the same reading apparatus previously described. In all other respects the three miniature versions perform identically with the larger prototype model initially described.

The relatively high temperature of the glow peak in CaF_2 : Mn would lead one to expect that the traps in this phosphor are deep and that there should be no loss of signal on room-temperature storage of the exposed phosphor. Surprisingly there is some loss, as shown in Fig. 27. Approximately

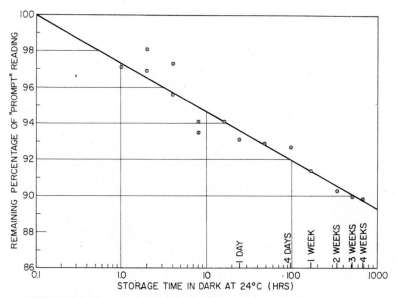

FIGURE 27   Loss of stored signal in thermoluminescent dosimeters using synthetic CaF_2 : Mn

6 to 10% of the initial exposure indication is lost during the first 16-hours of storage at room temperature. Further loss on storage thereafter proceeds very slowly, amounting to only a few per cent more in a month. This loss, comparable in magnitude to the latent-image fading observed with photographic film, is tolerable for personnel dosimetry. Other (natural mineral) CaF_2 phosphors reportedly show no fading over very long periods of time.[35] The fading observed with synthetic CaF_2 : Mn depends on the heating rate used in the thermoluminescence measurements; no fading is observed when the phosphor is heated at a slow heating rate ($\sim 1°C/min$) normally used in phosphor chemistry research. These results appear to be explicable on the basis that the apparently single glow peak in CaF_2 : Mn is really a superposition of several glow peaks due to traps of slightly different depths.[36]

It is characteristic of all thermoluminescent dosimetry systems that the process of reading the dosimeter expels the stored energy and makes the dosimeter ready for re-use. Although the reading can be obtained in the form of a chart record or printed number, which can be referred to repeatedly, the dosimeter itself can be read only once. In view of the speed of the reading operation, the very wide dose range encompassed by the dosimeter, and the usual lack of *a priori* information concerning the dose to be encountered, the recording instrument must be able to respond rapidly and automatically to a wide output range, lest the reading be inaccurate or lost altogether. This fast wide-range response can easily be obtained from a multi-decade logarithmic recorder, or by other means having varying degrees of sophistication. A simple reading procedure has been developed which allows a number of repeated readings of the same exposed dosimeter without erasing the stored signal.[37] This procedure allows one to make trial runs to determine the proper sensitivity scale to be used for the final reading. It also permits the preliminary segregation of a large population of exposed dosimeters having readingx below or above some arbitrary pre-selected exposure level, in the event that such a segregation is desirable.

The method is based on the recognition that thermoluminescence is simply a thermally-accelerated phosphorescence. If a thermoluminescent material is heated only part way up its glow curve it will phosphoresce, but at a lower intensity and for a longer time than would be the case if it were heated to a higher temperature. If it is held at the lower temperature for

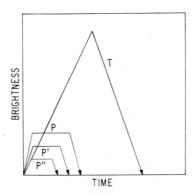

FIGURE 28   Schematic representation of normal thermoluminescence (curve *T*) versus "phosphorescence" (Curves *P*, *P′*, *P″*,) method of reading thermoluminescent dosimeters

only a short time, it will dissipate only a small fraction of the total light sum. This is illustrated in Fig. 28 where the normal glow curve is represented schematically by the triangle *T*, and various possible "phosphorescence" curves are represented by the Figures *P*, *P'*, *P''*. The phosphorescence brightness can be used as a measure of exposure. The choice of the heating schedule is quite flexible; the form of the heating curve, the maximum temperature achieved, and the time of observation all are conditioned by the minimum exposure one wishes to detect and the fraction of the stored energy one chooses to expend in the process.

Figure 29 shows the results achieved using the large prototype CaF_2 : Mn dosimeters, which were heated according to the schedule shown in Fig. 30.

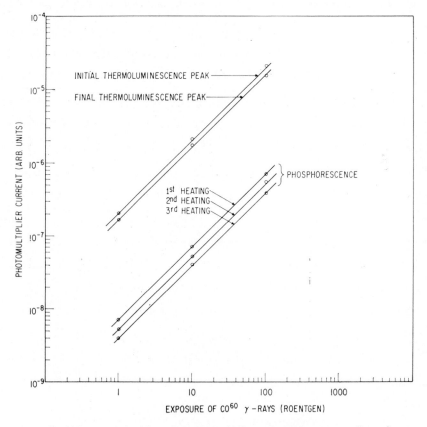

FIGURE 29 "Phosphorescence" and thermoluminescence reading of
CaF_2 : Mn dosimeters

The phosphorescence brightness at the point of cut-off of the heating current (about 0.033 of the peak brightness produced in a normal glow curve) was used as a measure of exposure. Response curves using this method of reading are shown for three successive phosphorescence readings on dosimeters exposed in the 1–100 R range. Figure 29 also compares the normal ("initial") thermoluminescent response, obtained from dosimeters read without preliminary phosphorescence runs, with the residual ("final") thermoluminescent response following three successive phosphorescence readings. The latter response is also linear, and is 0.84 of the response of dosimeters that have not been subjected to preliminary phosphorescence experiments. Thus, with relatively simple reading equipment, one can make a preliminary test of the reading of an unknown dosimeter, and then adjust

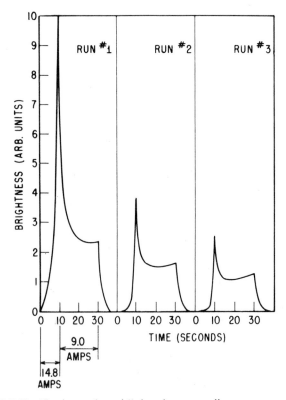

FIGURE 30   Heating cycle and "phosphorescence" curves corresponding to Fig. 29

10   Amelinckx (1347)

the sensitivity of the reader to obtain a final precise measurement of the exposure. Permanent records can be obtained of all the intermediate readings as well as of the final thermoluminescence reading.

Another obvious scheme by which it is possible, in principle, to make a repeat reading of the same dosimeter exposure is to use a phosphor having multiple glow peaks, all of which are stable enough to be useful for dosimetry. An initial reading could be made by selectively heating to "glow-out" the lowest temperature peak only. Repeat readings could then be made by a second, third, etc. heating, each of which is carried to a higher temperature than the last, thus emptying the more stable traps in sequence. Alternatively, with a phosphor that has only a single glow peak, multiple phosphor-coated filaments could be incorporated in the same dosimeter envelope, each filament being separately heatable. Finally, "memory" effects have been reported[35] in certain natural CaF_2 phosphors which present possibilities for repeat reading of the same dose, or even the reading of a total dose accumulated over many exposure, each of which has already been read out in the normal way. Some of these natural phosphors have a very deep trap (525°C) which is not discharged at ordinary "reading" temperatures (~400°C). However, a suitable light exposure transfers a small fraction of the charge carriers from this trap into the lower-temperature traps where they can be read out in the usual way, thus providing a repeatable measure of the total exposure received since manufacture.

In addition to the CaF_2 : Mn phosphor, current practical thermoluminescent dosimeters employ LiF, natural CaF_2, and $Li_2B_4O_7$,[38,39] each of which has certain advantages with regard to sentivity, linearity, resistance to radiation damage,[40] energy dependence, thermal neutron sensitivity, memory effects, or cost. A wide variety of devices and system designs has been developed, which include the use of loose powder, pressed or extruded phosphor blocks or rods, phosphorimpregnated plastic sheets or rods, with and without the encapsulation described in the text.[41,42]

VIII   OTHER LUMINESCENCE METHODS OF DOSIMETRY

A   Infra-red stimulated luminescence dosimetry

The principle underlying the use of optically stimulable phosphors for dosimetry has been described above in connection with thermoluminescence. Use of this class of phosphors permits one to illuminate the exposed dosimeter with light, generally infrared light, and observe luminescence in the visible region of the spectrum. Thus, *IR* illumination is substituted for the heating procedure used in thermoluminescence dosimetry. Unfortunately, there are relatively few phosphors which have sufficient *IR*-stimulability along with all the other characteristics desired in a dosimetry material. Antonov-Romanovsky *et al.*[3] described a system based on the *IR*-stimulable phosphor SrS : Eu, Sm which (after radiation exposure) emits visible light on stimulation by infrared light. Because of its relatively poor storage characteristics ($\sim 40\%$ loss of signal after two weeks post-irradiation storage) and other complications, this system has not received extensive acceptance. The optical stimulation method has obvious appeal, however, and interesting devices would certainly result if good phosphors could be developed.

B   Luminescence degradation dosimetry

The effect inverse to radiophotoluminescence—the destruction rather than the creation of photoluminescent centers—can also be used for dosimetry. Dosimetry based on this effect was first proposed using alkali halide phosphors activated with Pb^{+2} or Pb^{+2} and Mn^{+2}.[43-45] Under short wavelength ultraviolet excitation (2730A) the Pb^{+2} activator emits in the near ultraviolet and blue. With Mn^{+2} as an additional impurity the energy absorbed by the Pb^{+2} is transferred to the Mn^{+2}; the Pb^{+2} luminescence is suppressed and the orange luminescence characteristic of Mn^{+2} is emitted instead. When the phosphors containing Pb^{+2} are exposed to X-rays or γ-rays, Pb^{+2}-ions are radiochemically changed in amounts proportional to the exposure, apparently being reduced to Pb^0 atoms by electron capture. The characteristic Pb^{+2} absorption band at 2730A is thereby diminished. In the singly-activated phosphor the destruction of Pb^{+2} centers reduces the intensity of the Pb^{+2}-ion photoluminescence. In the phosphor which also contains Mn^{+2}, the orange Mn^{+2} photoluminescence is also diminished because of the removal of the primary absorbers of exciting ultraviolet light, the Pb^{+2}-ions.

Dosimetry systems based on the degradation of photoluminescence in organic materials[4] have received more attention than those based on inorganic phosphors. Ionizing radiation destroys the photoluminescence ability of many of the well known organic solids used in scintillation counting. The decrement of luminescence is large in comparison to most other measures of radiation damage on these materials, from which it is inferred

10*

that the radiation-damaged molecules not only lose the ability to luminesce themselves but also act as "poisons" or "quenchers" of some of the undamaged molecules.[46] Despite this relatively large yield, the radiation-sensitivity of these aromatic organic solids is still rather low. The threshold of detection is in the neighborhood of 10^5 rads. By the same token, massive doses ($\sim 10^9$ rads) are measurable with some of these organic solids.[47,48]

A system using pressed wafers of anthracene and *p*-quaterphenyl has been developed which encompasses the range 10^5–5×10^9 rads,[48] as shown in Fig. 31. The luminescence is measured before and after radiation exposure in a simple fluorimeter. Exposure is determined from the decrement of photoluminescence as shown in the Figure where I_0 is the initial photoluminescence brightness and I the post-irradiation photoluminescence brightness. The destruction of photoluminescence in organics such as those shown in Fig. 31 is fairly stable but at room temperature there is a slow recovery with time (i.e., "fading" of the dose indication). To overcome this a short post-irradiation heat treatment may be used. This accelerates the

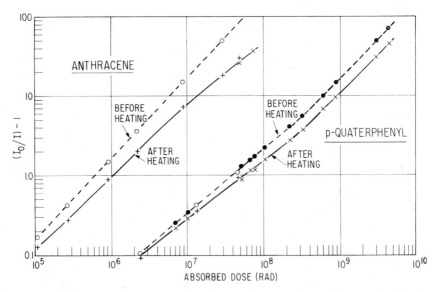

FIGURE 31 Luminescence degradation of organic phosphors exposed to
Co^{60} radiation.
Dashed curves: readings made within 1 hour after termination of exposure.
Solid curves: readings made after irradiation heat treatment of 1 hour at
100 °C

recovery and the remaining degradation persists, allowing repeated readings to be made over long periods of time.[48]

TABLE II   Optical effects employed in solid dosimeters

Type of centers induced by ionizing radiation	Measurement procedure	Effect	Description
I. Radiation-induced centers stable to measurement procedure	Illumination with light (generally ultra-violet or visible)	A. Coloration	Centers absorb light in originally transparent spectral region.
		B. Radiophoto-luminescence	Unirradiated solid is not luminescent. New centers absorb measuring light; emit luminescent light at longer wavelengths as long as measuring ligth is incident.
		C. Degradation of luminescence	Unirradiated solid is luminescent. New centers do not luminesce, and may even quench the normal luminescence. Emission continues as long as measuring light is incident.
II. Radiation-induced centers destroyed by measurement procedure	Heating	A. Thermo-luminescence	Energy stored in centers is released as luminescence. Luminescence debreases with time as sample is held at high temperature.
	Illumination with light of longer wavelength than is emitted in luminescence	B. Stimulated luminescence	Energy stored in centers is released as luminescence. Luminescence decreases with time as sample is exposed to stimulating light.

IX   CONCLUSION

The various optical effects described in the text are summarized in Table II.[49] It will be apparent from this table, as can also be inferred from the text, that dosimetry methods employing luminescence are closely related to those which depend upon the production of coloration in solids.[49-52] All these methods are very simple in principle, but it is not easy to synthesize or select materials that have the desired useful optical properties combined with many other necessary practical characteristics. Nevertheless, although development and evaluation of new phosphors and device designs are still proceeding, highly satisfactory luminescence-based-dosimetry systems are already available for most purposes except fast neutron dosimetry.

References

1. J. H. Schulman, R. J. Gitnher, C. C. Klick, R. S. Alger, and R. A. Levy, "Dosimetry of x-rays and gamma-rays by radiophotoluminescence," *J. Appl. Phys.* **22**, 1479–1487 (1951).
2. F. Daniels, C. A. Boyd, and D. F. Saunders, "Thermoluminescence as a research tool," *Science* **117**, 343 (1953).
3. V. V. Antonov-Romanovsky, I. D. Keirim-Marcus, M. S. Proshina, and Z. A. "Trapeznikova, Dosimetry of ionizing radiation with the aid of infra-red sensitive phosphors," *Conf. Acad. Sci. USSR on Peaceful Use of Atomic Energy*, July 1955. English translation prepared by U.S. AEC: 239–249 (1956).
4. J. H. Schulman, H. W. Etzel, and J. Allard, "Applications of luminescence changes in organic solids to dosimetry," *J. Appl. Phys.*, **28**, 792–795 (1957).
5. J. H. Schulman, W. Shurcliff, R. J. Ginther, and F. H. Attix, "Radiophotoluminescence dosimetry system of the U.S. Navy," *Nucleonics* **11**, (10) 52–56 (1953).
6. J. H. Schulman and H. W. Etzel, "Small volume dosimeter for x-rays and gamma-rays," *Science* **118**, 184–186 (1953).
7. R. J. Ginther and J. H. Schulman, "New glass dosimeter is less energy-dependent," *Nucleonics* **18**, No. 4, 92 (1960).
8. R. Yokota and S. Nakajima, "Improved fluoroglass dosimeter as personnel monitoring dosimeter and microdosimeter," *Health Physics* **11**, 241 (1965).
9. F. Daniels and W. P. Rieman, "Chemical Procurement Agency, Washington, D.C.," Final Report Project No. 4-12-80-001 (1954).
10. W. Kossel, U. Mayer, and H. C. Wolf, "Simultaneous dosimetry of radiation fields in living objects," *Naturwissenschaften* **41**, 209 (1954).
11. R. J. Ginther and R. D. Kirk, "The thermoluminescence of CaF_2 : Mn," *J. Electrochem. Soc.* **104**, 365 (1957).
12. J. H. Schulman, F. G. Attix, E. J. West, and R. J. Ginther, "New thermoluminescent dosimeter," *Rev. Sci. Instr.* **31**, 1263 (1960).
13. J. R. Cameron, F. Daniels, N. Johnson, and G. Kenney, "Radiation dosimeter utilizing the thermoluminescence of LiF," *Science* **134**, 333 (1961).
14. J. H. Schulman, F. H. Attix, E. J. West, and R. J. Ginther, "Thermoluminescent methods in personnel dosimetry," *Proceed. ENEA Symp. Pers. Dosimetry*, Madrid (1963).

15. F. H. Attix, *Present status of dosimetry by radiophotoluminescence and thermoluminescence methods*, U.S. Naval Research Laboratory Report No. 6145 (1964).
16. F. H. Attix, Editor, *Proceedings of the International Conference on Luminescence Dosimetry*, Stanford University, June 1965. Sponsored by U.S. AEC and U.S. ONR. Published by U.S. AEC.
17. Proceedings of a Symposium on *Solid State and Chemical Radiation Dosimetry in Medicine and Biology*, International Atomic Energy Agency, Vienna (1967).
18. K. Becker, "Radiophotoluminescence Dosimetry—A Bibliography," *Health Physics* 12 1367 (1966).
19. D. Curie, *Luminescence in Crystals* (Translated by G. F. J. Garlick), John Wiley and Sons, New York, (1963).
20. F. A. Kröger, *Ergeb. exakt. Naturw.* 29, 62 (1956).
21. C. C. Klick and J. H. Schulman, *Luminescence in solids, Solid State Physics*, Vol. 5, F. Seitz and D. Turnbull, Eds. Academic Press, New York, p. 97 (1957).
22. F. E. Williams, *Solid state luminescence, Advances in Electronics and Electron Physics*, Vol. 5, L. Marton, Ed., Academic Press, New York, p. 137 (1953).
23. H. W. Leverenz, *Luminescence in solids*, John Wiley and Sons, New York, (1950).
24. G. F. J. Garlick, *Luminescent materials*, Clarendon Press, Oxford, (1949).
25. P. Pringsheim, *Fluoriescence and phosphorescence*, Interscience Publishers, New York, (1949).
26. Luminescence of Organic and Inorganic Materials, (*Proc. Internatl. Conf. on Luminescence*), H. P. Kallman and G. M. Spruch, Eds., John Wiley and Sons, New York and London, (1962).
27. J. H. Schulman, Luminescence in Solids, p. 130 in *The Molecular Designing of Materials and Devices*, A. R. von Hippel, Editor, M.I.T. Press, Cambridge, Massachusetts (1965).
28. H. A. Klasens, *Photoconducting Phosphors*, p. 139, ibid.
29. J. H. Schulman and W. D. Compton, *Color Centers in Solids*, Pergamon Press, New York (1962).
30. H. W. Etzel and J. H. Schulman, "Silver-activated alkali halides," *J. Chem. Phys.* 22, 1549 (1954).
31. C. J. Delbecq, W. Hayes, M. C. M. O'Brien, and P. H. Yuster, "Paramagnetic resonance and optical absorption of trapped holes and electrons in KCl: Ag," *Proc. Roy. Soc.* A271, 243 (1963).
32. C. C. Klick, *High energy radiation dosimeter*, U.S. Patent 2,752,505, June (1956).
33. C. E. Mandeville and H. O. Albrecht, "The storage of energy in silver-activated potassium chloride," *Phys. Rev.* 91, 566 (1953).
34. J. H. Schulman, R. J. Ginther, R. D. Kirk, and H. S. Goulart, "Thermoluminescent dosimeter has storage stability, linearity," *Nucleonics* 18, No. 3, 92 (1960).
35. See article by R. Schayes, C. Brooke, J. Kozlowitz, and M. Lheureux, on "Thermoluminescent properties of natural CaF_2," in Ref. 16, p. 138.
36. J. H. Schulman, R. J. Ginther, F. H. Attix, S. Gorbics, E. West, and A. Nash, (In Press).
37. J. H. Schulman and E. J. West, "Phosphorescence method of reading thermoluminescent dosimeters," *Rev. Sci. Instr.* 34, 863–865 (1963).

38. J. H. Schulman, R. D. Kirk, and E. J. West, The thermoluminescence of lithium borate and its use in dosimetry, Proceedings of the **XIth** International Congress of Radiology, Rome, (September 1965), p. 1797. Also see Ref. 16, p. 113.

39. R. D. Kirk, J. H. Schulman, E. J. West, and A. E. Nash, "Studies on lithium borate for dosimetry," *Proceedings of Symposium on Solid State and Chemical Radiation Dosimetry in Medicine & Biology*, International Atomic Energy Agency, Vienna (1967).

40. See M. J. Marrone and F. H. Attix, Damage effects in CaF_2 : Mn and LiF dosimeters, *Health Physics* **10**, 431 (1964), for illustration of much greater radiation-damage resistance of CaF_2 : Mn as compared to LiF.

41. F. H. Attix, T. L. Johnson, E. J. West, A. E. Nash, and S. Gorbics, "Thermoluminescent dosimeters for personnel monitoring," *Report of NRL Progress*, March, (1968), U.S. Naval Research Laboratory, Washington, D. C.

42. F. H. Attix, Thermoluminescence dosimetry with CaF_2, U.S. Naval Research Laboratory, Washington, D. C., manuscript in "Manual on Radiation Dosimetry", N. W. Holm and R. J. Berry, Editors. (Marcel Dekker, Inc. New York), In Press.

43. J. H. Schulman, R. J. Ginther, and L. W. Evans, *Phys. Rev.* **76**, 459 (1949).

44. J. H. Schulman, R. J. Ginther, and L. W. Evans, U.S. Patent No. 2,506,749 (May 9, 1950).

45. J. H. Schulman, R. J. Ginther, and C. C. Klick, "Optical properties of NaCl: Pb phosphors," *J. Opt. Soc. America* **40**, 854 (1950).

46. H. Rosenstock and J. H. Schulman, "Models for luminescence degradation in organic solids," *J. Chem. Phys.* **30**, 116 (1959).

47. F. H. Attix, "Luminescence degradation," *Nucleonics* **16** (12), 48 (1958).

48. F. H. Attix, "High level dosimetry by luminescence degradation," *Nucleonics* **17** (4), 142 (1959).

49. J. H. Schulman, Solid state dosimeters for radiation measurement, "Progress in Nuclear Energy Series XII. *Health Physics* Vol. 1," page 150, Pergamon Press New York (1959).

50. H. Friedman and C. Glover, *Nucleonics* **10** (6), 24 (1952).

51. J. H. Schulman, C. C. Klick, and H. Rabin, "Measuring high doses by absorption changes in glass," *Nucleonics* **13** (2), 30 (1955).

52. N. J. Kreidl and G. E. Blair, "A system of megaroentgen glass dosimetry," *Nucleonics* **14** (1), 56 (1956).

Principles and basic dosimetric properties of radiophotoluminescence in silver-activated glasses*

K. BECKER

Health Physics Division
Oak Ridge National Laboratory
Oak Ridge, Tennessee

* Based on invited paper, HPS Midyear Topical Symp. on Pers. Rad. Dosimetry, Chicago, 1967, and a review article in *IAEA Atomic Energy Review* **5**, 43 (1967).

HISTORY, DEFINITION

In 1912, Goldstein[1] described alterations of the ultraviolet-excited luminescence spectrum of numerous inorganic compounds after exposure to beta
or gamma radiation. From about 1920, Przibram and his students in Vienna
(review papers[2]) extensively studied this effect which involved mainly rare
earth impurities in different minerals and synthetic inorganic solids. Przibram in 1922 also introduced the term "radiophotoluminescence" which
means, after redefinition in 1925[3], that a material which is originally non-
luminescent under visible or ultraviolet light is made responsive to such
excitation by pretreatment with ionizing radiation. In 1951 Schulman *et al.*[4]
restricted the term to the creation of new quasi-stable luminescent centres,
which are not or only to a minor degree destroyed by the excitation radiation. In this paper, radiophotoluminescence (RPL) is used in this sense.

While investigating the non-photographic effects of radiation on solids
under the aspects of radiography and dosimetry, Schulman, Weyl, and co-
workers[5,6], discovered that dilute solidified "solutions" of silver salts in
ionic crystals, such as alkali halides, Na_2SO_4 and $BaCl_2$ as well as in certain
glasses (an alumino-phosphate glass was mainly used) exhibit a strong
orange RPL under excitation with the 365 mμ mercury line (Fig. 1). Extensive studies of this effect, in particular in a metaphosphate glass (composition by weight 44% $Al(PO_3)_3$, 23% $Ba(PO_3)_2$, 23% KPO_3, 8% $AgPO_3$)[7],
led to the development of the first mass-produced solid state dosimetry
system, of which more than four million units have been made, mainly as
an accidental dosimetry system for the 10 to 1000 R exposure range by the
United States Navy[7-9]. In England and Sweden similar systems have been
developed[10,11], and a glass having a reduced energy dependence became
available in 1960[12]. Also small glass needles (fluorods) became quite popular
for high-dose personnel dosimetry and in radiobiological research.

In 1961, Yokota *et al.*[13] described a dosimeter glass with greatly improved
dosimetric properties (higher sensitivity, lower background luminescence,
reduced energy dependence, improved fading stability). If read with a
special fluorimetric reader small gamma exposures (less than 50–100 mR)
became measurable with good accuracy. This improved system stimulated
further research and extensive application of glass dosimeters in many
fields. Partly on the basis of Yokota's work, and partly independently, other
new glasses having a similar or even better background (pre-dose) sensitivity
and energy response have been made in several countries[14-16]. The experience of some investigators with early glass dosimetry systems, which had

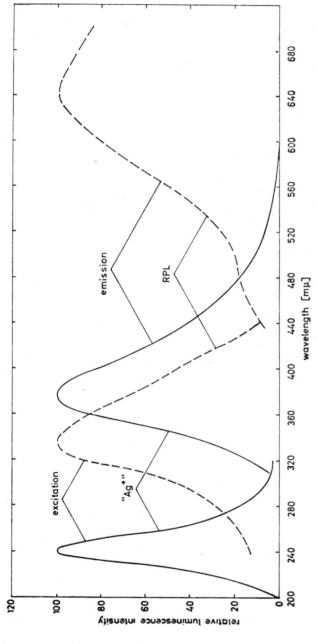

FIGURE 1   Luminescence excitation and emission of an undosed glass and of the radiophotoluminescence in a silver-activated metaphosphate glass (after J. H. Schulman *et al.*[4])

a high background (pre-dose) and relatively poor sensitivity, accuracy and stability, and the widespread interest in some countries such as the USA in LiF thermoluminescence dosimetry systems, has somewhat shaded the considerable progress in phosphate glass dosimetry in recent years. However, the development of glasses which have several times the sensitivity, only a small fraction of the energy dependence and only one hundredth of the pre-dose of the early glasses as well as the well-known basic advantage of RPL systems, in particular the permanence of the radiation effect which permits an unlimited number of remeasurements or interim measurements during dose integration, justifies the more extensive use of these devices in personnel routine and emergency dosimetry.

The progress in the field of RPL dosimetry[17] is quite rapid. Since 1966, for instance, electron spin resonance studies revealed the nature of the RPL centres in the glass[18], it was demonstrated that the measurability of low doses can be improved by orders of magnitude with a new reading technique[19], and new practically energy independent glasses based on lithium oxide/boron oxide systems with a reduced silver content have been studied which can also be used for sensitive radiation measurements at temperatures up to 300°C [20]. At the time of writing, about seven different readers for different purposes, and the same number of different dosimeter glasses, are commercially available. More than 300 publications[21,22] have been devoted to the properties and applications of glass dosimetry since the first publication in 1949 and this number is increasing at a rate of several publications per month.

THEORY OF RPL

The nature of centres and type of processes in dosimeter glasses is not yet completely understood. Relatively well studied are the radiation-induced effects in Ag^+-doped alkali halides which may, to a certain degree, serve as a model substance for the processes involved in glasses. According to Schulman[23], high-energy radiation induces several types of centres in such crystals (Fig. 2). Therefore, after irradiation, absorption bands in the near ultraviolet are produced. Illumination with this light produces visible luminescence. He originally ascribed the RPL to neutral silver atoms (centres E) or Ag^+-modified colour-(F)-centres (B). According to further studies more complex centres, such as (Ag^+ ion + hole + positive ion vacancy) and (Ag^+ ion pair + electron + negative ion vacancy) (C, D) are

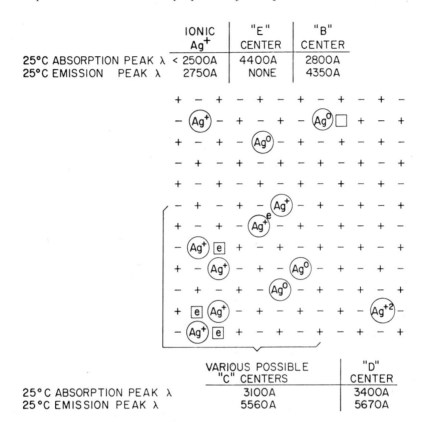

	IONIC Ag$^+$	"E" CENTER	"B" CENTER
25°C ABSORPTION PEAK λ	< 2500A	4400A	2800A
25°C EMISSION PEAK λ	2750A	NONE	4350A

	VARIOUS POSSIBLE "C" CENTERS	"D" CENTER
25°C ABSORPTION PEAK λ	3100A	3400A
25°C EMISSION PEAK λ	5560A	5670A

FIGURE 2   Models of various silver-bearing centres formed by irradiation of Ag$^+$-doped potassium chloride (after J. H. Schulman *et al.*[23])

more probable. It is, however, doubtful to which degree these effects in simple crystals parallel the processes in glasses containing a high silver concentration.

Dosimeter glasses show a peculiar behaviour after a short-time radiation exposure: immediately after exposure there is an increase in RPL intensity (build-up), which is later superimposed by fading. The kinetics depend mainly on temperature (Fig. 3), silver concentration in the glass, and on the glass base composition[24]. Vogel and Becker[25] suggested a mathematical treatment of the kinetics on the basis of a simplified band model (Fig. 4), assuming the following processes: ionizing radiation of sufficient energy

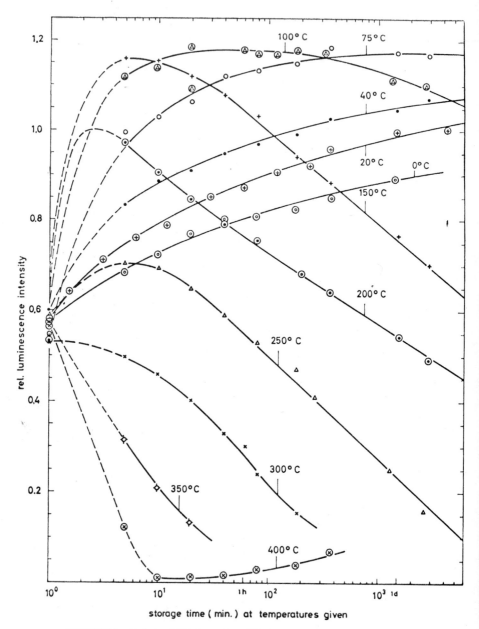

FIGURE 3 Relative RPL intensity of Yokota-type dosimeter glasses exposed to a constant dose of high-intensity gamma radiation at room temperature and stored at different temperatures (measurements taken at room temperature) as a function of storage time (after K. Becker[31])

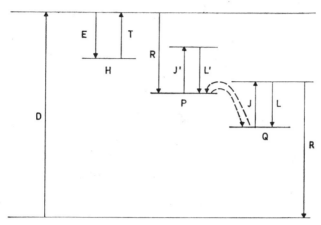

FIGURE 4   Band model of the main processes (RPL formation, build-up and fading) in Ag^+ activated phosphate glasses (after H. Vogel and K. Becker[25])

lifts electrons to the conduction band (D); they are partly directly trapped (R) by positively-charged silver atoms or aggregates (P), thus forming a new type of centre (Q); partly, they are first trapped (E) in traps which are ineffective for the glass luminescence (H) and then transferred thermally to the effective centres (T, R). This could explain the build-up; the increased RPL build-up with decreased silver concentration could be explained by the changes in the relation of the H to P centres by the increase of P. Fading or ultraviolet bleaching may be explained by a recombination of electrons from the excited state of Q with electron vacancies in "hole" traps (R'). J' and L' would correspond to the excitation and emission of the unexposed glass, J and L of the RPL after exposure.

From recent experiments using electron spin resonance techniques, Yokota and Imagawa[18] concluded that the most important centres in dosimeter glasses a room temperature are (Ag^+ + hole) having the capture level $dx^2 - y^2$ of $4d^9$ (Ag) and $2P\sigma$ of oxygen, the (Ag^+ + electron) with the $5S$ (Ag) orbital capture level, the latter being particularly important in glasses with a small $AgPO_3$ concentration, and a (Ag^+ + electron) pair coupled by exchange interaction. At higher doses exceeding several thousand R, higher aggregates of (Ag^+ + electron) (triads, etc.) are added to an increasing degree. According to these findings the main reason for RPL build-up with time is the increase of (Ag^+ + electron) triads and the decrease of holes in the PO_4 tetrahedrons. Despite these rather intense studies, however, several questions, such as a quantitative treatment of the fading processes, still remain unanswered, and interesting phenomena, such as the polarization of the RPL light[26], need a theoretical interpretation.

DOSIMETRIC PROPERTIES OF RPL GLASSES

So far, only silver-activated inorganic materials have been used, because silver seems to be superior to other activators, such as cadmium and lanthanides, which also exhibit RPL in certain minerals and crystals. There may, however, exist other elements with similar or even better RPL properties if combined with an optimal "solvent".

Suitable inorganic crystals are difficult to grow with identical properties and the solubility of silver ions is often rather limited. Only one system on the basis of polycrystalline pellets of silver-activated sodium chloride has been recommended for practical dosimetry[27]. In unpublished experiments, we also found RPL in silver-activated lithium fluoride. By chance, phosphate glasses turned out to be a good base material[4,7]. Most of the further studies therefore have been directed to the modification or improvement of the metaphosphate glass base. It has been demonstrated by some systematic studies that the glass components and their ratios can be very different without seriously affecting the RPL. For instance, experimental glasses having a high concentration of P_2O_5, B_2O_3, SiO_2, BeO and other oxides have been made. Most of these studies, of which only relatively few results have been published because of the commercial interests involved, led to glass bases consisting mainly of only a few metal metaphosphates, such as $Al(PO_3)_3$, $Mg(PO_3)_2$, $Ba(PO_3)_2$, KPO_3, $NaPO_3$, with additions such as B_2O_3 or SiO_2 for improvement of the weathering stability.

Recently, we found[20] that also lithium oxide/boron oxide glasses such as $(Li_2O \cdot 2B_2O_3)$ to $(Li_2O \cdot 6B_2O_3)$ are excellent solvents for silver salts such as silver metaphosphate and the resulting glasses exhibit a strong RPL in the same spectral region as the metaphosphate glasses. Probably quite different inorganic and maybe organic glass bases are also suitable. Each glass composition should represent an optimized compromise between the following main requirements:

Low pre-dose

The background luminescence of the unexposed glass was quite high in the Schulman-type glass (equivalent to about 10 to 40 R gamma exposure, depending on the fluorimetric reading technique). By using the purest materials (all luminescent ions, particularly those having a strong emission in the orange-red, such as Mn^{++}[10], as well as "quenching" ions such as Fe^{++}[28], have to be very carefully omitted), improved composition of the glass and special melting techniques (the crucible material, atmosphere in the oven, time and temperature of the melting and heat after-treatment may be among the factors which affect the pre-dose), it is possible now to produce glasses in large amounts and with reproducible properties which have pre-doses of less than 0.3 R.

High sensitivity

Silver concentration, glass base composition, and certain "quenching" cations, such as Fe^{++}, have a strong influence on the glass sensitivity. It is not yet possible to explain or to predict the effect of the glass base on the sensitivity. If, for instance, $Ba(PO_3)_2$ and KPO_3 in the Schulman-type dosimeter glass is replaced by $LiPO_3$, the sensitivity is increased by a factor of two. If, on the other hand, $LiPO_3$ in a special experimental glass[15] is replaced by $Mg(PO_3)_2$, a sensitivity drop by a factor of 20 was found[17]. Also the silver concentration is important. Depending on the glass base, maximum RPL is usually obtained with glasses containing 1 to 2% silver. The reason that conventional dosimeter glasses contain more silver (2.5 to 4.5%) is that the build-up of RPL in glasses with low silver content is a slow process. Recently, however, glass bases have been found which show a fast build-up, also with a low silver content and high final sensitivity[17].

Low energy dependence

For the most important application of RPL glasses in the dosimetry of X and gamma radiation a minimal energy dependence is desirable. Reduction of the effective atomic number $\bar{Z}$ of the glasses, which is a measure of the energy dependence in the photon energy range of interest (about 10 keV to several MeV), and can be calculated by the formula

$$\bar{Z} = \sqrt[3]{\frac{\sum_i n_i Z_i^4}{\sum_i n_i Z_i}} \qquad (1)$$

(n_i = molar fraction of element i in per cent, Z_i = atomic number of element i) is desirable. This is possible by replacing high-Z cations in the glass base by low-Z metals and reduction of the silver content. It has been established by experiments and calculations that the maximum sensitivity is between 40 and 50 keV, while the minimum is between 0.5 and two MeV. The energy dependence of the glass can therefore be expressed as

$$E.\,D. = \frac{\text{relative sensitivity at } \sim 45 \text{ keV}}{\text{relative sensitivity at } 1 \text{ MeV}} \qquad (2)$$

This value can be calculated under the assumptions of electron equilibrium, monoenergetic radiation and narrow-beam geometry, neglecting the self-shielding of the glass as well as the fluorescence and electron escape:

$$E.D. = \frac{[(\mu_{en}/\varrho)_{\text{gl.}}/(\mu_{en}/\varrho)_{\text{air}}] \, 50 \text{ keV}}{[(\mu_{en}/\varrho)_{\text{gl.}}/(\mu_{en}/\varrho)_{\text{air}}] \, 1 \text{ MeV}} \qquad (3)$$

(μ_{en}/ϱ) = mass energy transfer coefficients for air and glass, calculated from

$$\frac{\mu_{en}}{\varrho} = \sum_i \frac{(\mu_{en})_i}{\varrho_i} \, P_i \qquad (4)$$

P_i = percentage by weight of the element i.

If the fluorescence and electron escape from the glass[29] are considered, the calculated values have to be reduced by about 10%. Experimental values obtained with X radiation of 50 keV effective energy are about 60 to 80% of the calculated values, depending on the degree of filtration, because even well-filtered X radiation still has a rather broad energy distribution. If monoenergetic K fluorescence X radiation is used, the agreement is within the limits of accuracy of calculation and measurement. Using the lightest cations available the energy dependence can be reduced from about 30 (Schulman glass) to about 10 in conventional phosphate glasses. Because of the dominating effects of the Ag, however, further reduction is only possible if the silver concentration is reduced. In experimental metaphosphate glasses, factors of only 4 between maximum and minimum response have been obtained[15-17]. A further significant reduction seems improbable on the basis of conventional silver-activated phosphate glasses.

We have, therefore, studied glasses on the basis of lithium borates which have, if unactivated, an energy dependence of less than one, activated with small amounts of silver (0.3 to 3% $AgPO_3$)[20]. In Fig. 5, the energy dependence of such a glass is compared with the energy dependence of other conventional dosimeter glasses. It can be seen from Fig. 6 that the energy dependence of the glasses containing less than about 0.5% $AgPO_3$ can be

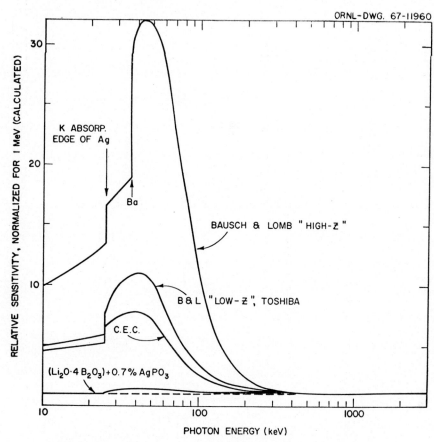

FIGURE 5   Calculated energy dependence of several dosimeter glasses (for composition, see Table II) (K. Becker and J. S. Cheka, unpublished)

compared with that of LiF. Those almost energy independent glasses, however, need an RPL developing and stabilizing temperature treatment prior to the RPL reading.

The energy dependence of dosimeter glasses can, of course, be compensated to a large degree between about 35 to 80 keV and several MeV by more or less sophisticated metal filters or filter combinations. Below this energy, several glasses behind different filters can be used as a "poor man's spectrometer" similar to the filter analytical techniques in film dosimetry. The discussion of those methods is, however, not subject of this introduction to the principles of RPL dosimetry.

11*

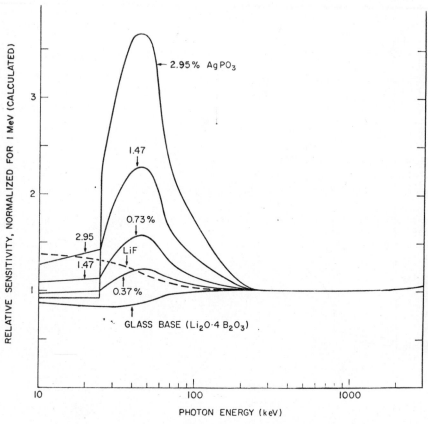

FIGURE 6   Calculated energy dependence of lithium borate glasses containing different amounts of silver phosphate, compared with lithium fluoride, unactivated (K. Becker and.J. S. Cheka, unpublished)

Stability

Phosphate glasses are less stable against humidity and certain chemicals than most other glasses. The surface of some glasses, such as ones containing much $LiPO_3$ or B_2O_3 may even soften when kept for several weeks in normal laboratory air. Improvement of the glass resistance against disturbing environmental effects, such as etching or softening of the glass surface, is usually not very important, because the glasses are humidity- and dust-proof encapsulated for use. For other purposes, such as in-vivo dosimetry, using small unshielded glasses, it is desirable to improve resistivity, for instance, by modification of the glass base[16] or by coating of the glass surface with inorganic (SiO_2) or organic materials[28].

Fast build-up and slow fading

Unfortunately, these requirements contradict each other to a certain degree. According to results with several commercial and experimental glasses[24], glasses having a fast build-up usually also exhibit a pronounced fading and vice versa. Glasses which exhibit an RPL constant within about $\pm 10\%$ between one hour and several years after irradiation at normal temperature will normally be a reasonable compromise.

Cheka[30] investigated the long-term stability of three commercial dosimeter glasses at room temperature (Fig. 7) and found the RPL intensity of two modern low-Z glasses to be constant within less than $\pm 10\%$, if the reading is done between one hour and several years after exposure. The maximum RPL is reached after about ten days. In these glasses, therefore, build-up and fading do not represent a serious problem for practical personnel dosimetry. Only under special conditions, such as accurate measurements immediately after exposure, a correction or "stabilization" may be desirable. Also measurements at increased temperatures require special precautions.

In the Schulman-type glass the maximum is already reached after less than one day, but the fading is much more rapid (30% in the first year). More extensive recent studies with glasses of different glass base composition and silver content[24,31] now permit a more general description of this effect.

In Fig. 3, the short-time kinetics of a common dosimeter glass in the 0 to 400°C temperature range are given. In this case maximum RPL may be obtained either by a one-day 75°C temperature treatment, by 15 to 20 min. at 100°C, or by 5 min. at 150°C (or values between). If the glasses are kept for extended periods at elevated temperatures, fading occurs. If, however, the glass is cooled to room temperature after the short heat treatment, the maximum RPL stays fairly constant over extended periods. In Fig. 8a, the kinetics of five commercial and one experimental glass at room temperature are compared. After a 15 min. 150°C stabilizing treatment (this time and temperature being a compromise between the requirements for the different glasses), the values given in Fig. 8b are obtained, if the storage temperature is 22°C. At elevated temperatures (Fig. 8c), some fading occurs, which amounts, for instance, after 10 weeks at 50°C to 6% less than the initial reading (after stabilization) in an experimental glass, and 18% less in the Schulman-type glass. Similar experiments by other authors led to similar

Solid state dosimetry

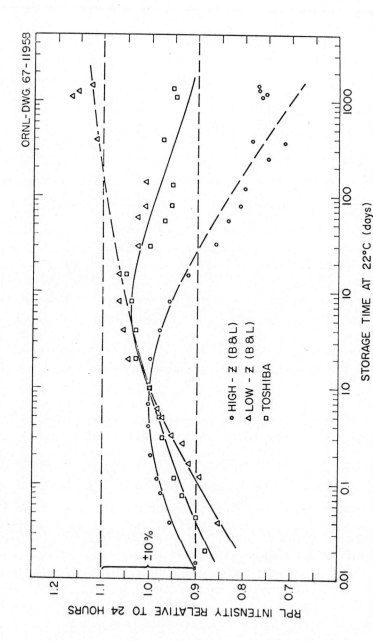

FIGURE 7   Long-term build-up and fading of three commercial dosimeter glasses at room temperature, artificial light, normalized for one day after exposure (after J. S. Cheka[30] and unpublished)

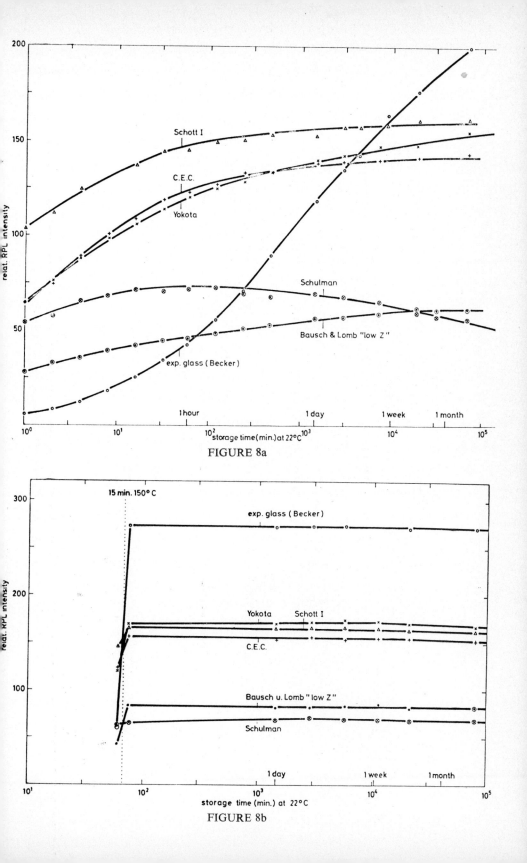

FIGURE 8a

FIGURE 8b

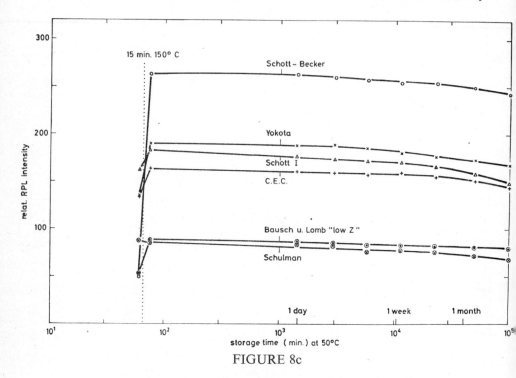

FIGURE 8c

FIGURE 8 Build-up and fading of the RPL of different dosimeter glasses exposed to the same high-intensity gamma dose (a) stored at room temperature, (b) stored ar room temperature after a 15-min 150°C heat treatment, (c) stored at 50°C after stabilization (15 min at 150°C) (after K. Becker[26])

results. There is no observable effect of the dose level on the kinetics up to exposures of about 1000 R.

Of the glasses in Fig. 8, all glasses but two (Schott-Becker and C.E.C.) contained the same amount of silver, but their sensitivity and RPL kinetics are obviously quite different. Even more drastic differences have been obtained using other glass base compositions: in a glass containing 8 % $AgPO_3$, 56 % $Al(PO_3)_3$ and 36 % KPO_3, for instance fading starts immediately after exposure and almost 20 % fading occurs during one day at room temperature (Fig. 9).

If the glass base composition is kept constant and the silver concentration is varied, curves like those in Fig. 10 result: a decrease in the silver concentration causes a decrease in the build-up speed. Therefore, the sensitivity of a certain glass, as well as the relation between silver concentration and sensitivity, depend on the time lapse between exposure and reading (Fig. 10 b). For this reason, in comparing pre-doses or sensitivities of glasses having different compositions, it should be considered that both characteristics depend on the storage time or temperature treatment of the glasses.

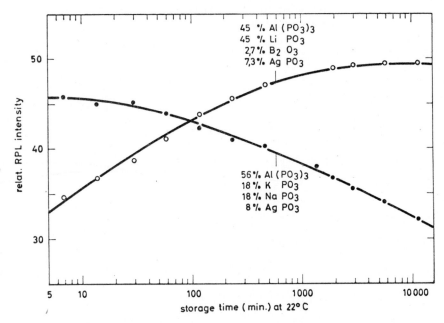

FIGURE 9   Build-up and fading in two metaphosphate glasses containing about the same amount of silver phosphate, but having a different glass base composition, at room temperature (after K. Becker[17])

Obviously, the thermal annealing kinetics of the RPL also depend on the glass composition. In Fig. 11 it is demonstrated that the RPL in glasses with low silver content first is more stable. Close to the end of the annealing process another process is superimposed. It follows from Fig. 3 that a 10 to 20-min 400°C treatment is sufficient to anneal the RPL in this glass completely. If the glass is kept at high temperatures for an extended period of time, a pre-dose increase may be observed. Also, after exposure of the glass to extremely high doses there may be some permanent pre-dose increase because of the formation of new luminescence centres.[31] There is no change in sensitivity even after numerous annealings. Glasses can be annealed many times for re-use. One should however, remove dirt carefully before heating the glasses because surface contaminations may become "burned-in" to the glass surface and cause an apparent pre-dose increase. Different kinetics may result because of the interference of RPL and discoloration kinetics at high doses.

For sensitive and accurate dose measurements at high temperatures (depending on the time which the glass has to be kept at those temperatures, between about 250 and 350°C), glasses with a low silver concentration may

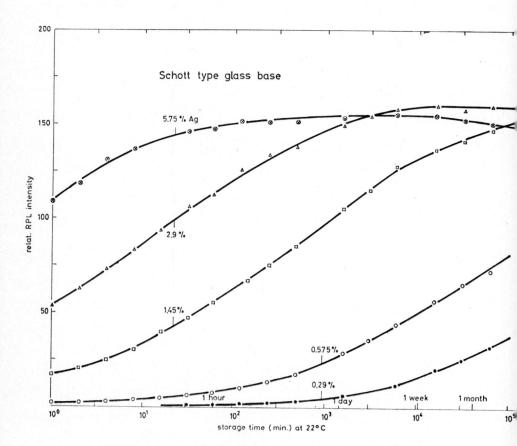

FIGURE 10(a)　RPL build-up kinetics of a dosimeter glass of constant glass base composition, but different silver content ar room temperature as a function of storage time.

be used. It can be seen in Fig. 12 that some of our recently studied energy independent lithium borate glasses[20] even show a build-up when kept for several days at 250°C. Of course, glasses of this type generally have to be stabilized by a heat treatment, for instance, two hours at 320°C prior to reading. After this, however, the RPL is remarkably resistant against fading even when stored at elevated temperatures for extended times.

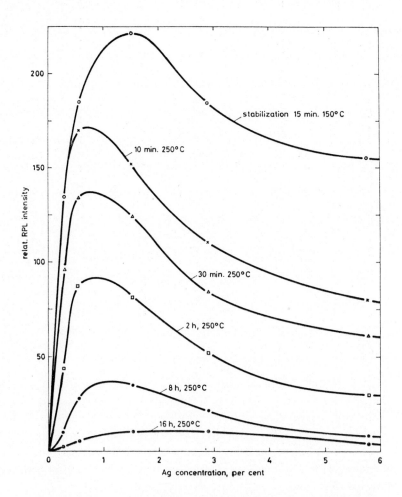

FIGURE 10(b)   RPL intensity as a function of silver concentration for different storage times and after stabilization (after K. Becker[24])

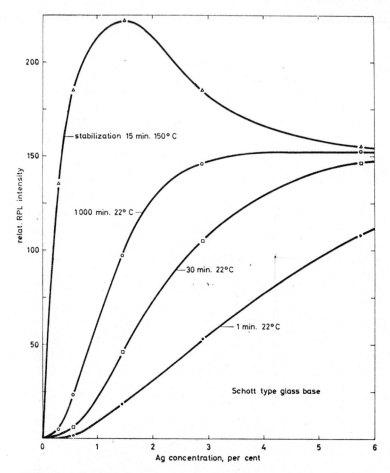

FIGURE 11   RPL intensity as a function of silver concentration for different storage times at 250°C (after K. Becker[24])

Desired neutron sensitivity

The thermal-neutron sensitivity of dosimeter glasses depends mainly on the following three parameters:

(a) The content of the thermal-neutron absorbers, such as Ag, Li, and B;

(b) The dimensions of the glass, because of the different percentages of reabsorption of beta and gamma radiation emitted by neutron-activated components (Ag); and

(c) The surroundings of the glass, in particular neutron-absorbing shielding materials.

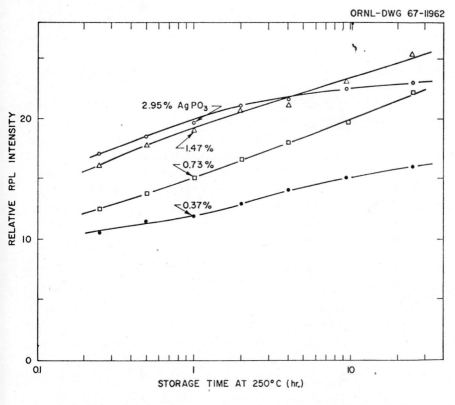

ORNL–DWG 67–11962

FIGURE 12   RPL build-up in lithium borate glasses containing different amounts of silver at 250°C (K. Becker and J. S. Cheka, unpublished)

Several authors have studied experimentally the relative sensitivities of DT-60 glass to thermal neutrons and gamma radiation. The relative sensitivity is expressed as the RPL reading of the glass in R gamma radiation, which is equivalent to the first collision dose in the glass, expressed in rads*. In the case of large glass blocks placed in a lead capsule, relative sensitivity values ranging from 0.4 to 0.38 have been reported[8,10]. For glass rods, one author[32] reports 0.4 and 1.0, if the rod is exposed inside a glass block; other authors, however, found 0.98 for unshielded glass rods[33]. In this high-Z glass, silver is mainly responsible for the thermal neutron effect.

---

* One rad of thermal neutrons is equal to 2.1×10^9 n/cm². To obtain the first collision dose in tissue the values should be multiplied by a factor of 11.

For the Li-containing low-Z glass rods, eightfold sensitivity has been reported[33]. In the Yokota-type glass, even higher sensitivities, between 10.4 and 15, have been measured by different authors for unshielded glass blocks or glass blocks shielded with brass, tin or bismuth[13,34-36]. By a 0.3 to 1mm cadmium shield, the sensitivity of blocks and of needles is reduced to 3.5[35,36]. With ^{6}Li shields of different thicknesses the sensitivity has been drastically reduced, for instance by 3 mm ^{6}Li down to 1% of the unshielded glass sensitivity[33]. This cannot be done by Cd shields because of the effect of the capture gamma radiation on the glass.

Kondo[32] used glasses with the same glass base, but a different silver content, for measurements of thermal-neutron fluxes in mixed radiation fields. Becker and Tuyn[38] studied the sensitivities of experimental glasses having the same silver content but a different content of Li and B. They found the experimental results in good agreement with the response values R calculated by the formula

$$R = 0.18 D + R_{Ag} \qquad (5)$$

where D = energy absorbed in the glass for the (n, α)-reactions of Li and B
    R_{Ag} = the component of the response due to the silver activation, and
    0.18 = the best value for the relative efficiency of the α particles.
D can be calculated by the formula

$$D = 1.6 \times 10^{-8} \frac{V\phi}{g} (N_{10_B} \sigma_{10_B} E_{10_B} + N_{6_{Li}} \sigma_{6_{Li}} E_{6_{Li}})$$

$$\left(\frac{1 - \exp\left(-\sum_i N_i \sigma_i L\right)}{\sum_i N_i \sigma_i L} \right) \qquad (6)$$

where V = glass volume in cm^3
N_i = number of ^{10}B or ^{6}Li atoms per cm^3
σ_i = cross-section of the (n, α) reactions in ^{10}B and ^{6}Li per cm^2
E = energy released by the reactions ($E_{10_B} = 2.5$ MeV, $E_{6_{Li}} = 4.78$ MeV)
g = weight of the glass in g
L = glass thickness in cm.

The silver effect has been calculated by the formula

$$R_{Ag} = 2.15 \text{ rad}/10^{10} \, n/cm^2 \times \frac{1 - \exp\left(-\sum_i N_i \sigma_i L\right)}{\sum_i N_i \sigma_i L}. \qquad (7)$$

The number 2.15 rad/10^{10} ncm^{-2} was obtained by Kondo[32] and Amato and Malsky.[37] Using the same formula, the effect of thickness, ^{10}B and/or ^{6}Li enrichment on the thermal-neutron sensitivity have also been calculated[34]. It has been found that the self shielding of glass blocks soon leads to a saturation value which, for blocks 4.7 mm thick, is around two to three times the normal sensitivity of Li-containing glasses. Also, the effect of strong neutron absorbers, such as gadolinium, is compensated by the self shielding.

Unfortunately, the fast-neutron sensitivity of dosimeter glasses is quite low and is difficult to measure. The results indicate an increase with increasing neutron energy. For 0.5 to 1.5-MeV neutrons, values of 0.003 to 0.007 (0.3 to 0.7 % of the gamma sensitivity in rad) have been measured[33,10]. For 14 MeV neutrons, 0.07 to 0.1 has been obtained for bare glass blocks and needles[32,36]. If the glass rod is encapsulated in Plexiglas (Lucite) a value of 0.21 has been found[32]. Also the effect of the fission spectrum of an unshielded reactor on glasses in different filters and environments[34] has been studied.

Several possibilities for increasing the low fast-neutron sensitivity have been discussed and studied. Unfortunately, it is difficult to make glasses with a high hydrogen content. By surrounding small glasses with organic materials for recoil proton registration, sensitivity may be somewhat increased. This effect can be further increased by mixing a fine glass powder with an organic material. However, because of the low efficiency of the recoil protons, even in a highly dispersed system only about 20 % of the gamma sensitivity can be expected.

Another method for fast neutron measurements is based on the use of moderating materials which thermalize the fast neutrons, either by using spherical moderators around the glass or by the use of the backscattering and moderating effect of the human body on the dosimeter. If, for instance, an unshielded Yokota glass at the front of a thorax phantom is exposed to a fission spectrum, neutron and gamma doses are indicated almost rad-equivalent. In free-air exposures only 1 cm polyethylene around the glass is sufficient to give a rad-equivalent response for fission neutrons. This system is, however, very neutron-energy dependent. If a glass is surrounded by 5 cm polyethylene, for example, fission neutrons are overestimated by a factor of 4 and Am/Be neutrons (about 4 MeV) are underestimated by 0.7 (Fig. 13). Almost rem-equivalent measurements between thermal and about 18 MeV are possible by surrounding the glass with a

20-cm diam. pressed-wood sphere[38]. Using a spherical moderator-absorber-moderator sequence based on the Andersson-Braun neutron rem counter an even better energy response is possible. These devices have the disadvantage of being quite heavy and voluminous and are, therefore, only of interest for dose measurements at fixed locations, for example around reactors or accelerators. In mixed thermal-neutron, X and/or gamma radiation fields,

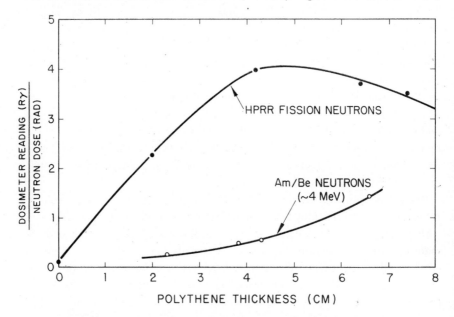

FIGURE 13   Ratio of the gamma to neutron radiation sensitivities of a Toshiba dosimeter glass block as a function of the moderator thickness surrounding the glass, for the HPRR fission spectrum and the Am/Be spectrum (after K. Becker and J. W. N. Tuyn[34])

the neutron and photon component can easily be separated by the use of dosimeter pairs encapsulated in different neutron absorbers. Several authors studied and used this technique, for instance, for neutron measurements in reactors mainly employing tin/cadmium pairs or lithium shields.

Encapsulation of glasses with a high thermal neutron sensitivity in Cd only reduces the neutron response by about a factor of 3 because of the effect of the capture gamma radiation and the neutrons above the Cd cut-off at 0.4 eV. To avoid encapsulation in thermal neutron absorbers, attempts have been made to reduce the thermal neutron sensitivity without affecting the gamma sensitivity. In one experiment, natural lithium was replaced by $^7Li^{39}$. More effective and less expensive is the method whereby neutron absorbers are omitted from the glass base and the silver concentration is reduced. For instance, one of a series of experimental glasses containing 60% $Al(PO_3)_3$, 19.5% KPO_3, and 19.5% $NaPO_3$, and 1% $AgPO_3$ had almost the same low pre-dose, sensitivity, and energy dependence for photons as the best commercial glasses, but only about 1% of their thermal neutron sensitivity[17].

Low dose-rate, LET, temperature and directional dependence

Several authors studied the dose-rate dependence of glass dosimeters up to 10^{10} R/sec[40] and did not find any dose-rate dependence.

For high LET radiation, there is a drop in glass sensitivity. For alpha particles, for instance, 16 to 20% of the gamma radiation sensitivity has been observed[32,40]. Using protons of variable energy the results in Fig. 14 were obtained for RPL glasses as compared to a LiF thermoluminescent dosimeter and a film dosimeter. There is not yet a theoretical explanation for this curve, nor have possibilities been studied to modify this response.

There is an effect of the temperature during irradiation on the glass response: betwen −10 and +50°C an increase of about 0.3%/°C was found[7], between 0 and 50°C an almost linear increase of 0.3%/°C and 0.2%/°C by other investigators. In most of these experiments, however, the effect will, in part at least, be simulated by the temperature influence on the build-up kinetics. Other experiments involving a stabilization treatment of the glasses have shown only a 0.1 to 0.2%/°C increase of sensitivity between −20 and +80°C.

Schulman *et al.* first observed an influence of the reading temperature on the RPL intensity. They determined the coefficient to be −0.77%/°C; other authors found somewhat higher values: −1.1%/°C, −0.86%/°C, −0.95%/°C, and −0.9%/°C. 0.9%/°C seems to be a good average of these values which will, however, be superimposed by the temperature dependence of the instrument, and the standards if the whole reader is used at different temperatures. It has been found with the US Navy CP-85 A/PD reader that the temperature dependence is much smaller than that of the glass alone[41]. This result has been confirmed by several authors who did not find a temperature dependence at all if the measurement is done in comparison with a Sm-activated standard.

The effect of light on glasses depends mainly on the pre-irradiation of the glass and the wave-length of the light. Like increased temperature, infra-red light increases the RPL build-up and fading rate. Visible light has only very little or no effect. Near ultraviolet light in the region of the RPL excitation causes a slow destruction of RPL centres ("bleaching"). This effect this too small to disturb the usual fluorimetric reading, which needs only a few seconds. It may, however, cause a considerable loss in RPL intensity if the glass is exposed for extended periods of time to bright sunlight. It has been found[42] that the bleaching at constant *UV* intensity is quite rapid at first and becomes smaller (linear function of log time). During the first hour of intense exposure with 365 mμ *UV* the RPL intensity dropped by almost 15%, and five hours are required to obtain a 30% fading.

It has been found[43] that short wave-length ultraviolet light can also create new RPL centres. Because of the strong absorption of this light in the glass (the *UV* absorption edge of modern glasses is around 300 mμ, and 254 mμ *UV* was used in the experiments), the effect is localized to the glass surface and the kinetics of the *UV*-induced RPL are different. If glasses are exposed to direct sunlight, all effects which have been mentioned may superimpose each other to a varying degree. Indirect natural or artificial room illumination, however, caused no observable effect on the glasses.

Contrary to the situation in photographic films, there is only a small directional dependence with glass blocks, plates and rods, also for low photon energies (less than $\pm 10\%$ for photon energies above 30 to 40 keV). A serious directional dependence can be introduced, however, by asymmetrical energy compensation filters or a badge design which results in a strong attenuation of the radiation under certain angles of radiation incidence. This directional dependence can be avoided by a symmetrical design, in particular by the use of conical holes which overlap in such a way that the projection in the glass volume stays constant under different angles of incidence[42].

Response to electrons and charged particles

For electrons and protons above 50 to 100 MeV, the sensitivity of the glass per rad is equal to the gamma radiation sensitivity. Below those energies, two effects may be superimposed:

(a) The penetration of the radiation (volume dose), the effect being small if only a thin layer of the glass surface is affected by the radiation;

(b) The LET dependence of the glass sensitivity (Fig. 14).

In cases in which the glass has been exposed to radiation of a low penetration power, only the uppermost layer contains RPL centres, and measurements of the range and depth-dose distribution are possible by a "peeling" method: the RPL of the exposed glass is measured, then a thin layer of known thickness is removed by chemical etching, and the glass is remeasured,

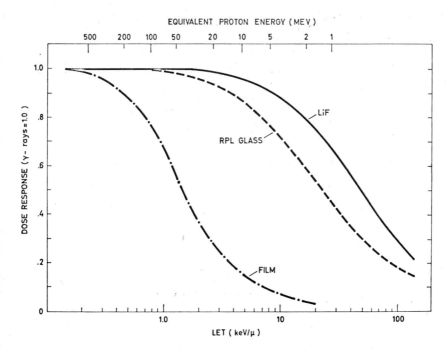

FIGURE 14   LET dependence of the dose response of RPL glass dosimeters and other detectors (E. Tochilin, unpublished)

etc., until the radiation effect is completely removed. The residual RPL may be plotted as a function of the thickness of the removed glass layer (Fig. 15). We have measured the range of beta radiation in glasses which had been submersed in solutions containing ^{3}H, ^{63}Ni, and ^{35}S, of alpha radiation from uranium, neptunium and plutonium, and of protons, deuterons and He$^+$ ions of different energies[44].

Heavy charged particles above a threshold LET which is not yet known, but is certainly above the maximum LET of alpha particles and below those

12*

of fission fragments, can be made directly visible by a preferential etching along the tracks of these particles at the dosimeter glass surface (Fig. 16). For the etching all chemicals attacking the glass surface at a sufficient speed, such as HF, NaOH, or EDTA solutions, can be used. The etching speed depends mainly on the glass composition, the etchant, and the etchant's concentration and temperature. The registration efficiency for fission frag-

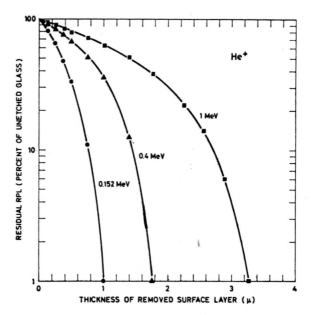

FIGURE 15   Residual RPL in a glass block (in per cent of the RPL of an unetched glass) as a function of the thickness of the unexposed layer (after K. Becker[44])

ments has, in contrast to the results of some other authors, been found to be over 90% in dosimeter glasses. For fissionable materials of a thickness greater than the range of the fission fragments, a sensitivity of 1.2×10^{-5} tracks per neutron per barn has been found[45].

In principle, the combination of a dosimeter glass and a foil of a fissionable material could be used as a neutron and gamma detector in mixed radiation fields (neutron dosimetry by track counting at the etched surface, gamma dosimetry by RPL measurement). Indeed, the RPL intensity measurement is not affected by the etching. However, the alpha, beta and gamma

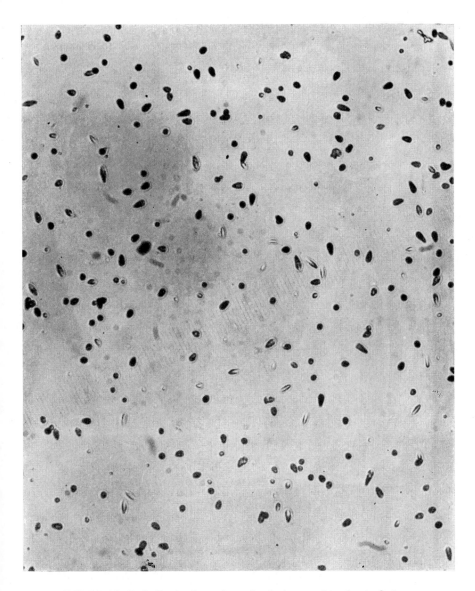

FIGURE 16   Etch pits in the surface of a dosimeter glass due to fission
fragments (after K. Becker[45])

radiation emitted by the fissionable foil causes a rapid linear increase in pre-dose and limits the usability of the method to relatively short times.

Good dynamic range and accuracy

The RPL intensity is a linear function of dose up to one or a few thousand R gamma exposure (or a comparable X-ray, beta or neutron dose), the exact dose depending somewhat on the glass dimensions and the type of reader. If the path length of the UV and RPL light is as small as 1 mm, the response may be linear up to 10^5 rad. At a dose level of 3 to 5×10^4 rad (the exact value also depending somewhat on the glass and the reader), the RPL intensity reaches a maximum and then decreases (Fig. 17). If the RPL is not

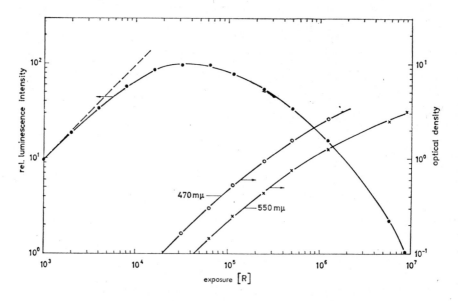

FIGURE 17   RPL intensity and optical density at different wave length of a dosimeter glass block (after K. Becker[46])

measured in the orange-red but at shorter wavelengths, for instance at 420 mμ, there is an increase of RPL output with dose up to 10^6 rad.[46]

The non-linearity is caused by the absorption of the excitation ultraviolet light in the glass, because an absorption band is formed with maximum intensity at 320 mμ, but extending into the visible. Gamma radiation exposures as low as several hundred R may be detected by density measurement at 320 mμ. Glasses which have been exposed to gamma doses higher than several thousand R become visibly discoloured: a usual dosimeter glass looks slightly yellow at 10^4 R, yellowishbrown at 10^5 R, deep brown at 10^6 R, and almost black at 10^7 R. The intensity of the 320 mμ absorption band is an almost linear function of the Ag concentration in the glass. If a glass which does not contain any silver is exposed to very high doses an absorption band in the red is created. It has also been found that, unlike the RPL build-up, fading of the 320 mμ absorption band starts immediately after exposure. Fading depends somewhat on dose and strongly on the Ag concentration. At low Ag concentration, there may even be an increase of the optical density after exposure[46]. Of course, it also depends on temperature, and the discoloration can be annealed by a high temperature treatment (Fig. 18). For correction of the errors caused during and after exposure special formulae have been used[47].

Because the absorption is less stable than the RPL, the kinetics for RPL build-up and fading are different if the glass has been exposed to levels above several thousand R gamma radiation (or the equivalent dose of other types of radiation). Because of superimposed effects of absorption fading, and

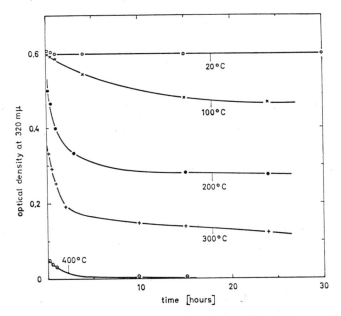

FIGURE 18   Fading of the 320 mμ absorption band in a dosimeter glass at different storage temperatures (after K. Becker[46])

RPL build-up, the build-up is more pronounced in this case[46]. If a glass is heated more absorption than RPL centres is destroyed, and the linear RPL response range is extended to higher doses.

More interesting than the high dose range, at least in personnel dosimetry, is the lower limit for dose measurements using RPL glasses. This limit is determined mainly by the following factors:

1) Pre-Dose of the Glass. If a glass has, like the US Navy DT-60 glass, a pre-exposure of around 40 R in a given reader system (in other readers it can be less), obviously exposures of a few R can only be read quite inaccurately. Modern glasses of different manufactures have pre-exposures of only a few hundred mR.

2) Dosimeter Consistency. Because the individual calibration (pre-dose and sensitivity determination) of each single glass dosimeter is not desirable, good consistency of the dosimetric properties within a large number of dosimeters is important. The deviations in the glass characteristics are determined by the size distribution of the pieces, inhomogeneities of the glass, luminescent contaminations of the surface and inaccuracies of the reading instrument. There have been considerable problems with older glass types, but in modern glasses the standard deviation for glass block pre-doses and sensitivities is only 0.1 to 0.6%[48]. To obtain low standard deviations accurate cleaning and positioning of the glasses in the reader are required.

3) Accuracy Requirements. The less the required accuracy is, the lower are the doses that can be measured by a given system.

4) Glass Size. In principle, accuracy is independent of the glass size. However, in practice it is more difficult to get accurate results if the volume of the glass is too small.

In Table I, some optimal accuracies which have been obtained with modern systems under laboratory conditions are given. These values may be improved by the use of other techniques. If, however, glasses are not properly cleaned from luminescent contaminations, for instance, by ultrasonic washing, less accurate results may be obtained. Also the DT-60 glasses had a considerably poorer accuracy of ±6 to 20%.

Under somewhat relaxed routine dosimetry conditions, the standard deviation for pre-doses and low gamma dose effects measured for three different dosimeter glasses (Toshiba) and a typical laboratory reader (Toshiba

TABLE I   Standard deviation of gamma radiation dose measurements under laboratory conditions

Glass type	Size (mm)	Reader	Dose level (rad γ-radiation)	Standard deviation (%)	Ref.
Yokota	8 × 8 × 4.7	FGD-3B	1–1000	<3	49
			pre-dose	<4	50
		FGD-6	0.010	4	51
			0.015	3.5	
			0.025	3	
			0.05	1.5	
	6 × 6 × 3.3	FGD-3B modified	0–35	ca. 0.35	48
		FGD-3B	0–20	ca. 1.6	
	1 × 6 (fluoroads)	FGD-3B	50	6.0	51
			1000	3.9	
			0–1150	ca. 2.5	48
Yokota, Bausch & Lomb		Bausch & Lomb Turner	10–5000	2–5	30

FGD-3) for 10 glasses each chosen at random averaged about ± 2.5 to 6%. About 20 mrad gamma radiation could be detected with the FGD-3 B without considering the individual glass block pre-doses, but using an average predose value. This detection limit is sufficient for most purposes in personnel dosimetry, but may be improved by better readers and other measures.

In order to get reliable information on the accuracy of film and glass dosimeters not under optimized laboratory, but under practical conditions, those conditions have been simulated in the following experiment: pairs of film badges (German standard type with open window, 1.2, 0.5, and 0.05 mm Cu, 0.5 mm Pb filters and Adox dosimeter film packets containing one sensitive and one insensitive film sealed in a plastic envelope) and glass dosimeter (FD-P8-1) blocks in a spherical Cd shield with conical holes at all sides have been exposed to monoenergetic and mixed X and gamma radiation in the 0.06 to 870 rad dose and the 45 to 1250 keV energy range. Partly the dosimeters were exposed frontally, partly under an angle of 80 to 90°. The dosimeters have been stored four weeks between irradiation and evaluation: 75% at room temperature (20 to 25°C), 25% at "summer" temperature (35°C). One half was stored in completely dry air, the other half at 75 to 80%

relative humidity. Series of ^{137}Cs calibration irradiations have also been made and stored at 22°C, 0% relative humidity. The actual doses were unknown to the glass and film evaluating technicians.

The results of this experiment (Fig. 19) may be summarized as follows: of all the film dosimeter readings, less than 20% are correct within ±30% of the actual dose (more than two thirds of the exposed films gained no meaningful results at all) but almost 90% of the glass readings. The percentage of "correct" readings (within ±30%) is about 13% for film badges at higher dose levels (>5 rad), but 100% for the glass dosimeter readings (inaccurate glass readings are only observed at low doses above 5 rad, the

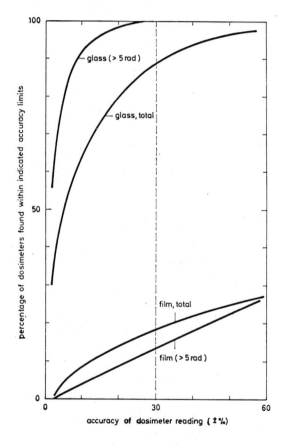

FIGURE 19   Percentage of film and glass dosimeters with dose indication within indicated accuracy limits (after K. Becker[17])

average error of 50 dosimeters was $\pm 4.6\%$). There was no effect of storage humidity and temperature on the percentage of correct glass readings, but a considerable effect on the films (at 0% relative humidity, 25% of the frontally exposed films, but only 6% of the slanting exposed films yielded the correct dose information). Even under conditions which are optimal for the film badge (dose 0.5 to 300 rad, frontal irradiation, dry storage at toom temperature) only 33% of the film readings, but 100% of the glass readings have been found within $\pm 30\%$ of the actual doses.

Recently, Kastner *et al.*[19] found that after *UV* laser pulse excitation the decay time for the pre-dose luminescence is smaller by a factor of ten than the RPL decay time, which is about 3 µsec. Using a delay time of one or two microseconds for the measurements they could easily detect 1 mR gamma radiation with a fluorod. It should be possible by this technique to measure doses in the 0.1-mR range.

Other factors, such as the price of the components and the manufacturing process, the desired size and shape of the glasses (blocks of different sizes, plates, needles, cylindrical units and spheres, have been made for different purposes), etc., also may be important factors for the development of a dosimeter glass.

In Table II, the composition and some dosimetric properties of several commercial and/or experimental dosimeter glasses are compiled.

Accurate knowledge of RPL spectra is important for choosing an optimal combination of optical filters and RPL detectors that give best sensitivity and high background (pre-dose) discrimination. Relative spectra measurements (without correction of the detector response characteristics) are, however, only of little value. Using a red-sensitive photomultiplier, the relative RPL spectra of Fig. 20a for different glasses exposed to the same gamma radiation dose have been obtained[52]. After correction for the PM tube response and normalizing to peak intensity $= 100$, the spectra in Fig. 20b with maxima between 610 and 640 mµ and a slow decrease into red were obtained. It has also been found that

a) At least for high doses, there seems to be no effect of the dose on the slope of the spectrum;

b) During build-up, no significant change in the spectrum takes place;

c) In the 0.5 to 5% silver range there is no effect of silver concentration on the spectrum, but there may be a considerable effect of the glass base:

TABLE II Composition and dosimetric properties of some radiophotoluminescent dosimeter glasses

Author, Manufacturer	Composition (wt. %)						Pre-dose rad (γ-equivalent) (approx.)	Relative γ-sensitivity (approx.)	Effective atomic number	Energy dependence sensitivity at 50 keV / sensitivity at 1 MeV calculated
	Ag	Al	Li	P	O	Others				
Schulman et al.[7] (Bausch & Lomb High-Z)	4.3	4.7		28.4	44.1	10.8 Ba 7.7 K	10.0	1.0	28.0	32.0
Ginther and Schulman[12] (Bausch & Lomb Low-Z)	4.3	4.7	1.9	33.7	52.3	3.1 Mg	10.0	1.0	17.6	10.0
Yokota et al.[13] (Toshiba)	4.2	4.6	3.6	33.3	53.5	0.8 B	0.2	2.2	17.5	10.0
François et al.[14] (C.E.C.)	2.4	3.5	2.5	33.8	52.5	0.5 Be 4.7 Na	0.7	1.9	15.4	7.3
Schott I, unpublished	4.6	3.1	4.7	34.1	52.8	0.9 Mg	0.15	2.1	17.9	11.0
Becker[15] (experimental glass)	0.6	0.5	7.3	34.7	55.9	1.0 B	0.1	3.1	12.6	4.0

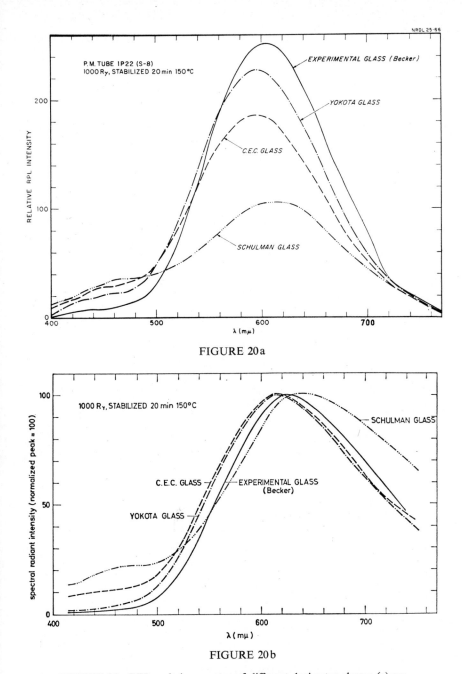

FIGURE 20a

FIGURE 20b

FIGURE 20   RPL emission spectra of different dosimeter glasses (a) uncorrected for the photomultiplier spectral response characteristics, (b) corrected for the PM tube response and normalized to peak intensity = 100
(after K. Becker and D. W. McQuilling[52])

As can be seen in Fig. 20, the RPL spectrum of a lithium borate glass is quite different from a phosphate glass;

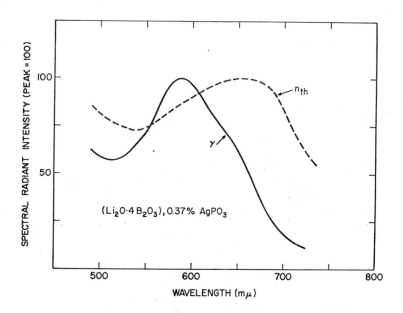

FIGURE 21 Absolute RPL spectra (excitation 365 mμ) in a silver-activated lithium borate glass after gamma radiation and thermal neutron exposure, peak intensity normalized = 1 (K. Becker, unpublished)

d) There is a considerable LET effect on the RPL spectrum. As can also be seen in Fig. 21, the high LET radiation caused by thermal neutrons creates RPL centres which have an RPL spectrum which is quite different from the gamma-radiation induced ones[53].

References

1. E. Goldstein, *Z. Phys.* **13**, (1912).
2. K. Przibram, *Z. Phys.* **20**, 196 (1924); **41**, 833 (1927); **44**, 542 (1927); **68**, 403 (1931); **102**, 331 (1936).
3. K. Przibram, *Ber. d. Akad. Wiss.* Wien (IIa) 134, 233 (1925).
4. J. H. Schulman, R. J. Ginther, C. C. Klick, R. S. Alger, and R. A. Levy, *J. Appl. Phys.* **22**, 1479 (1951).

5. J. H. Schulman, L. W. Evans, and R. Ginther, U.S. Patent No. 2.524.839 (filed 1948).
6. W. A. Weyl, J. H. Schulman, R. J. Ginther, and L. W. Evans, *J. Electrochem. Soc.* **95**, 70 (1949).
7. J. H. Schulman, W. Shurcliff, R. J. Ginther, and F. H. Attix, *Nucleonics* **11**, (10) 52 (1953).
8. E. R. Ballinger and P. S. Harris, LA-2298 Rep. 4526 (1959).
9. N. T. Kreidl, Final Developm. Rep. NObar-57010.
10. D. H. Peirson, AERE EL/R 2590 (1958).
11. J. H. Schulman, Tech. Rep. ONRL-11-61 (1961).
12. R. J. Ginther and J. H. Schulman, *Nucleonics* **18** (4), 92 (1960).
13. R. Yokota, S. Nakajima, and H. Sakai, *Health Phys.* **5**, 219 (1961).
14. H. François, V. Bourbigot, A. M. Grand-Clément, G. Portal, and G. Soudain, Paper *Internat. Congr. Dosimetry External Rad.* Paris (1965) and French Pat. 862.126 and 926.582.
15. K. Becker, *Nucl. Instr. Meth.* **36**, 323 (1965).
16. R. Yokota and S. Nakajima, *Health Phys.* **11**, 241 (1965).
17. K. Becker, *Health Phys.* **14** (1968), (in press).
18. R. Yokota and H. Imagawa, Paper *Int. Congr. on Glass*, Tokyo and Kyoto (1966).
19. J. Kastner, D. Eggeberger, A. Longnecker, D. King, and D. Schott, *Proc. IAEA Symp. Solid-State and Chemical Dosimetry*, Vienna, p. 115 (1967).
20. K. Becker and J. S. Cheka, (to be published).
21. K. Becker, *Health Phys.* **12**, 1376 (1966), and Dosimetry Bibliographies Series AED-C-21, Gmelin Institute, Frankfurt, Germany.
22. K. Becker, *IAEA Atomic Energy Review* **5**, 43 (1967).
23. J. H. Schulman, Proc. *IAEA Symp. Solid-State and Chemical Dosimetry* Vienna, p. 3 (1967).
24. K. Becker, *ibid.*, p. 131.
25. H. Vogel and K. Becker, *Nukleonik* **7**, 18 (1965).
26. T. Kishii and J. Sakurai, *J. Phys. Soc. Japan* **20**, 1271 (1965).
27. L. S. Druskina, *Jzv. Akad. Nauk SSSR, Ser. Fiz.* **29**, 434 (1965).
28. H. Brömer, A. May, A. Scharmann, and G. Weissenberg, *Proc. French-German Symp. Radiation Dosimetry*, Regensburg (1966).
29. Y. Feige, J. Sever and S. Alterovitz, IA-1003 (1965).
30. J. S. Cheka, *Health Phys.* **10**, 303 (1964), and ORNL-3849, 171 (1965).
31. K. Becker, *Proc. IAEA Symp. Pers. Dos. Rad. Accid.*, Vienna, 169 (1965).
32. S. Kondo, *Health Phys.* **4**, 21 (1960), and **7**, 25 (1961).
33. C. H. Bernard, W. T. Thornton and J. A. Auxier, *Health Phys.* **4**, (1961), and *Proc. IAEA Symp. Select. Topics Rad. Dos.*, Vienna, p. 503 (1960).
34. K. Becker and J. W. N. Tuyn, *Health Phys.* **11**, 1225 (1965), and *Proc. Conf. Luminescence Dosimetry*, Stanford 1965.
35. I. Miyanaga and M. Yamamoto, *Health Phys.* **9**, 965 (1963).
36. E. Piesch, *Atompraxis* **10**, 268 (1964).
37. G. G. Amato and S. J. Malsky, *Radiology* **76**, 290 (1961).
38. A. E. Nappi and C. Distenfield, Paper **8***th Meeting Health Phys. Soc.* (Abstract *Health Phys.* **9**, 889 (1963).

39. G. D. Kerr and J. S. Cheka, Paper *Health Phys. Soc. Symp. on Pers. Rad. Dosimetry*, Chicago 1967.
40. E. Tochilin and N. Goldstein, Paper **9***th Meeting Health Phys. Soc.* (Abstract *Health Phys.* **12**, 1705 (1966).
41. W. C. Bryan and W. P. Schaus, AFSWG-TN-61-4 (1960).
42. K. Becker, *Nukleonik* **5**, 154 (1963).
43. K. Becker, *Z. Naturforsch.* **19a**, 1233 (1964).
44. K. Becker, USNRDL-TR-1088 (1966).
45. K. Becker, USNRDL-TR-904 (1965).
46. K. Becker, *Health Phys.* **11**, 523 (1965).
47. H. Rabin and W. E. Price, *Nucleonics* **13**, (3) 33 (1955).
48. C. K. Menkes, *Health Phys.* **12**, 429 and 852 (1966).
49. K. Becker, *Kerntechnik* **6**, 199 (1964).
50. R. L. Kathren, *Health Phys.* **12**, 1624 (1966).
51. R. Yokota *et al.*, *Proc. Conf. Luminescence Dosimetry*, Stanford 1965, and *OECD/ ENEA Symp. Pers. Rad. Dosimetry*, Stockholm (1967).
52. K. Becker and D. W. McQuilling, USNRDL-TR-67-66 (1967).
53. K. Becker, to be published.

Production and properties of electron and hole centers in pure and doped alkali halide crystals

HEINZ PICK

University of Stuttgart, Germany

I SOME REMARKS ABOUT ALKALI HALIDE CRYSTALS

1 Introduction

1 *Alkali halide crystals*

Alkali halide crystals are among those, which have been treated from the first beginning of solid state physics. There are several good reasons, which have to do with the physical properties of the material. There are many different alkali halide crystals available as single crystals, most of which are face centered cubic (Fig. 1) (LiF, NaF, KF, LiCl, NaCl, KCl, RbCl, NaBr, KBr, RbBr, NaI, KI, RbI, CsI). This makes it easy to change certain parameters in a wide range.

2 *Binding energy*

The basic binding mechanism of the ion in the crystal is well understood. It is given by two terms: The one is the Coulomb interaction between charged ions

$$K_{\text{com}} = \pm \frac{1}{4\pi\varepsilon_0} \frac{e^2}{r^2},$$

13*

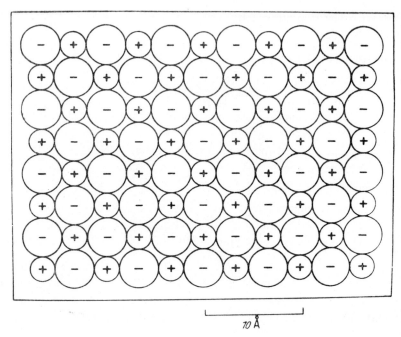

FIGURE 1   (100) plane of f.c.c. crystal (KBr)

it may be attractive $(-)$ or repulsive $(+)$. The other is the repulsive inter-action between neighbouring ion cores. This part is well described by

$$K_{rep} = \frac{b}{r^n} ; \quad u = 7\text{–}8.$$

The total binding energy is of the order of 6–10 eV. Similar considerations may be used to calculate the binding energy of local defects.

3   *Conductivity*

The crystals are insulating at low temperatures; there is ionic conductivity at high temperatures. Under normal conditions there is no electronic or hole conductivity. Therefore radiation induced carriers can easily be observed.

4   *Optical spectrum*

The optical absorptions spectrum is characterized by two well separated parts: the electronic absorption in the short wave ultraviolet and the lattice absorption due to ionic vibration in the far infrared (Fig. 2). There is no absorption in the wide range of the spectrum between 0.2 and 50 μ (6 eV and 25 meV). This wide spectral range is open for the optical detection of defects, chemical impurities, electronic and hole centers, they may be present or produced by radiation or heat treatment.

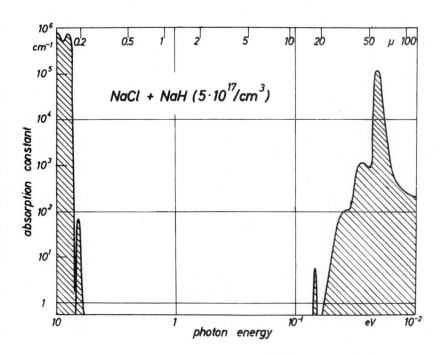

FIGURE 2   Optical absorption spectrum of alkali halide crystal

5   Magnetic properties

The ions of the lattice as well as the bulk crystals are diamagnetic. Paramagnetic defects, which normally are produced by high energy radiation may easily be measured.

For these and other reasons very many investigations have been carried out and there is a very high amount of information available with respect to alkali halide crystals.

2   The defect structure of alkali halide crystals

1   *Lattice defects*

Alkali halide crystals may be grown from aqueous solution or from the melt. The optically clear crystals are cubic with equal numbers of positive and negative ions. There is only very little overlap of the ion cores. At high temperatures the precise geometric order of a crystal is thermodynamically unstable. There is always a small concentration of point lattice defects. This is true also in semiconductors, other ionic crystals, metals and so on.

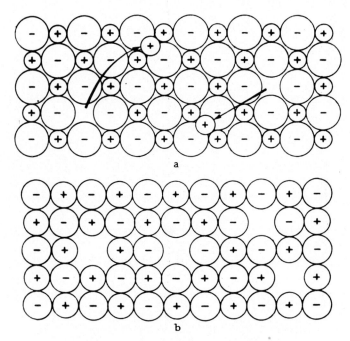

FIGURE 3   Schottky and Frenkel defect structure

In alkali halides an equal number of positive and negative ion lattice sites is unoccupied (Fig. 3). The concentration n of these empty lattice sites (so called Schottky defects) depends on temperature and is controlled by an activation energy E_1 for the production of anion and cation vacancy pairs according to

$$n^2 = n_+ \, n_- = A \exp \left(-E_1/kT \right).$$

E_1 is of the order of 2.5 eV. The defect concentration near the melting point is of the order of 10^{-4}.

2 *Vacancy motion*

The anion and cation vacancies are mobile at high enough temperatures. The activation energy E_2 for thermally activated vacancy motion is of the order of 0.9 eV. Self-diffusion and ionic conductivity at high temperatures are mainly given by vacancy production and vacancy motion.

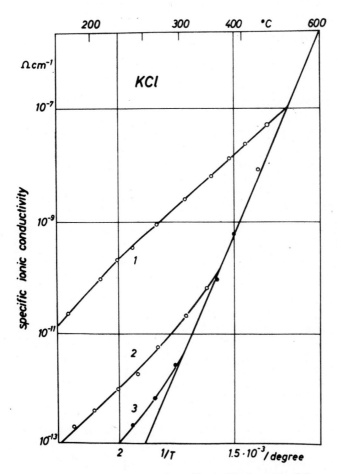

FIGURE 4 Temperature dependence of ionic conductivity

The temperature dependence of the diffusion constant D, defined by

$$\frac{1}{F}\frac{dN}{dt} = -D\frac{dn}{dx},$$

for cation or anion self-diffusion is

$$D_0 = \text{const. exp}\,(-E_{12} + E_2/kT)$$

(for example in KBr at $650°C$ $D_s = 5.2 \cdot 10^{-8}$ m^2/sec this is equivalent to mean displacement of 10 cm per day).

The ionic conductivity of alkali halides is based upon diffusion of vacancies, which are charged entities, and is given by the drift of the randomly moving vacancies along the lines of the applied electric field (Fig. 4).

3   *Defect induced reactions*

Diffusion, self-diffusion and ionic conductivity play an important role for most photochemical processes especially at higher temperatures; the aggregation of lattice defects e.g. produced by high energy radiation, is only possible because of the vacancy motion. Internal stress fields and electric fields provide the driving forces for such processes (like photographic process in silver halides).

3   **Chemical impurities**

Very much effort is needed to grow alkali halide crystals with chemical impurity concentrations below 10^{-6}.

1   *Divalent cations*

The most common cation impurities are divalent ions like Mg^{++} or Ca^{++}. For reasons of charge compensation the incorporation of such divalent ions into the growing crystal is combined with the introduction of one cation vacancy. At low temperatures the cation vacancy and the divalent impurity ions are associated. The dissociation energy is of the order of 0.5 eV; at temperatures above a few hundred degrees centigrade divalent cations and cation vacancies are dissociated. Because of the mass action low an increase in cation vacancy concentration is followed by decrease in anion vacancy concentration holding the product of both concentrations at a given temperature constant. Because of the increase in total number of vacancies and because of the higher mobility of the cation vacancies the ionic conductivity increases with increasing divalent impurity concentration. Because of the presence of divalent impurities in all alkali halide crystals the low temperature range of the ionic conductivity is always governed by these additions, it is called the extrinsic range (Fig. 4). The high temperature range which is given by the thermodynamic defect structure is called the intrinsic range of the conductivity. The same is true for the temperature dependence of the diffusion constant. Low temperature measurements of conductivity or diffusion constant can be used to measure the total concentration of divalent impurities.

2 *Anion impurities*

The most common anion impurity is the monovalent OH^- molecular ion. It has no direct influence upon ionic conductivity. But it is quite effective in binding divalent impurity ions thus compensating the conductivity effect of divalent ions. The OH^- impurity plays on important role as sensitizer of photochemical reaction and of secundary process following primary radiative defect production. Whereas the divalent cations mentioned above cannot be detected optically, the OH^- ions give rise to optical absorption near 2000 Å and fluorescence emission near 4000 Å according to electronic transitions of the lattice impurity center. Furthermore there is an infrared absorption near 2.5 µ because of the vibration of the molecular ion. There are other molecular anion impurities found in alkali halide crystals like O_2^-, O_2^-, N_2^-.

3 *Heavy metals*

Monovalent heavy metal impurity cations like Ag^+, Cu^+, Tl^+ have been found to be very effective fluorescent or phosphorescent centers. Furthermore they are trapping centers for free electrons, which may be produced by high energy radiation. This is a very important property for the reduction of the electron hole pair anihilation and the stabilization of the products of photochemical reactions under X, γ and β rays.

4 *Purification and doping*

To be shure of the special composition of a given crystal and to be able to make certain predictions with regard to the reaction of a crystal upon high energy radiation special purification and doping procedures are needed. Chemical methods, ion exchange chromatographic treatment, zone refining and sublimation of the molten material are such purification methods. To get rid of the anion impurities heat treatment under halogen is very effective.

The crystals are grown under rare gas atmosphere from highly purified crucibels. Under such conditions the total impurity content may be hold below 10^{-7} or 10^{-8} mole per mole. Much more effort is needed to reach higher degrees of purity. For special purpose the crystals can be doped with special additions, like divalent cations, heavy metal ions, rare earth elements, hydrogen, or stechiometric excess of one of the components of the crystal. A few examples will be treated later on.

4　Color centers

1　*The name color center*

The first to observe the coloration of uncolored, clear crystals of sodium chloride by β and γ rays was E. Goldstein in 1896. He observed the yellow NaCl, the violett KCl, the blue KBr and so on.

Later on in 1926 Z. Gyulai found that the same type of colorations is produced by stechiometric excess of the metal component of the crystal. The coloration was found due to optical absorption in the visible range of the spectrum. In 1936 E. Mollwo found ultraviolett absorption bands due to stechiometric excess of the halogen component of the crystal. It was in 1949/50 that it became clear that both types of absorption bands—due to excess alkali and due to excess halogen—appear at the same time, if alkali halide crystals are irradiated with high energy radiation (x, β, γ-rays). This shows clearly, that in a certain sence the high energy radiation produces photochemical dissocation of the polar crystal into alkali and halogen components. In fact, this is a very rough and unprecise description. Physicists prefer terms like "Trapped-Electron-Centers" and "Trapped Hole Centers" referring to the fact that the primary radiative effect is the production of free carriers: electrons and holes, which in a secondary step are trapped to neutralize cations and anions or more complicated entities within the crystal. The concept "Color Center" originally created to name the excess alkali center was finally used for both types, the trapped hole and the trapped elctron centers. Occasionally the word "V Center" for the hole center is used.

2　*The methods of coloration*

Many different methods have been reported to produce color centers. Some are developed for the production of one of the two types, others are efficient for the production of both types, the trapped hole and electron centers.

a) Additive colorations means heat treatment of a crystal in an atmosphere of the alkali metal vapor or the halogen gas. The stechiometric excess of one of the components is reached by a diffusion mechanism. Normally this type of coloration is used only for the production of "Trapped Electron Centers" (*F*-centers mainly).

b) Electrolytic coloration means injection of electrons and holes from injecting electrodes at high temperatures. This rather complicated process is controlled by the underlying ionic conductivity.

c) Photochemical coloration needs specially doped crystals. These "sensitized" crystals contain centers, which may be decomposed by ultraviolett light. One example is KCl doped with KH. It will be discussed later.

d) Coloration by high energy radiation has been mentioned earlier. The production of crystal point defects (vacancies and interstitials) and the production of free mobile carriers (electrons and holes) are the primary effects. They normally are followed by secondary processes, which stabilize the products of the reaction. In many cases the effeciency of the radiative coloration is enhanced by unknown sensitizers. Mostly the crystals colored by high radiation bleach under heat or light. The coloration is optically unstable, because of electron hole recombination and anihilation.

3   *Electron and hole centers*

a) The most simple "Trapped Electron Center" is the *F* center (Farbzentrum = Color center). It consists of one electron, trapped in an anion vacancy. There are many other electron centers, but they all contain at least one *F* center as a constituent: the *F'*, *M*, *R*, *N* centers will be discussed later. Some are combined with foreign cations as F_A centers (foreign alkali ion like Na^+ in KCl) or *Z* centers (foreign divalent ions like Ca^{++} in KCl). The easiest way to produce crystals with only trapped electron centers is the additive coloration in alkali vapour followed by special heat or light treatment.

b) The trapped hole centers are normally rather complicated. Those produced by additive coloration under halogen gas, are really not yet fully understood. The most simple types of trapped hole centers are produced by high energy radiation at very low temperatures. One of these is the V_K center, another is the *H*-center. These two will be considered more carefully later.

4   *Impurity centers*

There is a very high variety of impurity centers. We will consider only a few of them.

The *U* center, which is a negative hydrogen ion on normal anion lattice site, will be one of them. It is extremely effective as sensitizer for *F* center production or coloration in the original meaning of the concept "Color Center". Furthermore it is one of the few examples for which the total photochemical reaction is well understood.

The OH^- molecular ion center may be another example to be treated. This may be useful because most crystals, which have been grown without special care, contain OH^- as impurity and again because possible steps of the photochemical process have been analized. The heavy metal ion impurities will not be discussed in this lecture. They will be mentioned in Prof. Schulmans and Prof. Scharmanns papers.

II   TRAPPED ELECTRON CENTERS

5   The *F* center

1   *The model of the F center*

The *F* center may be described as one unpaired electron trapped in an anion vacancy. It replaces the negative halogen ion and holds the total charge

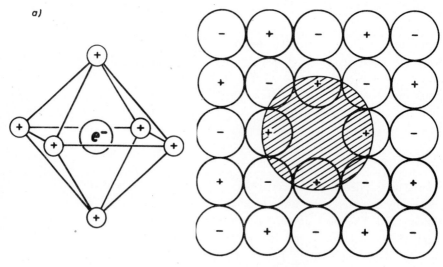

FIGURE 5   Model of *F* center

unchanged (Fig. 5). Chemically the center may be considered as a combination of a positive alkali ion with one electron, forming an alkali atom occupying the site of one pair of vacancies (anion and cation). This consideration supports the idea of stechiometric alkali excess. A much better concept, which holds the chemical picture unchanged, shares the electron around the six neighbouring cations. The precise charge distribution of the electron considered is one of the main problems of a physical description of the *F* center. The following discussions of certain properties provide informations to develop a more detailed description.

2   Optical absorption

The optical absorption of the *F* center—for most alkali halide crystals in the visible range of the spectrum—consists of one broad band (Fig. 6). Peak

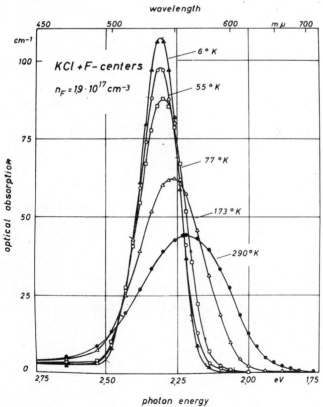

FIGURE 6   The *F* band

position and half width depend on temperature holding the total absorption—the area under the absorption curve—constant. It may be described as electronic transition from a $1S$ ground state to a $2p$ excited state. The electronic transition is coupled to lattice vibrations, which are responsible for the temperature dependent broadening. From the quantum mechanic theory of electron–phonon interaction one derives in accordance with experimental results the frequency ω_0 of the coupled lattice vibration (Fig. 7)

$$\left(\frac{H(T)}{H(0)}\right)^2_{\text{abs}} = \coth\left(\frac{\hbar\omega_0}{2kT}\right)$$

and finds for $\omega_0 = 2 \times 10^{13}/\text{sec}$ in KCl. Similar values are found for other alkali halides.

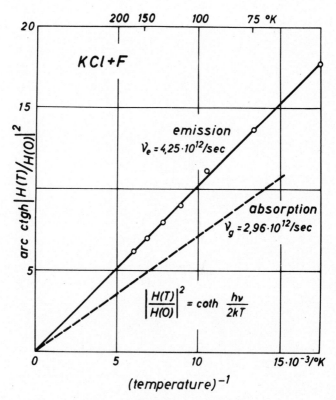

FIGURE 7 Temperature dependence of the half width of the absorption and emission bands

From the fact that the peak frequency of the absorption curve compared for different alkali halides is strongly correlated with the lattice constant d: (Fig. 8)

$$va^2 = \frac{3}{8} \frac{n}{m^*},$$

and not with special atomic properties of the ions forming the crystal one can easily see, that the F center is a typical lattice defect center and not an atomic center imbedded into a cristalline medium. The total integrated absorption is proportional to the number N of F centers per cm³. N may be found by measuring the absorption constant K_{max} at maximum frequency and the half width H' of the absorption band.

$$N = A \times K_{max} \times H.$$

The factor A contains constants of the crystal and can be derived theoretically or experimentally . The highest concentrations of normal undisturbed F centers, so far observed, is of the order of $3 \times 10^{18}/\text{cm}^3$, corresponding to a mole fraction of 10^{-4}.

On the high frequency side of the F band very small bands called K and L_1, L_2, L_3 are observed. They belong to electronic transitions from the $1S$

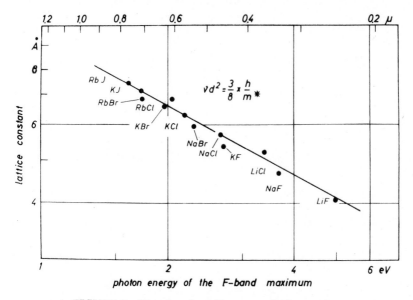

FIGURE 8 F band peak position versus lattice constant

ground state to higher excited states. They will not be discussed in more detail.

3   *Fluorescence emission*

The reverse optical transition form the first excited state ($2p$) to the ground state is a fluorescent emission with quantum efficiency $\eta \sim 1$. Again a broad band is observed and again the half width is given by the interaction of the electronic system with the vibrating lattice: (Fig. 9)

$$\left(\frac{H(T)}{H(0)} \right)_{em}^{2} = \coth \frac{\hbar\omega_e}{2kT},$$

with $\omega_e = 2.7 \times 10^{13}/\text{sec}$ in KCl (Fig. 7).

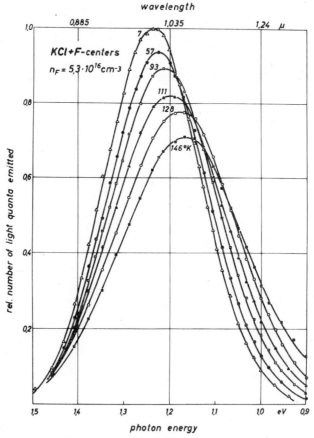

FIGURE 9   The *F* center fluorescence band

The most surprising and important fact is a big so called "Stokes shift" of the emission band (at 1.24 eV photoenergy in KCl) as compared with the absorption band (at 2.31 eV). The Stokes shift of 50% of the excitation energy is found for F centers in all alkali halides. It is explained by a very effective displacement of the ions surrounding the vacancy after optical excitation. The reason for this is given by the change in charge distribution of the F center electron; which has spheric symmetry in its ground state and a more complicated distribution in its first excited state. Because of the electrostatic interaction between electron and ions the relative positions and the total electrostatic potential distribution are changed after optical excitation. Therefore after light absorption the F center and its surrounding are trans-

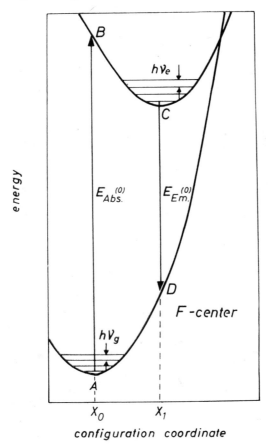

FIGURE 10   Configuration coordinate diagram

14   Amelinckx (1347)

ferred to a so called "relaxed excited state" from which the optical decay, the fluorescence emission, takes place. After light emission another relaxation to the original ground state follows. During the relaxation processes lattice vibrations are excited by the moving ions. Therefore the loss in quantum energy, given by the Stokes shift, is equivalent to an increase in thermal energy (temperature) of the crystal. (Simplified description is given by a $C - C$ diagram, Fig. 10).

4   Ionisation of the excited F center

It should be mentioned that the lifetimes of the (relaxed) excited states are of the order of microseconds. During this life-time of the excited state (F^*) ionisation of the center may happen. The ionisation energies are of the order of 0.15 eV and by a factor of 10 or more smaller than those of the ground state.

Thermal ionisation (at temperatures above 100°K) as well as electric field ionisation (at fields of 10^5 Volt/cm) has been observed. Photoconductivity and trapping of the free mobile carriers can be measured. One finds electron mobilities of the order of 8×10^3 cm²/Volt sec at low temperatures and at small F center concentrations in rather clean crystals.

Trapping centers for free carriers are F centers themselves as well as empty anion vacancies. Trapping of electrons in anion vacancies corresponds to reformation of F centers. Trapping of electrons at F centers is possible at low temperatures. These centers consisting of two electrons in one anion vacancy are called F' centers. They are rather unstable and are ionized thermally at temperatures above 100°K.

5   Magnetic moment of the F center in its optical ground state

It was briefly mentioned earlier that the electronic structure of the F center ground state is spherically symmetric. This has been proved by careful study of the magnetic properties of F centers containing crystals: The ions forming the crystal are diamagnetic, the number of core electrons in each is even, the electrons are paired and all orbital and spin moments are compensated. There is no electronic magnetic moment left.

The F center however contains an unpaired electron which at least contributes spin momentum, of $1/2\hbar$ and magnetic moment of one Bohr unit for each F center. The total paramagnetic moment of an F center crystal is very small according to the small concentration of paramagnetic particels.

In addition to the paramagnetic moment of the *F* centers there is a small contribution according to the nuclear magnetic moments of the nuclei of the lattice ions.

Without external magnetic field both magnetic moments of the crystal, that of the *F* centers and that of the nuclei are zero because of the random

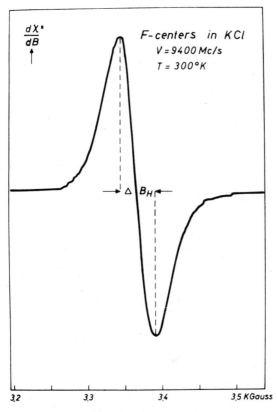

FIGURE 11   ESR line, hf-broadening

statistical distribution of the spinvectors. With external magnetic field there is some temperature depending alignment of the paramagnetic particles. Quantummechanically this means: There are certain possible orientations of the magnetic dipoles with respect to the direction of the field. They are different in energy, the lowest energetic state belonging to magnetic moments which are antiparallel to the external field and the highest energetic states

14*

belonging to those moments which are parallel to the external field. The difference in energy between two magnetic states is

$$\Delta E = \mu \cdot H \cdot \Delta m,$$

(μ = magnetic moment, H = magnetic field, Δm = difference in magnetic quantum numbers, normally $\Delta = 1$).

The distribution of all magnetic particals (F centers) over all possible magnetic states (2 in the case of the F center, namely parallel and anti-parallel) depends on temperature and field strength. There is allweighs a majority of the population in the lower energetic states.

According to the difference in population density magnetic excitation (absorption) of microwave fields is possible at frequencies which obey a resonance condition

$$h\nu = \mu H \Delta m.$$

From measuring the resonance frequency ν at given and known magnetic field H one gets the magnetic moment μ. The method to measure resonance frequencies of electronic systems with unpaired spin is called *ESR* (Fig. 11). For the F center the magnetic moment is found to be roughly equal to that of a free electron, or to the $1S$ electron of a hydrogen atom.

This means only the spin momentum and no orbital momentum contributes to the total magnetic moment of the F centers. Orbital momentum zero is found for spherically symmetric electron distribution only.

6   Electronic structure of the F center ground state

The ESR method tells us about the symmetric of the F center electron. It does not give details about the density distribution or the wave function ψ of the unpaired electron. Information about these questions may be derived from the so called hyperfine interaction between electronic and nuclear magnetic moments. The existence of such *hf*-interactions is shown by the *hf*-splitting or broadening of a ESR line (Fig. 12). This may be understood in the following way: If the F center electrons in KCl spend some of their time, let say 1 %, near one of the neighbouring potassium nuclei (K^{39}) which has spin 3/2 and therefore 4 different possible orientations with respect to the external magnetic field, it does not see the undisturbed external field, H_0 but a field which is changed by the contribution of the potassium nucleus. Because of the 4 different possible orientations of the nucleus there are 4 different effective magnetic fields and consequently 4 different resonance frequencies to be measured. If the nuclear magnetic moments are known (and this is normally the case) the spin density and the electron wave function can be derived from the hyperfine splitting of the resonance line. One of the numbers estracted from the hyperfine splitting, the isotropic hyperfine constant a is a direct measure for the electron density of the nucleus considered:

$$a = \frac{2}{3\mu_0} \mu_u \cdot \mu_{uuc} |\Psi(0)|^2 .$$

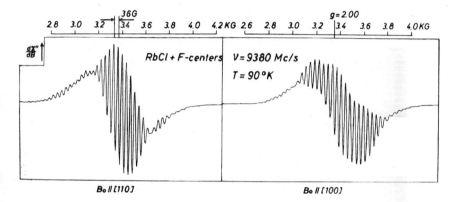

FIGURE 12   ESR line, hf-splitting

In fact, the total procedure to find the a values for the neighbouring lattice ions is very complicated because of the high number of nuclei contributing to the total *hf*-interaction. A special experimental method, the *E*lectron *N*uclear *D*ouble *R*esonance technique (ENDOR) and a special theoretical treatment, the spin hamiltonian, has been developed for this purpose. As a result one gets the square of the special distribution of the *F* center wave function $(\psi)^2$.

One finds that the electron spends 95% of its time within the first shell of 6 cation neighbours, and only 1% outside the second shell of 12 anion neighbours.

These are the results for the optical ground state. Corresponding results for the first or higher excited states are not yet available. What one knows from other data, is, that the relaxed first excited state is much more spread out and that the unrelaxed excited state has two parts contributing to the magnetic property: the spin momentum and the orbital momentum. The discussion of these properties would lead us into very complicated details. Nevertheless the proceeding remarks give us a rather comprehensive picture of the *F* center.

6   The *F* aggregate centers *M, R, N*

1   *Production of aggregate centers*

An *F* center containing crystal is not in thermal equilibrium. As a result of heating at higher temperatures one observes either bleaching, because of recombination and anihilation with trapped hole centers, or production of *M, R* and *N* centers as aggregates of *F* centers. The easiest way to produce aggregate centers is treatment of an additively colored crystal with *F* light near room temperature. The first product of the photochemical reaction is

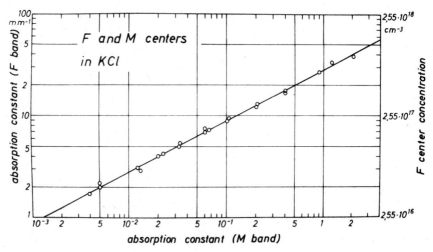

FIGURE 13   *M* center concentration as a function of *F* center concentration

the *M* center which is identical with two neighbouring *F* centers; it is followed by the *R* center which is a combination of three *F* centers, and higher aggregates as *N* centers and finally colloidial particles. Another method uses high energy radiation. As mentioned earlier the first result of trapping of electrons are *F* centers. The formation of *M* centers and *R* centers increases with *F* center concentration according to $[M] \times [F]^2$ and $[R] \times [F]^3$

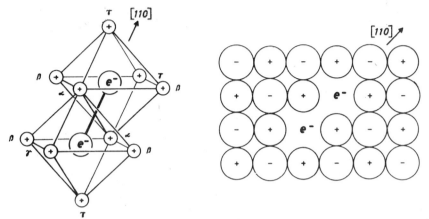

FIGURE 14   Model of the *M* center

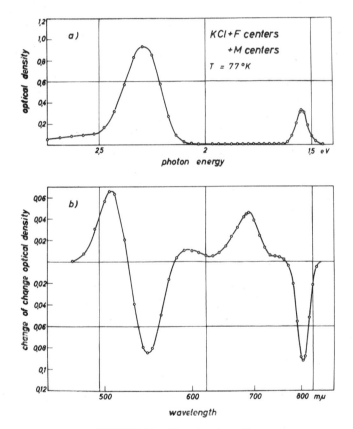

FIGURE 15   *M* center absorption

$= [M] \times [F]$ (Fig. 13). The M and R centers are noncubic. Under normal conditions there are 6 different crystallographic orientations of the M center and 4 different orientations of the R centers. Alignment of the M and R centers along one of the equivalent directions can be achieved by excitation with polarized light at temperatures below room temperature.

2 Properties of the M center

The M center consists of two anion vacancies with two trapped electrons (Fig. 14). According to the orthorhombic symmetry (D_2h) the M center has two different optical transitions or absorption bands (Fig. 15a). The long wave band belongs to the excitation with transition vector along the [110] axis, the short wave band—which is similar to the F band—represents the

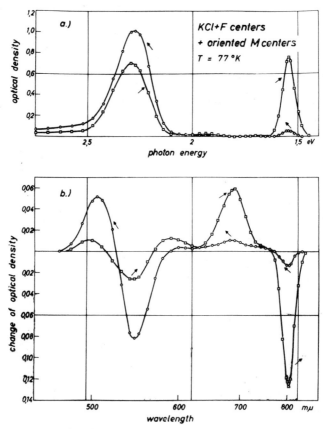

FIGURE 16   Dichroic M center absorption

two perpendicular transitions [1$\bar{1}$0], [100]. As a result of center alignment the crystal becomes dichroic (Fig. 16a).

There is only one fluorescence emission band (Fig. 17) in the near infrared which corresponds to the axial transition: After optical excitation the center relaxes to the lowest excited state very fast (10^{-12} sec.) The lifetime of the relaxed excited state from which the fluorescence emission originates is of the order of 10^{-7} sec. As one would expect the fluorescence emission of a crystal with M centers aligned along one of the [110] directions is linearly polarized along this same direction.

The M centers normally have no paramagnetic moment (singlet state) because of the spin compensation of the two trapped electrons. But there exists a metastable triplet state with lifetimes of the order of 10–50 seconds

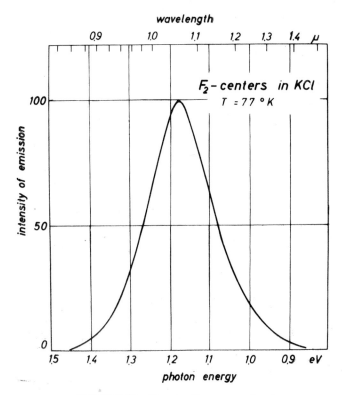

FIGURE 17 M center fluorescence band

with parallel spins or total spin $S = 1\hbar$. This triplet ground state is reached optically by singlet excitation. Whereas most of the excited M centers return to the singlett ground state under fluorescence emission, a small fraction decays into the lower lying triplet ground state. Optical absorption (Fig. 15b, 16b) ESR and ENDOR spectra of this triplet state have been taken. The results are in good agreement with expectations. Especially the values of the electron density at the neighbouring nuclei are the same as calculated on the basis of the well established F center model.

3   Properties of the R center

R centers consists of three anion vacancies forming a triangle in one of the (111) planes with three trapped electrons (Fig. 18). There are three different absorption bands (Fig. 19) and one infrared fluorescence band. Partiel alignment of the R centers along one of the four [111] directions is possible. As a result the crystal becomes dichroic and the fluorescence polarized.

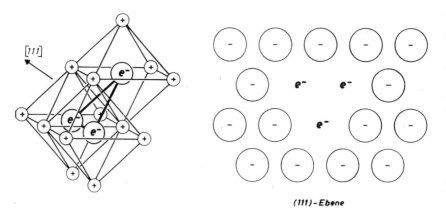

FIGURE 18   Model of the R center

The normal ground state of the R center is characterized by total spin $S = 1/2\hbar$, the center is paramagnetic. In addition a metastable quartet state with total spin $S = 3/2\hbar$, (parallel orientation of the three spins) has been observed. As in the case of the M center the ESR and ENDOR data are in good agreement with the F and R center models.

As mentioned earlier for the F band the optical absorption bands are broadened because of the modulation of the electronic transition frequency

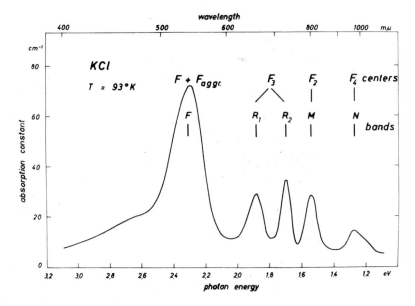

FIGURE 19   Absorption of *F, M, R, N* centers

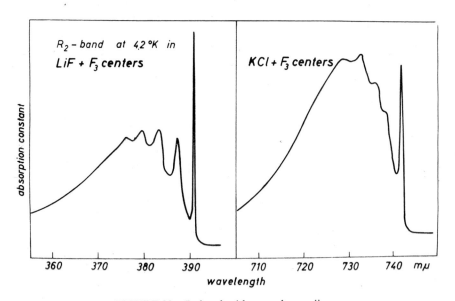

FIGURE 20   *R₂* band with zero phonon line

by frequencies of the lattice vibrations. In the case of long wave *R* bands the lattice vibration has been resolved partially at very low temperatures. The so called "zero phonon line" with no additional excitation of the lattice phonon spectrum the "one phonon spectrum" and higher phonon spectra have proved to be very useful for special symmetry considerations of the coupling between the electronic and the vibrational system (Fig. 20).

4   *Higher F aggregate centers*

There is no question that higher aggregates of *F* centers exist. One of them is the *N* center. It may be a complex of 4 anion vacancies with 4 trapped electrons (Fig. 21). None of the higher aggregates is really understood. So far

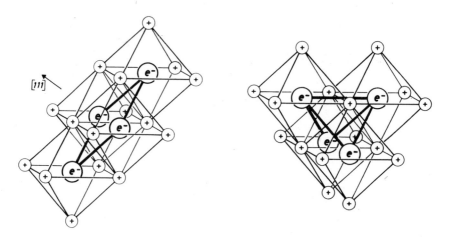

FIGURE 21   Models of the *N* center

it is unknown if the absorption bands which have been observed have something to do with aggregates near foreign ions. Nevertheless the tetraedral combination of 4 *F* centers is especially interesting because it could be the basic element for the formation of colloidial particles: 4 of the 16 cations which are nearest neighbours of the *M* center are neighbours of 3 anion vacancies respectively. The binding forces of these 4 cations to the lattice are strongly reduced. Therefore it may happen that these cations combine with 4 trapped electrons to form one metallic particle in the interior of a cubic crystalline hole.

7 *F* Centers with foreign ions

1 *Common remarks*

There are several possibilities for F centers to reduce the thermal non-equilibrium of the crystal by combining with other lattice defects.

The process of aggregation of F centers has been discussed before. In crystals with foreign cations another process has been observed: Under certain conditions the impurity ions are centers of attraction for F centers, or anion vacancies and electrons. Coulomb fields, dipole fields and stress fields may be responsible for the build up of such potential valleys. In crystals with foreign monovalent and divalent cations such associations have been observed. Centers containing smaller foreign alkali ions (Na or Li in KCl) are called F_A centers and centers containing alkaline earth ions are called Z centers (The nomination has historical reason and should not be discussed during this lecture). These centers are worth to be considered briefly because alkali halide crystals normally contain such impurity ions.

2 *The F_A centers*

F_A center consists of a F center with one foreign alkali ion as nearest neighbour (Fig. 22). These combinations have found to be stable only if the foreign ion is smaller than the normal lattice cation.

Because of the strong reduction in symmetry the threefold degeneracy of the F absorption is lifted and two absorption bands are observed (Fig. 23), with transition vectors along and perpendicular to the center axis [100]. As

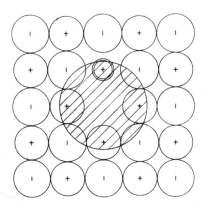

FIGURE 22   Model of the F_A center

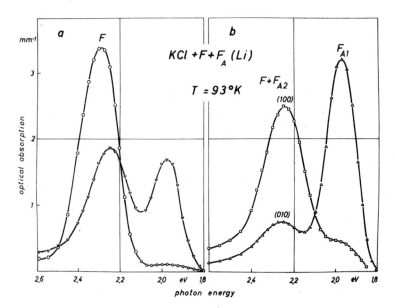

FIGURE 23   Dichroic F_A center absorption

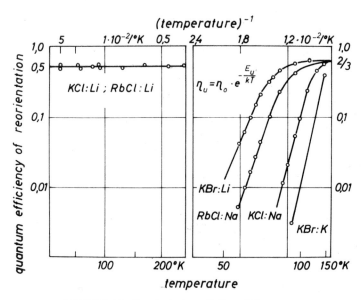

FIGURE 24   Reorientation of aligned F_A centers

in the case of the M center alignment along one of the 3 axes can be achieved by polarized light giving the crystal dichroic properties. There is one fluorescence emission band. The paramagnetic behaviour is quite similar to that of the undisturbed F center with little changes in electron density distribution because of the one foreign ion and because of certain displacements of the lattice ions. The orientation of an F_A center is easily lost in the optically excited state. One group of F_A centers (type I) needs activation

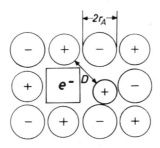

F_A - center		$D/2r_A$	activ. energie	
RbCl	: Li	1,00	—	⎫
RbBr	: Li	,99	—	⎬ II
KCl	: Li	.93	—	⎭
KBr	: Li	.85	0,05 eV	⎫
RbCl	: Na	.73	0,07	⎬ I
KCl	: Na	.66	0,09	⎭
RbBr	: K	.53	0,11	

FIGURE 25   Saddle point configuration of type II F_A centers

energies of the order of 0,2 eV for reorientation. One other group (type II) does not need any activation (Fig. 24). The question to which of the two groups one given F_A center does belong depends on the radius of the foreign ion as compared with the lattice parameter. Type II F_A (Fig. 25) centers with very small foreign ions (Li in KCl), when excited to the first excited state, probably change their local arrangement from the one described above into a saddle point configuration with two anion vacancies separated by one interstitial anion. There is no preference to move back from this excited state configuration to one of the two ground state configurations. The reason for the formation of such special ion configuration is given by the *p*-type excited state wave function, which fits extremly well into such a local potential distribution. The observation of a very short excited state life time, a remarkably narrow emission band and an extremely large Stokes shift (70%) are in good agreement with these ideas.

3   *The Z centers*

The *Z* centers represent some kind of a combination of *F* centers with divalent cations ($CaCl_2$ in KCl). From optical measurements one knows that there are at least 3 different types of *Z* centers (Fig. 26). The local configuration of none of them has fully been established. From optical, ESR and ENDOR measurements good arguments could be given for the Z_1 center to be composed of an *F* center, an additional cation vacancy and the divalent ion. The most probable configuration in KCl is described by a model in which

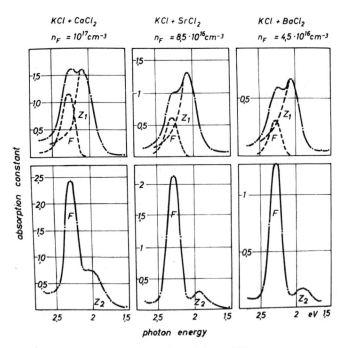

FIGURE 26   Absorption of Z_1 and Z_2 centers

the F center, the cation vacancy, one lattice anion and the divalent foreign cation follow each other along one [100] direction of the lattice (Fig. 27).

The kinetics of the Z_1 center production under F light follows a bimolecular reaction

$$\frac{d[Z_i]}{dt} = C \cdot [F'] \cdot [Me^{++}] \exp\left(-E/kT\right).$$

F' stands for ionized F centers or anion vacancies, the concentration of which is identical with that of the F' centers; the activation energy $E = 0.6\,\text{eV}$ is the same as observed for the production of M centers and F_A centers and is probably given by the energy needed for the anion vacancy motion. No dichroism and no fluorescence has been observed so far.

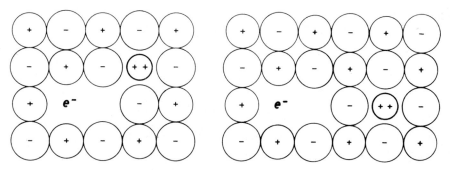

FIGURE 27   Models of the Z_1 center

From recent observations one knows that divalent ions easily combine with OH⁻ impurity centers. At the moment it is unknown how much earlier results have been influenced by such complications. Most of the measurements have to be repeated with very clean doped crystals.

III   TRAPPED HOLE CENTERS

8   General remarks

1   *Comparison between trapped electron and trapped hole centers*

There is remarcable difference between electron and hole centers. The F type electron centers are lattice defect centers. Their properties are mainly given by lattice parameter, lattice energy, lattice polarization, lattice vi-

15   Amelinckx (1347)

brational spectrum, lattice defect structure and so on. The V centers or hole centers however may primarily be considered as molecular centers (Cl_2^-, Cl_4^{--}). Their properties reflect the binding energy, the vibrational structure and the steric configurations of a group of atoms, which are surrounded by some dielectric material. The special influence of the lattice properties is of second order.

2 Production of trapped hole centers

The most successful method to produce the simplest hole centers is the photochemical decomposition of the crystal by high energy radiation at very low temperatures. Under these conditions trapped electron centers are found at the same time. Most of the electrons and holes produced by radiation normally recombine under emission of radiation. The anihilation can be reduced remarkably by foreign cations as Tl^+, Ag^+, Pb^{++}, which are effective trapping centers for electrons. Nevertheless the trapped hole centers are stable only at low temperatures. At higher temperatures they recombine with electron centers.

9 The V_K center

1 The model of the V_K center

The V_K center may be considered as diatomic molecular ion (F_2^-, Cl_2^-, Br_2^-) formed by trapping of one position hole (Fig. 28). This means, there is one hole in the two filled electronic shells of two neighbouring halogen ions,

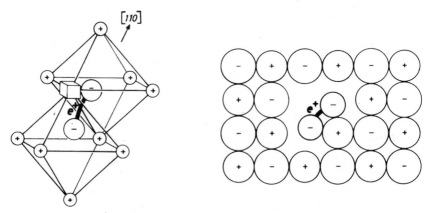

FIGURE 28   Model of the V_K center

reducing the total number of electrons in the *p* orbits from $2 \times 6 = 12$ to $12 - 1$. The hole concept is the easiest way to describe such an electronic system properly. Because of the anihilation of one negative charge the Coulomb repulsive force and consequently the interatomic distance of the two neighbouring halogen atoms is reduced. Occasionaly the V_K center is described as self trapped hole. This means that no special lattice defects like vacancies or interstitial atoms are needed to bind the extra positive charge. The hole itself forms the trapping center by bringing two lattice anions together and creating an attractive potential. The V_K center has [110] orientation.

2 Optical properties of the V_K center

The optical absorption spectrum consists of several absorption bands, a strong one in the near ultraviolett and a week one in the visible range of the

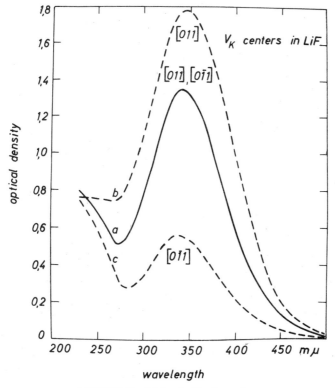

FIGURE 29   Dichroic V_K absorption

15*

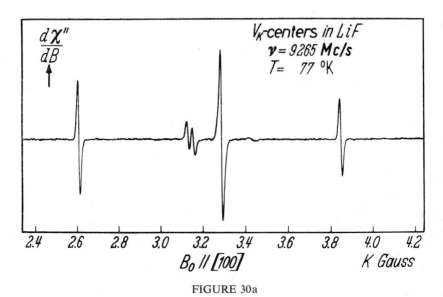

FIGURE 30a

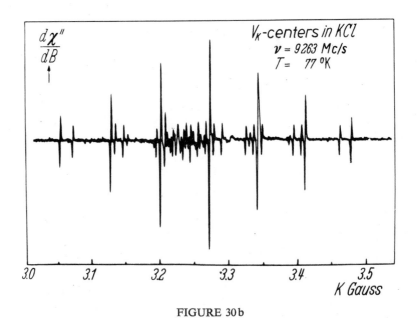

FIGURE 30b

FIGURE 30   ESR spectrum of the V_K center in LiF and KCl

spectrum. Dichroic absorption has been observed after optical excitation with polarized light (Fig. 29). V_K centers may be distroied optically by photoionization of electronic centers (F, Tl⁰, Ag⁰). The free mobile electrons recombine with the trapped hole reproducing the undisturbed lattice configuration:

3 *The ESR spectrum of the V_K center*

The most important results for the analysis of the V_K centers were delivered by ESR measurements. The ESR spectrum of the V_K center in LiF consists of 3 lines that of the V_K center in KCl of 7 main lines (Fig. 30). This fits exactly into the model given above, if one considers the hyperfine interaction of the unpaired hole with two halogen nuclei. In the case of LiF these are two F^{19} nuclei with nuclear spin 1/2 for each and magnetic quantum numbers 1, 0, -1 for the diatomic system. The results are three ESR lines. In the case of KCl with Cl^{35} nuclei there are seven lines according to total nuclear spin 3 with magnetic quantum numbers 3, 2, 1, 0, -1, -2, -3. The intensities of which reflect the statistical weights: $1:2:3:4:3:2:1$. There is some complication because of the two isotopes Cl^{35} (75%) and Cl^{37} (25%) with different magnetic moments (1,37/, 14). There are three possible combinations of two nuclei, namely $Cl^{35} - Cl^{35}$, $Cl^{53} - Cl^{37}$ and $Cl^{37} - Cl^{37}$. The main spectrum of seven lines belongs to the $Cl^{35} - Cl^{35}$ species. The other two produce additional and more complicated spectra, which should not be treated in detail. The V_K center and the distribution of the unpaired hole is nonspheric. The ESR spectrum therefore is anisotropic.

4 *ENDOR results*

Besides the strong hyperfine interaction between the unpaired hole and the two halogen nuclei there is a much weeker superhyperfine interaction with neighbouring lattice ions which surround the V_K center. The hyperfine constants for 20 more nuclei have been determined. These data give some information upon the hole density distribution and the polarization of the ion cores by the V_K center.

10 The *H* center

1 *The model of the H center*

H centers are simultaneously produced with V_K centers at temperatures below 20°K by high energy radiation. The *H* center consists of four halogen ions, along one [110] line, bound togheter by one trapped hole. It may be regarded as Cl_4^{---} in the case of alkali chlorides. There is one important difference with respect to the V_K center:

The four chlorines share the space of only three lattice sites (Fig. 31). In total there is one interstitial anion plus hole, or one additional interstitial halogen atom. The creation of such an interstitial is necessarily correlated

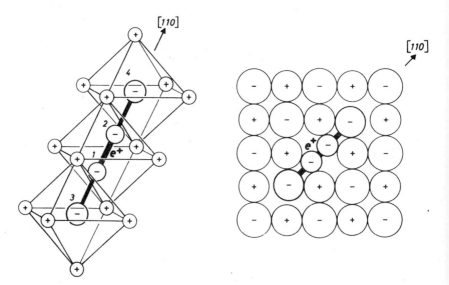

FIGURE 31   Model of the *H* center

with the production of an anion vacancy. The creation of the hole on the other hand is combined with the production of an electron. The trapping of both the positive hole and the negative electron results in creation of an *H* and an *F* center. *H* center and *F* center are complementary to each other.

2   *Properties of the H center*

The optical absorption spectrum is quite similar to that of the V_K center and characterized by a broad band (3.6 eV in KCl). Dichroic absorption due to alignment of the *H* centers along one of the [110] directions of the lattice with polarized light has been observed. The ESR spectrum is fully described by considering strong hyperfine interaction of the trapped hole with 2 halogen nuclei and weeker hyperfine interaction with 2 more halogen nuclei. The hole density distribution is anisotropic.

11 Other hole centers

Besides the V_K and H center at least two more hole centers have been analized.

1 *The V_F center*

The V_F center is a combination of a V_K center (Cl_2^-) with a cation vacancy (which represents a negative lattice charge) (Fig. 32). Whereas the V_K is

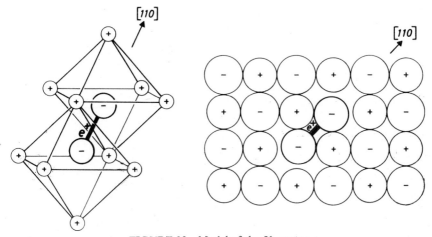

FIGURE 32   Model of the V_F center

positively charged, the V_F center is neutral. In a certain sence it is the antimorph of the F center. The V_F center combined of a trapped hole and a cation vacancy, the F center combined of a trapped electron and an anion vacancy. Nevertheless the electronic structures are completely different.

2 *The V_t center*

An other hole center is the neutral V_t center which combines one hole with 3 anions and 3 vacancies (2 cation and 1 anion vacancy) (Fig. 33).

3 *The V_1 center*

There is a strong genetic relation between the H center and the V_1 center, which can be produced by additive coloration. One believes the V_1 center is formed by trapping a second hole at an *H* center. This would mean the V_1 center is like a neutral halogen molecule in normal lattice anion position. The V_1 center then carries positive lattice charge.

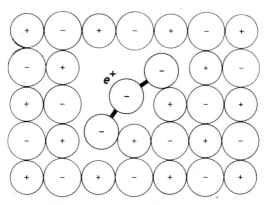

FIGURE 33   Model of the V_t center

IV   IMPURITY CENTERS

12   The *U* centers

1   *Introduction*

Negative hydrogen ions on anions lattice sites are called *U* centers, because of their ultraviolett absorption near 2200 Å. *U* centers containing crystals are mixed crystals of alkali halides with small additions of alkali hydrides

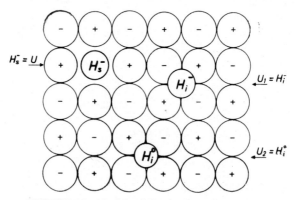

FIGURE 34   Models of the *U*, U_1 and U_2 centers

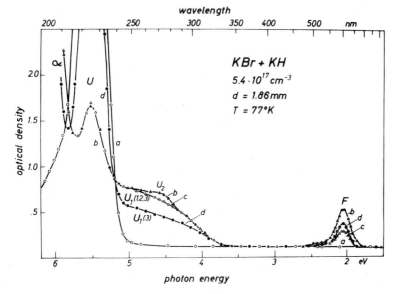

FIGURE 35a

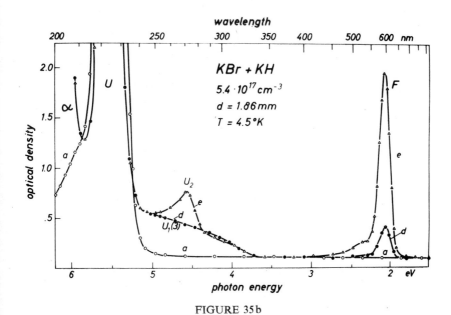

FIGURE 35b

FIGURE 35   Photochemical reactions in *U* center crystal

(KBr + 10^{-4} KH) (Fig. 34). The easiest way to get such crystals is to aneal additively colored (*F* centers containing) crystals under hydrogen atmosphere at temperatures of 300–500°C. These crystals are of special interest for two reasons: They are sensitized for coloration of crystals by *UV* light or high energy radiation. They are highly efficient for the study of the coupling between localized impurity modes and nonlocalized lattice modes of vibration.

2   *The photochemical decomposition of the U center*

At temperatures below 100°K the following reaction of ultraviollett excitation of the *U* center is observed: (Fig. 35). The negative hydrogen ion is transferred into interstitial position, forming an U_1 center, an empty anion vacancy is left behind. These two praticals recombine if the temperature is above 150°K.

The U_1 center which is characterized by a very broad absorption band around 2300 Å undergoes photoionization down to liquid helium tempera-

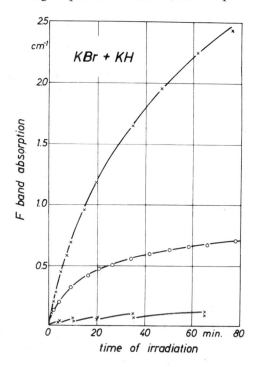

FIGURE 36   Sensitization by *U* centers for x-ray coloration

tures (4.5°K). A neutral hydrogen atom remains (U_2) in interstitial position, the free electron is trapped at the empty anion lattice site as a normal F center.

3 Sensitization for radiative coloration by U centers

As mentioned earlier most of the products of high energy radiation are lost by recombination of electrons and holes. Only a small fraction is trapped as electron and hole centers according to the production of lattice defects, as vacancies and interstitials. Certain impurity atoms, ions or molecules may be used as sensitizers providing effective trapping centers for electrons or holes.

U centers are such sensitizers for x-rays. Crystals doped with U centers get a very stable coloration under x-irradiation, the efficiency being enhanced by a factor of 10–100 (Fig. 36). What happens is the following: The hydrogen ion is transferred into interstitial space and neutralized by a trapped hole, the electron is trapped as F center in the anion vacancy. Every two neutral hydrogen atoms combine to stable H_2 molecules which do not react with the F centers unless the temperature is enlarged to temperatures of a few hundred degrees centigrade.

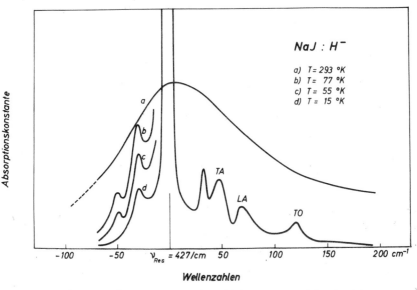

FIGURE 37 Infrared absorption of U centers containing crystal

4   *The infrared spectrum of the U center*

Besides the ultraviolet electronic absorption there is an infrared absorption near $20\,\mu = 500\,\text{cm}^{-1}$, due to excitation of localized oscillation of the hydrogen against the surrounding lattice (Fig. 37). Because of the small mass of the impurity ion the absorption is on the high frequency side of the fundamental absorption of the lattice. Much interest has been given to the sidebands of the infrared absorption spectrum. They are produced by the coupling of the localized hydrogen oscillator with nonlocalized lattice

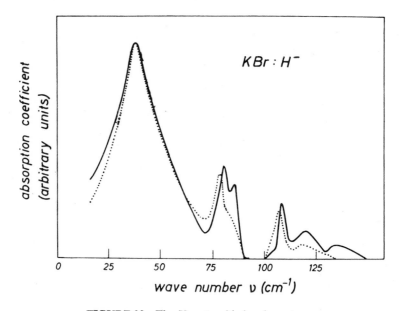

FIGURE 38   The *U* center side band spectrum

vibrations. From group theoretical consideration one gets information about the types of lattice vibrations which are responsible for the sideband spectrums. In those cases, in which the lattice phonon spectrums is well know spectrums. In those cases, in which the lattice phonon spectrums is well known from neutron scattering experiments one has found very good agreement between theoretical calculation and experimental observation (Fig. 38). One other result is of some importance for crystal physics. The half width of the main absorption band is strongly temperature dependent. There are two effects responsible for this. The one especially important at higher temperatures is the elastic scattering of lattice phonons at the impurity centers. The other is the decay of the localized phonon into 2 or 3 nonlocalized lattice phonons.

5   The U_2 center

The U_2 center (Fig. 39) which is a neutral hydrogen atom in interstitial position has been investigated carefully by ESR (Fig. 39) and ENDOR methods to learn something about the distribution of the hydrogen $1S$ elec-

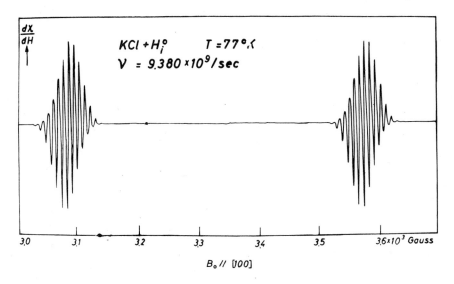

FIGURE 39   ESR spectrum of the U_2 center

tron if incorporated into a polar lattice. From hyperfine interaction of the unpaired electron with the proton and the surrounding nuclei of the lattice the electron density distribution has been measured. It was found that the spherically symmetric orbit of the free hydrogen atom is disturbed remarcably by the overlap of the electronic ion cores, the polarization of the neighbouring ions and the localized vibration of the impurity and defect center.

13   The OH⁻ center

1   *Introduction*

OH⁻ impurity centers are normally present in alkali halide crystals grown in air or without special precautions. They have found much interest during the last years for different reasons. Change in orientation of the dipole molecule from one crystallographic orientation to some other due to applied electric or elastic fields, paraelectric resonance, paraelectric cooling are such topics. We will confine ourselves to the optical properties and photochemical reactions mainly at low temperatures. We will refer to crystals, grown from purified material with less than 10^{-4} molefraction of OH⁻ anion doping and no detectable amount of divalent cations and other impurities present.

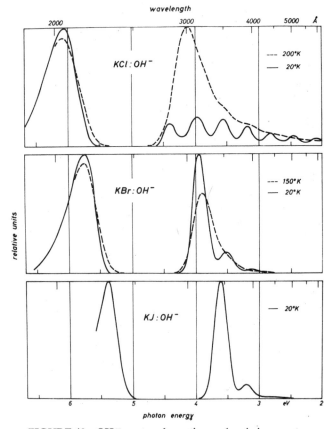

FIGURE 40   OH⁻ center absorption and emission spectra

2   *Absorption and emission spectra*

The absorption spectrum in the short wave ultraviolett shows a broad unsymmetric, temperature independent band (Fig. 40). It has to be considered as disturbed excit on band, this is an electronic lattice absorption disturbed by and near the foreign anion. It is not much effected by the molecular properties of the OH radical. There is a strongly temperature dependent fluorescence emission spectrum with Stokes shift of the order of 1.8 eV, with vibrational structure due to the OH streching vibration. The fluorescence emission has to be attributed to desexcitation of the OH molecule. Between optical absorption of a disturbed lattice state and the fluorescence emission of an excited molecular state an electronic conversion takes place which is responsible for the large Stokes shift.

A certain fraction of the excited OH^- centers undergoes a thermally activated dissociation into O^- on lattice site and H^0 in interstitial position. At temperatures above 100°K thermoluminescent recombination takes place. The spectrum is the same as the fluorescence spectrum. Besides the radiative desexcitation the nonradiative plays an important role. The ratio of radiative and nonradiative transitions depends strongly upon the special lattice surroundings. It is very different in KCl and KJ.

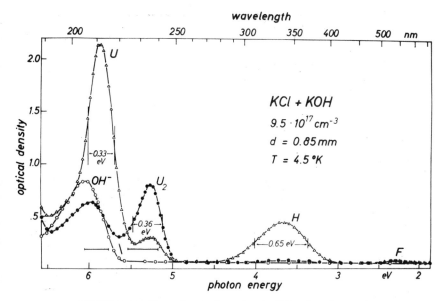

FIGURE 41   Photochemical reaction in OH^- doped crystal

3   *Photochemical reactions*

At liquid helium temperatures the OH⁻ center may be decomposed by ultraviolet light into O^- ions on anion lattice sites and hydrogen atoms in interstitial space ($\dot{U}_2$ center). (Fig. 41). Continuing the photochemical procedure, a very interesting observation was made. Optical excitation of the U_2 center at 4.5°K with U_2 light (5.3 eV quantum energy) is followed by production of U centers (negative hydrogen ions in anion position) and H centers (interstitial halogen atom) (Fig. 42). This means one halogen atom has been ejected from a normal lattice site into interstitial position. The hydrogen atom takes its place and ionic charge. This combination is rather unstable. Recombination takes place at temperatures of 10–50°, depending on the distance between H center and U center. Recombination of the U_2 center with O^- to reform OH⁻ centers in observed at temperatures around 100°K.

References

1. James H. Schulman and W. Dale Compton, *Color Centers in Solids*, International Series of Monographs on Solid State Physics, Oxford, London, New York, Paris: Pergamon Press, 1962.
2. Heinz Pick, *Struktur von Störstellen in Alkalihalogeniden.* Springer Tracts in Modern Physics, Volume 38, Berlin, Heidelberg, New York: Springer 1965.

CHAPTER II–5

The physics of the photographic process*

LAWRENCE SLIFKIN

University of North Carolina, Chapel Hill, N. C., U.S.A.

The silver halide photographic emulsion is one of the most efficient and versatile tools available for the recording of signals and images of visible light. Moreover, as compared to electronic recording devices, it is both convenient to use and extremely economical. In large part, these advantages derive from the fact that in the photographic emulsion, the amplifying

* Preparation of this manuscript supported by the U.S. Atomic Energy Commission (Contract AT-(40-1)-2036) and Office of Aerospace Research (Grant AF-AFOSR-450-66).
Reference

"electronics" is built-in; the silver halide microcrystal itself contains all of the components necessary to enhance the original signal by a factor of 10^9, once the amplifier is turned on by the addition of a developing agent.

Nevertheless, in spite of more than half a century of very vigorous research, some aspects of the photographic process are still quite uncertain and the subject of spirited controversy. The reason for these obscurities is that many steps in the process take place at a few special sites, often on the surface of the silver halide grain. Thus, it is the very efficiency and micro-miniaturization of the photographic process that makes its essential ingredients often invisible, both chemically and physically, so that inferences must frequently be drawn from indirect experiments rather than from direct observation.

The present discussion attempts to summarize our current understanding of the physical phenomena underlying photographic recording. In those aspects of the process for which this understanding is still rather speculative, prime alternative models will be outlined without recounting all of the circumstantial evidence *pro* and *con* that could be mustered up from the scientific literature. A much more detailed treatment is given in a comprehensive volume edited by C. E. K. Mees and T. H. James.[1] Another recent review of the photographic process may be found in a solid state physics textbook by F. Brown.[2]

It should become apparent from what follows that the photographic process is truly a marvel. If it is not impossible, then the very efficient functioning of a modern photographic emulsion is at least highly improbable. Had the photosensitive properties of silver halides not been recognized as a result of the frequent appearence of these compounds in chemical laboratories, it seems rather unlikely that a modern engineer would ever base the design of a proposed recording system on the possibility that a medium could be found having all of the properties now known to be possessed by silver halide microcrystals.

1 THE PHOTOGRAPHIC PROCESS

A photographic emulsion consists of small crystals of silver bromide or chloride, often with several per cent dissolved silver iodide, suspended in gelatin. The grains typically have dimensions of the order of 0.1 micron to 1 micron and, depending on how they were precipitated, may have {100} or

[111] crystallographic surfaces.[3] A common morphology is a triangular or hexagonal tabular grain, the two large [111] surfaces being about 1 micron across, and with a thickness of about 0.1 micron.

These grains are imbedded in a gelatin matrix, which serves as an emulsifying agent to prevent coagulation and provides mechanical support. The gelatin also plays an active role in the photographic process, providing substances which adsorb to the surface of the grain and make it more photosensitive, and acting as an acceptor for some of the halogen produced by photolysis. Commercial emulsions may also contain small deliberate additions of other sensitizers, such as sulfur compounds or gold salts, and the grains may carry adsorbed layers of dye molecules, which extend the range of photosensitivity out to longer wavelengths than would be possible with undyed silver halide.

The initial act in the photographic process is the excitation, by absorption of a photon of sufficiently large energy, of an electron from the valence band of the microcrystal into the conduction band, thus producing a free photo-electron and a free positive hole. Each of these charge carriers undergoes a displacement by a combination of random diffusion and drift in any electric field that may be present, and each is ultimately trapped. If an electron and hole are both trapped at the same site, they recombine; the input signal from the photon is then lost. If, on the other hand, they are trapped at separate sites, the electron can convert to an atom of silver metal any silver ion which also migrates to this trap, while the hole can disappear by the conversion of a halide ion into a halogen atom. The net result of the absorption of the quantum of light is then the photolytic decomposition of one molecule of silver halide into separated silver and halogen atoms.

If this process were repeated many times over, and if the halogen thus formed could continually be removed from the vicinity of the grain (by, for example, chemical reaction with substances in the medium surrounding the grain), then eventually large portions of the grain would be converted to metallic silver (known as "print-out"), and one would have achieved photographic recording. Modern photographic films, however, are designed to operate under exposures which produce only a few atoms of metallic silver per grain. The invisible product thus formed is known as the latent image, and when the emulsion is subsequently immersed in a developing solution, it is this latent image which rapidly catalyzes the reduction of the entire grain to metallic silver. It is here, in the formation and the action of the latent image, that the amplification of the input signal is achieved, and a

16*

major share of the physics of the photographic process is thus centered about the formation and properties of the latent image.

Perhaps the most important characteristic of a given emulsion is the degree of opacity produced in it after exposure and development. The opacity of a developed emulsion may be measured by the optical density, defined as the logarithm (base 10) of the ratio of the intensity of an incident measuring beam to that transmitted by the partially transparent film. A plot of the density versus the logarithm of the exposure is referred to as the Hurter and Driffield, or H. & D., plot, and is shown schematically in Fig. 1.

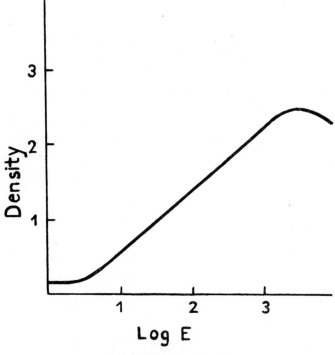

FIGURE 1   H. & D. Plot

The fact that this curve does not pass through the origin tells us that there is a non-zero density even in regions which received no exposing light at all; this is known as fog, and results from the fact that even before exposure a small number of grains have surface centers which will catalyze development. The horizontal region of the curve at the lowest exposures is due to the existence of a threshold exposure for the formation of the latent image, and constitutes a strong indication that absorption of more than one photon per grain is necessary to produce a latent image: if only one photon could produce a latent image speck in a grain, then the H. & D. curve should have a finite slope at zero exposure. The "speed" of the emulsion is determined by the value of the exposure at which the H. & D. curve turns upward, and the approximately linearly rising region which follows is that normally employed in photography. The horizontal projection of this rising portion determines the latitude of the emulsion, while the slope is a measure of the contrast. The slope is not infinite (i.e., the H. & D. plot is not step-shaped) because of the statistical distribution of photon absorptions among the various grains, the probabilistic nature of the processes of latent image formation and development, and because of the distribution of grain sizes and grain sensitivities within a given specimen of emulsion. The reversal in slope at very great exposure is known as solarization.

Emulsions with relatively larger grains generally have greater speeds because (a) for a given exposure, more photons are absorbed by a larger grain, and (b) since development of one latent image speck converts the entire grain to metallic silver, the amplification factor can be greater in the case of larger grains. Another measure of the efficiency of the process, however, is the number of photons that must be absorbed in order to make the grain probably developable. This information can be extracted from an analysis of the H. & D. plot, and in the best emulsions studied it has been found[4] that *absorption of only four photons per grain is sufficient to render an appreciable fraction of the grains developable!*

2   ELECTRON BAND STRUCTURE OF SILVER BROMIDE AND CHLORIDE

Since the formation of the latent image involves the optical and electronic properties of the microcrystals, an understanding of this process might well begin with an inquiry into the electronic energy band structure of the silver halides. Extensive optical and photocarrier transport experiments by Brown and co-workers[5] agree with results of band structure calculations[6] that while the conduction bands in silver chloride and bromide are "simple," with an approximately isotropic energy minimum at the origin of k-space (the propagation vector k is a measure of the momentum of the electron of hole), the maximum energy of the valence band electrons occurs at the edge of the Brillouin zone, as indicated in Fig. 2. The shape of the valence band is a result of the fact that in silver chloride and bromide crystals, the energy levels of the silver d-electrons almost coincide with those of the halide p-electrons, resulting in extensive mixing of the wave functions. The optical transitions of importance to photography with visible light are those requiring the smallest photon energy, shown as a dashed line in the figure. At room temperature, such non-vertical transitions are accomplished

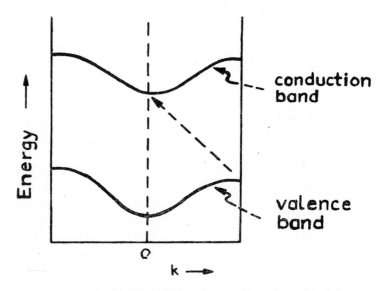

FIGURE 2   Silver halide band Structure (schematic)

by the simultaneous absorption or emission of a quantum of lattice vibration, a phonon, such that crystal momentum is conserved. The threshold for this transition at room temperature is at approximately 420 mμ in AgCl, 480 mμ in AgBr, and at somewhat longer wavelengths for AgBr containing a few per cent AgI. Silver halide crystals themselves are thus photosensitive only to the blue-green and ultraviolet regions of the spectrum. The extension of this range throughout the visible and well into the infrared region is accomplished by the adsorption of dyes which absorb light at long wavelengths. It is not obvious that such dye sensitization should indeed be possible, since a red photon, for example, has too small an energy to effect the transition shown in Fig. 2, and we will return to this question later.

3 FORMATION OF THE LATENT IMAGE

Some thirty years ago, Gurney and Mott[7] proposed a model for latent image formation which has served as the starting point for discussion of the photographic process ever since. In this theory, the latent image is formed at a surface electron trap, perhaps a foreign atom or molecule (Gurney and Mott suggested Ag_2S) adsorbed at a singular point, such as a surface kink site. Absorption of a photon within the grain produces a free photoelectron, which ultimately wanders to the trap. This trapped electron is then neutralized by the appearance of a mobile interstitial silver ion, forming a silver atom. If the trap-plus-atom is now at least as good a trap as before, then upon absorption of another photon, the process may be repeated, thus adding another silver atom to the speck. By repeated cycles of this sort, a speck consisting of many silver atoms is built up; this speck constitutes the latent image.

There is a great deal of varied experimental support for the essential correctness of the general principles of this model. An elegant corroborative demonstration has been provided by Haynes and Shockley.[8] They exposed a large single crystal of silver chloride to repeated flashes of ultraviolet light and synchronously applied electric field pulses. The decay of the field due to ionic conduction is sufficiently slow (of order of a millisecond) that the field remains essentially constant during the lifetime of the electron (microseconds). Thus, the photoelectrons are swept into and through the crystal. It was found that particles of print-out silver formed wherever the electrons were trapped—at isolated points within the specimen, in deformed regions of deliberately strained crystals, or even at the opposite surface, about a centimeter from the surface at which the photoelectrons were produced. This experiment represents a convincing argument for the electronic–ionic cycle proposed by Gurney and Mott.

The Gurney–Mott cycle thus consists of two stages, an electronic and an ionic stage. It requires that there be mobile interstitial silver ions present and ignores the fate of the photohole which was also produced by the absorption of light, implying thereby that the hole does not recombine with the electron before the arrival of the interstitial silver ion.

Now the bulk concentration and mobility of interstitial silver ions in silver halides is known. Unlike the alkali halides, where the dominant lattice defect is the Schottky pair (a cation vacancy plus a dissociated anion vacancy), the predominant lattice defect found in AgCl and AgBr is the cation Frenkel pair (interstitial silver ion plus silver vacancy). At room temperature, both vacancy and interstitial are mobile, the vacancy making approximately 10^8 jumps per second and the interstitial about 10^{11} per second. The concentration of Frenkel pairs as a function of temperature has been determined, most recently by Müller[9] and by Abbink and Martin.[10] If these results are extrapolated to room temperature, one obtains fractional concentrations of defects of approximately 10^{-11} for AgCl and 3×10^{-8} for AgBr. It could thus be concluded that there are virtually no interstitial silver ions in a microcrystal of AgCl, but perhaps a small number in a typical AgBr microcrystal. This deduction, however, si valid only for perfectly pure material, and if one takes account of the usual presence of several parts per million of divalent metal impurity (introducing an equal concentration of additional silver vacancies), then the calculated concentration of interstitials is greatly decreased and it would seem that only a negligible fraction of the emulsion grains should have in them even one interstitial ion.

On the basis of reasoning similar to this, Mitchell,[11] in an exposition of a detailed model of the photographic process, proposed that after the absorption of a photon, the hole is first trapped (he suggested that the main function of sensitization with sulfur compounds was the efficient trapping of holes by Ag_2S) and that an interstitial silver ion was then ejected from the neighborhood of the trapped hole. Thus, the interstitial is thought to be created during the photographic process.

There is now, however, considerable evidence that in a region within, say, 0.05 micron of the surface, the concentration of interstitial silver ions is much greater than the bulk value. Hamilton and Brady[12] have applied the Haynes-Shockley photoelectron sweeping technique to an emulsion of large tabular silver bromide grains. The total exposure from the flashes was kept sufficiently small that photolysis proceeded only to the latent image stage, rather than forming visible print-out. The location of the latent images was made visible by partial development, to enlarge the specks, followed by observation with electron microscopy. As expected, the distribution of sites of the latent image specks was found to have been shifted in the direction in which electrons would drift in the applied field. Hamilton and Brady then introduced a delay between the application of the sweeping field and the light flash. During this delay period the ionic conductivity of the microcrystal produces an increasing surface polarization such that the internal filed decays with time. Thus, the longer the delay between application of the field and the light flash, the smaller was the resulting displacement of the latent image specks; from these results, it was possible to deduce the ionic conductivity of the grains. This was found to be 100 times larger than the expected bulk value, and was attributed to an excess of interstitial silver ions lying within the surface regions of the grain. Support for this interpretation was provided by the observation that addition of Cd^{++} (which, by introduction of vacancies, would suppress the concentration of interstitials) or adsorption of agents forming strong complexes with silver ions reduced the effective ionic conductivity.

Now, a surface region rich in interstitial silver ions should not be unexpected after all. It has been known for some time[13] that in order for the surface of an ionic crystal to be in equilibrium with the charged lattice defects in the interior there must exist a potential difference between the surface and interior. If, for example, the free energy required to form a silver ion vacancy is less than that for an interstitial silver ion, then in perfectly pure silver halides, more vacancies than interstitials will evaporate from surface to interior, leaving a net positive charge on the surface which is compensated by an extended negative space charge consisting of the cloud of excess vacancies. In real material, on the other hand, cation impurities are present which introduce an excess of silver vacancies in the interior, tending to reverse the sign of the potential difference and the field in the space charge region. To a good approximation, the potential difference is zero at an "isoelectric" temperature T_c such that $c = e^{-G_v/kT_c}$, where c is the concentration of vacancies introduced by the impurities and G_v is the free energy of formation of the vacancy. Thus, the surface will be negatively charged at temperatures below T_c and is positive above T_c, the field will then be a function of both temperature and purity.

A detailed calculation of this space charge distribution in the silver halides has been given by Kliewer.[14] Measurements of the effects of this field in silver chloride, using both internal friction techniques and deformation-induced voltages, have been made by Slifkin, McGowan, Fukai, and Kim.[15] This work demonstrated that in silver chloride of moderate purity, the surface carries a negative charge at room temperature and that the isoelectric temperature is normally well above room temperature. From the variation of T_c with impurity content, it was found that the formation free energy of the vacancy is indeed less than that of the interstitial. Inserting the numerical results obtained into the relations derived by Kliewer leads to the conclusion that there must be a substantial excess of interstitials throughout a subsurface layer of about 0.05 microns thickness, in qualitative agreement with the observations of Hamilton and Brady.

4 ELECTRONS AND HOLES

The Gurney–Mott model demands that the electron produced by the absorption cf light be sufficiently mobile and long-lived to reach a surface trap before being trapped in the interior; otherwise, an internal, rather than surface, latent image would be formed, an image which would be incaple of promoting development in any developer that does nor also contain a solvent for silver halide. Moreover, in view of the Mitchell alternative to the sequence of steps proposed by Gurney and Mott, it is of interest to inquire into evidence as to whether the hole or the electron is trapped first. We therefore wish to know the lifetimes and mobilities of the photocarriers, as wel as the nature of the traps that limit their lifetimes.

In discussing mobility (the drift velocity per unit electric field) one must distinguish between the microscopic mobility, which is characteristic of the free particle, and what is known as the drift mobility, which is measured by the displacement of the particle over a period of time in an applied field. If there is no temporary trapping of the particle, the two are the same; if, on the other hand, the particle spends portions of its travel time in temporary, shallow traps, then the measured drift mobility will be smaller than the microscopic mobility by a factor which is equal to the fraction of the time the particle is free. The mobility determined from a Hall effect measurement is essentially the microscopic mobility, while a photoconductivity experiment or a measurement of latent image displacement by an electric field measures the drift mobility of electrons. The drift of holes can similarly be monitored by their action in annihilating latent image specks and print-out particles. Lifetimes can also be determined in a drift experiment by delaying the application of the field after the light flash, and observing the effect of the decay of the electrons or holes during the delay period.

A summary of the room temperature results obtained by a large number of workers[8,12,16−21] is as follows. In silver chloride both the microscopic and drift mobilities of the photoelectron have a value of 50 cm^2/volt-sec. Temporary trapping is thus negligible. The lifetime of the photoelectron is of the order of a few microseconds for crystals grown in air (for crystals grown in vacuum or in chloride, the lifetime is smaller by a factor of 10 to 100). Comparable data for the holes in silver chloride are not available.

In large silver bromide crystals, the microscopic mobility of the photoelectron is 60 cm^2/volt-sec. For photoelectrons in AgBr emulsion grains, a drift mobility of 0.2 cm^2/volt-sec was observed, this low value implying that the carrier spent the majority of its lifetime in temporary traps. Values of the electron lifetime itself are found to be of the order of microseconds in both large crystals and in emulsion grains. The hole in AgBr has a room-temperature microscopic mobility of approximately 1 cm^2/volt-sec, but the drift mobility is often several factors of ten lower than this. The hole lifetime is several microseconds, and in emulsion grains is reported to be several times that of the electron.[12] In addition to these values of the hole lifetime, Georgiev,[22] Malinovski and Platikanowa,[23] and Heukeroth and Süptitz[24] have reported a surface component of the order of several hundred microseconds in the decay kinetics of photoholes in silver bromide.

One can calculate the diffusion range of a particle from its mobility and lifetime. The mean diffusion distance during a lifetime τ is approximately twice $(D\tau)^{\frac{1}{2}}$, where D is the diffusion coefficient, and in turn is equal to kT/e times the mobility. At room temperature, e/kT is 40 volts. If, from the data given above, we take the lifetime to be one microsecond and the mobility to be, say 1 cm^2/volt-sec, then the mean diffusion distance is seen to be several microns. Thus, one expects both the photohole and the photoelectron to be able to diffuse from the interior of a photographic grain to the surface within their respective lifetimes.

Such estimates, however, ignore the effect of the electric field in the space charge region near the surface. These fields are quite large, averaging something like 10^5 volt/cm over much of the volume of the grain, and they probably contribute significantly to separating the photoelectronhole pair. Moreover, since the surface is negatively charged, the electron will be repelled from it. It has been estimated[15] that the electron makes some 50 attempts before finally reaching the surface and becoming permanently trapped. This effect may be of significance to the high efficiency of the photographic process, since in the most efficient emulsion, there would only be one latent image speck formed per grain. This, in turn, requires that the electron be somewhat selective in choosing its trap; all photoelectrons must be concentrated into one site. The repulsive surface field would help provide just such a selectivity, encouraging the electron to become trapped at that particular site of least negative or most positive potential.

Although it is not known just what defects constitute the best traps for the electron and hole, there is some information as to what will and what will not trap carriers. Growing latent image specks must surely be deep electron traps. Some impurity ions, such as Ni^{++}, have been shown to trap electrons,[25] while Cu$^+$ is known to be a deep hole trap.[26] There have been many observations of print-out on dislocations,[27] implying electron trapping along these line defects. This is surprising in view of the negative charge on dislocations,[15] and suggests that in annealed crystals the electrons may really be becoming trapped at impurity ions segregated at or near the dislocations.

This notion is strengthened by the observation of Childs[28] that the effect in doped crystals is very sensitive to the nature of the dopant. In freshly deformed crystals, on the other hand, the dislocations are expected to be highly jogged. Seitz[29] has pointed out that certain configurations of jogs must always be charged, either $+\frac{1}{2}e$ or $-\frac{1}{2}e$, and such jogs would be expected to trap charge carriers. Miller[30] has indeed observed a finer scale print-out formation on fresh dislocations as compared to widely spaced specks formed at aged dislocations. Interestingly, dislocations do not trap holes.[23] There is some evidence, however, that silver vacancies act as shallow hole traps[31,32] and Mitchell[11] has argued that Ag_2S specks on the grain surface must be permanent hole traps, although there is also much evidence that Ag_2S is a good electron trap.

5 RECIPROCITY FAILURE AND THE LATENT IMAGE

Over a considerable range of exposing intensity, the density produced in the developed emulsion depends only on the total exposure; i.e., on the product of the exposing intensity and the time of exposure. This fact is known as the reciprocity law (for a given density, the intensity needed is proportional to the reciprocal of the exposure time). At either extremely low intensity or very high intensity, however, the efficiency of the emulsion decreases, and the density produced is less than would be expected from the reciprocity law.

High intensity reciprocity failure occurs when the photoproduction of electrons and holes takes place more rapidly than the Gurney–Mott cycle can operate. Two effects now enter to decrease the sensitivity of the grain. First, at high light intensity electron-hole recombination may become more important. The extent of this process, being second order, is expected to increase as the square of the intensity. Second, since the incipient latent image site cannot trap a second electron until the intervening ionic step (capture of an interstitial silver ion) has taken place, then excess electrons may become trapped at other, "second-choice" sites. The number of latent image specks which are nucleated is thus increased, and a greater number of absorbed quanta will be required in order to induce growth in any one of them to a size sufficient to catalyze the subsequent development. Electron microscopic observations by Spencer, Brady, and Hamilton[33] on fine-grain emulsions do indeed show that under high intensities the number of latent image specks per grain increases from one up to four or five.

Hamilton and Brady have analyzed their measurements[12] of the ionic conductivity of silver bromide microcrystals to yield estimates for the time required for the ionic step in latent image formation. This time is found to be 1.5 μsec for ion capture at a center with a charge equal to -1 (in electronic units), 3 μsec at a center with charge $-\frac{1}{2}$, and 5 milliseconds or greater at a neutral or positively charged center. They conclude that only negatively charged centers can capture silver ions rapidly enough to explain the observed sensitivity found at high light intensities. Since each such center has just previously captured an electron, and since it is unlikely that electrons would have been deeply trapped at sites which were already negative before the arrival of the electron, it seems likely that the electron traps are either electrically neutral (such as a speck of neutral silver or Ag_2S) or else have a charge of $+\frac{1}{2}$, as in the case of a surface jog.[29] The charge of the incipient latent image speck is thus proposed to alternate during the operation of the Gurney–Mott cycle between 0 and -1 or between $+\frac{1}{2}$ and $-\frac{1}{2}$.

Low intensity reciprocity failure indicates that more than one quantum is required in the nucleation of the speck which will ultimately grow into the latent image. Statistical analyses of the sensitivity of emulsions at low intensities and of the initial region of the H. & D. curve indicate that this nucleation requires the delivery to the trap of two silver atoms (in the form, of course, of photoelectrons and silver ions) within a few seconds; the two-atom speck thus formed is stable for several days, but is too small yet to act as a latent image speck. Experiments in which an emulsion is first exposed for a period at one intensity and then for another period at a different intensity[34-36] have shown that once the two-atom speck is formed, there is no further lowintensity reciprocity failure (i.e., it is quite stable), but that the total exposure must be approximately doubled in order to produce a latent image speck. Moreover, the growth stage from Ag_2 to formation of the latent image speck is subject to high-intensity reciprocity failure, further indicating the need for more than one quantum to convert. Ag_2 into a viable latent image. The conclusion drawn from this work is that the minimum aggregate of silver atoms which can act as a latent image speck is four. It will be recalled that work described earlier shows that in a sensitive emulsion, absorption of four photons by a grain renders it rather probably developable. The photographic process must be very efficient indeed.

6 LATENT IMAGE REGRESSION EFFECTS

Our discussion thus far has centered mainly on the photoelectron, but the hole must also be properly disposed of. Mitchell[11] emphasized that the latent image must not be a good hole trap if the quantum efficiency of the process is to be high. He suggested that an interstitial silver ion is captured *before* each photoelectron, thus assuring that the trap never acquire a negative charge which could attract a hole. The details of Mitchell's model have been challenged by Hamilton and Brady.[37]

Not only is it essential that the hole not be annihilated at the latent image site, but it is also important that there be adequate halogen acceptor near to the grain surface; otherwise, halogen would accumulate and could ultimately convert the surface latent image back to the halide. The solarization phenomenon, displayed in Fig. 1 as a reversal of slope at high exposures, is probably an illustration of this effect. Although it is possible that the H. & D. curve begins to bend down at high exposures because of a change in the nature of the latent image specks as a result of excessive growth, a more commonly accepted explanation is that after all of the nearby halogen acceptor has been consumed, any further halogen excess will remain free to attack surface latent image specks. If, now, at these high exposures, a fraction of the photoelectrons are trapped in the interior of the grain, forming an internal latent image, then the net effect of further light absorption is to destroy the surface image as this internal image grows. The developability of the grain thus dimishes.

The latent image may also be destroyed by irradiating the exposed but undeveloped emulsion within or near the red region of the spectrum. This is known as the Herschel effect. It appears to involve the photoelectric emission of an electron from the silver of the latent image into the conduction band of the silver halide, requiring approximately 1 to 1.5 eV. This is followed by migration away of the silver ion thus formed. The electron and ion may ultimately recombine, but not necessarily at the latent image. Süptitz[38] has shown that visible print–out specks, formed inside a large silver chloride crystal by the Naynes–Shockley technique, are indeed bleached by yellow light, only to reappear in unirradiated regions of the crystal. The net effect of the Herschel irradiation of an emulsion is thus presumably a dispersal of the latent image into units each of which is too small to initiate development.

7 SENSITIZATION

The photosensitivity of commercial emulsions is greatly enhanced by the addition of various chemical sensitizers. These may be reducing agents, gold salts, or sulfur compounds. The nature of chemical sensitization is not established, but a number of likely possibilities have been suggested. The action of reducing sensitizers may be to produce small quantities of atomic silver, which may serve either as halogen acceptor or as the nuclei for formation of latent image. It is apparent that sensitization represents a delicate balance, since if it is overdone, the grains will be developable even without prior exposure (i.e., the emulsion will display excessive "fog"). Presumably sensitization by means of gold salts results in the ultimate incorporation of atomic gold into the latent image, but whether this simply involves the replacement of a silver atom by a gold atom (i.e., $Au^+ + Ag^0 \rightarrow Au^0 + Ag^+$) or an actual increase in the number of metal atoms (perhaps by the reduction of Au^+ to Au^0 by agents in the gelatin) is not known.

Sulfur sensitization probably involves the formation of Ag_2S at the surface of the grain. The silver sulfide has been considered both as a hole trap (in the form of a reagent for halogen atoms) and as an electron trap. There is evidence that sulfur sensitization enhances the formation of surface latent image at the expense of internal latent image, and that it also increases the number of nuclei for latent image formation. Both of these observations point to a role of the adsorbed Ag_2S primarily as a trap for electrons. An elegant demonstration of the ability of Ag_2S to act as nucleation site for latent image formation was provided by West and Saunders.[39] They irradiated a thin sheet of AgBr with light absorbed very near to the surface. The reverse surface was within the diffusion range of electrons but not for holes, and some latent image was found to form there. Upon treating this reverse surface with Ag_2S, it was found that the formation of latent image there increased considerably, thus demonstrating the electron trapping ability of the added Ag_2S.

Photographic emulsions are also sensitized by the addition of small amounts of dyes which adsorb onto the grain surfaces. There are a number of dyes which thereby confer on the microcrystal a photographic sensitivity in the spectral region in which the adsorbed dye itself absorbs. The spectral range of emulsions has thus been extended out to 1300 mμ, where the quantum energy is less than 1 eV.

Even though the energy gap between valence and conduction bands in silver halides is 2.5 to 3 eV, there is no violation of energy conservation in this process, since the hole may be formed in a state well above the top of the valence band. It is not yet known whether the mechanism of dye sensitization is (a) one in which energy os transferred from the excited dye molecule, or aggregate of molecules, to the silver halide, there producing a photopair (there is evidence that the electron energy levels at the crystal surface may be considerably distorted,[40] so the hole could well be formed there rather than in the dye layer); or (b) one in which a free electron is transferred directly from the dye to the conduction band of the crystal. In either case, a free electron and a bound hole are produced. That the electron is really free has been convincingly demonstrated, most recently by Saunders, Tyler, and West,[41] who performed a Haynes-Shockley drift experiment on electrons produced by irradiation in the spectral region of the dye absorption. The electron had the normal free electron mobility while the holes were found to be bound to the sites of their production.

A necessary, but not sufficient, condition that dye sensitization proceed by electron transfer rather than by energy transfer is that the first excited singlet state of the dye lie above the bottom of the conduction band of the silver halide. There is conflicting evidence on this point in the recent literature[42,43] and the issue is certainly not resolved.

A discussion of a possible energy transfer by means of excitons in the dye layer and in the crystal has been given by LuValle.[44] One of the most convincing demonstrations that dye sensitization can occur by energy transfer is a recent experiment of Kuhn *et al.*[45] Using monolayer adsorption techniques, they prepared specimens in which a 50 Å thick layer of hydrocarbon chain (presumably electronically inert) separated the dye monolayer from the silver bromide surface. They showed that the time required for electron tunnelling from the excited dye to the silver bromide was much longer than the lifetime for fluorescence. Nevertheless, the silver halide crystal effectively quenched fluorescence and was sensitized for production of latent image. Thus, at least in this particular case, efficient dye sensitization resulted from transfer of excitation energy, not charged particles.

8   HIGH ENERGY RADIATION AND PARTICLES

The essential new feature that appears when a photographic emulsion is exposed to energetic radiation (x-rays, gamma rays, beta rays, etc.) is the high density of ionization that occurs all along the track of a fast charged particle and at the sites of ionizing events in the track of an uncharged photon. For example, the absorption of an x-ray of 1 Å wavelength results in the production of about 200 atoms of silver. Exposure to energetic radiation, even at low rates of incidence, is thus equivalent to a very high intensity exposure within those grains affected, and no horizontal threshold region is seen on the H. & D. curve. As in the case of exposure to visible light of high intensity, many small latent image specks are formed, and much of the image is in the form of internal rather than surface specks. In the case of exposure to high energy beta rays, the distribution of many small and less effective latent image specks, instead of a few large ones, makes it necessary to prolong the development time. Also, chemical sensitization is even more effective for exposure to beta rays than for visible light.

It has been demonstrated that the tracks of particles of charge greater than 1 can be made visible within the bulk of large single crystals of silver chloride.[46] After the exposure to the nuclear particles, photoelectrons are then swept through the crystal by the technique of Haynes and Shockley. Some of the electrons become trapped along the tracks, presumably at the fresh dislocations formed by a thermal spike in the wake of the energetic particle. The formation of print-out at the trapped electrons then delineates the track. It has been found that the effect is rather sensitive to the presence of impurities in the part-per-million range.[28] Doping very pure silver chloride with copper or iron results in the decoration of grow-in dislocations, but not tracks; doping with lead enhances track decoration, but not that of aged dislocations; and doping with nickel suppresses decoration of both, presumably because nickel is itself such a good trap for electrons. As compared with photographic emulsions, single crystal track recording is not subject to development distortion, offers a thicker detector than an emulsion pellicle, and produces sharper tracks with a thickness that increases with particle charge. A major disadvantage of this detector is its inability to make visible the tracks of singly charged particles.

9   WHY SILVER HALIDES?

It may be of interest to summarize those properties of silver halide emulsions which have been seen to be important to the efficient functioning of the photographic process for visible light.

1) There must be no appreciable dark electronic conductivity.

17   Amelinckx (1347)

2) There must be a high quantum yield for production of photoelectron-hole pairs by absorption of visible light. If the action spectrum does not extend to the red end of the spectrum, a dye sensitization process must be possible.

3) The electron-hole recombination rate must be low, at least at low intensities.

4) Both the electron and hole must have sufficiently large mobilities and lifetimes in order for them to reach the surface of the grain before becoming permanently trapped.

5) The cation must be very mobile when in a defect state (the interstitial, here) which has a relatively low formation energy, so that it can seek out and combine with the trapped electron.

6) It must be possible to permanently remove the hole.

7) High photographic efficiency demands that successive photoelectrons become trapped at the site of the first; i.e., a concentration mechanism is required. The site of this concentration must be on the grain surface.

8) The development process must proceed only slowly in the absence of latent image, but autocatalytically in the presence of the image speck.

Many of these requirements are individually found only rarely. That all of them should be present in one system is surely a fortunate coincidence.

References

1. C. E. K. Mees and T. H. James, eds. *The Theory of the Photographic Process*, 3rd edition, New York, The Macmillan Co., (1966).
2. F. Brown, *The Physics of Solids*, New York, W. A. Benjamin, Inc. (1967).
3. C. Berry and D. Skillman, *J. Appl. Phys.* **35**, 2165 (1964).
4. A. Marriage, *J. Phot. Sci.* **9**, 93 (1961); E. Klein, *ibid.* **10**, 26 (1962).
5. A. Tippins and F. Browm, *Phys. Rev.* **129**, 2554 (1963); G. Ascarelli and F. Brown, *Phys. Rev. Letters* **9**, 209 (1962); B. Joesten and F. Brown, *Phys. Rev.* **148**, 919 (1966).
6. F. Bassani, R. Knox, and W. B. Fowler, *Phys. Rev.* **137**, A1217 (1965); P. Scop, *ibid.* **139**, A934 (1965).
7. R. Gurney and N. Mott, *Proc. Roy. Soc.* (*London*) **164A**, 151 (1938).
8. J. Haynes and W. Shockley, *Phys. Rev.* **82**, 935 (1951).
9. P. Müller, *Phys. Stat. Sol.* **12**, 775 (1965).
10. A. Abbink and D. Martin, *J. Phys. Chem. Solids* **27**, 205 (1966).
11. J. Mitchell, *Rept. Prog. Phys.* **20**, 433 (1957); J. Mitchell and N. Mott, *Proc. Roy. Soc.* (*London*) **2**, 1149 (1957); J. Mitchell, *J. Phys. Chem.* **66**, 2359 (1962).

12. J. Hamilton and L. Brady, *J. Appl. Phys.* **30**, 1893, 1902 (1959); *J. Phys. Chem.* **66**, 2384 (1962); L. Brady and J. Hamilton, *J. Appl. Phys.* **35**, 1565 (1964).
13. J. Frenkel, *Kinetic Theory of Liquids*, New York, Oxford Univ. Press, (1946); J. Eshelby, C. Newey, P. Pratt, and A. Lidiard, *Phil. Mag.* **3**, 75 (1958).
14. K. Kliewer, *J. Phys. Chem. Solids* **27**, 705, 719 (1966).
15. L. Slifkin, W. McGowan, A. Fukai, and J. S. Kim, *Phot. Sci. and Eng.* **11**, 79 (1967).
16. R. Ahrenkiel and R. van Heyningen, *Phys. Rev.* **144**, 576 (1966).
17. L. Chollet and J. Rossel, *Proc. Int. Conf. on Semiconductors*, Prague, (1960).
18. P. Süptitz, *Z. Phys.* **153**, 174 (1958).
19. R. Hanson, *J. Phys. Chem.* **66**, 2376 (1962).
20. F. Hamm, *J. Appl. Phys.* **30**, 1468 (1959).
21. V. Saunders, R. Tyler, and W. West, *J. Chem. Phys.* **37**, 1126 (1962).
22. M. Georgiev, *Phys. Stat. Sol.* **15**, 193 (1966).
23. J. Malinowski, *Contemp. Phys.* **8**, 285 (1967); J. Malinowski and W. Platikanowa, *Phys. Stat. Sol.* **6**, 805 (1964).
24. U. Heukeroth and P. Süptitz, *Phys. Stat. Sol.* **13**, 285 (1966).
25. A. Michel, *Phys. Rev.* **121**, 968 (1961); T. Sliker, *ibid.* **130**, 1749 (1963).
26. F. Moser, N. Nail, and F. Urbach, *J. Phys. Chem. Solids* **3**, 153 (1957).
27. The first report was J. Hedges and J. Mitchell, *Phil. Mag.* **44**, 223 (1953).
28. C. Childs, private communication.
29. F. Seitz, *Phys. Rev.* **80**, 239 (1950); *Rev. Mod. Phys.* **23**, 328 (1951); *ibid.* **26**, 7 (1954).
30. M. Miller, Ph. D. Thesis, University of North Carolina (1961).
31. L. Cordone and M. Palma, *Phys. Rev. Letters* **16**, 22 (1966).
32. F. Kröger, *J. Phys. Chem. Solids* **27**, 1697 (1966).
33. H. Spencer, L. Brady, and J. Hamilton, *J. Opt. Soc. Am.* **54**, 492 (1964).
34. J. Webb and C. Evans, *J. Opt. Soc. Am.* **28**, 249 (1938).
35. J. Enns and E. Katz, *J. Opt. Soc. Am.* **47**, 758 (1957).
36. P. Burton and W. Berg, *Phot. J.* **86B**, 2 (1946); *ibid.*, **88B**, 84 (1948).
37. J. Hamilton and L. Brady, *Phot. Sci. and Eng.* **8**, 189 (1964).
38. P. Süptitz, *Z. Wiss. Phot.* **53**, 201 (1959).
39. W. West and V. Saunders, Phot. Sci. and Eng. **3**, 258 (1959).
40. C. Berry and D. Skillman, *J. Appl. Phys.* **35**, 2165 (1964); C. Berry, *Phys. Rev.* **153**, 989 (1967).
41. V. Saunders, R. Tyler, and W. West, *J. Chem. Phys.* **46**, 199 (1967).
42. P. Gilmer, *Phot. Sci. and Eng.* **11**, 222 (1967).
43. I. Akimow, V. Bentsa, F. Vilesov, and A. Terenin, *Phys. Stat. Sol.* **20**, 771 (1967).
44. J. LuValle, *Phot. Sci. and Eng.* **8**, 229 (1964).
45. H. Bücher, A. Kuhn, B. Mann, D. Möbius, L. v. Szentpály, and P. Tillman, *Phot. Sci. and Eng.* **11**, 233 (1967).
46. C. Childs and L. Slifkin, *Rev. Sci. Instr.* **34**, 101 (1963); *Brit. J. Appl. Phys.* **16**, 771 (1965).

Some aspects of radiation damage in covalent crystals*

E.W.J. MITCHELL

J.J. Thomson Physical Laboratory,
University of Reading,
Whiteknights, Reading, Berks.

I INTRODUCTION

The emphasis of the Summer School is on radiation effects for dosimetry. Some lectures are specifically related to problems of dosimetry, while in other cases, lecturers have been asked to deal more generally with radiation effects in a particular class of materials. My lectures are in the latter category and deal with some of the wide ranging radiation effects in some covalent crystals.

---

* Part of this paper first appeared in *Nature*, **208**, 638, (1965).

One of the reasons for discussing these materials as a class is that they exhibit a number of properties which change primarily as a result of the displacement of atoms by nuclear encounter. It is true that thermoluminescent effects exist in diamond arising from ionization processes, similar to those occurring in ionic crystals used as thermoluminescent dectectors. However, there are also effects which only occurr following the displacement of atoms, although the effects of ionization on the defects so produced may seriously affect the changes brought about on the physical property. Some examples of this will occur in these lectures. The practical consequences of this would be that if one was utilizing a *displacement effect* and measuring changes in optical absorption, electron spin resonance, resistivity ... one may have to take care to put the sample in a standard ionization state following the irradiation with the dose to be monitored.

In spite of these qualifications the covalent materials* that I shall be dealing with exhibit a number of effects primarily related to atomic displacements. Furthermore, the displacements are produced by direct nuclear encounter rather than by two stage processes only involving ionization as in the alkali halides. In this respect the covalent materials resemble metals but they would have the advantage over metals if used for "displacement radiation" dosimetry that the simpler types of defects tend to be stable to higher temperatures than in metals.

This practical distinction between ionic crystals (particularly alkali halides) and covalent crystals is an expression of the greater stability in the latter of an abnormally charged atom (ion) in a normal lattice site. Calculations about these stabilities are in a primitive state but the observations are that low energy ionizing radiation can produce a number of displacement effects in the alkali halides but that these effects are not detected in the covalent materials dealt with here.

In these lectures I shall be giving examples from experiments on diamond, graphite, silicon, germanium and gallium arsenide. While I have been emphasizing the possibilities of these materials for dosimetry of radiation capable of producing displacements by direct nuclear encounter, there are also well-known instances where sensitive dose rates of ionizing radiation may be monitored. In the electron (photo) voltaic effect associated with a space charge barrier in a semiconductor junction the voltage developed is related to the number of electron-hole pairs produced in the barrier region. The

---

* Polymers are excluded from this discussion.

efficiency of such a device depends on the elimination of recombination centres for the electrons and holes in the barrier region. In these cases one would have to avoid using the devices with ionizing radiation capable of producing displacements. Displaced atoms provide recombination centres and the magnitude of the electron (photo) voltaic effect is rapidly reduced. So much so that the electron (photo) voltaic effect is also used as one of the most sensitive means of detecting atomic displacements produced in the barrier region and has been used in a number of displacement threshold determinations. A similar effect is observed in gallium arsenide when recombination centres produced by atomic displacements rapidly quench edge luminescence. The recombination centre apparently provides a much more effective path to electron-hole recombination than the direct luminescence.

In this introductory discussion I have emphasized so far "cumulative" dosimetry rather than the counting of individual events. Covalent crystals may also be utilized as counters. A considerable amount of work has been done on the particle counting properties of the various types of diamond. The difficulty has been that the internal recombination rates are too high so that all the charge resulting from the event is not collected. Trapping of carriers contributes to the same difficulty and also introduces unwanted polarization of the crystal. In these cases a field is maintained externally in insulating material in which an enhanced pulse may be built up, following an initial ionization, by various processes of internal secondary ionization.

Metal-semiconductor, or $p-n$, space charge barriers may be used in the same way thus giving the semiconductor particle detectors. They essentially utilize the electron (photo) voltaic effect under conditions that all the charge resulting from an initial event is collected. Since in silicon the energy required to produce an electronhole pair is 3.6 eV there is a potential gain of almost an order of magnitude over gas counters (requiring 31 eV). The semiconductor particle counters germanium and silicon have relatively long minority carrier lifetimes and high mobilities both of which help to give complete charge collection and hence accurately proportional counters. Silicon is generally to be preferred because of its higher resistivity and thus greater ability to maintain a larger field, but germanium has the greater stopping power. Particle detectors will be discussed elsewhere in the School; I mention them here for completeness because the most successful ones are made from covalent crystals. Recent reviews have been given by Dearnaley and Northrop (1966) and Gunnersen (1967).

II   OPTICAL EFFECTS (electronic spectra)

a   General

Defects give rise to localized electron energy levels and these in turn lead to absorption of light when excitation from the ground to excited state is possible. The amount of absorption is related to the number of centres and to the probability of absorption.

$$\mu \cdot \Delta E = \left(\frac{\pi e^2 h}{3mc}\right) Nf = 10^{-16} \, Nf$$

for $\mu \, \Delta E$ in (cm^{-1} eV) and where f, the oscillator strength for the transition, (f_{ge}, for $g \to e$) is related to the wave functions of the two states

$$f_{ge} = \frac{8\pi^2 m}{e^2 h} \gamma_{ge} \, |\textstyle\int \psi_e| \, ex \, |\psi_g \, d\tau|^2 .$$

As with atoms and molecules, to which the localized electronic structures of defects are very similar, the matrix moments are large when there is considerable overlap in the wave functions, as for example to atomic $s \to p$ transitions. f-values for transitions depend sensitively on the form of the wavefunctions and are not accurately calculable for defect transitions in covalent crystals.

Some convenient orders of magnitude are given in Table 1:

TABLE 1   Orders of magnitude of defect concentrations and irradiation doses relevant to optical absorbtion experiments.

	$f = 1$			$f = 0.1$		
	No. of defects cm^{-3}	eg. e$^-$ dose	eg. n^0 dose	No. of defects cm^{-3}	eg. e$^-$ dose	eg. n^0 dose
$\mu = 2$ cm^{-1} $\Delta E = 0.5$ eV	10^{16}	ca. 10^{16} e$^-$ cm^{-2}	ca. 10^{14} fast n^0 cm^{-2}	10^{17}	ca. 10^{17}	ca. 10^{15}
$\mu = 200$ $\Delta E = 0.5$	10^{18}	ca. 10^{18}	ca. 10^{16}	10^{19}	ca. 10^{19}	ca. 10^{17}

The dose figures stated in this table are the sort of figures which can occur—they are given as illustrations. It should also be born in mind that the measurement of an absorption coefficient of 2 cm^{-1} requires a crystal of ca. 1 cm thick whereas ca. 0.1 mm is required for comparable accuracy for absorption coefficients of 200 cm^{-1}.

b Form of spectra

The form of the spectrum depends upon how the ground and excited electronic functions couple to the lattice vibrations. According to the Frank–Condon principle only the vertical transitions are possible in Fig. 1 since other transitions involve changes in the configuration of atoms which are much slower than the electronic transition. In cases where the change of the configuration of atoms between the minimum in the ground electronic state to the minimum in the excited electronic state is small the zero point motion associated with the two lowest vibronic states may allow the lower energy absorption transition (or higher energy emission) to occur as shown diagrammatically in Fig. 1. This gives a sharp zero–phonon line in some crystals. An example of a radiation induced defect in diamond is shown in Fig. 2. This curve also shows structure on the broader band from inter-action with particularly prominent higher energy lattice vibrations. In general the luminescence spectra may be excited anywhere in the absorbing region of the spectrum but the efficiency will be expected to be greater nearer the zero–phonon spike when radiationless returns to the ground state become less probable.

The spike to band ration is given by

$$\frac{\text{absorption in spike}}{\text{absorption in band}} = \exp\left\{\frac{\Delta E}{2.5\,\omega_0}\right\}^2$$

$$\text{or } \exp\{-S\}$$

where ΔE is the half-width of the band, ω_0 an average phonon energy and S is the average number of phonon involved in the "normal" transition. When minima separations are large, and phonon energies relatively small, S may be large and only broad bands observed (F & M centres in alkali halides). In the diamond case in Fig. 2 $S = 3.6$ corresponding to $\omega_0 = 0.10$ eV.

c Charge occupancy

An important aspect to the study of lattice defects by optical methods—and one which is of special importance when optical methods are considered for dosimetry—is the charge occupancy of a defect. It is well known in the alkali halides that the absorption spectrum associated with a defect is extremely

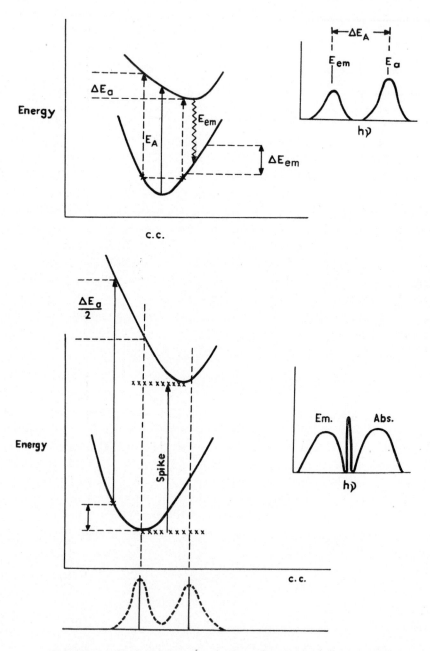

FIGURE 1   Frank–Condon effect in absorption and emission in crystals

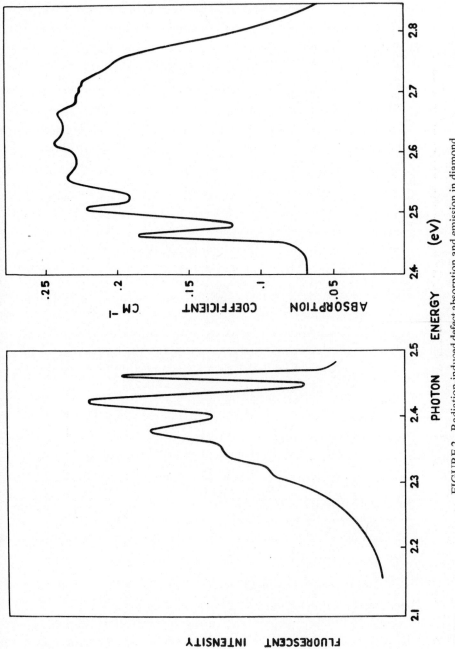

FIGURE 2   Radiation-induced defect absorption and emission in diamond

sensitive to charge occupancy. Thus an anion vacancy can exist as a **vacancy** (α-band), as a vacancy with one trapped electron (F-band) or as a vacancy with two trapped electrons (F'-band). The absorption occurs in the ultraviolet, visible and near infrared respectively. Clearly if using one band to monitor the concentration of a defect one would have to know that a fixed proportion of the defects at different stages of monitoring was in the particular charged state. The same problem arises in a different connection— when one uses an optical absorption to monitor the removal of defects by annealing. This problem was discussed by Mitchell and Paige (1957) and by Levy (1961) who was one of the first to adopt the procedure of a standard ionizing dose following an annealing treatment.

Dyer and Ferdinando (1966) and Ferdinando (1967) have observed an interesting effect of charge accupancy in diamond. The G-band (spike 1.673 eV, broad band peak at about 2 eV) produced by particle irradiation of diamond occurs in all types of diamond. However, in experiments in which semiconducting diamond (IIb) was electron irradiated it was found that although the G-band occurred at higher doses it did not at, for example, for a dose of 3.8×10^{18} e$^-$ cm^{-2}. Yet at this dose in type IIa diamond the G-band was easily observed.

The explanation seems to be that in type IIa diamond the Fermi level is somewhere near the centre of the band gap and the lowest state of the defect is lower such that the defect always contains a trapped electron. In the semiconducting diamond on the other hand, owing to the aluminium acceptor centre, the Fermi level is much closer to the valence band edge. Initially, therefore, the ground state of the defect lies above the Fermi level and no electrons are trapped in the defects. Wuth further irradiation the Fermi level moves towards the middle of the gap, increasing the fraction of defects which trap electrons. This enables one to conclude that the band corresponds to the defect containing a trapped electron.

This is a particularly striking effect occurring in the visible part of the spectrum. In silicon the work of Watkins (e.g. 1964) has shown a wide variety of charge states of vacancies in silicon and their associated electron spin resonance (e.s.r.) spectra.

d   Some optical experiments on gallium arsenide

The study of radiation effects has had influence on many aspects of solid state physics and some experiments we carried out on gallium arsenide have led me to believe that it can be a valuable way of examining disordered systems. The experiments were optical and again may be of interest to this School.

The problem of the energy levels of disordered systems is a major one for physicists interested in condensed matter. We can divide the problem into:

i) specifying the energy levels;

ii) specifying the disorder;

iii) solving the Schroedinger equation for the disordered system.

In the semiconductor field (i) has been attempted for liquids, for amorphous films and for highly chemically doped materials. If an amorphous structure is produced by heavy particle irradiation (as in the case of many insulators, e.g. quartz) one has the ability to measure over a wider range of amorphous phase. The energy levels then have to be determined by spectroscopy and the disorder can in principle be specified by position correlation functions obtainable from neutron and x-ray spectroscopy. The final problem has not been solved for any particular system but notable progress has been made in recent years, e.g. Gubanov (1963), Lax and Halperin (1966).

In a number of semiconductors (e.g. Ge, GaAs) it appears that fast neutron irradiation produces two kinds of effect:

i) point defects and simple aggregates;

ii) large disordered regions ($20 \simeq 2000$ Å?).

The qualitative features of the theoretical work on disordered systems are shown in Fig. 3. In the region of the band edges of the perfect crystal further energy levels are introduced extending into the forbidden gap. Away from the band edges these levels are expected to be localized becoming non-localized nearer to the original band edges. Such levels would be expected to have major effects on optical absorption near the band edges and also on any system showing edge emission. We have made an initial survey of the effects in gallium arsenide.

Point defects can also affect the energy states in the region of the band edges, particularly when charged. They then provide a strong local electric field perturbation as discussed by Franz and Keldysh. Some measurements of such an effect on the absorption edge have been reported by Lucovsky *et al.* (1965). Because of these we have examined the spectrum out to greater photon energies than used by Lucovsky for his work on impurities and also

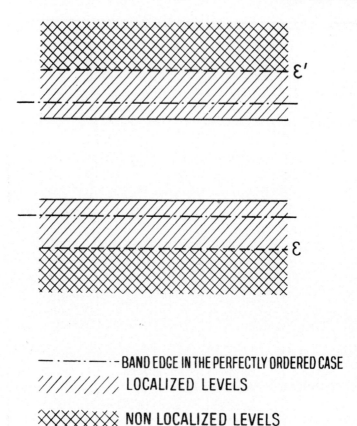

$- \cdot - \cdot - \cdot -$ BAND EDGE IN THE PERFECTLY ORDERED CASE

$/////////$ LOCALIZED LEVELS

$\times\times\times\times\times\times$ NON LOCALIZED LEVELS

FIGURE 3   Qualitative features of energy level scheme in a disordered
system (after L. Banyai, 1964)

have looked at a range of samples to see whether effects were dependent on the initial Fermi level.

The optical results for *n*-type material (Mitchell and Norris, 1966) are shown in Fig. 4 from which we find that there is a considerable absorption tail induced by a fast neutron irradition of 4.3×10^{16} n° cm^{-2} (fast n° Ni scale). The change of absorption closely follows

$$\Delta\mu = A \exp. \{B(hv)\}.$$

A is found to be 2.82 cm^{-1} and $B = 3.05$ eV^{-1} giving for example $\Delta\mu = 83$cm^{-1} at 1.12 eV. The details of the original samples are given in Table II.

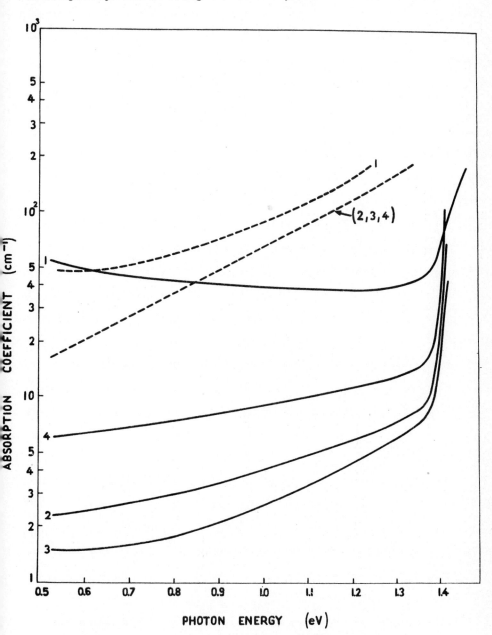

FIGURE 4   The absorption spectra of four samples of *n*-type gallium
arsenide before (bold lines) and after (dotted lines) neutron irradiation

TABLE II. Summary of characteristics of gallium arsenide specimens

Sample types and number	Deliberate dopant	R.T. carrier concentration cm^{-3}	R.T. carrier mobility cm^2/volt/sec.	Emission peaks (eV)		
N1	Te	3.0×10^{18}	2500	1.53	—	1.28
N2	—	2.6×10^{16}	5480	1.49	1.33	—
N3	Compensated semi-insulating	4.5×10^{7}	2300	—	1.35*	—
N4	—	1.5×10^{17}	2400	1.50	(2.41*, 1.36*)	1.24
P5	Zn	1.0×10^{19}	84	1.46	—	—
P6	Zn	7.8×10^{17}	150	1.48	1.35	—

(* emission weak)

The results with *p*-type material are more complicated because of the free carrier absorption present initially. Before irradiation the free carrier absorption ratio at a photon energy of 0.99 eV was $\dfrac{\text{P.5}}{\text{P.6}} = 12$. This is in good agreement with the carrier concentration measured electrically of 12.8. The free carrier absorption is obviously affected by irradiation induced traps and it is difficult to assess what edge absorption has been induced by irradiation. In the case of P.6 one can see (Fig. 5) that the absorption approaches the exponential form increasing towards the band edge and is comparable with the *n*-type results—e.g. P.6 $\Delta\mu - 10^2$ at 1.12 eV.

From the decrease in free carrier absorption in P.5 and from the initial Hall effect measurement we can also find that 17.7 holes cm^{-3} are removed per fast n° cm^{-2}.

Thus qualitatively we see that band tailing effects are present which extend much farther from the absorption edge in the original crystals than could be ascribed to the effects of point defects.

e Photoluminescence

We have also observed large changes in the photoluminescence of the irradiated samples. The luminescence was measured at 80°K before and after irradiation, using an unirradiated sample of the same impurity concentration in each case to monitor the apparatus response. The luminescence is se-

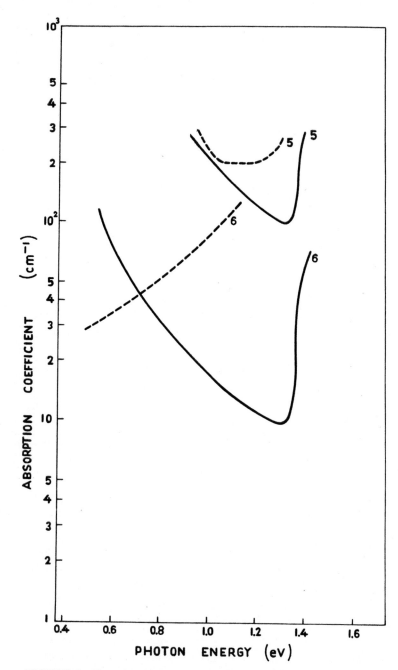

FIGURE 5   The absorption spectra of two samples of *p*-type gallium
arsenide before (bold lines) and after (dotted) neutron irradiation

verely quenched by the neutron irradiation and we use the ratio of intensities

$$\frac{I_0 - I_R}{I_0}$$

as a measure of the effect.

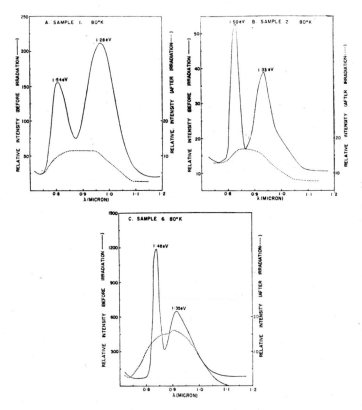

FIGURE 6   The quenching of photoluminescence at 80°K in neutron-irradiated gallium arsenide: A. Sample N1; B. Sample N2; C. Sample P6

The effects are shown in Figs. 6 and 7 and summarized in Table III.

Quenching of photoluminescence was also observed following 2 MeV electron irradiation (3.6×10^{15} e$^-$ cm^{-2}). The e$^-$/n$^\circ$ ratio for equivalent effects is 1.4 for P.5 and 6.6 for P.6 but in the absence of rate curves these ratios must be regarded as approximate. On the other hand it is the same

TABLE III.   Quenching of photoluminescence by irradiation in gallium arsenide
(I_0 intensity before irradiation, I_R after irradiation, $\Delta = I_0 - I_R$;
I_0 and I_0* not same relative scale)

Sample types and number	Peak position (eV)	n^0 Irradiation			e^- Irradiation		
		I_0	I_R	Δ/I_0	I_0*	I_R*	Δ*$/I_0$
N1	1.53	155	10	0.93	4.77	0.64	0.87
	1.28	211	10	0.95	5.70	1.30	0.77
N2	1.49	52.8	16	0.68	—	—	—
	1.33	38.8	15.8	0.59	—	—	—
N3	1.35	85.2	15	0.82	—	—	—
N4	1.50	31.6	15	0.53	—	—	—
	1.24	38	12	0.68	—	—	—
P5	1.46	371	19	0.95	9.05	0.80	0.91
P6	1.48	1188	15	0.99	8.40	0.83	0.91
	1.35	645	16	0.97	6.36	3.32	0.48

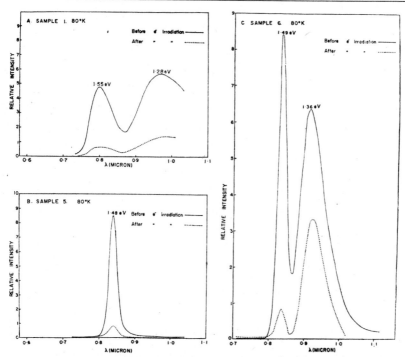

FIGURE 7   The quenching of photoluminescence at 80°K in electron-
irradiated gallium arsenide: A. Sample N1; B. Sample N2; C. Sample P6

18*

order of magnitude as the e^-/n° ratio for identical carrier removal rate in *p*-type samples of about 3.

The value of 3 is much lower than found for many effects in other co-valent crystals (e.g.—500 for diamond). This is consistent with the fact that GaAs appears to be very susceptible to damage by electrons as shown by the dimensional changes presented by Vook (1964) at the Paris Conference.

f   Remarks

The results reported on gallium arsenide show that its optical properties are considerable modified by irradiation. The recombination centres respon-sible for the quenching of photoluminescence would very likely affect electro-luminescence properties. Thus (a) would seriously affect opto-devices used in radiation fields, or (b) might in some circumstances be suitable for mo-nitoring radiation. The optical absorption produced by neutron irradiation shows a strong exponential tail to the original absorption edge.

III   OPTICAL EFFECTS (vibrational spectra)

A radiation effect which occurs only in some covalent crystals is the pheno-menon of induced 1-phonon vibrational absorption. In perfect crystals of diamond, silicon or germanium there is no dipole moment associated with the fundamental vibrations and, therefore, no optical absorption occurs. After neutron irradiation infrared absorption occurs in the 1-phonon region (Diamond $-\lambda > 7.5\,\mu$; silicon $-\lambda > /6\,\mu$; germanium $-\lambda > 33\,\mu$).

This effect is associated with the local charge deformation produced by the defects such that the main lattice vibrations give rise to a dipole moment in the vicinity of the defect. Thus optical absorption becomes possible at frequencies at which it was previously forbidden. Spectra for diamond and silicon are shown in Fig. 8. The effect is not a sensitive monitor of defect concentration and has primarily been of interest as a new phenomenon in solid state physics. Only in diamond has it been observed after electron irradiation and then high doses (ca. $10^{19}\,e^-\,cm^{-2}$) were needed.

An associated effect which occurs is the production of vibrational bands at higher frequencies than the above. These are frequencies characteristic of the *localized* vibrations of the defect complexes (or defect plus neigh-bouring lattice atoms). Examples may be seen in Fig. 8 on the high frequency side of the 1-phonon cut-off in diamond and silicon.

The neutron dose range producing these effects is 10^{17}–$10^{19}\,n^\circ\,cm^{-2}$.

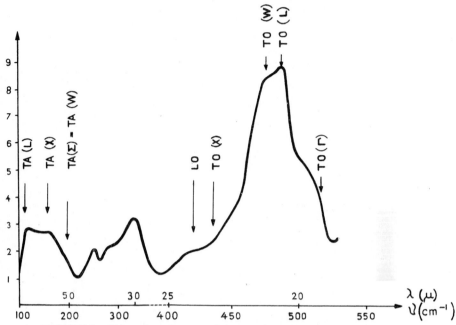

FIGURE 8 Absorption spectrum of (upper diagram) neutron-irradiated diamond and (lower diagram) neutron irradiated silicon

IV GRAPHITE

a Introduction

Apart from its practical significance, graphite is an unique substance physically. Within a layer each carbon atom contributes three electrons to strong in plane sp^2 trigonal covalent bonds. There is considerable space between layers (spacing 3.36 Å) which are held together by the relatively weak Van der Waals forces. The fourth electron of each atom (π electron) is much more loosely bound and it is the π electrons which give rise to the conduction properties.

Considering a two-dimensional structure, the π electrons are in bands 3–4 eV higher than the bands containing the sp^2 electrons. With two atoms per two-dimensional cell there are two π bands and these are degenerate at the corners of the hexagonal Brillouin zone. The two π electrons per cell normally occupy the lower of the two π bands. (See Fig. 9). Even in this extremely simplified model one can see that graphite will have unusual properties since the valence and conduction bands touch at zone corners such that an activation energy is not needed for conduction.

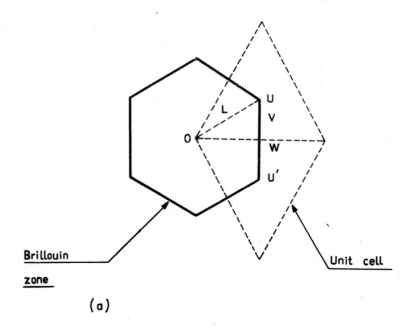

Brillouin zone

Unit cell

(a)

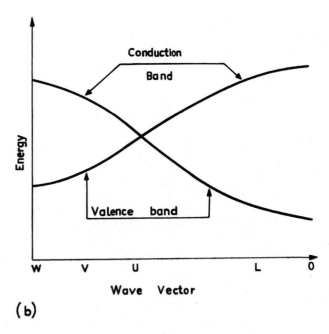

(b)

FIGURE 9   Two-dimensional energy band model for graphite

If, more realistically, one considers a three-dimensional Brillouin zone, containing four atoms, degeneracies occur along the zone edges and conduction can take place by both electrons and holes which form ellipsoidal energy surfaces in the overlapping bands along the zone edge.

The detailed band scheme, illustrated in Fig. 10 gives a constant carrier concentration for temperatures up to 80°K but one increasing with temperature at higher temperatures. Below 80°K the increase of resistivity with temperature arises from increasing carrier scattering. The orders of magnitude of parameters in the best single crystals at 80°K are electron and hole concentrations ca. 2×10^{18} cm^{-3} and mobilities ca. 6×10^4 cm^2/volt-sec. and at 300°K are ca. 7×10^{18} and 1×10^4.

Carrier densities in polycrystalline graphite are somewhat less than these values and mobilities considerably less corresponding to the large crystallite boundary scattering. Thus the room temperature resistivity of polycrystalline graphite is ca. 10^{-3} Ωcm compared with ca. 5×10^{-5} Ωcm for single crystal.

The resistivity of graphite increases with irradiation, the change resulting from a combination of changes in both carrier scattering and concentration. Changes in the latter are complex and at 80°K in polycrystalline graphite the carrier concentration has been observed to *increase* on irradiation, although this was more than outweighed by the mobility decrease giving a net resistivity increase. Small shifts in the Fermi level can have complex results when the electronic structure is as sensitively balanced as in graphite. Thus a small change in Fermi level arising from electron trapping will release further holes in the hole band, but because of the higher density of hole states will release more holes for conduction. This may explain the otherwise odd effect mentioned above.

It is clear from this resumé of the electronic band structure of graphite that it is going to be extremely difficult to predict the effects of a particular defect. Without some distortion of the structure it is difficult to see how there can be a localized trapping state. With such a sensitive balancing of Fermi level and band edges, the strain around a defect may well provide the necessary distortion to give rise to localized levels, although detailed calculations cannot at present be made with any useful reliability.

b Radiation effect on electrical resistivity

The changes in electrical resistivity in graphite during reactor irradiation have, in fact, been used by Bell *et al.* (1962) to monitor the damaging flux

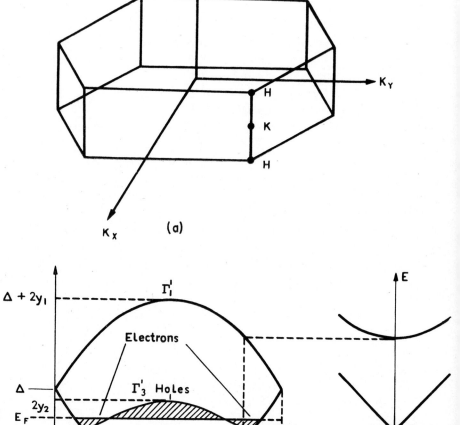

FIGURE 10   Energy band structure of graphite (three dimensional model,
after Simmons, 1965) (a) Brillouin zone. (b) Variation of energy along *HKH*:
$\xi = k_z C_0$. (c) Variation of energy in plane perpendicular to *HKH*: $\sigma = a_0 k$,
where k is the wave vector measured from a zone corner

in a reactor. They have also used the effect to compare damaging fluxes in different parts of a reactor, and also between different reactors.

The resistivity of polycrystalline graphite changes linearly with fast neutron dose up to about 10^{18} n° cm^{-2}. It then begins to saturate. The defects present under these conditions with temperatures of about 50°C are not the original displacement configuration. Although the vacancy in graphite is not thought to be mobile until ca. 1000°C the interstitial is believed to be able to migrate easily between the planes well below room temperature. Thus for room temperature or near one has the possibility of trapped interstitials, interstitial aggregates and only the postulated interstitial-vacancy repulsion potential prevents large amounts of interstitial-vacancy recombination.

In spite of the large amount of work on graphite one does not yet have unequivocal models for the defects present after a reactor irradiation at, say 30°C, nor of the processes involved in the Wigner energy release.

It is clear that interstitial carbon is mobile well below room temperature. This has several consequences:

i) interstitial aggregates can form, and even when nothing as drastic as dislocation loops have formed there still could be present di-interstitials and higher complexes;

ii) interstitials may be anchored by impurities, dislocations or grain boundaries;

iii) the vacancy concentration has to be substantially preserved to account for the high temperature stage which appears undoubtedly to be associated with vacancy motion. It is assumed, therefore, that there is a repulsive potential between vacancy and interstitial such that up to moderate temperatures (possible 100°C) separation is kinetically easier than recombination.

We have been studying the effects of electron irradiation at low temperatures to examine the effects of "simple" defects and the changes which occur on warming to room temperature. It is well known that several processes must occur because of the observation, first by Austerman and Hove (1955), of the reverse annealing peak as shown in Fig. II. Both Austerman and Hove (1955), and Lucas and Mitchell (1964) showed that no annealing effects on the resistivity were observed between 10 and 80°K.

A possible model for the effect was proposed by Reynolds and Goggin (1960). This model has been extensively used. According to the model electron irradiation produces separated Frenkel pairs and close Frenkel

pairs. It is assumed that the increase of resistivity in the first stage corresponds
to the separation of the pair, and that at a higher temperature the interstitials become freely mobile leading to di-interstitial formation and possibly
higher aggregates.

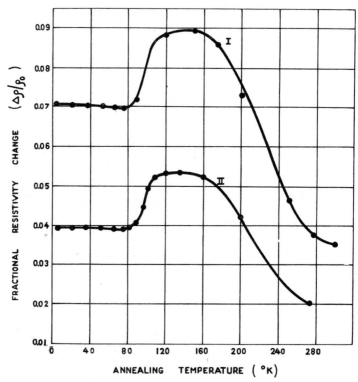

FIGURE 11   Pulse annealing of two graphite samples irradiated at liquid
helium temperature with 1.25 MeV electrons (resistivity measured at 4°K)

Davies and Mitchell (1969) have carried out a simple analysis of this
process and have shown that the peak height is related to the initial fraction
(f_{iv}) of close interstitial-vacancy pairs as follows:

$$H_A = \frac{\Delta\varrho_{Pk}}{\Delta\varrho_0} = \frac{1}{f_{iv}\dfrac{\varrho_{iv}}{\varrho_i + \varrho_v} + (1 - f_{iv})} \tag{1}$$

$$\text{or} \quad = \frac{1}{f_{iv}\eta_s + (1 - f_{iv})}$$

and that in the extreme case of $\eta_s \to 0$ the expression reduces to

$$H_A \text{ (limit)} = \frac{1}{1 - f_{iv}}. \tag{2}$$

It is easy to show that to account for a peak height of 1.5 commonly found in polycrystalline graphite f_{iv} has to be at least *0.3* and higher for value of $\eta \neq 0$. This being so we have calculated the fraction of close pairs by assuming that recoils within an energy x of E_d, the displacement energy remain as close pairs. Thus

$$f_{iv} = \frac{\displaystyle\int_{E_d}^{3E_d + x} N_p(E)\,dE}{\displaystyle\int_{E_d}^{E_{mx}} N_p(E)\,dE}$$

if only primary knock-ons have to be considered. (E_{mx} is the maximum knock-on recoil energy.) Including secondaries we write the following (Mitchell, 1964)

$$f_{iv} = \frac{\displaystyle\int_{E_d}^{E_d + x} N_p(E)\,dE + \int_{3E_d}^{3x_d \cdot x} N_p(E)\,\frac{E}{3E_d}\,dE}{\displaystyle\int_{E_d}^{3E_d} N_p(E)\,dE + \int_{3E_d}^{E_{mx}} N_p(E)\,\frac{E}{3E_d}\,dE}. \tag{3}$$

Some results for calculations using primaries only are shown in Fig. 12 for $E_d = 60$ eV and different values of x. In order to obtain a value of $f_{iv} = \frac{1}{3}$ at 2.0 MeV we require $x = 23$ eV ($E_d = 60$ eV) or $x = 13$ eV ($E_d = 30$ eV) and with these relatively large values of x we predict a large energy dependence of f_{iv} and consequently of the peak height. This conclusion is not significantly altered when we consider secondaries also.

We have measured the peak height as a function of energy in the range 0.4 to 2.0 MeV and it will be seen that the peak height is largely independent of energy, and in fact decreating slightly with decreasing energy at low energies (Fig. 13).

In considering this result we have come to the conclusion that there are a number of models which can be justified as plausibly as the Reynolds/ Goggin model. These are described in Table IV. They differ principally in

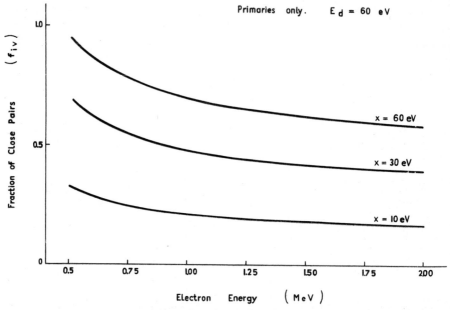

FIGURE 12　Calculated values of f_{iv} as a function of electron energy
for different values of E_d and x

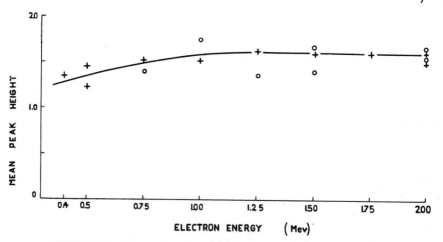

FIGURE 13　Reverse annealing peak height as a function of bombarding
electron energy

TABLE IV. Possible models for reverse annealing peak in electron-irradiated graphite

Model	Defects produced on irradiation $T_{irrad} \ll 85°K$	Stage α 80 — 130°K	Stage β 130 — 240°K
A INTRINSIC Close Frenkel pairs Interstitial mobile ~160°K	Close $i–v$ pairs Single vacancies Single interstitial	Separation of close $i–v$ pairs	Formation of di-interstitials
B INTRINSIC Close Frenkel pairs, di-interstitial Interstitial mobile ~85°K	Close $i–v$ pairs Single vacancies Single interstitials	Formation of more close pairs (di-interstitials)	eparation of close pairs, more di-interstitials
C IMPURITY Interstitial mobile ~160°K	Single vacancies Close $i–v$ pairs Single interstitials Trapped interstitials (impulse)	Separation of trap and interstitial	Separation of close pairs, formation of di-interstitials
D IMPURITY Interstitial mobile ~85°K	Single vacancies Close $i–v$ pairs Single interstitials Trapped interstitials (impulse)	Release of interstitial from traps → formation of di-interstitials and more close pairs	Separation of close pairs; formation of larger agregates of interstitials
E IMPURITY Interstitial mobile at $\ll 85°K$	Single vacancies Close $i–v$ pairs Trapped interstitials Di-interstitials	Release of trapped interstitials → more close pairs and di-interstitials	Separation of close pairs, formation of larger aggregates of interstitials

whether impurities are involved and in the activation energy of motion of the free interstitial. In the Reynolds/Goggin model (Model A in Table IV) the interstitial is free at temperatures ca. 160°K and according to the Davies and Mitchell (1965) analysis would have an activation energy of 0.45 eV. This is higher than all calculated values; 0.016 eV, Iwata *et al.* (1961); 0.14 Coulson *et al.* (1966). On the other hand, the calculated values depend sensitively on the potentials used and may not be sufficiently accurate to use as a method of distinguishing between the various models.

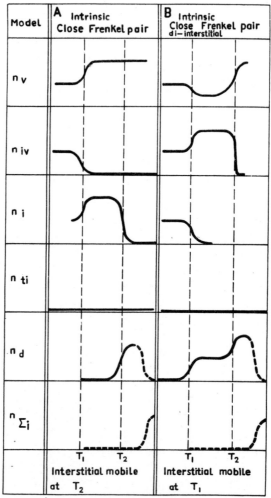

where n_x's are concentrations of each type of defect

$x \equiv v$ – vacancies   ti – trapped interstitials

iv – close Frenkel pairs   d – interstitials in di – forms

Σi – interstitials in aggregates

FIGURE 14   Diagrammatic plots of the variation of the concentration of different defects during an isochronal anneal for Models A and B

Comparison of models with experiment

The temperature variation of the concentration of various kinds of defect according to the models set out in Table is shown schematically in Figs. 14 and 15. It is clear from these diagrams which defect concentration/temperature curves correspond to a single reverse annealing peak and, therefore, which

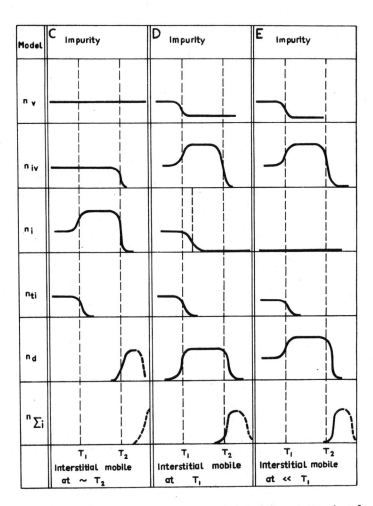

FIGURE 15 Diagrammatic plots of the variation of the concentration of different defects during an isochronal anneal for Models C, D and E

defect has to be assumed to have the major effect on the resistivity. Thus we have:

Intrinsic Model A	Single Interstitials
Intrinsic Model B	Close Frenkel pairs, with some contribution from di-interstitials.
Impurity Model C	Single Interstitials.
Impurity Model D	Close Frenkel pairs with some contribution from di-interstitials.
Impurity Model E	Either close Frenkel pairs or di-interstitials.

Defects in graphite may affect the resistivity by both trapping of carriers and by scattering and there is no experimental or theoretical work which provides any indication of the relative effectiveness of the defects listed above. However, we have isolated the nature of the defects necessary for different models and it is quite clear that the single interstitials (a) effectively postulated by Reynolds and Goggin (1960) is not the only plausible possibility.

We may now examine the models in relation to three experimental facts about the peak height in electron irradiated graphite:

a) The magnitude of the peak height is almost independent of electron energy except for a tendency to decrease slightly at lower energies;

b) It is independent of the electron dose up to at least 1.8×10^{18} e$^-$/cm^{-2};

c) The magnitude of the peak height is ~ 1.5.

The important parameters in the models are discussed from the point of view of energy dependence are f_{iv}, the initial fraction of close Frenkel pairs or f_{it} the initial fraction of trapped interstitials.

MODEL A.   Close Frenkel Pairs—Interstitial mobile—160°K.
If we consider the peak height of 1.5 at 2.0 MeV on model A (Reynolds and Goggin) we require $f_{iv} \geqq 0.33$ depending on the resistivity ratios. It is clear from Table V that to obtain this value we need

a) a fairly large value of x, at least 25 eV ($E_d = 60$ eV);

b) the consequent strong energy dependence of peak height which is contrary to the experimental results (see Fig. 16).

MODEL B. Close Frenkel Pairs/di-interstitials; Interstitial mobile −85°K. In model B the peak height is primarily related to the additional close Frenkel pairs which form during stage α. It can be shown that

$$H_B = 1 = \frac{f'_{iv}}{f_{iv}}$$

and although as noted we now can use a smaller value of f_{iv} to explain the observed peak height, the energy dependence of the peak height is still determined by the energy dependence of f_{iv}. Suppose that a fraction g of the interstitials form further close Frenkel pairs, then

$$H_B = 1 + \frac{g(1 - f_{iv})}{f_{iv}}$$

$$= (1 - g) + \frac{g}{f_{iv}}.$$

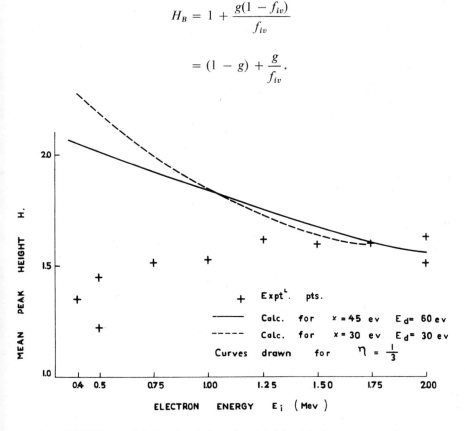

FIGURE 16   Calculated variation of peak height with electron energy for
Model A

19   Amelinckx (1347)

TABLE V. Calculated fraction f_{iv} of close pairs in electron-irradiated carbon (E_i is the energy of the incident electrons)

E_i / MeV \ x / eV	$E_d = 60$ eV					$E_d = 30$ eV				
	10	20	30	40	50	10	20	30	40	50
0.50	0.3200	0.5390	0.6920	0.8015	0.8820	0.4313	0.6766	0.8150	0.8995	0.9584
0.75	0.2648	0.4544	0.5780	0.6891	0.7590	0.3742	0.6005	0.7506	0.8556	0.9316
1.00	0.2351	0.4095	0.5430	0.6475	0.7306	0.3360	0.5447	0.6814	0.7910	0.8693
1.25	0.2134	0.3744	0.5000	0.6004	0.6823	0.3082	0.5023	0.6371	0.7368	0.8136
1.50	0.1968	0.3467	0.4649	0.5606	0.6394	0.2869	0.4691	0.5968	0.6922	0.7665
1.75	0.1837	0.3245	0.4362	0.5272	0.6029	0.2700	0.4423	0.5639	0.6552	0.7270
2.00	0.1731	0.3063	0.4124	0.4993	0.5719	0.2561	0.4203	0.5365	0.6243	0.2935

In this case the peak height would decrease as the electron energy decreased. The magnitude of this decrease will depend on the value of g; for $g = 0.12$ we require a value of $x = 10$ eV ($E_d = 60$ eV) to fit the observed result (Fig. 17). A higher value of g would enable a lower x value to be

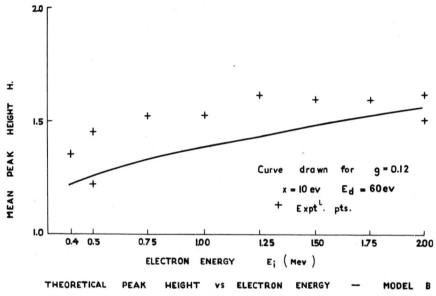

THEORETICAL PEAK HEIGHT vs ELECTRON ENERGY — MODEL B

FIGURE 17   Calculated variation of peak height with electron energy for Model B

employed, and give a smaller energy dependence. In this model di-interstitials could contribute to the peak height but if $\varrho_{iv} = \varrho_d$ one would not obtain a decrease in stage B.

Similar considerations apply to model D and to model E(i).

Although the simple claculations of close pair fractions may not be a colmpetely accurate description of the processes involved it does show that models of this kind can account at least qualitatively for the observed effects.

The Energy Dependence of f_{it}

We consider first models C and E(ii). In model C interstitials have become trapped as a result of impulse motion following the original collision. In order that the peak height shall not be dose dependent for electron doses up to

19*

$(\sim 1.8 \times 10^{18}$ e$^-$ cm^2) we have to assume that the trapping impurities are present to a concentration of ca. 10^{19} cm^{-1} (cf. <10 p.p.m. revealed by chemical analysis of chemically purified polycrystalline graphite). The average spacing between impurities therefore is ca. 50 Å so that we are interested in knock-ons having a range of ca. 20 Å. To explain the observed peak height at least 30% of all knock-ons have to have this average range at 2.0 MeV. This fraction must fall as one approaches the threshold and the peak height would be expected to fall away sharply. In making statements about average ranges we are ignoring the effects of long range correlated motion. This would seem only to be possible between the graphite planes and the fraction of all displaced atoms capable of such motion would be expected to be much less than that required to give $f_{iv} \geqq 30\%$.

MODEL E (iii)
This model also depends on the trapping of interstitials. They are assumed to be mobile at the temperature of irradiation and, therefore, f_{it} can be independent of energy. The important defect in this model is the di-interstitial and in the simple case when we neglect close Frenkel pairs:

$$H_E = 1 + \frac{f'_{id}}{f_{id}} = \frac{1}{f_{id}}.$$

We can explain an energy independent peak height by taking $f_{id} = 67\%$.

A further feature of this model is that one can build in a slight energy dependence which can be made closely to resemble the experimental situation where the peak height is not quite independent of energy at low energies. Suppose some close Frenkel pairs are formed initially, we are assuming that they do not affect the resistivity significantly but the energy dependence of their production affects the possible values of f_{it} and hence f'_{id}. This may be seen qualitatively in the calculation shown in Fig. 18 where initially $f_{it} = 1 - f_{iv}$, and at the top of the peak $f_d = (1 - f_{iv})$.

c Stored energy release
Mitchell and Taylor (1965) have recently questioned whether the origin of the 200°C energy release can be due to the rearrangement of interstitial atoms among themselves. In this Sec. I give the discussion presented by these authors including a brief account of their experiment.

As is well known for irradiations of low neutron doses the energy is released primarily in the 200°C peak in the warm-up curve, although there

is a tail to the curve extending to much higher temperatures. Samples irradiated to higher neutron doses, or at higher irradiation temperatures, release
relatively less energy in the 200°C peak, compared with the higher temperature region (Bridge *et al.*, 1962). The energy release has been related to
neutron dose and temperature systematically by Bell *et al.* (1962).

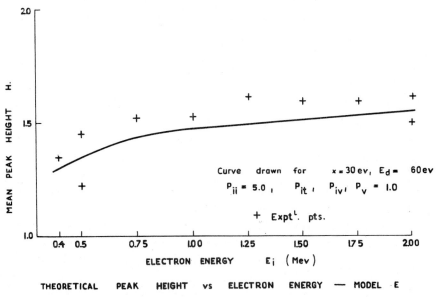

THEORETICAL PEAK HEIGHT vs ELECTRON ENERGY — MODEL E

FIGURE 18   Calculated variation of peak height with electron energy
for Model E (di-interstitial version, iii)

The origin of the 200°C peak has remained uncertain. Although there
had originally been suggestions that it arose from the recombination of
interstitial atoms and vacant sites (Kinchin, 1956; Neubert and Lees,
1957) more recently it has been generally considered that the energy was
associated with a re-arrangement of displaced atoms in which the vacancy
concentration was not significantly altered. The types of model which have
been considered may be illustrated by referring to those put forward by
Bollman (1963) and Iwata and Suzuki (1963). Bollman has suggested that
the process involves the recrystallization of small amorphous regions of up to
60 Å diameter which he assumes are produced by neutron irradiation.
According to Bollman, the recrystallized regions may contains some disloca-

tion dipoles, but the regions is considered to be of much lower energy than the amorphous region.

On the other hand, it has frequently been suggested that the stored energy is released when interstitial atoms re-arrange themselves between graphite planes into a lower energy configuration. In the Iwata-Suzuki (1963) model it is assumed that relatively loose aggregates of C_2 molecules have formed at about room temperature. These aggregates are assumed to produce the c-axis until cell expansion and to be loosely held together through the elastic strain, the electronic binding between the C_2 molecules being assumed to be small. At 200°C, Iwata and Suzuki suggest that this loose configuration is converted into the much more stable configuration of the tongue dislocation—not unlike Bollman's dislocation dipole—with a considerable relase of energy. Such a process would be accompanied by a recovery in unit cell expansion but the crystal would remain longer than before irradiation.

Each of these models possesses the feature that some disordered arrangement of carbon atoms is converted into a more or less perfect crystal without any interstitial-vacancy recombination occurring. Normal graphite has a relatively large interplanar spacing in the c-direction and the binding between planes is weak. We expect that the differences between elastic strain energies associated with various interstitial combinations will be small. Energy differences between different structures will then arise primarily from the electronic terms. These can be treated as more or less isolated from the rest of the crystal such that a two-dimensional perfect structure between the planes would have an energy not very different from a two-dimensional layer in the perfect crystal. We can therefore expect that the energy gain from the re-arrangement of the interstitials will be less than the energy required to dissociate graphite into free carbon atoms in their *tr.* $^3\pi$ graphite valence state. Accordingly, from such models the stored energy (S) will be expected to be less than the sum of the heat of sublimation (E_s) and the promotional energy (E_p):

$S < E_s + E_p = 7.44$ (Knight and Rink, 1958) $+ 6.93$ (Goldfarb and Taffe, 1959; Coulson *et al.*, 1963) eV

per atom involved in the ordering process, or $S <$ about 14–15 eV, there being uncertainty in E_p.

In order to decide by how much S is less than 14–15 eV on these models we have to specify the electronic state of the distributed interstitials before re-arrangement. If their electronic state were not *tr.*$^3\pi$ but tended more to the free atomic state ^3P, then S would tend to 7.44 eV ($E_p \rightarrow 0$). Similarly, if pairs resembling C_2 molecules between the planes are the starting point of the rearrangement we should expect $S \approx 7.44$–$3.03 \approx 4.4$ eV/atom, since 3.03 eV is the energy release per atom for the formation of C_2 from carbon atoms in ^3P states (Glocker, 1954). Thus, while precise values of S cannot be calculated without considerable difficulty fo different interstitial re-arrangement models, we can say with fair certainty that $S < 14$–15 eV and in a plausible case we find $S \sim 5$ eV.

The process of radiation damage by reactor irradiation is complex, and it has not been possible to determine accurately from the stored-energy measurements the amount of energy released per atom involved in the process. During the past three years we have been engaged on measuring the energy release in electron irradiated graphite. The objects have been, first, to determine whether the 200°C peak is present—we should not expect to see it if Bollman's hypothesis were correct because of the very much lower mean carbon recoil energy resulting from 2.0-MeV electron irradiation (mean recoil about 131 eV) compared with neutron irradiations (mean about 10^5 eV). Secondly, if the peak were found we should be able to determine the energy involved per original displacement event, the number of which can be calculated in an electron irradiation with much more certainty than in a reactor irradiation. The experiment has now been completed and in this article we give a preliminary account of the results.

Stored-energy determination

An adiabatic differential power method was used to measure the stored energy released on annealing between 20°C and 400°C. The principle of operation is similar to that of Clarebrough *et al.*, and to the linear-rise calorimeter of Henson and Mounsey. Two specimens, one irradiated, the other unirradiated, were mounted in a cavity which was heated at approximately 6°C/min. Individual heaters mounted axially in each specimen were used to maintain both specimens at the same temperature as the cavity. The difference in the power supplied to the two heaters was measured between 20°C and 400°C. After the initial run the calorimeter was allowed to cool, and then a second run was performed to establish the small power difference which was necessary in the absence of any stored-energy release. The stored-energy release was obtained by subtracting the power difference required in the second run from that required in the first run. Individual runs were reproducible to within ± 0.001 cal deg^{-1} g^{-1}. The performance of the apparatus was checked by carrying out an experiment in which some small pieces of copper were introduced into one of two unirradiated graphite samples. Full details of the method and the various procautions which have to be taken will be published later.

The specimens, which were of reactor grade *A* graphite, were irradiated with 2.0-MeV electrons from the University's Van de Graaff accelerator, two specimens at 95°C and the remainder at 65°C. The irradiation flux was 7.7 μamp cm^{-2} (4.9 × 10^{13} e$^-$ sec^{-1} cm^{-2}) and the specimens were irradiated in four directions, the maximum dose used being 1.87 × 10^5 μamp min cm^{-2} (7.0 × 10^{19} e$^-$ cm^{-2}) in each direction. This was done to ensure as uniform as possible a distribution of damage throughout the thick specimens. Five specimens, irradiated to the different doses shown in Table VI, have been measured.

TABLE V: Summary of results for electron-irradiated polycrystalline graphite

Electron dose (e$^-$ cm^{-2})	Concentration of displaced atoms ($E_d = 60$ eV) (cm^{-3})	Stored energy released between 20° and 400°C (cal g^{-1})	Stored energy released per incident 2 MeV electron eV per incident e$^-$	Stored energy release per original displacement eV per displacement
1.7 × 10^{19}	0.53 × 10^{19}	1.9 ± 0.2	3.4	15 ± 3*
3.4 × 10^{19}	0.07 × 10^{19}	2.4 ± 0.2	2.4	11 ± 2
		2.9 ± 0.25	2.9	13 ± 2
5.3 × 10^{19}	1.6 × 10^{19}	5.3 ± 0.1	3.1	14 ± 2
7.0 × 10^{19}	2.1 × 10^{19}	6.8 ± 0.1	3.1	14 ± 2

* These are the estimated overall uncertainties.

Calculation of the number of displacements

The concentration of displaced atoms has been determined using the cross sections computed by Mitchell and Salisbury (1963) for the displacement energy (E_d) of 60 eV indicated by the electrical resistivity measurements of Lucas and Mitchell (1964). The latter experiments showed that the displacement energy must be greater than the commonly assumed 25 eV and their analysis of the energy dependence of the resistivity changes indicated a value of 60 ± 10 eV. In using this cross-section (σ_s, column 20 of Table 1 of Mitchell, 1964) we have allowed for the production of displacements by the more energetic primary knock-ons (Lomer *et al.*, 1962; Snyder and

Neufeld, 1956; Kinchin and Pease, 1955). The energy-loss of the electrons in the specimens has been estimated from the range-energy relation as previously described by Clark *et al.* (1961). The results are shown in column 2 of Table 1; they correspond to the production in the present conditions of 0.30 displacements cm^{-3} per incident 2.0 MeV e^{-} cm^{-2}.

It has been suggested by Goggin and Reynolds (1963) that close interstitial-vacancy pairs have less effect on the electrical resistance than separated defects. If close pairs were preferentially produced at low energies in the Lucas and Mitchell experiment they would have the effect of making the estimate of $E_d = 60$ eV too high. Current calculations suggest that it would be unlikely that this effect could reduce the value to as low as 50 eV, the effect of which would be to increase the number of defects in the crystal above that calculated (0.30 cm^{-3}/e^{-} cm^{-2}) to at most 0.41.

This is one of the various sources of error considered, and their net effect is difficult to estimate precisely. The details of the discussion of errors will be included in the fuller publication. The conclusions is that 0.30 displacements cm^{-3}/e^{-} cm^{-2} is our best estimate (column 2) and that although the true value might be higher it is unlikely to be as high as 0.41.

Results and discussion

The results of the stored-energy measurements are given in column 3 of the Table in cal/g. Further methods of computing the stored energy in the 200°C peak from the results are being examined, and these may lead to some minor adjustments to the values given here. In subsequent columns the results are expressed as energy in eV per incident electron, and in eV per displaced atom. The slope of the best line of energy versus defect concentration gives a mean value of 13.5 eV per original displacement. (see Fig. 19.) (For a displacement energy of 50 eV we would obtain 9.9 eV per original displacement.) (Taylor (1968) quotes corrected values of 12.70 ± 0.86 eV and 9.55 ± 0.65 eV respectively.)

Thus from measurements on electron-irradiated specimens we find that: (*a*) there is an energy release peak at 200°C; (*b*) the total energy released in the peak is 3.0 eV per incident 2.0-MeV electron; and that, combining this result with the calculation of the number of displaced atoms, (*c*) using a displacement energy of 60 eV the energy released in the 200°C peak can be expressed as 13.5 eV per original displaced atom.

The observed energy release in electron-irradiated graphite cannot be explained by Bollman's mechanism. Furthermore, the value of 13.5 eV per displaced atom makes it improbable that the results can be explained by the aggregation of inters tial C_2 molecules for which we have argued that the energy release should be about 4–5 eV. Indeed, it seems impossible to account for the derived value of 13.5 eV per displaced atom without assuming the recombination of interstitial atoms and vacancies. In the following discussion we give reasons for assigning the value of 13.5 eV per displaced atom to interstitial-vacancy recombination.

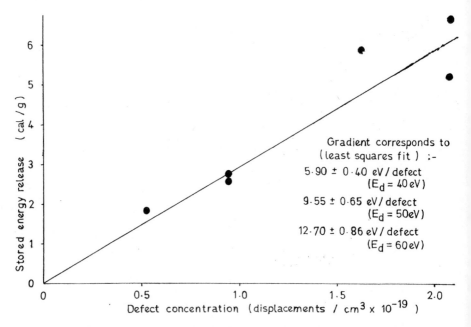

FIGURE 19   Stored energy released in electron-irradiated graphite between 70 and 370°C as a function of defect concentration ($E_d = 60\,\text{eV}$)

(1) Lidiard and Perrin (1965) have shown in their analysis of the kinetics of the dimensional changes in neutron-irradiated graphite that recombination has to be taken into account at 150°C.

(2) Using the same cross-sections as those used in calculating the concentrations given in column 2, we find that for the flux used in our experiments of $4.9 \times 10^{13}\ e^- \text{cm}^{-2}\ \text{sec}^{-1}$ we produce 1.5×10^{13} displacements $\text{cm}^{-3}\ \text{sec}^{-1}$. It is generally agreed that interstitial migration occurs between atomic layers in graphite with little diffusion across the layers. In the ex-

periments recorded here, therefore, we expect that displacements were produced at the rate of 5.1×10^5 per cm^2 per interatomic layer per sec.

(3) A single interstitial will diffuse rapidly at $338°K$ and, using the activation energy of 0.45 eV determined recently by Davies and Mitchell (1965) from their detailed analysis of the reverse annealing peak, we find that an interstitial will jump at the rate of 2.0×10^6 per sec (assuming a frequency factor of 10^{13} sec^{-1}). For the lower activation energy derived theoretically (Iwata and Suzuki, 1963) we should get an even higher jump frequency.

(4) In electron-irradiated polycrystalline graphite in which the displacements are produced primarily as single interstitial-vacancy pairs, we now consider the obstacles to interstitial aggregation. The most likely obstacles are the grain boundaries the separation of which is about 10^3 Å. In fact, it has often been assumed (for example, Goggin and Reynolds, 1963) that interstitials cannot pass through a grain boundary for temperatures of about room temperature and below. The grains define an interlayer volume of 3.4×10^{-18} cm^3 and an average number of jumps of about 10^5 for an interstitial produced in this volume to reach a boundary.

(5) For an interstitial diffusing with a jump rate of 2×10^6 sec^{-1} the vicinity of a grain boundary would be reached after 5×10^{-2} sec. This is very much shorter than the time interval between the production of interstitials in the interlayer volume by the irradiation, given by $(5.1 \times 10^5 \times 10^{-10})^{-1}$ or 2×10^4 sec.

Thus in the case of electron irradiation, defects are not produced sufficiently rapidly, within a mutually accessible volume, for diffusive interstitial aggregation to occur. We consider that the interstitials are most likely to be trapped in the vicinity of grain boundaries. Other obstacles or trapping points may be operative and similar conclusions could be drawn for dislocation trapping and impurity trapping (reactor grade A graphite may contain up to 50 p.p.m. of some impurities).

We propose, therefore, that during our irradiation at $65°C$ interstitial atoms become trapped singly in the vicinity of one or more of the obstacles and that interstitial-vacancy recombination does not occur at $65°C$. In the region of the $200°C$ peak we suggest that these trapped atoms are released and that, predominantly, recombination occurs. This is expected because initially the number of accessible vacancies will be greater than the number of free interstitials. Undoubtedly a small amount of interstitial aggregation could occur. The activation energies involved in the process (a spread of about 0.2 eV around 1.38 eV from our measurements) corresponds to the spectrum of interstitial obstacle binding energies. Our conclusion is that the 13.5 eV per atom derived from our experiment corresponds to the energy associated with interstitialvacancy recombination in graphite. From the difference between the detrapping activation energy (1.38 eV) and the interstitial migration energy (0.45 eV) we estimate that the energy to form a Frenkel pair in graphite is (13.5 + 0.93) ≈ 14.4 eV. (For a displacement energy of 50 eV we would find the formation energy to be 10.8 eV.)

It is interesting to note that Coulson *et al.* (1963) calculated the formation energy of a Schottky defect, in which the ejected atom is on the surface, in graphite to be 10.7 eV. If the atom had been put in an interstitial position the energy of formation would have been higher. Thus, although we should not over-emphasize the agreement, it is encouraging that the value we obtain for the stored-energy release per interstitial vacancy recombination is consistent with Coulson's calculation.

The mechanism described here does not affect the explanation put forward by Goggin and Reynolds (1963) of the reverse annealing peak which is found after electron irradiation below $80°K$. In this case the interstitial atoms are immobile at the temperature of irradiation so that the interplanar concentration of interstitials may grow. When the interstitials become mobile simple aggregates may be formed.

Finally, we comment on the significance of our conclusion to the interpretation of the stored-energy release in the $200°C$ peak in neutron-irradiated graphite. For three low-dose neutron irradiations up to 2.5×10^{18} fast $n°$ cm^{-2} Ni scale we have measured the release of stored energy in our apparatus and find, for example, 21.5 cal g^{-1} at a dose of 2.5×10^{18}, and a mean of 0.9 cal g^{-1} per 10^{17} fast $n°$ cm^{-2} (see Fig. 20 for the results of Taylor, 1968) Åström (1961) reported 5.3 cal g^{-1} for a thermal dose of 3.8×10^{18} and an estimated fast dose of 3.8×10^{17} (1.4 cal g^{-1} per 10^{17} fast $n°$). We cannot be certain about the comparability of the fast dose estimate, and in view of this the two measurements are in reasonable agreement. For our experiment and using the damage function of Thompson and Wright (1964) we find that the energy release corresponds to about 2 eV per displaced atom. In the reactor irradiation we expect the energy per displaced atom to be less than the value of 14 eV per interstitial-vacancy recombination discussed already because: (1) some multiple interstitial groups are expected to be produced directly by the irradiation; (2) the higher effective damage flux means that there is a much greater chance of interstitial aggregates forming by diffusion. (This is the basis of the homogeneous theory for the nucleation of dislocation loops used by Reynolds and Thrower (1963) to account for the observed rates of growth in high neutron fluxes.)

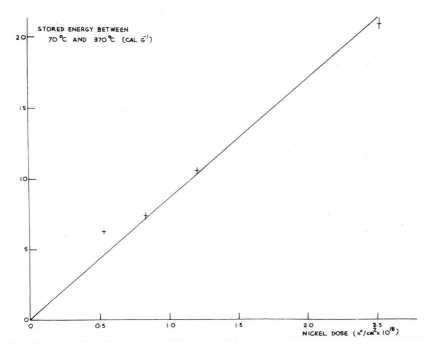

FIGURE 20   Stored energy released in neutron-irradiated graphite between 70 and 370°C as a function of neutron dose

Both these factors mean that, relative to the total number of interstitials produced, fewer single interstitials will be trapped by obstacles. Thus only a fraction of the interstitials will be a source of stored energy when they are released in the 200°C peak. Furthermore, continuing re-arrangements of the various interstitial aggregates would yield some stored-energy release on the high-temperature side of the peak. At the highest neutron fluxes the fraction of trapped single interstitials will become progressively smaller and the stored-energy release at 200°C will become a relatively smaller part of the whole.

Conclusions

The stored-energy release in electron-irradiated graphite corresponds to 13.5 eV per displaced atom. The major uncertainty in this value comes from the calculation of the defect concentration which may be too low.

It is shown that, for the electron-beam currents used, an interstitial atom moving between graphite layers could be trapped by grain boundaries, dislocations or impurities long before the production of the next interstitial by the electron in the appropriate volume (for example, interatomic layer in a crystallite). Thus interstitial aggregates will not accumulate and we interpret the measured stored-energy release in the 200°C peak as the recombination of interstitial atoms and vacancies, the interstitials being freed with a range of activation energies around 1.4 eV.

In reactor-irradiated graphite we expect that relatively fewer interstitials are trapped in this way, other interstitial formations occurring because of the higher recoil energies involved and the much higher effective damaging flux. Thus, although the same process of interstitial-vacancy recombination is assumed to be the major contribution to the stored-energy release at 200°C, the energy involved per original displacement is considerably less. This will be true particularly at high fluxes, and the fraction of the total stored energy released in the peak will become progressively smaller as irradiation flux and temperature are increased.

The proposed model therefore accounts for the qualitative features of the energy release in reactor-irradiated graphite. The value of about 14 eV per interstitial-vacancy recombination deduced from electron-irradiated graphite is consistent with the vacancy formation energy of 10.7 eV calculated by Coulson *et al.* (1963). In the latter case the ejected atom has been put on the surface and the defect formation energy would be higher if the ejected atom remained in an interstitial position.

V BORON DOPANT ENHANCED DAMAGE IN SILICON

Clark and Thompson (1969) have recently studied the effects of reactor irradiation at 80°K on the Hall constant and electrical conductivity in silicon. The irradiations were carried out in the Science Research Council cryostats in HERALD at Aldermaston. Samples were transferred to a storage Dewar by a small bucket filled with liquid nitrogen. They were subsequently mounted in a specialy designed measuring cell, which allowed them to be

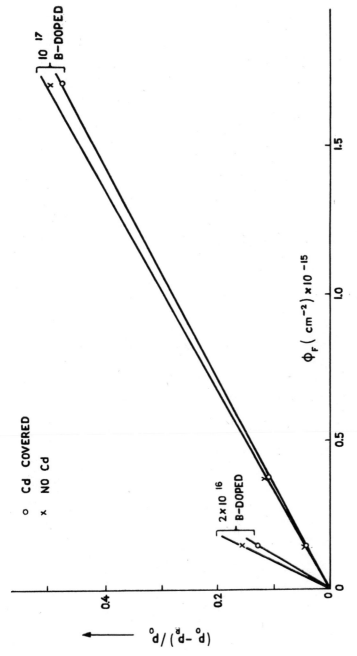

FIGURE 21 Fractional change of carrier concentration with fast neutron dose for 2×10^{16} and 10^{17} boron doped silicon

mounted under liquid nitrogen. During operation the sample was cooled by a liquid nitrogen filled reentrant cavity. Pulse annealing could be carried out up to room temperature.

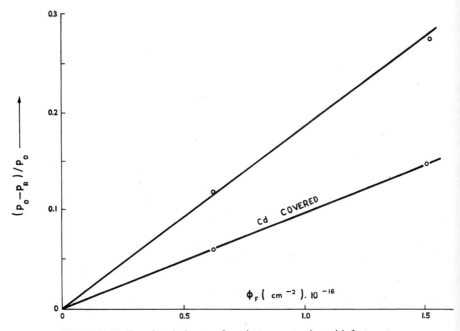

FIGURE 22   Fractional change of carrier concentration with fast neutron
dose for 3×10^{18} boron doped silicon

The results, which might be of interest to this School are shown for boron doped silicon in Figs. 21 and 22. Experimental points are shown for sets of samples covered in cadmium foil (eliminating 95% of thermal neutrons) and for sets uncovered. It will be seen that the fractional change in carrier concentration is lower for the covered material and the difference represents the effect of thermal neutrons on the properties of boron doped silicon. No such difference was observed between cadmium covered and uncovered phosphorus doped n-type material. This also shows that the thermal neutron reaction with silicon $(n\alpha)$ does not contribute a significant part of the damage.

Clark and Thompson (1969) have calculated the effect of thermal neutrons on the samples arising from the $B^{10}(n\alpha) Li^7$ reaction. Although B^{10} is only

18.8 % abundant its cross-section is high (4090 b) and there is a large energy release of 1.02 MeV for the Li^7 and 1.78 MeV for the α-particle. They have applied the Thompson and Wright (1964) method to these conditions and determined the total number of displacements produced by the Li^7, He^4 and the Si knock-ons. The details of these calculations are being prepared for publication.

The result they find is that the number (cm^{-3}) of displacements N_d is

$$N_d = 3.1 N_B \phi_T 10^{-18} \tag{4}$$

where N_B is the boron concentration and ϕ_T the thermal flux. Using the Thompson and Wright method on the fast neutron damage it is found that

$$N_d \text{ (fast)} = 19.1 \phi_F \tag{5}$$

where ϕ_F is the fast (>1 KeV) flux. Experimental results may be expressed as

$$y = \frac{\left(\dfrac{\Delta P}{P_0}\right)_T}{\left(\dfrac{\Delta P}{P_0}\right)_F + \left(\dfrac{\Delta P}{P_0}\right)_T}$$

and compared with calculated values of

$$\frac{N_D(Th)}{N_D(\text{fast}) + N_D(Th)} .$$

The experimental values are:

N_B	y
2.3×10^{16}	$17(\pm 2)\%$
1.2×10^{17}	$4.6(\pm 1)\%$
3×10^{18}	$48(\pm 3)\%$

The theoretical values are in very good agreement (within the limits of experimental error) for the two higher boron concentrations. For the lowest boron concentration the experimental value is approximately $8\times$ the calculated value. In the higher concentration samples the carrier removal rate (C.R.R.) was linear with dose and the Fermi level below the boron acceptor. For the 2×10^{16} cm^{-3} boron concentration the C.R.R. was not linear and this may account for the discrepancy.

20   Amelinckx (1347)

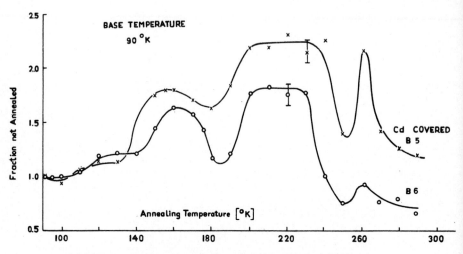

FIGURE 23   Isochronal annealing of carrier concentration in two *p*-type
silicon samples, cadmium covered (B5) and unshielded (B6)

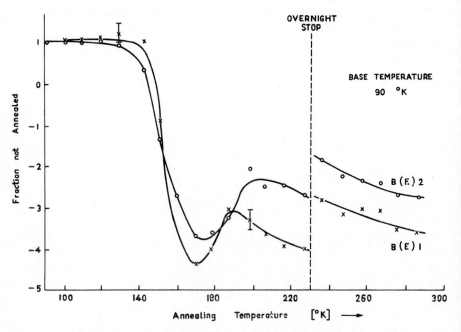

FIGURE 24   Isochronal annealing of carrier concentration in two electron-irradiated samples of *p*-type silicon

It is also interesting to note that the $B^{10}(n\alpha)$ Li^7 reaction also affects the pulse annealing curve, with the 270°K annealing peak being considerably reduced (Fig. 23). We do not have an explanation for this effect at present, nor for the remarkable effect shown in the annealing of electron irradiated silicon (Fig. 24). Here there is a strong annealing stage in *p*-type silicon at ca. 150°K which leads to a conductivity and carrier concentration greater than in the unirradiated crystals.

VI ELECTRONIC INFLUENCES ON THE STABILITY OF DEFECTS IN GERMANIUM

a General

It is well known that the covalent semiconductors are very sensitive to the presence of defects and also consequently as detectors of radiation capable of producing displacements. To get some idea of the orders of magnitude consider germanium, which in a particular electron irradiation experiment to be described below, gave a carrier removal rate (C.R.R.) of 2.6 e⁻ cm⁻³/ 2 MeV e⁻ cm⁻². Excluding the possibility of double trapping, the defect production rate must have been $\gtrsim 2.6$ defects cm⁻³/e⁻ cm⁻². Doses were in the range 10^{13}–10^{14} e⁻ cm⁻² and we were, therefore, studying fractions of defects as low as

$$\frac{2.6 \times 10^{13}}{4.5 \times 10^{22}} \sim 6 \times 10^{-10} \; \underline{\hspace{2cm}}.$$

This is of great interest when studying the properties of defects but this sensitivity to displacements is a disadvantage when utilizing germanium or silicon for detecting ionizing radiation by the electron (photo) voltaic effect in a space charge barrier as in particle counters.

Physically one is again interested in the nature of the defects giving rise to the damage. For concentrations as low as that quoted above and if the radiation induced defects are mobile, defect/impurity complexes will form since impurities probably greater than 10^{14} cm⁻³ are present even when the specific doping impurities have been eliminated. This leads us to want to know about the stability and mobility of defects in covalent semiconductors like germanium and silicon.

The energy of self-diffusion (E_{SD}) in germanium is about 3 eV and the mechanism of diffusion is believed to be by vacancy motion. An acceptor level is quenched in with a formation energy (E_F) of 2 eV and anneals with

20*

an activation energy of about 1 eV. It appears that this acceptor is associated with the vacancy and that the energy of motion (E_m) of the vacancy is about 1 eV. ($E_{SD} = E_F + E_m$). The vacancy, therefore, is only likely to take place in processes around room temperature or above. Thus if n-type germanium is irradiated at 80°K no annealing occurs until $T > 300$°K. Then several stages appear with activation energies in the range 0.8–1.4 eV and are attributed to vacancy motion and to vacancy/impurity complex motion. Similar experiments on p-type germanium show that the annealing stages are sensitive to the Fermi level, and presumably, therefore, on the charge state of some defect or complex.

In order to avoid the effects of the association of defects with impurities one should irradiate at low temperatures when the defects are not mobile. While as indicated above 80°K may be sufficient to inhibit motion of vacancies it is necessary to go to 5–10°K to eliminate other processes.

The first irradiations in this temperature range on germanium were by McKay and Klontz (1962) who reported the remarkable result that while for 1 MeV electron irradiation they observed a C.R.R. in n-type of 2/cm, in p-type the C.R.R. was <0.1/cm. For doses up to about 10^{16} e⁻ cm⁻² the annealing started at about 60°K. (At higher doses there was a further stage at 35°K which was attributed to some modification of the defects produced at lower doses having different annealing characteristics).

The possibility that the defects were present in the p-type material but were electrically inactive was eliminated by very careful stored energy measurements. Stored energy measurements in the range 15–80°K showed an energy release at 60°K in low dose n-type samples but nothing in p-type. It was concluded, therefore, that irradiation at about 10°K produced defects—stable up to 60°K—in n-type but not in p-type. Thus one is led to the idea that the charge state affects the stability of a defect.

We have to ask, therefore, what is the nature of the defect in n-type germanium and the 60°K annealing stage, a defect which while electrically active in n-type must either be absent or in a charge state which renders it *both* inactive and immobile in p-type.

An early experiment of McKay and Klontz (1962) showed evidence of an electronic effect. Following irradiation at 1.1 MeV, when carriers were removed as described above, they irradiated at 0.3 MeV when the defect production rate would be expected to be considerably smaller. Instead of observing a much smaller carrier *removal* rate, however, the carrier concentration increased with the 0.3 MeV irradiation. They concluded that because of the higher *ionizing* power of the lower energy irradiation defects which previously were stable were now no longer so. In particular, they suggest that during fast electron irradiation a fraction of the defects is in the form of close Frenkel pairs. They further suggest that there is an attractive potential between the components of the pair such that "normally" they rapidly recombine. If the close interstitial-vacancy pair captures an electron, however, the potential is rendered less attractive and there is a much higher barrier to recombination (Fig. 25).

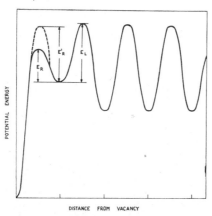

FIGURE 25   Model representing the potential energy an interstitial may have for sites it can occupy near the vacancy. Nearest the vacancy is the metastable site associated with the primary defect. When occupied by an interstitial which has trapped an electron the barrier to recombination is E_R'. Release of the trapped electron reduces the barrier to E_R'. Deeper minima further from the vacancy are stable positions for the interstitial

Such a defect would have the observed characteristics of being present in *n*-type, but not in *p*-type. Furthermore, in the presence of intensely ionizing radiation the concentration of such defects would be expected to drop. Following this McKay and Klontz considered that the 60°K annealing stage corresponds to the thermal activation of the trapped electrons, after which the defects would be separated by the much lower barrier allowing easy recombination.

b   Stability of the defect in the presence of light

If the explanation proposed by McKay and Klontz (1962) is correct then the defect should be unstable on illumination with low energy light. This effect was examined by Ishino and Mitchell (1966) who studied the annealing characteristics in the presence of infrared light whose photon energy was less than the band gap (thereby not causing band to band ionization).

Antimony doped materials were used, *Sb-M*, $\varrho_{RT} = 1–2$ Ωcm and *Sb-H*, $\varrho_{RT} = 25$ Ωcm. Electrical measurements could be made down to

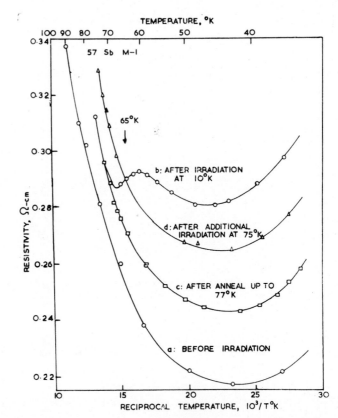

FIGURE 26 The results of warm-up runs for a lower resistivity germanium sample showing the annealing which occurs in the dark (from Ishino and Mitchell, 1966)

7°K and the samples could be irradiated through thin aluminium windows, or by rotating an external collar, could be illuminated from a tungsten lamp through a germanium filter. Annealing of the effects of 2.0 MeV electron irradiation was studied by the three curve warm-up technique for which results are shown in Fig. 26, 27 and 28.

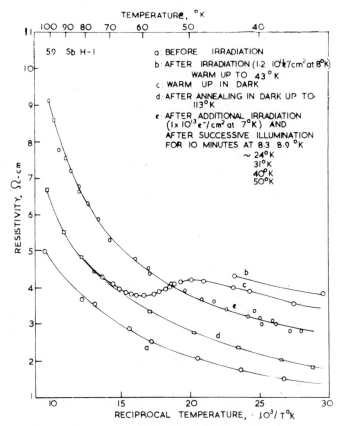

FIGURE 27 The results of warm-up runs for a higher resistivity germanium sample (from Ishino and Mitchell, 1966)

i *Temperature dependence of Hall coefficient and resistivity before and after irradiation and after annealing*

Since the samples used in the experiments were not degenerate, the Hall coefficient and the resistivity have a strong temperature dependence, especially below 25°K. Therefore, a fixed reference temperature could not be used for the measurements. Instead, the variation of resistivity and Hall coefficients was measured as a function of temperature in the temperature range below each annealing temperature. If there are no annealing stages, the resistivity and the Hall coefficient curves should coincide with those obtained before the warm-up. In this way, we found that the annealing around 60°K is the only annealing stage between 7 and 80°K. In these experiments, typical electron doses were of the order of 10^{13} electrons/cm² for *Sb-H* and of 10^{14} electrons/cm² for *Sb-M* samples.

In many of the samples, it was found that the resistivity after the 60°K annealing almost coincides with that before annealing (after irradiation) in

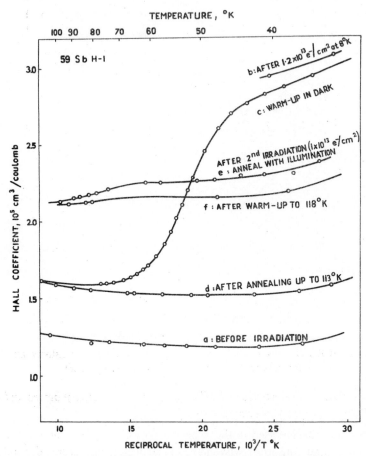

FIGURE 28   Temperature dependence of the Hall coefficient of the sample
as in Fig. 27 (from Ishino and Mitchell, 1966)

the temperature range below 10°K. This might be caused by introduction of an acceptor level near the chemical donor level during the 60°K annealing or by a change in the degree of compensation, bu the measurements below 10°K were not sufficiently accurate to comment in more detail on this point.

ii Annealing in dark

As mentioned in the previous section, no annealing was observed until the sample was warmed up to about 60°K.

Two Sb-M and two Sb-H samples were irradiated at temperatures near to 10°K and the resistivity and the Hall coefficient were measured as a function of temperature and time during warming up to liquid nitrogen temperature. An interesting difference in annealing temperature in the two kinds of samples was found.

Figure 26 shows the temperature dependence of resistivity in one of the Sb-M samples. The curve (a) was obtained before irradiation. After irradiation with 6.3×10^{13} electrons/cm² at about 10°K, the sample was allowed to warm up slowly to liquid nitrogen temperature. Curve (b) obtained during this warming up, shows that the centre of the annealing stage is 65°K. After keeping the sample at liquid nitrogen temperature for about 8 hours, the temperature dependence of resistivity was as shown in curve (c). From this curve it is obvious that the step on the curve (b) around 65°K is caused by removal of the defect rather than by a change in charge state of a defect. Curve (d) was obtained after an additional irradiation of a similar amount (6.9×10^{13} electrons/cm²) at 70°K.

Figure 27 shows a similar set of curves obtained with one of Sb-H samples. Hall coefficient data obtained in the same sample are given in Fig. 28. It is clearly seen that the annealing takes place at much lower temperature than in the Sb-M sample. The centre of the annealing stage in the case of Figs. 27 and 28 is 55°K. In this sort of experiment, the rate of warming up is obviously important. In order to confirm that the difference in annealing temperature described above is due to the difference in the doping levels, two samples 58Sb-M-6 and 58Sb-H-3, were warmed up at almost the same rates. The central temperatures of the annealing stage were 66.7 and 60.6°K in 58Sb-M-6 and 58Sb-H-3 respectively. In this case the effect of heating rate on the temperature of the annealing stage is eliminated and the observed change must arise from the difference of doping level.

iii The effect of infrared illumination on annealing

According to McKay and Klontz (1963) the defects responsible for the 60°K annealing stage become metastable when electrons are trapped being otherwise unstable. The annealing process is governed by the thermal release of these electrons. If this model is correct, it is of interest to study

Solid state dosimetry

the annealing when the trapped electron is excited by illuminating the crystal with infrared light. The effect of infrared illumination was examined on several samples. The illumination was carried out by using an ordinary 30 watt tungsten lamp at about 4 cm from the specimen. The light was incident on the sample through a thick germanium filter and a thin polyethylene film. During illumination, the sample temperature was controlled by adjusting the vacuum in the thermal switch chamber—a stainless steel can connecting the helium reservoir with the sample chamber—and by applying a heater current so that the sample temperature did not change significantly.

Figure 29 shows a result obtained using one of Sb-H samples. Curve (a) represents the resistivity before irradiation*. The sample was irradiated

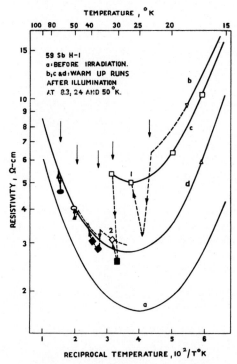

FIGURE 29   The effect of warm-up runs for a higher resistivity sample showing the effect of infrared illumination

---

* This curve refers to the resistivity before the second irradiation of the sample which had previously been irradiated to 1.2×10^{13} electrons/cm² followed by annealing to 113 °K. The curve is the same as curve (d) in Fig. 27.

with 1×10^{13} electrons/cm^2 at 7°K and was illuminated at 8.3°K for ten minutes. No annealing was observed. Then the sample was allowed to warm up to about 24°K, Hall and resistivity measurements being made [curve (b)]. The second illumination was carried out at 24.0–26.5°K forten minutes. The point indicated by an inverse full triangle shows the resistivity measured during illumination. After illumination the sample was cooled down to 9.4°K and then warmed up to 32°K [curve (c)]. The third illumination was performed at 31–32°K for ten minutes. A substantial change was induced by the third illumination. Similarly, ten minute illuminations were further carried out at 40, 50 and 72°K. After the annealings with illumination were completed, the temperature dependence of resistivity was as shown in curve (d). It should be noticed that with infrared illumination the annealing takes place at much lower temperature than it does in the dark. One can completely eliminate the 60°K annealing stage by illumination at lower temperatures.

iv *Defect introduction*

In several samples, Hall coefficient data before irradiation, after irradiation at low temperature and after annealing up to liquid nitrogen temperature are all available. If the defect responsible for the 60°K annealing is called a "primary defect" and if one electron is removed per one primary defect, a cross-section for the production of the primary defect as well as a total cross-section for the carrier removal can be calculated.

In Table VII, these cross-sections are tabulated. They were obtained from the Hall data at 40°K. Although the dose measurements in these runs were not made to better than 10%, the calculated cross-section values are in reasonable agreement with each other. The macroscopic cross-section is defined by $N\sigma_d$ where σ_d is the microscopic cross-section and N the number of atoms per unit volume. From simple displacement theory the micro- and macroscopic cross-section for producing primary displacements are 61×10^{-24} cm^2, 2.7 cm^{-1} and 45×10^{-24} cm^2, 2.0 cm^{-1} for the displacement energies of 25 eV and 31 eV, respectively at an electron energy of 2 MeV.

The temperature dependence of the carrier removal rate is also of interest. Figure 30 shows the reduction of conductivity after successive irradiations at various temperatures. The data were extrapolated to 50°K and the rate of change in conductivity per unit amount of irradiation was calculated for the various irradiation temperatures. These values are plotted in Fig. 31. Unfortunately, the Hall coefficient was not measured in this sample, so that one could not obtain the carrier removal rate from this

TABLE VII. Calculation of macroscopic cross-sections from Hall data at 40°K

Sample	Irradiation temperature (°K)	Carrier concentration (cm^{-3})			Δn Total carrier removal (cm^{-3})	Δn^2 Permanent defect (cm^{-3})	Δn_1 Primary defect (cm^{-3})	ϕ Dose $10^{13}\dfrac{e}{cm^2}$	Macroscopic cross section (cm^{-1})	
		before irradiation	after irradiation	after annealing					total $\Delta n/\phi$	primary defect $\Delta n_1/\phi$
58Sb-M-3	11	2.13×10^{15}	1.64×10^{15}	1.84×10^{15}	4.9×10^{14}	2.9×10^{14}	2.0×10^{14}	15	3.3	1.3
58Sb-M-6	11.5	1.09×10^{15}	7.69×10^{14}	9.0×10^{14}	3.2×10^{14}	1.0×10^{14}	1.3×10^{14}	14	2.3	0.93
58Sb-H-3	17	5.14×10^{13}	3.30×10^{13}	4.38×10^{13}	1.84×10^{13}	7.6×10^{12}	1.08×10^{13}	1.0	1.84	1.1
58Sb-H-1	8	5.25×10^{13}	2.11×10^{13}	4.07×10^{13}	3.14×10^{13}	1.18×10^{13}	1.96×10^{13}	1.2	2.62	1.63
								Average	2.6 ± 0.8	1.3 ± 0.4

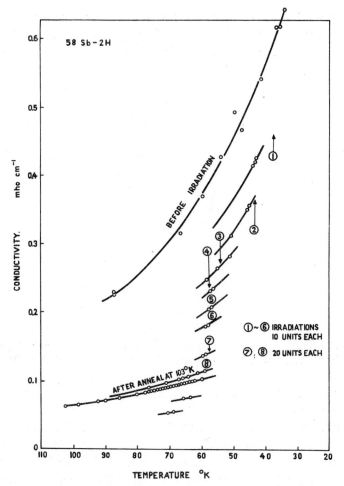

FIGURE 30 Temperature dependence of conductivity before irradiation and after successive irradiations at various temperatures (from Ishino and Mitchell, 1966)

measurement. However, is is clearly shown that the rate of change in conductivity decreases rapidly around 40°K with increasing irradiation temperature and becomes nearly constant above about 50°K.

DISCUSSION

As mentioned earlier MacKay and Klontz (1963) have proposed the model that the 65°K annealing stage is of a primary defect and that the defect is stabilised by trapping an electron. They also suggested that the annealing mechanism is limited by the thermal detrapping of the trapped electron (1963). All of the present experimental results seem to support this proposed mechanism.

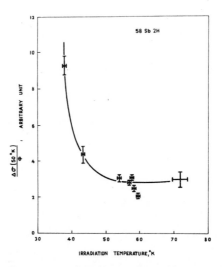

FIGURE 31   Temperature dependence of rate of change of conductivity by irradiation with 2 MeV electrons (from Ishino and Mitchell, 1966)

a) First, we shall consider the result of doping level dependence of annealing temperature.

According to MacKay and Klontz (1963) the depth of the trapping level is estimated to be 0.1 eV from the bottom of the conduction band based on the assumption that the 65°K annealing is partially limited by the rate of excitation of the trapped electron from the defect state. It is, therefore, expected that the higher resistivity samples will have lower annealing temperatures than the lower resistivity samples, because the Fermi level lies deeper in the higher resistivity samples at the same temperature. This is exactly the case of our experiment. The Fermi level of Sb-M samples at 65°K, i.e. at the central annealing temperature, is at 0.04 eV from the conduction band edge, whereas in Sb-H samples it is about 0.05 eV from the conduction band edge at about 55–60°K. If it is considered that the occupation of a given energy level is appreciably affected if the Fermi level comes within about 2 kT of the level, the acceptor level in question would be situated about 0.06 eV from the conduction band. The possibility will be discussed later that the rate of annealing of the defect may be limited by the lifetime of the defect when no electrons are trapped.

b) Secondly, we shall discuss the effect of infrared illumination.

The fact that the "optical bleaching" is observed seems to provide the most direct evidence of the validity of the MacKay-Klontz mechanism because, if the annealing is due to the excitation of the trapped electron by thermal means, the same phenomenon should occur when the electron is excited by other means, i.e. by optical means.

The experiment may also be used to give some quantitative information about the barrier height when no electrons are trapped (E_R) which can be estimated by the equation:

$$E_R = -kT \ln \frac{n_j}{\nu_0 t},$$

where n_j, the necessary number of jumps for the annealing to occur, which is assumed to be 1, ν_0 the vibrational frequency of the order of 10^{13}/sec, t, the annealing time and k and T have their usual meanings. In the present experiment, annealing took place effectively at 30°K with illumination. This implies that E_R should be of the order of 0.08 eV, based on the assumption, that about half of the total anneal proceeds during illumination for 10^3 sec at 25°K. In this calculation we also assumed that the infrared illumination is sufficiently intense so that the rate of annealing is determined by overcoming the barrier E_R, and not by an excitation rate of the trapped electron.

The present experiments give some insight to the mechanism of annealing at low temperature and show that charge occupancy affects the stability of the defect.

References

Astrom, H. U., 1961, *Ark. Fys.* **20**, 10, 161.

Austerman, S. B., Hove, J. E., 1955, *Phys. Rev.* **100**, 1214.

Banyai, L., 1964, *Int. Conf. on the Physics of Semiconductors.* Vol. 1, p. 417 (Dunod Paris, 1964).

Bell, J. C., Bridge, H., Cottrell, A. H., Greenough, G. B., Reynolds, W. N., Simmons, J. H. W., 1962. *Phil. Trans. Roy. Soc.* A. **254**, 361.

Bollman, W., 1963, *Proc. Fifth Carbon Con.* **2**, 303 (Pergamon Press, Oxford 1963).

Bridge, H., Kelly, B. T., Gray, B. S., 1962, *Proc. Fifth Carbon Con.* **1**, 289 (Pergamon Press, Oxford).

Clark, C. D., Kemmey, P. J., Mitchell, E. W. J., 1961, *Disc. Faraday Soc.* No. 31, 96.

Clark, C. D., Thompson, D. A., 1969a, To be published. 1969b to be published.

Clarebrough, L. M., Hargreaves, M. E., Michell, D., West, G. W., 1952, *Proc. Roy. Soc.* A. **215**, 507.

Coulson, C. A., Herraex, M. A., Leal, M., Santos, E., Senent, S. 1963. *Proc. Roy. Soc.* A. **274**, 461.

Coulson, C. A., Senent, S., Herraex, M. A., Leal, M., Santos, E., 1966. *Carbon*, **3**, 445.

Davis, C. B., Mitchell, E. W. J., 1965, Unpublished report.

Davies, C. B., Mitchell, E. W. J., 1969, *Phil. Mag.* **19**, 57.

Dearnaley, G., Northrop, D. C., 1966. *Semiconductor Counter Nuclear Radiations* (2nd edition) (E. & F. N. Spon Ltd., London).

Dyer, H. B., Fernindando, P., 1966, *Brit. J. Appl. Phys.* **17**, 419.

Ferninando, P., 1967, Ph. D. thesis (University of Reading).

Glockler, G., 1954, *J. Chem. Phys.* **22**, 159.

Goggin, P. R., Reynolds, W. N., 1963, *Phil. Mag.* **8**, 265.

Goldfarb, I. J., Jaffe, H. H., 1959, *J. Chem. Phys.* **30**, 1622.

Gubanov, A. I., 1963, *Quantum Electron Theory of Amorphous Conductors* Chap. 4 (1963) (Translation New York, Consultant Bureau 1965).

Gunnersen, E. M., 1967, *Rep. Progr. Phys.* **30**, 27.

Henson, R. W., Mounsey, J. A., *U.K. A.E.A. D.E.G. Rep.* 328 (W).

Ishino, S., Mitchell, E. W. J., 1966. *Proc. of the Symposium on Lattice Defects in Semiconductors*, Kyoto, (University of Tokyo Press 1968). See also Werner, Z. G., Whitehouse, J. E., Ishino, I., Mitchell, E. W. J., *9th Int. Conf. on the Physics of Semiconductors*, *Proc.* Vol. 2 p. 1070 (Publishing House "Nauka" Leningrad 1968).

Iwata, T., Fujita, F. E., Suzuki, H., 1961, *J. Phy. Soc. Japan* **16**, 197.

Iwata, T., Susuki, H., 1963, *Radiation Damage in Reactor Materials* p. 565 (Int. Atomic Energy Agency Vienna 1963).

Kinchin, G. H., 1956, *Proc. Int. Con. Peaceful Uses of Atomic Energy* **7**, 472 (U.N., New York, 1956).

Kinchin, G. H., Pease, R. S. 1955, *Rep. Progr. Phys.* **18**, 1.

Knight, H. T., Rink, J. P., 1958, *J. Chem. Phys.* **29**, 449.

Lax, M., Halperin, B. I., 1966. *Proc. of the International Conference on the Physics of Semiconductors*, Kyoto, (*J. Phys. Soc. Japan*, Vol. 21 Supplement) p. 218.

Levy, P. W., 1961, *Disc. Faraday Soc.* No. 31, 118.

Lidiard, A. B., Perrin, 1965, Private communication from A.E.R.E. report.

Lomer, J. N., Mitchell, E. W. J., Niblett, D. J., 1962. *Radiation Damage in Solids* **1**, 205 (International Atomic Energy Agency, Vienna, 1962).

Lucas, M. W., Mitchell E. W. J., 1964. *Carbon* **1**, 345.

Lucovsky, G., Varga, A. J., Schwartz, R. F., 1965 *Solid State Commun.* **3**, 9.

McKay, J. W., Klontz, E. E., 1962, *Radiation Damage of Solids* Vol. III, p. 27 (Int. Atomic Energy Agency, Vienna 1963).

McKay, J. W., Klontz, E. E., 1963, *Radiation Damage in Solids*, (International Atomic Energy Agency, Vienna) Vol. III, p. 27.

Mitchell, E. W. J., 1964, *Proc. Symp. Radiation Damage in Semiconductors* 367, (Dunod, Paris).

Mitchell, E. W. J., Norris, C., 1966. *Proc. of the Int. Conf. on the Physics of Semiconductors*, Kyoto, 1966 (*J. Phys. Soc. Japan* Vol. 21 Supplement) p. 292.

Mitchell, E. W. J., Paige, E. G. A., 1957, *Phil. Mag.* **1**, 1085.

Mitchell, E. W. J., Salisbury, C., 1963, Limited Circulation of Folio of "Cross section calculations for displacement of atoms by fast electrons".

Neubert, T. J., Lees, R. B., 1957, *Nuclear Science and Engineering* **2**, 748.

Reynolds, W. N., Goggin, P. R., 1960, *Phil. Mag.* **58**, 1049.

Reynolds, W. N., Thrower, P. A., 1963, *Radiation Damage in Reactor Materials* p. 553 (Int. Atomic Energy Agency, Vienna 1963).

Simmons, J. W. H., 1965, *Radiation Damage in Graphite* (Academic Press, London 1965).

Snyder, W. S., Neufeld, J., 1956, *Phys. Rev.* **103**, 862.

Thompson, M. W., Wright, S. B., 1964, *U.K.A.E.A. Rep. A.E.R.E.-R.* 4701.

Vook, F. L., 1964, *Proc. Symp. Radiation Damage in Semiconductors* p. 51 (Dunod, Paris 1964).

Watkins, G. D., 1964, *Proc. Symp. Radiation Damage in Semiconductors* p. 97 (Dunod, Paris 1964).

Radiation induced defects in ferromagnetic materials

D. DAUTREPPE

CEN Grenoble

A large number of magnetic materials have radiation sensitive properties which can be used as monitors for dosimetry. But if radiation sensitivity is a necessary condition, other requirements must be fullfilled to get a useful dosimeter. Among these the following seem to be the main ones:

Selectivity: specific response to a special kind of radiation

Independance of instantaneous flux
Relative independance of the irradiation temperature

Practicability: easy measurement of the physical property used, small dosimeter, reproducibility of sample elaboration, etc ...

As our time is limited, we shall look into one particular class of magnetic material i.e. the *ferromagnetic metals*; trying to discuss the experimental results on the basis of the preceeding points. Anyhow a large part of our conclusions can be applied to other classes of magnetic materials such as ferrites and superparamagnetic alloys for instance. On the other hand, when talking about magnetic materials, one thinks immediately to this class of ferromagnetic

metals which are widely used for permanent magnets, high voltage transformers, transformers for electronics, etc ...

The most useful and straightforward property of these materials is the
hysteresis loop, which can be characterized by the following quantities as
shown on Fig. 1:

initial permeability μ_0
maximum permeability μ_m
remanent induction B_r
coercive force H_c
saturation induction B_s.

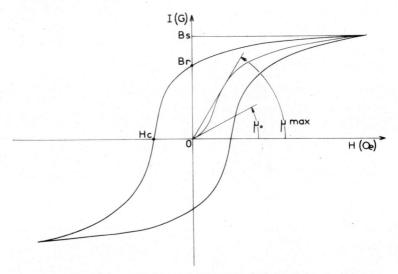

FIGURE 1   Hysteresis cycle. B_s: saturation induction, B_r: remanent
induction, H_c: coercive force, μ_0: initial permeability, μ_{max}: maximum
permeability

This hysteresis loop which is related to the first magnetization curve, can
be explained by the presence of Weiss domains separated by Bloch walls. In
order to supress the flux outside the sample and in this way minimize the
energy, Weiss domains appear where the magnetization is uniform. Two
domains are separated by a region (Bloch Wall) where the magnetization
turns progressively from the direction it has in the first domain to the direction if has in the second. On Fig. 2 is shown as an example a 180° Bloch
wall. The thickness of these Bloch walls depends on the result of the compe-

TABLE 1   D. C. Magnetic properties: Percentage change as result of irradiation with $\sim 2 \times 10^{18}$ neutron/cm^2

Material	$\dfrac{\Delta \mu_{20}}{\mu_{20}}$	$\dfrac{\Delta \mu_{max}}{\mu_{max}}$	$\dfrac{\Delta H_c}{H_c}$	$\dfrac{\Delta B_r}{B_r}$	$\dfrac{\Delta B_m}{B_m}$	$\dfrac{\Delta B_r/B_m}{B_r/B_m}$
Supermalloy	−93	−93	815	−38	−3	−36
4 · 79 Mo Permalloy	−89	−79	403	−44	<1	−44
Mumetal	−65	−38	158	−26	−3	−23
48 Nickel–iron	−70	−10	99	−26	−2	−26
50 Nickel–iron (oriented)	−31	15	−28	−24	−4	−21
3.5 Silicon–iron	8	−1	6	1	0	1
3 Silicon–iron (oriented)	18	1	−2	−3	−1	−1
3.1 Silicon–aluminium–iron	1	1	−2	−2	1	−1
16 Aluminium–iron (ordered)	34	15	−8	8	−5	13
16 Aluminium–iron (disordered)	−4	−4	−2	—	—	—
2 V Permendur	3	2	−2	−1	−1	0

μ_{20} = permeability at induction of 20 gausses.
μ_{max} = maximum permeability.
H_c = coercive force.
B_r = residual induction or remanence.
B_m = induction at field intensity of 30 oersteds.
B_r/B_m = loop rectangularity or squareness ratio.

tition of two main energy terms: the exchange energy which tends to keep parallel two neighbouring atomic magnetic moments and the magneto-crystalline anisotropy energy which tends to keep these magnetic moment along an easy axis of magnetization. The greater the anisotropy energy is the thinner the wall is. In iron, a 180° wall is approximally 2000 Å thick, while a 90° wall is 500 Å thick. In the range of small applied magnetic fields, the measured induction increases by the reversible motion of the Bloch walls; in medium magnetic fields the motion is irreversible and in higher magnetic fields the rotation of the magnetization gives the main contribution to the induction increase.

The ferromagnetic materials are divided into soft magnetic materials mainly used in transformer cores and hard magnetic materials mainly used as permanent magnets. The former have a high permeability and a low coercive force while the latter have a high coercivity and a high remanence ($B_r X H_c$ must be as large as possible).

The hard magnetic materials are mainly made of highly anisotropic ferromagnetic particles embedded in a non magnetic matrix. In this way, when the

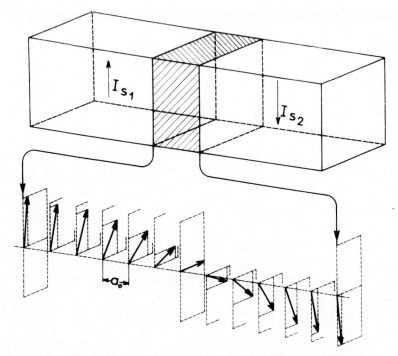

FIGURE 2   Magnetization rotation in a 180° Bloch wall

magnetization has been fixed in a special direction by applying a large
magnetic field, it stays in this direction. Only if the radiation is able to
change in a appreciable amount the structure of the precipitated particles,
the hysteresis loop will be changed and consequently the magnetic properties.
Due to this fact, and as we shall see later, the hard magnetic materials will
remain unaffected by radiation.

The soft magnetic materials can be divided into pure metals or diluted
solid solution (such as Fe–3 % Si) and alloys. The former would be affected
by the radiation produced defects if their size is comparable to the Bloch
walls thicknesses. Point defects would have practically no influence on the
hysteresis loop, though they can give rise to "magnetic after effects" which
eventually can be used as monitors. In alloys, the situation is completly
different, since enhanced diffusion can take place, and change the structure
of the alloy, and consequently the magnetic properties which are the most
structure sensitive, i.e., the initial permeability and the coercive force. The
saturation induction B_s would be practically unaffected ...

So let us explain what is this phenomenon called "magnetic after effect" and another related to the magnetic behaviour of ferromagnetic alloys called "induced magnetic anisotropy".

1 MAGNETIC AFTER EFFECT

A typical example is given by carbon in αFe. The carbon atoms enter the b.c.c. αFe lattice into interstitial sites which are approximatly on the middle of the edges of the unit cell cube. These sites are energetically equivalent from symmetry considerations. But a magnetic coupling between these carbon atoms and the local magnetic moments, introduces a small energy difference between the sites lying on the direction of the magnetization and the sites perpendicular to this direction. This energy difference ($\sim 10^{-3}$ eV) is sufficient to introduce a difference between the population of the inequivalent sites. The establishement of the equilibrium population distribution when the magnetization is suddenly turned from one easy direction (say 001) to another (say 100), occurs with a time constant $\tau = \tau_0 \exp \dfrac{W}{kT}$, where W is the potential barrier the carbon atoms have to cross to jump from one site to a neighbouring one. The anisotropic distribution around the magnetization introduces a supplementary anisotropy energy (small in comparison with the magnetocrystalline anisotropy) which impede an eventual rotation of the magnetization and consequently an eventual motion of a Bloch wall. So if after a demagnetization, which changes complettly the distribution of the Weiss domains, the initial permeability is measured as a function of time, a decrease will be observed. The time dependance will be governed by the time constant τ. The amplitude of the phenomena as defined by the reluctivity $\left(r = \dfrac{1}{\mu} \right)$ difference: $r(t = 0) - r(t \gg \tau)$ is proportional to the carbon concentration.

A great number of defects created by irradiation on pure or doped ferromagnetic metals give rise to large magnetic after effect of this kind.

2 INDUCED MAGNETIC ANISOTROPY

This effect can only occur in alloys. Let us take as a typical example Fe–Ni (50%–50%). We use a polycrystalline circular sample with a large number of grains; in this way our sample is isotropic as far as magnetic anisotropy is concerned, since the easy axis of magnetization are randomly distributed.

If this sample is heat treated in an applied saturing magnetic field and then quenched, an easy axis of magnetization appears in the direction of the applied field. This phenomenon can be explained by assuming magnetic coupling between the Ni–Ni, Fe–Fe and Ni–Fe bonds and the magnetization. This coupling tends to produce, a diffusion proceeds, a bonds distribution with cylindrical symmetry around the magnetization. This distribution is frozen in by the quenching and tends to stabilize the magnetization in the treatment field direction, explaining the macroscopic easy axis.

The same effect can be produced by irradiation with an applied magnetic field in a temperature range where normaly no diffusion occurs. Even if this induced magnetic anisotropy is not the physical property measured after the irradiation of a ferromagnetic alloy, its role is very often predominant in the behaviour of the hysteresis loop. This behaviour will be different if no external magnetic field is applied, since the magnetization will have different directions in the different Weiss domains.

Some observations can now be derived, which concerned the different properties needed for a good dosimeter. As we have focussed our attention on ferromagnetic metals, as far as selectivity is concerned, they have the same behaviour as the normal metals, i.e., the main part of the damage produced in a reactor is caused by fast neutrons. In alloys most of the change in magnetic properties will come from enhanced diffusion changing the structure, and consequently will be generally temperature dependant, excepted in special cases. The magnetic properties of these alloys depend on the history of the alloy (heat treatment, deformation, etc...), consequently the reproducibility of the sample is difficult; and of course the most radiation sensitive alloys would be the most irreproductible. The easiest magnetic measurement which can be performed is the hysteresis loop recording or the initial permeability measurement. In this case, the sample will be a small disc ($\sim$20 mm in diameter and 0.1 to 0.5 mm thick) with a central hole ($\sim$10 mm in diameter). Two coils would be wounded around. A wire can also be used if the ratio of the length over the diameter is sufficiently large ($\sim$20). This wire can be put after irradiation into a measuring coil. This latest sample shape seems the most suitable for dosimetry applications. Magnetic after effect measurements can be made in the same way since they are permeability measurements. The induced magnetic anisotropy which can be more easily quantitatively connected to the defects creation and migration, than the hysteresis loop modifications, implies a much more complicated apparatus (torque magnetometer and electromagnet).

A   Ferromagnetic pure or doped metals

We shall only give some examples concerning Iron, since the same general behaviour is valid for Nickel or Cobalt. First let us look rapidly to the recovery curve of the electrical resistivity after a 78°K neutron irradiation (Fig. 3). Of course we shall not discuss the use of electrical resistivity since we are mainly concern with the magnetic properties, but we shall only point out that the electrical resistivity increase remaining at room temperature

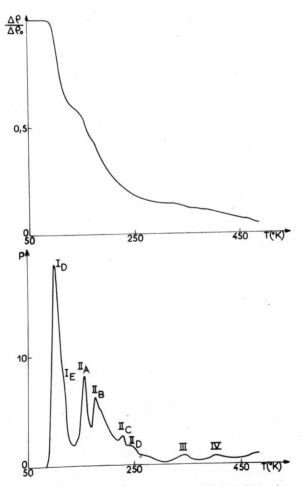

FIGURE 3   Isochronal annealing of the electrical resistivity after a neutron irradiation at 78°K with 8.10^{17} nvt $(E > 1 \text{ MeV})$

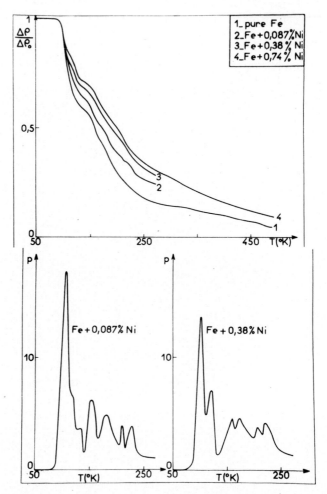

FIGURE 4   Effect of Nickel on the isochronal annealing of the electrical
resistivity of neutron irradiated Iron at 78°K. Dose 8.10^{17} nvt ($E > 1 \, MeV$)

can be increased by the addition of foreign atoms (Fig. 4). This doping effect
can also be used in connection with magnetic after effects. On Fig. 5 is shown
the isochronal annealing of the amplitude of different magnetic after effects,
after a 78°K neutron irradiation. On Fig. 6 the dose dependance of the
108°K magnetic after effect compared to the energy released. New magnetic
after effects appear when foreign substitutionnal atoms are introduced as

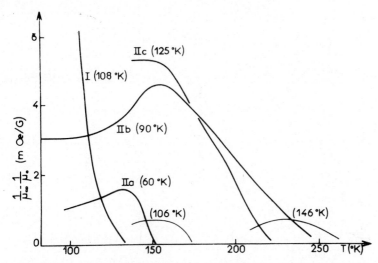

FIGURE 5   Isochronal annealing of the m.a.e. zone II after a neutron irradiation at 78°K. Dose 10^{18} nvt ($E > 1$ MeV)

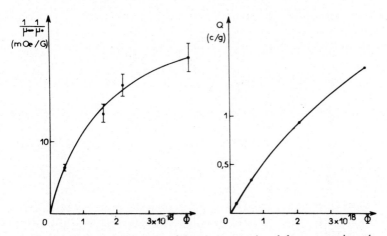

FIGURE 6   Dose dependence of the m.a.e. zone 1 and the energy released during peak 1

shown on Fig. 7. Of course all these magnetic after effects which anneal out below 0°C are not very useful for dosimetry, but others appear to be stable at room temperature as shown on Fig. 8 and 10, and their stability can be modified by doping (Fig. 9). Special studies would be necessary for a practical use of this effect for dosimetry.

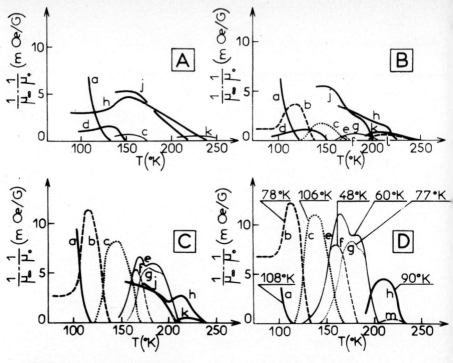

FIGURE 7 Isochronal behaviour of the new magnetic after effect zones obtained on Nickel doped Iron neutron irradiated at 78°K as the Nickel content incerases   A. Pure Iron;   B. 0.02% Nickel doped Iron;   C. 0.07% Nickel doped Iron;   D. 0.5% Nickel doped Iron

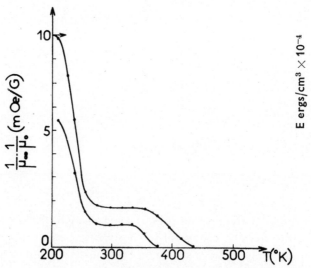

FIGURE 8 Isochronal annealing of the magnetic after effect (m.a.e.) zone III after ueutron irradiation at 77°K Dose 5.10¹⁸ nvt ($E \geqq 1$ MeV) Upper curve: m.a.e. zone III$_b$ (223°K) Lower curve: m.a.e. zone III$_a$ (183°K)

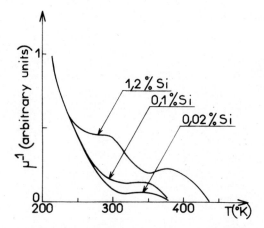

FIGURE 9   Isochronal annealing of the m.a.e. tone III_b after neutron irradiation of Iron containing different amount of Silicon

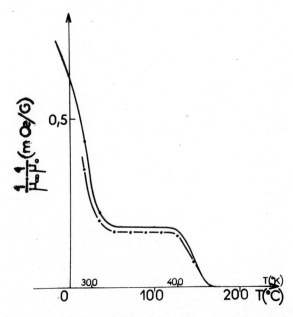

FIGURE 10   Isochronal annealing (20°–15 mn) of the magnetic after effect (m.a.e.) zone IV after neutron irradiation of pure Iron at 78°K. Dose 10^{18} nvt ≥ 1 MeV. Solid curve: m.a.e. zone IV_a. Dotted curve: m.a.e. zone IV_b

B   Ferromagnetic alloys

We shall take some examples in the Fe–Ni system since again the general behaviour is valid for other alloys. The induced magnetic anisotropy is certainly one of the most radiation sensitive property in these alloys, since some 10^{15} n.v.t. can give a well measurable effect. The irradiation does not need to be performed in the presence of a magnetic field since a larger effect

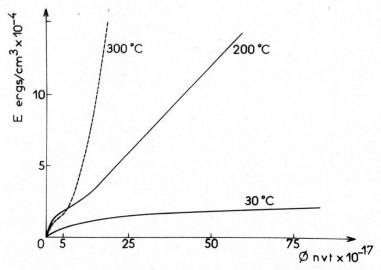

FIGURE 11   Variation of the induced magnetic anisotropy at different temperatures during neutron irradiation for a 50%- 50% polycrystalline FeNi alloy

can be obtained by an annealing in a saturing magnetic field after irradiation. Some defects such as vacancies can only be mobile at a temperature higher than room temperature and consequently are stocked during the irradiation. During a further annealing they anneal out producing the necessary diffusion for the induced magnetic anisotropy to occur. On Fig. 11 is shown for example the induced magnetic anisotropy increase during irradiation of a Ni–Fe (50%–50%) alloy with an applied magnetic field at different temperatures. At room temperature even at low doses the rate is small in comparison with the 200°C and 300°C irradiation, but a further annealing after irradiation gives a large increase. The behaviour can be changed if the alloy composition is changed. Unfortunaty as we said the measurement implies a relatively large apparatus.

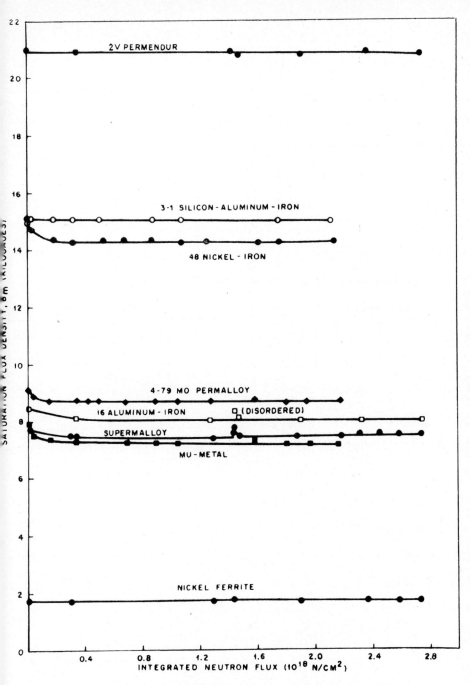

FIGURE 12 Saturation induction as a function of neutron flux for different magnetic materials

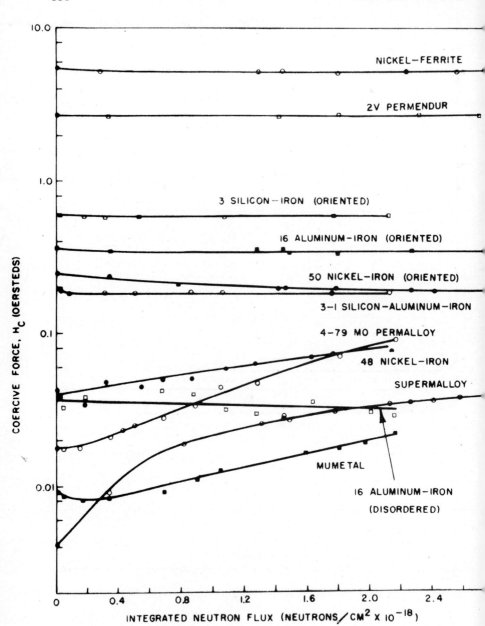

FIGURE 13   Coercive force as a function of neutron flux for different
magnetic materials

Let us now look at the modification of the other magnetic properties connected with the hysteresis loop. On Fig. 12 one can see that the saturation induction is practically unaffected in doped iron, alloys or ferrites. Figure 13 and 14 show the behaviour of the coercive force and the initial permeability. As can be seen the most radiation sensitive materials are

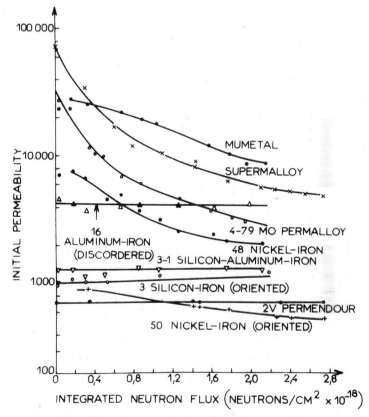

FIGURE 14   Initial permeability as a function of neutron flux for different magnetic materials

those with low coercive force and high permeability. In all the Fe–Ni alloys considered, the permeability decrease as well as the coercive force increase, can be explained by the effect of the induced magnetic anisotropy. In each Weiss domains as well as in the Bloch walls this anisotropy build up around the local direction of the magnetization and consequently impede the further motion of the Bloch walls.

Sensitivity of engineering materials to fast neutron irradiation*

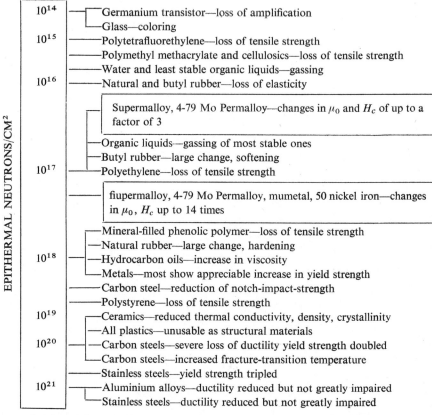

* Adapted from O. Sisman and J. C. Wilson, *Nucleonics* **14**, No. 9, 58 (1956).

On Fig. 15 is shown how the hysteresis loop is deformed. The reluctivity seams to be linearly dependant on the integrated flux (Fig. 16). On Fig. 17 is shown how these magnetic materials take place in the fast neutron sensivity scale.

To summarize, in the pure or doped ferromagnetic metals only the magnetic after effects can be used in the range of some 10^{18} n.v.t.; in alloys the most sensitive property is the induced magnetic anisotropy (some 10^{15} n.v.t.) but a rather complicated apparatus is needed. The initial permeability can be used but in that case the sample reproducibility would certainly needs some special studies. On the other hand the temperature dependance must be tested in the dosimetry conditions.

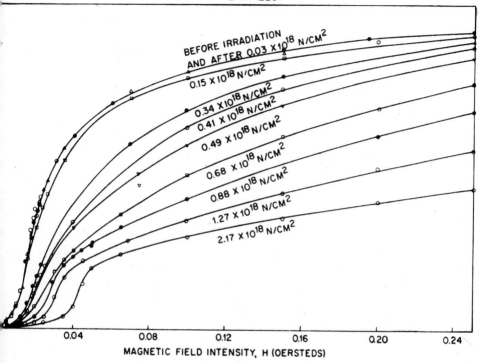

FIGURE 15   Effect of irradiation on normal induction curve

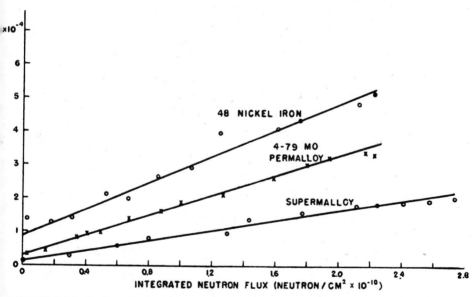

FIGURE 16   Reciprocal of initial permeability as a function of integrate neutron flux

22*

Bibliography

Magnetic after effect

1. L. Neel, *J. Phys. Rad.*, **13**, 249 (1952).
2. G. De Vries, D. W. van Geest, R. Gersdorf, and G. W. Rathenau, *Physica*, **25**, 1131 (1959).
3. P. Brissonneau, *J. Phys. Chem. Sol.* **7**, 22 (1958).

Magnetic after effects in irradiated pure or doped ferromagnetic metals

4. P. Moser, *Mem. Scient. Revue de Métallurgie*, **63**, n° 4, 343 (1966) and **63**, n° 5, 431 (1966).
5. P. Moser and D. Dautreppe, *IAEA Vienna* **1962, tome I**, p. 299.
6. E. Balthesen, K. Isebeck, and H. Wenzl, *Phys. Stat. Sol.* **8**, 603 (1965).
7. J. Verdone, P. Peretto, P. Moser, D. Dautreppe, and J. Verdier *C. R. Acad. Sci. (Paris)* **260**, 5209 (1965).
8. P. Vigier, V. Hivert, P. Moser and E. Bonjour, *C. R. Acad. Scien. (Paris)* **260**, 3359 (1965).
9. P. Vigier, Thesis 1966, C.E.N.-Grenoble, SPSRM, B.P. 269–38 – France.
10. P. Peretto, D. Dautreppe and P. Moser, *Phys. Stat. Sol.* **13**, 325 (1966).
11. L. Neel, *C. R. Acad. Sci. (Paris)* **237**, 1613 (1953); *J. Phys. Rad.* **15**, 225 (1954).
12. S. Taniguchi and M. Yamamoto, *Sci. Rept. Res. Inst. Tohoku Univ.* **A6**, 330 (1954).
13. S. Taniguchi, *Sci. Rept. Res. Inst. Tohoku Univ.* **A7**, 269 (1955).
14. S. Chikazumi and T. Oomura, *J. Phys. Soc. Japan*, **10**, 842 (1955).
15. E. T. Fergusson, *C. R. Acad. Sci. (Paris)*, **244**, 2363 (1957).

Induced magnetic anisotropy in irradiated ferromagnetic alloys

16. J. Pauleve, D. Dautreppe, J. Laugier and L. Neel, *C. R. Acad. Sci. (Paris)* **254**, 965 (1962).
17. W. Chambron, D. Dautreppe, L. Neel, and J. Pauleve, *C. R. Acad. Sci. (Paris)* **255**, 2037 (1962).
18. L. Neel, *C. R. Acad. Sci. (Paris)* **257**, 2917 (1963).
19. E. A. Nesbitt, G. Y. Chin, A. J. Williams, R. C. Sherwood and J. Moeller, *J. Appl. Phys.* **37**, 1218 (1966).
20. L. Neel, J. Pauleve, R. Pauthenet, J. Laugier, and D. Dautreppe, *J. Appl. Phys.* **35**, 871 (1964).
21. J. Pauleve, K. Krebs, A. Chamberod, and J. Laugier, *C. R. Acad. Sci. (Paris)* **260**, 2439 (1965).
22. A. Marchand and A. Chamberod, *C. R. Acad. Sci (Paris)* **261**, 3113 (1965).
23. W. Chambron, A. Chamberod, J. Pauleve, and D. Dautreppe, Baden-Baden (June 1966).
24. P. Moser and D. Dautreppe, *J. Phys. Rad.* **24**, 516 (1963).
25. H. D. Dietze and E. Balthesen, *Nukleonik*, **3**, 93 (1961).
26. M. Wuttig, J. T. Stanley, and H. K. Birnbaum, (to be published).
27. P. Peretto, Thesis (1967), C.E.N.-Grenoble, PSRM, B.P. 269-38-France.

28. P. Peretto, J. L. Oddou, C. Minier-Cassayre, D. Dautreppe, and P. Moser, *Phys. Stat. Sol.* **16**, 281 (1966).
29. P. Peretto, P. Moser and D. Dautreppe, *C. R. Acad. Sci (Paris)* **258**, 499 (1964).
30. E. Balthesen, K. Isebeck, and H. Wenzl, *Phys. Stat. Sol.* **8**, 593 (1965).
31. H. Kronmuller, H. E. Schaefer, and H. Rieger, *Phys. Stat. Sol.* **9**, 863 (1965).
32. A. Seeger, F. Walz and H. Kronmuller, 12th Annual Conference Magnetism and Magnetic Materials, Washington, November 1966.
33. P. Moser, P. Peretto, D. Dautreppe, and P. Vigier, *J. Appl. Phys.* **36**, 1227 (1965).

Induced magnetic anisotropy

34. G. A. Kelsall, *Physics*, **5**, 169 (1934).
35. J. F. Dillinger and R. M. Bozorth, *Physics*, **6**, 279 (1935); R. M. Bozorth and J. F. Dillinger, *Physics*, **6**, 285 (1935).

General survey

36. D. I. Gordon and R. S. Sery, *I.E.E.E. Transactions on Communication and Electronics* **83**, 357 (1964).
37. D. I. Gordon and R. S. Sery, *Solid State Physics in Electronics and Telecommunications.* Acad. Press. Inc. London and New York (1960) **4**, 824–58.
38. R. S. Sery, R. H. Lundsten, and D. I. Gordon, *Materials in Design Engineering* Reinhol Publishing Corp. N.Y.
39. D. I. Gordon, *Proceedings Institute of Environmental Sciences* M.T. Prospect. Illinois, p. 205–228 (1960).

Effect on hysteresis loop

40. A. I. Schindler, NRL Report 5686 (1961).
41. A. I. Schindler, E. I. Salkovitz, and G. S. Asell, *J. Appl. Phys. suppl.* **30**, 2825 (1959).
42. A. I. Schindler and E. I. Salkowitz, *J. Appl. Phys. suppl.* **31**, 2455 (1960).
43. E. A. Nesbitt, B. W. Batterman, L. D. Fullerton and A. J. Williams, *J. Appl. Phys.* **36**, 1235 (1965).
44. D. I. Gordon and R. S. Sery, *J. Appl. Phys.* **35**, 879 (1964).
45. D. I. Gordon and R. S. Sery, *I.E.E.E. Transactions on Nuclear Science* NS-II, 105 (1964).
46. D. S. Billington, R. H. Kernohan, W. L. Harman and P. G. Huray, ORNL 3213, p. 137 (1961).
47. A. I. Schindler, R. H. Kernohan, and J. Weertman, *J. Appl. Phys.* **35**, 2640 (1964).
48. R. S. Sery and D. I. Gordon, *J. Appl. Phys.* **34**, 1311 (1963).

PART III

Applied topics

_____

Dosimetry of high-energy radiation for radiobiology and radiation protection purposes

J. BAARLI

CERN, Geneva

INTRODUCTION

Radiation dosimetry forms an essential part of science in view of its importance in providing the basic knowledge required for quantitative measurements of radiation. Such measurements are essential to any study of radiation effects, as well as any prediction of a radiation danger for protection purposes.

Historically, since the discovery of ionizing radiation, dosimetry has developed from the use of a qualitative estimation of radiation quantity by the skin-erytherma to the large number of disometers existing today.

A measurement of radiation might depend upon what the measured quantity is to be used for. Initially, the ionization of air by radiation was utilized for this purpose. Then later, the basic for measurement was changed to that of the energy absorbed in the medium at the place of interest. The unit first used was the roentgen, defined as the production of 1 ESU of charge in 1 cm^3 of air at NTP. For the latter case, the rad was defined as being equivalent to the deposition of 100 ergs per gram of the irradiated material.

If one considers that the principal unit to be used when measuring radiation dose is that of the energy delivered by the radiation to the medium, it is of interest to provide information about the processes responsible for the energy deposition in the medium under consideration.

The unit rad can be considered to be an integral of a number of individual processes occurring within the medium, which causes the energy deposition in the space under consideration. In many cases, this unit might therefore not be sufficient to help in explaining radiobiological effects or other effects observed. The reason for this might be due to the composition of the medium with respect to the radiation effects observed.

An attempt to arrive at an explanation is made by using the LET concept. LET is defined as the linear energy transferred to the medium along the track of the absorbed ionizing particle. Careful consideration of this concept has revealed some severe limitations. The limitation is due mainly to the lack of a precise definition of a particle track in the absorbing medium. More correctly, the absorption processes are distinct and distributed in space within the absorbing medium around the track of the ionizing particle.[1] As a result, it has been suggested to describe the radiation dose statistically by means of micro-dosimetry[2]: the distribution in space, on a microscopic scale of the individual absorption processes and their quantities, which are responsible for the radiation dose.

It is convenient to distinguish between the dosimetry for the purpose of radiobiological studies and the dosimetry for radiation protection. The essential quantity of radiation for radiobiological investigations is the rad, together with a specification of the radiation utilized. This specification might also be given by a more detailed description of what happens in the absorber.

In the case of radiation protection, the biological efficiency of the radiation under consideration has to be considered. This results in the utilization of another unit called the rem, defined as the product of the dose in rad, the QF (which is approximately proportional to the LET), and any other relevant factors. In the following, we will start by discussing the radiation dosimetry for biological purposes, and then follow this with a discussion of dosimetry for radiation protection purposes.

1 RADIATION DOSIMETRY OF VERY HIGH ENERGY RADIATION FOR RADIOBIOLOGICAL STUDIES

1.1 General

The vast amount of radiobiological studies have mainly been carried out by the use of gamma-rays, X-rays, protons, and neutrons. In these cases, the dosimetry problem is relatively simple because definitions and procedures of such measurements are well established. For example, if radiobiological studies are carried out with Co gamma radiation, it is possible to utilize any dosimetry system if the system chosen has been calibrated. Calibrations are normally made against a standard such as an ion chamber or a chemical dosimeter.[3] The same might be the case if the irradiation were carried out with X-rays. For more fundamental radiobiological studies, information on the LET distribution or a similar quantity is required. This physical study presents considerable difficulties which are apparently due to the rather loose definition of the LET.

If neutrons are to be used, the dosimetry problem becomes more difficult. The reason for this is that the processes which are leading to a radiation dose depend greatly upon the energy distribution of the neutrons as well as on the composition of the absorbing material. Fast neutrons will cause recoil-protons, as well as nuclear interactions with subsequent emission of gamma-rays. The radiation which is responsible for the energy absorption will therefore be quite complex. It will consist of densely ionizing protons and short-range nuclear recoil-particles, as well as gamma and beta radiation.

To ensure a complete and correct measurement of the absorbed dose under any possible condition presents considerable difficulties, which are resolved only in a very few special cases. The additional information about LET distribution raises additional problems.

The dosimetry of high-energy radiation is even more complex on account of the radiation field composition. Utilization of protons with energies exceeding the threshold for pion production can result in radiation fields which it might not be possible to describe in detail. The description of the radiation might therefore only be made in a qualitative manner. It is as a result of such complicated situations that one would like to see a dosimeter for radiation which responds to the radiation, independently of the type and composition of the radiation field, i.e. independently of the processes resulting in the energy deposition.

Very few dosimeters with such characteristics have been developed so far. But there are some processes which have been studied in sufficient detail, and which are utilized for this purpose.

At the present time, there does not exist any proof that the Bragg–Gray relation is not fulfilled under the circumstances mentioned. As a consequence of this, one may adopt the ionization in a tissue–equivalent gas, enclosed inside a tissue-equivalent medium defining the energy absorbed per gram, as being the absorbed dose in tissue.[4]

If one would like to make dose measurements in a different tissue, for example, a similar arrangement could be utilized. In the case of bones, bone-equivalent material and bone-equivalent gas could be used; in the case of lung tissue, one could use lung-equivalent gas and lung-equivalent material, and so on. In this way, there exists a possibility for establishing the total energy absorbed or the dose in rad at the point of interest.

Now there are in addition other parameters which are of equal importance for the fundamental study of radiobiology. It is known that the effects on living tissue depend on the LET or the linear energy transfer, i.e. the energy deposition per unit length along the track of a particle penetrating the medium. A first approximation for evaluating this property could be to use the stopping power of the radiation under consideration. One could measure the average stopping power in water, because water is near to tissue, and most of the body is, to a great extent, water. However, this approach will not resolve the entire problem, since the energy deposition along the track of a particle is also associated with absorption processes, lateral to the track, which might be important when compared to the location of biologically active entities. In order to establish a more fundamental quantity for describing the way in which the radiation is absorbed, and which bears a relation to the biologically important centres, another approach is required. At present, such a field of research is just beginning to develop and, as mentioned before, is called micro-dosimetry.

Micro-dosimetry tries to formulate a statistical description of the individual absorption process on a macroscopic scale within the biological medium. A spherical tissue-equivalent proportional counter has been developed for this purpose, and utilizes the variation in the gas pressure for the definition of the volume in the tissue in which the dose is to be measured.[5]

Calculations based on known radiobiological effects might also help in clarifying the fundamental biological quantity which could assist in defining spatial limits for the statistical description of absorption processes of interest to radiobiology.[6] Another device has been developed based on columnar recombination in a gas, and it has been found that effects observed bear a known relationship to the LET.[7]

1.2 High-energy radiation

At the present time, approximately 30 different subnuclear particles are known. Table 1 indicates those particles, as well as some of their known properties such as mass, lifetime, decay mode, etc. Most of the particles are unstable and decay within rather short lifetimes.

Existing high-energy accelerators are able to provide beams of some of these particles. The most useful beams provided are those of protons, neutrons, electrons, pions, muons, and kaons. The energy of these beams depends on the available accelerating potential, which also partially determines the intensity of the particular radiation. Normally, intensity of such particle beams from present-day accelerators range up to 10^6–10^7 part/sec, when it concerns secondary neutrons or mesons. Proton beam intensities can be much higher, up to 10^{13} part/sec.

1.3 Dosimetry of high-energy proton beams

High-energy proton beams from accelerators have been utilized extensively for high-energy nuclear physics studies, and recently also for radiobiological research. The dosimetry of these beams, at energies up to 200 MeV, has normally been done for radiobiology by counting the number of protons, using a Faraday cup and then calculating the dose to the specimen with the help of information about the stopping power for the medium. Use of air or aother ionization chambers, as well as chemical dosimeters, has also been made.

The study of dosimetry of high-energy proton beams at CERN has been limited to the study of the 600 MeV ejected beam from the synchro-cyclotron. The dosimetry has been based essentially on the use of an air-equivalent ion chamber calibrated against a tissue-equivalent chamber, and the use of the Fricke chemical dosimeter.[8]

TABLE 1   Elementary particles

Particle	Electric charge	Mass in MeV	Spin	Strangeness	Mean lifetime in seconds	Common disintegration products	Antiparticle
Baryons							
Ξ^- (xi minus)	$-e$	1321	$\frac{1}{2}$?	-2	1.2×10^{-10}	$\pi^- + \Lambda$	$\bar{\Xi}^+$ (antixi plus)
Ξ^0 (xi zero)	0	~ 1311	$\frac{1}{2}$?	-2	$\sim 2 \times 10^{-10}$	$\pi^0 + \Lambda$	$\bar{\Xi}^0$ (antixi zero)
Σ^- (sigma minus)	$-e$	1196	$\frac{1}{2}$	-1	1.6×10^{-10}	$\pi^- + n$	$\bar{\Sigma}^+$ (antisigma plus)
Σ^0 (sigma zero)	0	1192	$\frac{1}{2}$	-1	$\approx 10^{-20}$	$\gamma + \Lambda$	$\bar{\Sigma}^0$ (antisigma zero)
Σ^+ (sigma plus)	$+e$	1189	$\frac{1}{2}$	-1	0.8×10^{-10}	$\pi^+ + n$ or $\pi^0 + p$	$\bar{\Sigma}^-$ (antisigma minus)
Λ (lambda)	0	1115	$\frac{1}{2}$	-1	2.5×10^{-10}	$\pi^- + p$ or $\pi^0 + n$	$\bar{\Lambda}$ (antilambda)
n (neutron)	0	940	$\frac{1}{2}$	0	1.0×10^3	$e^- + \bar{\nu}_e + p$	$\bar{n}$ (antineutron)
p (proton)	$+e$	938	$\frac{1}{2}$	0	stable	—	$\bar{p}$ (antiproton)
Bosons							
K^0 (K zero)	0	498	0	$+1$	10^{-10}	$\pi^+ + \pi^-$	$\bar{K}^0$ (anti-K zero)
K^+ (K plus)	$+e$	494	0	$+1$	1.2×10^{-8}	$\mu^+ + \nu_e$ or $\pi^+ + \pi^0$	K^- (K minus)
π^+ (pi plus)	$+e$	140	0	0	2.5×10^{-8}	$\mu^+ + \nu_\mu$	π^- (pi minus)
π^0 (pi zero)	0	135	0	0	1.01×10^{-16}	$\gamma + \gamma$	itself
γ (photon)	0	0	1	0	stable	—	itself
Leptons							
μ^- (mu minus)	$-e$	106	$\frac{1}{2}$	undefined	2.26×10^6	$e^- + \nu_e + \nu_\mu$	μ^+ (mu plus)
e^- (electron)	$-e$	0.511	$\frac{1}{2}$	undefined	stable	—	e^+ (positron)
ν_e (neutrino)	0	0	$\frac{1}{2}$	undefined	stable	—	$\bar{\nu}_e$ (antineutrino)
ν_μ (neutrino)	0	0	$\frac{1}{2}$	undefined	stable	—	$\bar{\nu}_\mu$ (antineutrino)

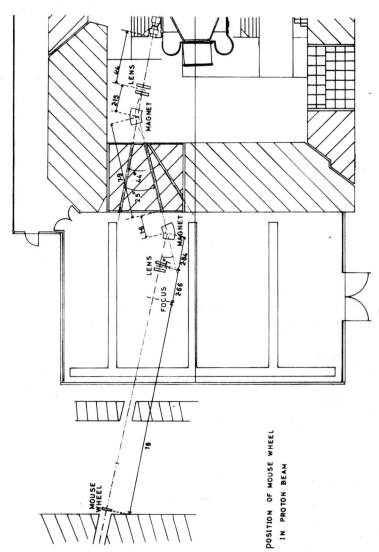

FIGURE 1   Position of mouse wheel in proton beam

Vertical Profile

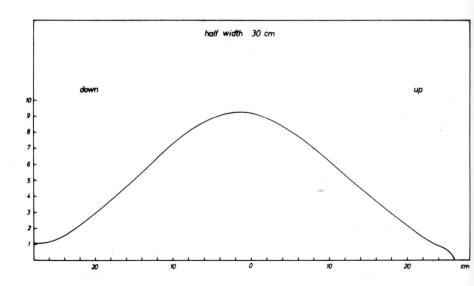

Horizontal Profile

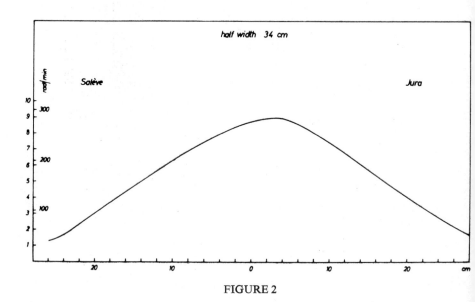

FIGURE 2

Figure 1 shows the layout of the ejected proton beam of the CERN Synchro-cyclotron. After leaving the cyclotron, the protons are focused by a pair of quadrupole lenses and deflected through 25° into the beam channel of the main shielding. Outside the shielding, the protons pass through a bonding magnet which deflects them 27° in the opposite direction to remove unwanted radiation and to select the protons of a defined energy of 592 MeV. Another quadrupole lens is placed in front of this magnet to defocus the beam in order to vary the beam size. The beam is trapped in a 10 m deep beam-catcher.

Figure 2 shows typical dose distribution across the beam. It is seen that this distribution is very near to a Gaussian, having values at half-height of about 30 cm. Without the last pair of defocusing lenses, this value will only be of the order of a cm or two, making measurements with conventional chambers rather difficult.

Figure 3 shows the depth dose distribution of the 600 MeV proton beam absorbed in water. It indicates a dose build-up in the first 10 to 15 cm, after which there is a decrease in dose-rate which rises again at the end and produces the well-known Bragg peak. Its location is at a depth of about 150 cm in water.

In order to understand the complexity of the dosimetry problems of a beam of high-energy charged particles, it may be of interest to consider the interaction processes occurring for the ideal case of a single proton at near-relativistic energy.

Absorption processes take place between the particle and the electrons or the atomic nuclei of the absorber. In other words, energy might be lost both by a number of small energy losses in ionization or excitation events, and in nuclear events with large single losses. As a consequence of this, the concept of the range of a particle in an absorber has to be considered with some care. For example, if a proton has caused a nuclear interaction, it is lost for a range determination. The variety of processes involved also influence the localization of the energy deposition in the medium with respect to the location of the particle. This is easily understood if secondaries from nuclear interactions, as well as δ-rays, are considered. It is also normal at such energies to use the principal concept of the linear energy transfer (LET), in spite of the fact that it might be difficult to establish this for the case of nuclear reactions. However, usually it is wrongly used, and identified as equivalent to the stopping power of the particle. For example, for a proton with near-relativistic energy of 600 MeV, the initial LET will be of the order

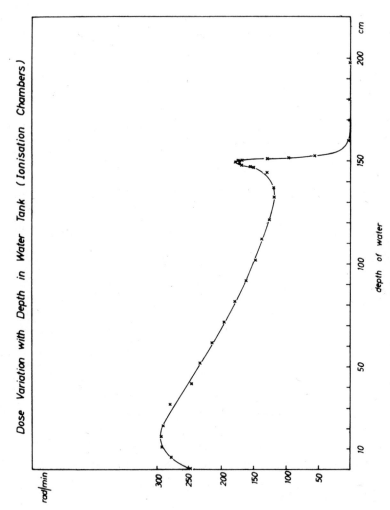

FIGURE 3   Dose variation with depht in water tank (ionisation chambers)

of 2.0 keV/μ, increasing as the particle is lowed down, and at the end of its range reaching a value of about 90 keV/μ. As the particle reaches the end of its range, the LET concept is more in accordance with the stopping power.

Due to particular processes which occur at the end of the range of the proton (charge exchange processes), the energy deposit per unit length, just before the particle is brought to rest, again decreases.

The problem of estimating the average ionization per unit path length from the rate of energy less which the particle suffers, dE/dX, requires knowledge of the energy dissipation of the particle itself and its long-range secondaries. In addition to the ionization and excitation along the track of the particle, which might occur as single events or in clusters, a whole spectrum of δ-rays up to a characteristic maximum will result from primary interactions. The relative number of electrons or δ-rays produced in this way, having an energy between T and $T + dT$, can be calculated from the following distribution law:

$$dN = Z^2 f\left(\frac{dT}{T^2}\right),$$

where Z is the effective charge of the moving ion. The maximum energy which can be transferred into δ-rays is given by the following formula:

$$T_{max} = 2m_0 c^2 \left(\frac{\beta^2}{1 - \beta^2}\right),$$

where β is the velocity of the moving ion, relative to that of light c, and r_0 is the rest mass of the electron. Under these circumstances, the ranges of the δ-rays are considerable, and therefore the conception of local energy deposit as used in the LET definition is not well established. Due account has then to be taken of the electromagnetic form-factor at high energies.

Beams of high-energy protons are easily produced by existing high-energy accelerators, and the definition of such beams by momentum spread and divergence is rather good. When such a beam of high-energy protons penetrates an absorber it is scattered and nuclear interactions takes place. These processes contribute to a distribution of the ranges of the protons, which means that the end of the tracks will be located within a certain distance. This is seen from Fig. 3.

It can also be seen that the value of the peak at half-height amounts to roughly 3 cm when water is used as an absorber. However, this distribution

23*

depends largely upon the initial proton energy, and decreases as the proton energy is lowered.

Of particular interest are the nuclear interactions, the spallation processes, or nuclear evaporation processes. The nuclear interaction process which takes place, for example, in water, or in any other material containing C, N, and O, depends on the geometrical cross-section of the atomic nuclei.

Theoretical studies of nuclear interaction processes caused by high-energy particles in light nuclei (CNO) have been carried out. Such studies have been compared with experimental investigations. It is possible in this way to distinguish between slow cascade particles and evaporation particles, and so arrive at the results presented in Table 2. In addition to this, a contribution to the dose is also caused by the recoil nuclei. Considering the momentum transferred in such interactions as well as the masses involved, it is concluded that the ecoil nuclei might possess an energy of about 4.8 MeV with a mass of about 6.

TABLE 2   Charged particles emitted on an average from a nuclear interaction of light nuclei

Particle	Slow cascade particles		Evaporation particles	
	Number	Energy (MeV)	Number	Energy (MeV)
Protons	0.28	6.0	1.1	5.0
α particle	0.20	7.5	1.65	7.5
Li nuclei	0.09	6.0	—	—

As long as the nuclear interaction probabilities are low the contribution to the energy absorbed from these interactions will be small and depend very little on energy (Fig. 4). Theoretical studies have shown that for a 400 MeV proton incident on a 30 cm slab, about twice as much absorbed dose is caused by the primary ionization compared to the secondaries resulting from nuclear interactions.[9] Secondaries are mainly high-energy protons, and the dose due to heavily ionizing particles is relatively important. The recoil nucleus accounts for less than 1%. As the energy becomes greater, the relation changes such that at 2 GeV the contribution is about half and half. The evaluation of this can be done by using the information given in Table 2, together with the cross-section shown in Fig. 4.

With this explanation, it can be concluded that the dosimetry of very high energy charged particle beams of protons can be carried out by using

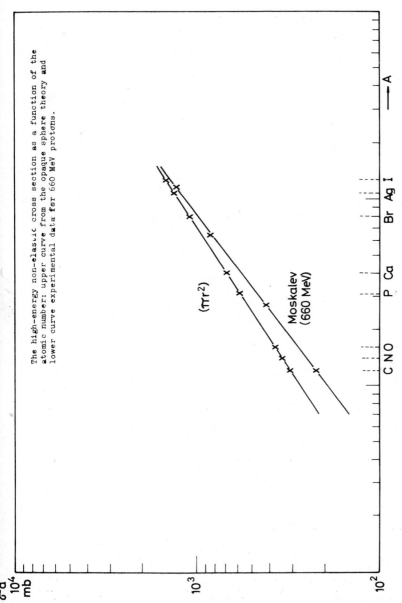

FIGURE 4   The high-energy non-elastic cross section as a function of the atomic number: upper curve from the opaque sphere theory and lower curve experimental data for 660 MeV protons

the same methods as those developed for any other ionizing radiation. The reason for this is that protons with relativistic energy have minimum ionizing power and behave more or less like electrons with energies around 1 MeV, and that the nuclear interaction is of relatively small importance.

When the dosimetry of a beam of particles is to be considered, then there are two quantities which are normally required. First, one would like to have the dose at the point of interest and, secondly, information about the LET variation. It is commonly assumed that the LET in the Bragg peak increases substantially as a result of the slowed-down protons. For a beam of high-energy protons, the energies are distributed in space to such an extent that on an average the LET will not change substantially along a beam of this type.

Very few direct measurements have been made under actual conditions of the LET distribution in such beams. Calculations have shown that the LET values are not much greater than those found for X-rays.[9] This is confirmed by a few measurements based on the ion recombination of a tissue-equivalent gas and by a number of radiobiological experiments with such proton beams[10].

Biological experiments have shown that the biological effectiveness of high-energy protons is equivalent to X-rays, both in the beam itself as well as in the Bragg peak.[8,11]

1.4 Dosimetry of pion beams

Beams of high-energy pions are of considerable interest, for several reasons. Such beams have been proposed for therapeutic application in connection with cancer treatment, and have also been required for use in radiobiological investigation. The reason for this is due primarily to the special behaviour of the negative pions. These particles can be made to interact at rest with atomic nuclei, causing the emission of heavily ionizing, atomic nuclear fragments. A beam of negative pions is therefore producing a Bragg peak when absorbed in water, for example, which, in addition to the ionization from the sloweddown pions, is composed of ionization from products from strong nuclear interactions.

A negative pion has a rest mass of 140 MeV and has one electrical charge. The lifetime is about 10^{-8} sec. The energy required in order to produce negative pions lies in the range of about 400 MeV. It is normally produced by irradiating a beryllium target with high-energy protons.

The particles produced in this way are focused by the fringing field of the accelerators and guided by quadrupole lenses through the channel in the main machine field. Momentum selection is made by a stabilized magnet; the pion beam utilized at CERN is shown in Fig. 5.

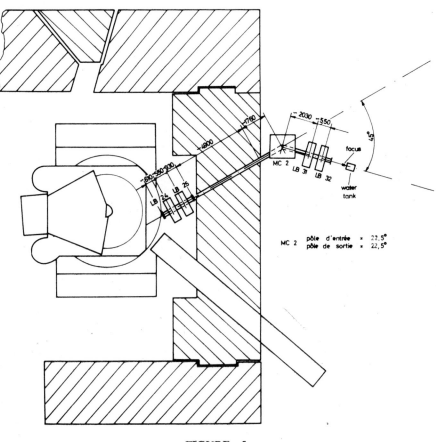

FIGURE 5

When a negative pion penetrates an absorber, it will ionize more or less like an electron. After being slowed down to rest, it forms a mesic atom and the pion will be captured by the nuclei and will interact strongly. This interaction will result in the emission of particles similar to these indicated in Table 2.

Now, if a beam of high-energy negative pions is absorbed, in water, it will cause a dose distribution with depth characterized by just these properties. The Bragg peak will be produced as a result of the ionization from the slowed- down pions and the products from the nuclear interactions. Measurements made in water using an ionization chamber along the axis of an absorbed negative pion beam are shown in Fig. 6.

In order to elucidate the particular problems associated with the dose measurement of such beams, it is necessary to use a method which does not depend upon the specific ionization of the particle responsible for the energy absorbed. As indicated before, no unique method exists at present for this purpose. As a consequence, normal measurements are carried out by the use of small ionization chambers, as well as some measurements with Si–In detectors.[12]

The beam of negative pions is the only radiation produced so far, where a substantial part of the dose within a well-defined region is caused by strong nuclear interactions. This dose contribution from strong nuclear interactions can also be estimated, since the use of positive pions does not result in such interactions. Positive pions of the same momentum will ionize the medium in the same way as will the negative pions, but will come to rest without the nuclear interactions. Depth dose distribution in water for negative and positive pions is shown in Fig. 6.

Any study of dosimetry of strong nuclear interactions requires a region where the dose is duo principally to the interactions and their products. So far, all negative pion beams lack intensity, and for this reason dosimetry is not studied very extensively.

The Bragg peak as observed by an ion chamber in a water phantom indicates that the Bragg peak has a width at half-height of about 3 cm for the 70 MeV negative pion beam from the CERN Synchro-cyclotron. This width is partially caused by the intial momentum spread of the pions, and then the straggling caused by the absorption processes. A reduction of an initial momentum spread results in loss of intensity, and therefore compromises are required for optimizing the conditions.

The results of an investigation of the variation in average specific ionization along the beams absorbed in water are shown in Fig. 6, and refer to the numbers indicated on the upper curve. These results have been obtained by an ionization chamber functioning as a result of ion recombination along the particle tracks.[12] The results show that the relative specific ionization compared to Ra–γ rays varies from 1.0 to 3.4, with a value of 2.7 in the Bragg peak.

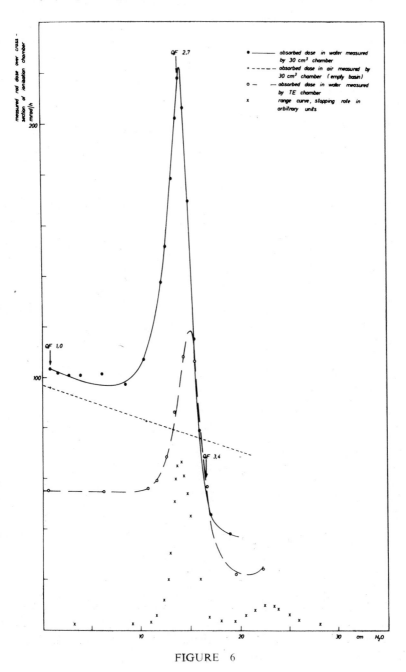

FIGURE 6

In Fig. 7 is shown the relative dose distribution as a function of the LET for the same beams, as measured with a LET proportional counter.[13] It indicates clearly the presence of heavily ionizing products in the peak of the negative pions, which is absent from the positive beam.

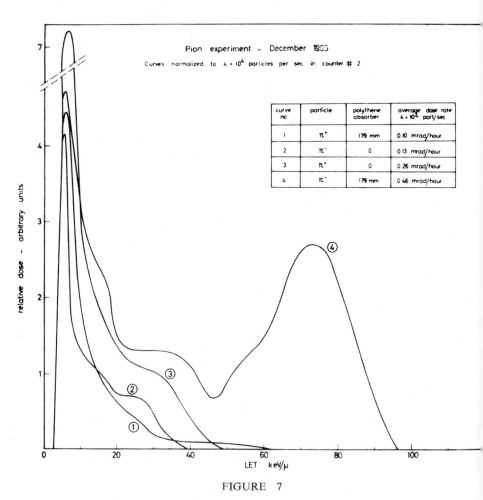

Pion experiment – December 1965

Curves normalized to $4 \cdot 10^4$ particles per sec in counter # 2

curve no	particle	polythene absorber	average dose rate $4 \cdot 10^4$ part/sec
1	π^+	179 mm	0.10 mrad/hour
2	π^-	0	0.13 mrad/hour
3	π^+	0	0.26 mrad/hour
4	π^-	179 mm	0.46 mrad/hour

FIGURE 7

Several problems regarding the dose measurements of stopped negative pions are still not resolved. This refers, among others, to the absolute dose from the nuclear interactions and the information regarding LET or the distribution of the energy absorption processes.

1.5 The dosimetry of muons

The principal production mode of muons is by the decay of pions. The muons have a lifetime of 2.2×10^{-6} sec, such that it has a small chance of decaying during passage through an absorber of moderate dimension.

Muons interact weakly with nuclear matter and the cross-section for interactions is extremely small (10^{-30} cm^2). In coming to rest in an absorber, positive muons and electrons form a particle such as an atom (muonium). This "atom" decays into a positron and a neutrino-antineutrine pair with a maximum energy up to about 50 MeV.

High-energy muons penetrating an absorber ionize the medium with minimum ionization power, and because of the small probability for nuclear interactions almost the entire energy is dissipated through ionization processes.

Beams of muons are commonly produced by existing high-energy accelerators, and they form an excellent tool for the study of radiation doses from a random distribution of ionization processes.

Up to the present time, no attempt has been made to explore experimentally the problems existing in dosimetry under such "pure" conditions. It is expected that all the ionization processes in this case will be randomly distributed, and no particular problem should arise from the variation in space of the ionization processes. No radiobiological experiments have yet been done using such beams, and it is to be hoped that efforts in this direction will be made in the future.

1.6 Dosimetry of very high energy neutron radiations

Particular difficulties in evaluating the absorbed dose are arising from high-energy neutron radiations. This is caused by the fact that high-energy neutrons are able to deliver energy to the absorber only through nuclear interactions. The nuclear interactions which can take place vary greatly from knock-on collisions to spallation interactions in which the whole available energy is utilized to form nuclear fragments. In addition, sub-nuclear particles such as pions might also be produced. Due to this variety of interactions, spatial distribution of energy absorption processes vary over an extremely large range, making the averaging of the dose on a macroscopic scale meaningless.

Beams of very high energy neutrons are already available, although monoenergetic beams are extremely difficult to provide. This is due to the production of high-energy neutrons.

Figure 8 shows measurements of a high-energy neutron beam, and it is easily seen that the momentum spread covers a rather wide range.[14]

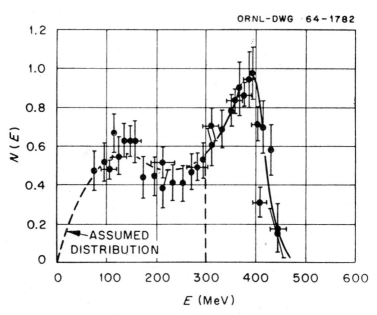

FIGURE 8   Energy spectrum of neutrons resulting from the charge exchange of 480-MeV Protons in Beryllium

If one of these high-energy neutron beams is utilized for irradiating an absorber of water, depth dose distribution, as shown in Fig. 9, is obtained in the first 15 to 30 cm. It is seen that the dose variation with depth from 1 to 15 cm increases extremely rapidly. This is due to the production of the secondary radiation resulting from the interaction process. Of particular interest in this connection is the variation of the specific ionization in depth under these conditions. Table 3 shows some measurements in water for beams of neutrons of energies between 180–525 MeV, which illustrates this.

It is observed that the average specific ionization decreases from the entrance of the absorber to depths of maximum dose-rate. This experimental evidence can be understood because of the relativistic behaviour

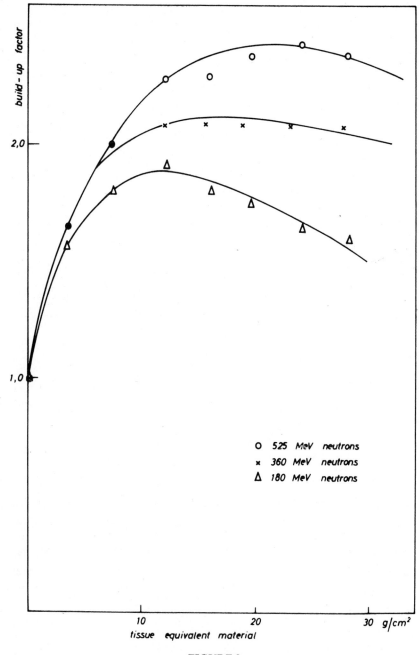

build - up factor

2,0

1,0

10   20   30 g/cm²

tissue equivalent material

O 525 MeV neutrons
x 360 MeV neutrons
Δ 180 MeV neutrons

FIGURE 9

of the particles and their interaction products. It means that the dose per high-energy particle will be loss effective at greater depth, than it would be at the surface. This fact is of importance when judging, for example, the radiation danger from very high energy particles as found near large accelerators, or in space (for the astronauts). No unique dosimetry system has yet been developed which can give adequate information on this subject.

TABLE 3   Dose-rate, build-up factors and relative specific ionization for beams of 180–525 MeV neutrons

Beams Neutron Energy	Dose-rate (rad/h)		Build-up factors	Quality factor	
	Depth 1 g	Depth 20 g		1 g	20 g
525 MeV	1.83	4.6	2.5	2.6 ± 0.6	1.7 ± 0.5
400 MeV	3.03	7.5	2.5	3.5 ± 0.7	2.0 ± 0.5
360 MeV	1.11	2.2	2.0	2.4 ± 0.6	2.0 ± 0.5
180 MeV	0.85	1.6	1.85	2.8 ± 0.5	2.4 ± 0.5

Radiobiological experiments in beams of very high energy neutrons are highly desirable, but radiobiologists seem at present to prefer proton or pion beams to the energetic neutron beam. However, the principal problem when evaluating radiation dangers cannot be resolved without an extensive study of the biological effects from radiation by very high energy neutrons.

2   DOSIMETRY FOR PROTECTION FROM HIGH-ENERGY RADIATIONS

The protection problems of very high energy radiation were not studied in great detail until recently, when it became necessary to judge the radiation hazard near high-energy accelerators.

Such accelerators are new in regular use for the study of elementary particle physics. The interest in the field of radiation protection is also greatly stimulated by the possibility of space travel and the associated hazard from cosmic rays. The difficulties in applying conventional dosimetry methods to very high energy radiation arise from the difference in the interaction with matter. Also, high local energy deposition and high linear energy transfer values are associated with products from nuclear interactions. The measurement problem is complicated by the presence of a wide variety and a great energy range of secondary radiation, accompanying the high-energy particle radiation.

Existing accelerators produce primary beams of protons up to 30 GeV. These accelerators are able to produce the sub-nuclear particles shown in Table 1. Fortunately, not all of these particles are of equal importance for radiation protection purposes, and Table 4 indicates these which are of particular concern.

The particles—those which transform a large portion of the energy of an initial energetic particle into dose—are, in roughly their order of importance: the proton, the neutron, the pion, the muon, and the photon. The next particle of importance is the kaon which, in many respects, behaves like a heavy pion. Kaons are produced in negligible quantities in present-day accelerators but might become important in connection with future high-energy machines, for example, the 300 GeV CERN accelerator. The kaons and the pions are important as a source of muon radiation which penetrate the shielding of the accelerators. Outside the shielding of a high-energy accelerator, a mixture of the radiation indicated in Table 4 will exist.

TABLE 4   Particles contributing to the radiation hazard outside high-energy accelerators

Particle		Mass (MeV)	Lifetime (sec)	Decay products	Remarks
Proton	p	938	stable	—	—
Neutron	n	939	10^3	$p + e^- + \nu$	—
Pion	$\pi^\pm$	140	2.5×10^{-8}	$\mu^\pm + \nu$	Source of muons
	π^0	135	10^{-16}	$\gamma + \gamma$	outside shield
Kaon	$K^\pm$	494	1.2×10^{-8}	$\mu^\pm + \nu$	Source of muons
	K^0	498	10^{-10}	$\pi^\pm + \pi^0$	outside shield
				$\pi^+ + \pi^-$	
Muon	$\mu^\pm$	106	2.3×10^{-6}	$e^+ + 2\nu$	—
Electron-positron	$e^\pm$	0.51	stable	—	Source of bremsstrahlung
Photon	γ	0	stable	—	—

The evaluation of the hazard of this mixture requires, on the one hand, that a complete measurement be made and that the relative efficiency with respect to biological effects be taken into account. Due to the variation in operation of the accelerator, the radiation composition might change. Furthermore, this might also vary from one place to another, due to shielding efficiency and targeting.

An approach to the radiation protection measurement problem might be to utilize an instrument which measures the dose, independently of the type of radiation existing, at the same time taking into consideration the biological efficiency of this existing radiation mixture.

No such instrument has so far been developed, and therefore the practical approach to health physics measurements differs considerably from one laboratory to another.

Particular attention is always paid, for protection purposes, to the measurement of stray neutron radiations.[15] Other approaches have emphasized the utilization of tissue-equivalent ionization chambers, combined with a LET proportional counter.[16] Another method is that of a particular tissue-equivalent ionization chamber utilizing the columnar recombination process in gases to account for the biological efficiency of the existing radiation.[17]

Still another approach is based on the use of a set of six different instruments which basically are measuring the dose from the neutron component as well as the charged particles and γ-rays, together with the dose from slow neutrons and the strong nuclear interaction processes.[10] In all cases, the important problem to resolve is the interpretation of the observed information.

Neutron radiation is normally measured by activation of the various materials selected. These are chosen to have a particular interaction threshold value and a known cross-section for producing certain isotopes. The combination of the threshold and the known cross-section is often utilized to evaluate the spectral distribution of neutrons, and this is then converted to the radiation dose for protection purposes by applying the ICRP recommended conversion values[15].

Experience has shown that behind the shielding of accelerators having moderate energies, the principal part of the radiation is neutron radiation, and the dose estimate shows that this radiation, accounts for the principal danger.

The combination of a tissue-equivalent ionization chamber and a LET proportional counter has not been studied sufficiently to be able to judge the precision with which hazard can be evaluated by this method. There are two principal difficulties associated with this method, one of which concerns evidence regarding the behaviour of this instrument in the presence of radiation able to produce strong nuclear interactions, and the other the fundamental difficulties with regard to the interpretation of the observed spectrum from a LET counter.

The utilization of the ion recombination process in an ionization chamber is equally loosely founded. It is more by chance that the saturation is found to coincide with the LET variation from the various radiation mixtures. Until more studies on the mechanism of gas recombination have been carried out, no further progress in the precision of this method can be envisaged.

The use of six different instruments which measure separately the slow neutrons, fast neutrons, gamma-rays and charged particles, together with the strong nuclear interactions, represents a compromise between the above-mentioned methods and the possible measurement of radiation hazard. It is based on the utilization of commercially available instruments, and the interpretation is made by combining the recommendations of the ICRP and standard calibration procedures. Special experimental studies have been made in order to select the instruments, such that these processes causing a dose in tissue exposed to a mixed radiation field are measured. This is shown in Table 5. Table 6 shows the instruments utilized and the principle radiations measured.[18]

TABLE 5   Correspondence between interaction processes in tissue for various types of radiation and the instruments utilized for their detection

Instrument	Radiation measured	Corresponding interactions in tissue
Boron chamber	Thermal neutrons	Thermal capture
		Resonance capture
Long counter	Fast neutrons	Proton recoil
P. R. counter		
Carbon-11 activation	High-energy particles	Strong interactions
Ion chambers	Gamma radiation and direct ionization	Electromagnetic interaction

Unfortunately, the instruments chosen do not have an ideal response for each of the interactions taking place and, in addition, they do not discriminate satisfactorily between the different processes they are supposed to measure individually. The system has been developed at CERN, and considerable effort has been made to interpret the results obtained. This interpretation has been compared with recommendations made by the ICRP.

TABLE 6 Survey Instruments and Methods (CERN HP-group)

Purpose of measurement	Radiation measured				Total absorbed dose (D)	Total DE evaluation
	Thermal neutrons 0.025–1 eV	Fast neutrons $<0.1 > 14$ MeV	High energy particles >20 MeV	γ and charged particles		
a) Rapid measurements	Long Counter	H_2-filled ionization chamber			TE chamber	$(\phi/7) \times 2$ under study $D \times 10$
b) Radiation analysis	BF_3 chamber (mrem/h)	Long Counter (n. cm^{-2} s^{-1}) + Proton Recoil Counter (MeV. cm^{-2} s^{-1})	^{11}C production (part. cm^{-2} s^{-1})	Air or CO_2 filled ionization chamber in relation with TE chamber	Tissue-equivalent chamber	$\sum$ of partial DE's and check of DE/D = QF
c) Radiation analysis under special conditions	Activation of Au or In (n. cm^{-2} s^{-1})	Activation of Au or In in moderators and/or S, P, Al (n. cm^{-2} s^{-1})	^{11}C production (part. cm^{-2} s^{-1})	γ films or TLD dosimeters	TE capacitor chambers	$\sum$ of partial DE's and check of DE/D = QF
d) Monitor stations	Long Counter			Argon chamber		Ref. [7].

Measurements in experimental halls in the neighbourhood of shielded primary and secondary particle beams, as well as far away from the accelerators, show a large contribution to the dose equivalent coming from fast neutrons. In most cases, at the mentioned places, only 20% of the DE is normally found to be caused by strong nuclear interactions, gamma-rays, and charged particles. Studies of the radiation composition and its variation cannot support the assumption of a simple model of radiation equilibrium outside the shield of a high-energy accelerator. The method usually applied in high-energy radiation shielding studies assumes that the high-energy particle component controls the composition of particles in the lower energy ranges, and the dose estimate is made from measurement of the high-energy component alone. Such flux measurements apply the ICRP factors to obtain the DE. When comparing the two different approaches of interpretation of measurements, large discrepancies are found. These are shown in Table 7.

By comparing the deduced DE with a TE chamber reading, reasonable values for the QF are found. If, however, the ICRP interpretation mode is utilized, unreasonable QF values are obtained.[18]

From such comparison it is seen that it is questionable to assume radiation equilibrium outside the shield of a high-energy accelerator, if one uses the ICRP procedures. In addition, it is also found that the radiation composition can vary greatly ever a small distance for one reason or another.

In conclusion, it can be said that several problems regarding dosimetry of high-energy radiation have not been resolved. The most important problem is related to the dose estimate of strong nuclear interaction processes and the dose estimate from an unknown mixture of radiation.

TABLE 7   Dose contribution on top of main CPS shield

Target	Position long.	Position transv.	Shielding thickness g/cm²	GeV	Contribution to DE HEP %	FN %	ThN %	γ %	DE mrem/h	D mrad/h	Apparent QF	Apparent mrem/h φ HEP	Dose equivalent 20 MeV	1 GeV	Apparent QF 1 GeV
32	+12	0	720	25.6	55	32	2	12	53	11.1	4.8	0.18	79	750	58
32	+6	0	720	25.6	59	30	1.0	12	83	16.4	5.1	0.17	130	1260	77
32	0	0	720	25.6	61	30	1.0	8.5	70	9.7	7.3	0.16	117	1130	116
32	+6	0	720	13.8	50	37	0.2	11.6	42	11.5	3.8	0.20	57	545	47
32	0	0	720	13.8	46	43	0.4	9.0	28	6.9	4.0	0.22	35	340	49
32	0	+2	720	13.8	39	45	0.4	12.5	14	4.9	2.9	0.26	15	140	29
32	+3	+4	720	13.8	52	36	0.4	13	9.3	3.6	2.6	0.19	13	130	36
32	+5	0	720	13.8	49	36	0.2	15	32	9.7	3.3	0.20	43	410	42
32	+5	0	720	13.8	56	35	—	11	18	—	—	0.18	27	260	—
32	+6	0	720	13.8	51	38	0.2	12	41	11.5	3.8	0.20	56	540	47
32	+6	+2	720	13.8	61	31	0.3	8.3	26	7.7	3.3	0.17	42	400	52
82	0	0	730	25.6	70	19	1	8	40	5.3	7.5	0.14	76	700	132
82	0	0	730	18.4	63	33	1	3	19	3.6	5.3	0.16	3	287	80
82	+10	0	730	18.4	55	29	2.3	13	26	5.6	4.6	0.19	38	350	63
82	0	0	730	11.2	51	33	2.5	12.5	12	2.7	4.4	0.20	16	153	57
82	0	0	580	25.6	89	10.2	—	1.3	167	35	4.7	0.11	415	3700	106
82	0	0	580	18.4	61	37	0	1.0	120	16	7.5	0.16	197	1825	114
82	0	0	580	11.2	65	33	0	1.2	84	13	6.5	0.15	149	1375	106

2	0	2	500	18.4	42	42	—	16	171	45	3.7	0.24	195	1800	40
2	+2	0	500	18.4	49	51	—	—	588	170	3.5	0.21	770	7130	42
2	+6	0	500	18.4	58	42	—	—	755	150	5.0	0.17	1175	10900	73
10	+6	0	450	18.4	41	53	—	6.4	2530	341	7.4	0.25	2780	25800	76
10	+6	+5	450	18.4	39	52	—	8.9	985	195	5.1	0.25	1070	9930	51
10	+6	-5	450	18.4	42	57	—	1.3	966	143	6.7	0.24	1100	10100	71
10	+9	0	450	18.4	39	55	—	6.7	2350	341	6.9	0.26	2450	22600	66
10	0	0	450	18.4	32	63	—	4.3	2210	244	9	0.31	1930	17850	73
6	+3	0	730	18.4	28	67	—	5	36	6	6	0.36	27	250	42
6	+3	+5	650	18.4	44	49	—	7	45	11.4	4	0.23	54	500	44
6	+3	-6	650	18.4	31	64	—	5	39	6.7	5.7	0.32	32	300	45
6	+7	0	650	18.4	32	59	—	9	147	19	7.7	0.31	127	1175	62
6	+21	0	650	18.4	25	57	—	18	37	7.2	5.1	0.28	35	325	45
6	+36	0	450	18.4	31	60	—	9	111	14	7.9	0.33	92	850	61
8	+5.3	+4	650	19.5	38	52	0.4	9.3	144	54	2.7	0.26	148	1375	25
8	+5.3	+2	650	19.5	40	51	0.4	7.9	235	72	3.3	0.25	2.57	2370	33
8	+5.3	0	650	19.5	41	48	0.4	10.4	194	59	3.3	0.25	210	1950	33
8	+5.3	-2	650	19.5	35	57	0.5	7.0	122	44	2.8	0.28	116	1075	24
8	+5.3	-4.6	650	19.5	41	52	0.5	5.7	81	27	3.0	0.25	89	825	30
8	+5.3	-7	650	19.5	28	64	0.8	6.4	25	5	5.0	0.35	19	175	35

— = no measurements; long. + = downstream target; transv. + = exterior to orbit; HEP = high energy particles

long. — = upstream target; transv. — = interior to orbit; FN = fast neutrons

ThN = thermal neutrons

ϕ_{HEP} = flux of high energy particles

References

1. G. Jaffé, *Z. der Physik* **30**, 849 (1929).
2. H. H. Rossi, *Micro-dosimetry, biophysical aspects of radiation quality*, IAEA No. 58, 81 (1966).
3. ICRP Handbook 85 (1964).
4. J. Baarli, K. Goebel, and A. H. Sullivan, "The calibration of health physics instruments to measure high-energy radiation," *Health Physics* **9**, 1057 (1964).
5. H. H. Rossi and W. Rosenzweig, "A device for the measurement of dose as a function of specific ionization," *Radiology* **64**, No. 3, 404 (1955).
6. A. H. Sullivan, "Radiobiological cell survival data and the principles of radiation dosimetry," Health Physics (on press).
7. A. H. Sullivan and J. Baarli, "An ionization chamber for the estimation of the biological effectiveness of radiation," CERN 63–17 (1963).
8. J. Baarli and P. Bonét-Maury, "Relative biological effectiveness of 592 MeV protons on mice," *Nature* **205**, 361 (1965).
9. Kazuaki Katch and J. E. Turner, "A study of elementary particle interactions for high-energy dosimetry," *Health Physics* **13**, 831 (1967).
10. J. Baarli and A. H. Sullivan, "Radiation dosimetry for protection purposes near high-energy particle accelerators," *Health Physics* **11**, 353 (1965).
11. M. J. Lamb, T. W. McSheeby, C. E. Purdom, J. Baarli, and A. H. Sullivan, "The mutagenic effect of 600 MeV protons in Drossophylla melanogaster," *Rad. Bio.* **12**, 27 (1967).
12. J. Baarli, "Radiological physics of negative pions," *Rad. Res.* (in press).
13. T. Overton, "Experience with a linear energy transfer (LET) chamber at CERN," CERN 66–33 (1966).
14. V. P. Dzhelepov, *Izv. Akad. Nauk, SSSR Ser. Fiz.* **19**, 573 (1955).
15. H. W. Patterson, "Accelerator radiation monitoring and shielding," *Symposium on Accelerator Radiation Dosimetry and Experience*, Brookhaven (1965), p. 3.
16. R. F. Dvorak, R. L. Mundis, and R. V. Wheeler, "Radiation environment at the zero gradient synchrotron," *Symposium on Accelerator Radiation Dosimetry and Experience*, Brookhaven (1965), p. 34.
17. M. Zielczynski, V. N. Lebedov, and M. Salatskaya, "Instrument for determination of recommended relative biological effectiveness of radiation." *Inst. for Exp. Techniques* No. 6, 1217 (1964).
18. K. Goebel, A. Rindi, A. H. Sullivan, and J. Baarli, "The purpose, interpretation, and utilization of area monitoring measurements near the CERN accelerators," *OECD Symposium*, Stockholm (1967), p. 435.

Semiconductor junction detectors and their application to radiation dosimetry

R. P. PARKER

Physics Department,
Institute of Cancer Research,
Sutton, Surrey. U.K.

INTRODUCTION

This paper is concerned with the application of semiconducting materials to radiation dosimetry using essentially dose-rate and non-destructive techniques. As such it is complementary to the radiation damage methods described by other lecturers; the characteristics considered here are primarily a result of ionizing events within the crystal, the free charge carriers liberated being collected by the use of an electric field. The methods are in many ways analogous to the use of a gaseous ionization chamber and the dose-rate levels considered range from a few rad/min to around 10^5 rad/min.

Owing to the close proximity of its atoms a solid has an inherent advantage over a gas in that less energy is required to produce a hole-electron pair. This results in larger signals and less statistical spread (hence the current interest in semiconductors for high resolution γ-spectrometry). Furthermore the stopping power of a solid is greater than that of a gas, leading to the possibility of small but sensitive devices.

The objects of the present paper are to consider briefly the basic principles of semiconductor electrical conductivity detectors in so far as they affect their use as radiation detectors and to describe their relevant characteristics. Attix (1962) and Fowler (1963) have surveyed such systems in relation to other solid state methods of dosimetry, whilst comprehensive treatments of semiconductor detectors and their applications have recently been given by Dearnaley and Northrop (1966) and Gunnersen (1967).

PHYSICAL PRINCIPLES OF SEMICONDUCTOR DETECTORS

In both the gaseous ionization chamber and the semiconductor detector charge carriers released by ionizing events in the sensitive volume of the device are swept apart to the electrodes by means of an electric field, the charge deposited in the detector capacitance being ideally proportional to the energy lost by the incident radiation in the sensitive volume.

The gaseous detector imposes less stringent requirements for complete charge collection compared with the solid-state device, where high carrier mobility, low trapping and recombination rates, and a large yield of carriers per unit of energy expended are all desirable. A low background current is also essential for most applications. In general these requirements can be satisfied only by a semiconductor and Table 1 lists some possible materials, together with their relevant physical properties. The elements silicon and germanium stand out, particularly since they are the only materials which can at present be obtained in a state of high purity and crystalline perfection. However, the energy gap determines the intrinsic conductivity of a semiconductor at a given temperature and it can be seen that for Si and Ge this precludes their use as bulk conductivity detectors at room temperature, although operation at 77°K has been successfully accomplished in the case of silicon (Gibbons and Northrop, 1962).

In the present state of technological development of the other materials listed gallium arsenide (Northrop, 1960) and cadmium telluride (Mayer, 1967) are probably the most promising, particularly for room temperature

TABLE I Semiconductor properties

Semiconductor	Energy gap (eV) at 300 °K	Energy per electron-hole pair (eV)	Atomic number(s)	Electron mobility (cm² volt⁻¹ sec⁻¹) at 300 °K	Hole mobility (cm² volt⁻¹ sec⁻¹) at 300 °K	Electron life-time in p-type material (sec)	Hole life-time in n-type material (sec)
Germanium	0.67	2.94	32	3800	1800	10^{-3}	10^{-3}
Silicon	1.08	3.66	14	1500	500	3×10^{-3}	3×10^{-3}
Diamond	~6	10–20	6	1800	1200	—	—
Cadmium selenide	1.67	—	48, 34	650	—	$10^{-2} - 10^{-3}$	—
Cadmium sulphide	2.41	7.3	48, 16	350	15	$\sim 10^{-3}$	$<10^{-8}$
Cadmium telluride	1.44	4.65	48, 52	1050	80	4×10^{-8}	10^{-8}
Gallium antimonide	0.7	—	31, 51	5000	1000	$\sim 10^{-8}$	$\sim 10^{-8}$
Gallium arsenide	1.43	6.3	31, 33	8500	420	10^{-7}	10^{-7}
Gallium phosphide	2.25	—	31, 15	140	150	10^{-8}	10^{-8}
Indium antimonide	0.17	0.6	49, 51	$\sim 10^{5}$	$\sim 10^{3}$	$\sim 10^{-7}$	$\sim 10^{-7}$
Indium arsenide	0.33	—	49, 33	3×10^{4}	500	—	—
Indium phosphide	1.25	—	49, 15	5000	200	—	—
Lead sulphide	0.41	—	82, 16	400	650	2×10^{-5}	—
Zinc selenide	2.7	—	30, 34	530	28	—	—
Zinc sulphide	3.6	—	30, 16	140	5 (700 °K)	—	—
Zinc telluride	2.26	—	30, 52	340	110	—	—

operation, but for dosimetric application where tissue equivalence is desirable silicon is the most suitable. True tissue equivalence must await the development of relatively large volume organic semiconductors, a field which is of increasing importance (Guttman and Lyons, 1967).

For most practical purposes the level of impurity conduction, even in silicon and germanium, is too high for the construction of simple bulk conductivity detectors. Fortunately the resulting noise can be drastically reduced, at least in a restricted volume, by utilising the properties of a reverse-biassed junction between p- and n-type semiconductors. This was first achieved by McKay (1949) and further developed by Mayer and Gossick (1956).

When the n- and p-type materials are joined together some carriers will diffuse into the opposite region (Fig. 1 a), the net result being a flow of current from the p- to the n-type material. This current flow will continue until the Fermi levels on both sides of the junction are coincident; in this condition a space-charge will be set up by the ionized impurities remaining near the junction (Fig. 1 b), thus developing a potential barrier whose magnitude is about 0.7 volt for a gold surface barrier on silicon. The region of non-zero electric field is termed the "depletion volume" because it is depleted in free charge carriers and forms the sensitive region of the device. When this reverse bias is increased by the application of an external biassing potential it can be shown (Dearnaley and Northrop, 1966) that the depletion layer thickness is proportional to $(\varrho V)^{1/2}$, where ϱ is the base material resistivity and V is the applied voltage.

In this depletion region there exists both a low free carrier concentration and an electric field: the background current flowing will therefore be low (typically a fraction of a microamp) and any additional charge carriers produced by ionization processes initiated by incident nuclear radiation will be swept apart in the electric field and the charge collected at the electrodes.

The sensitive thickness of the detector may be increased by raising either the resistivity or the bias. In silicon thicknesses of a few hundred μm are typical and by careful fabrication and the use of very high resistivity material (50000 ohm-cm and higher) sensitive thicknesses in excess of 1 mm have been achieved. The manner in which the sensitive thickness is easily varied by altering the applied bias voltage is a useful feature of these devices which is not found with the gaseous ionization chamber; it has been utilized in the construction of instruments for dose measurement in mixed radiation fields

(Moncaster, Northrop and Raines, 1963; Blanc, Casanovas and Soudain, 1965).

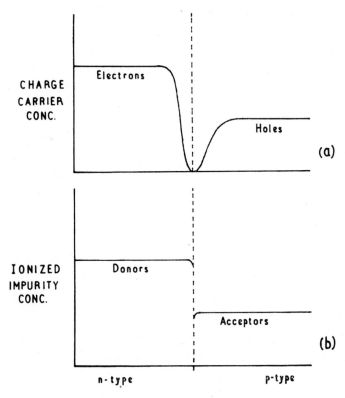

FIGURE 1   (a) free charge carrier concentrations; (b) ionized impurity concentrations at a *p–n* junction (Parker, 1967)

Although the charge collection efficiency is very close to 100% in a well-constructed device made from high purity material there will always be some current flow due to diffusion, space-charge generated carriers and surface leakage. The resultant noise will restrict the lowest energy loss detectable to typically 30 keV in silicon at room temperature, but by cooling this may be reduced to a few keV. For a comprehensive discussion on noise reference should be made to Goulding and Hansen (1961) and Dearnaley and Northrop (1966).

TYPES OF SEMICONDUCTOR JUNCTION DETECTOR

Various methods for the fabrication of junction detectors have been devised and are described in detail elsewhere (Dearnaley and Northrop, 1966). Silicon is the material generally used since room temperature operation is possible; owing to its higher atomic number germanium is of increasing performance for γ-spectrometry but operation at liquid nitrogen temperatures is necessary. Since this paper is primarily concerned with dosimetric applications the following discussion will be limited to silicon.

Brief descriptions of the construction methods in common use are given below: in all cases the starting material is the same namely a slice of cleaned, etched, high-purity silicon.

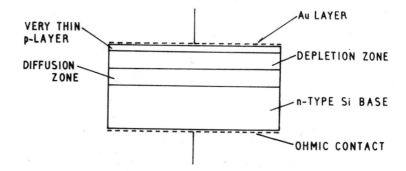

Regions of Charge Generation in PN Junction

FIGURE 2   Diagrammatic construction and regions of charge collection for *p–n* junction surface barrier detector. (Parker and Morley, 1967)

1   Diffused junction detectors

For these devices the starting material is usually *p*-type and the *p–n* junction is formed by the diffusion of an *n*-type impurity (such as phosphorus) at a temperature of $\sim 800°C$, the back contact being ohmic (for example, silver loaded epoxy cement). The resultant device (see Fig. 2) is robust and relatively easy to construct, but owing to the high temperatures required there is some degradation in the minority carrier lifetime of the material, resulting in higher currents and inferior charge collection (Walter and Bates, 1966).

2   Surface barrier devices

These are straightforward junction counters similar to the diffused variety but the *p–n* junction is obtained by spontaneously forming a *p*-type layer on *n*-type material in the presence of oxygen at room temperature. Electrical connection is made via an evaporated gold film and again the back contact is ohmic. Since no high temperature treatment is necessary the silicon should retain its minority carrier lifetime but the device is less robust than the diffused junction and more susceptible to contamination.

3   Lithium drifted devices

The sensitive thickness of simple junction counters is restricted by the resistivity of the material and the potential which can be conveniently applied without excessive surface leakage current. In order to make thicker devices the lithium ion drift method is used (Pell, 1960). Lithium, which is a donor to silicon, is diffused into *p*-type material to a depth of about 100 μm at a temperature of $\sim 400°$C. A reverse bias is then applied and the temperature reduced to 100–200°C. The lithium ions are very mobile and migrate interstitially through the silicon, distributing themselves so as to minimise the electric field and therefore compensate the initial acceptors present, creating an effectively intrinsic zone. The resulting detector is designated *p–i–n* and by this method of fabrication compensation has been achieved to depths of over 1 cm.

4   Amplification devices

Detectors constructed as described above all suffer from the disadvantage that they possess no internal amplification and therefore require low-noise electronic amplifiers.

Multiplication type counters would have the advantage of very large output pulses and this has recently been achieved (see Huth, 1966). The multiplication is achieved by biasing the counter to a point where internal amplification in the bulk material occurs before surface breakdown, the high electric fields being obtained by contouring the edges of the device. The amplification factor obtained is a function of the particle range and factors approaching 10^3 have been achieved for short range particles, values of 20–50 being normal for minimum ionizing particle traversals.

At present the detector thickness and area are very limited but nevertheless thay are already showing promise as dosimeters (Jones, 1967).

X-RAY AND γ-RAY DOSIMETRY

The application of semiconductor detectors to x-ray and γ-ray dosimetry has been described by Jones (1962a, 1963), Baily and Kramer (1964), Parker and Morley (1967) and Parker (1967); reference should be made to these publications for detailed information.

In order to detect an incident photon it must interact with the detector to produce a charged particle, which in turn causes ionization. The event need not occur within the depletion volume since minority carriers created within a diffusion length of the depletion volume can diffuse into it and be collected provided that the time constant of the system are appropriately chosen. By choosing good minority carrier lifetime material (2–3 msec) diffusion lengths of several millimetres are possible thus providing a useful way of effectively increasing the sensitive volume of the detector for dosimetric measurements (see Fig. 2).

The devices may be used in both the pulse-counting and *DC* modes and these will be considered in turn.

1   Pulse-counting mode

This is the most sensitive method of operation of junction devices and is the method normally adopted for the detection and spectrometry of charged particles.

The major problem is the inherent noise of the device and the time constants and applied voltage must be chosen for optimum signal/noise ratio. The time constants normally used (0.1 to 1.0 μsec) are small compared with the diffusion time and so the sensitive volume is restricted to the depletion zone. In *p–n* devices this is usually up to 0.5 mm thick but may extend to several millimetres in Li-drifted devices.

The electrical pulses may be counted with or without note being taken of their size and Fig. 3 shows the number of counts obtained plotted as a function of the discriminator level. The different curves were obtained with a needle probe of sensitive volume 0.04 ml using γ-emitting radionuclides of different energies, the radiation exposure being 1 roentgen in each case. At low discriminator levels the counts/roentgen are all of the same order and for this particular detector, operated at a discriminator level equivalent to 115 keV, the total variation over an incident energy range of 0.4 MeV is less than $\pm 30\%$ about a mean sensitivity of 8.75×10^6 counts/ roentgen.

At room temperature the noise level is such that dose rates down to 10 μr/min may be measured even with this small volume detector; the sensitivity may be increased by using a detector of larger volume. No alteration in pulse-counting sensitivity over a temperature range of 0–40°C has been observed although an increase in ambient temperature does necessitate an increase in discriminator level if the background due to noise is to kept be constant.

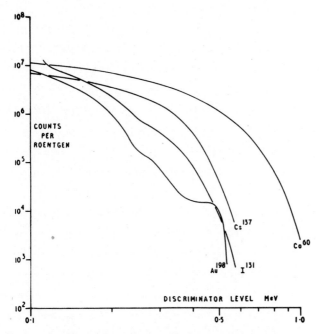

FIGURE 3 Discriminator curves obtained in pulse-counting mode, depletion depth 300 μm. (Parker and Morley, 1967)

The absorbed dose, D, in rads is given by

$$D = (\text{constant}) \times \sum_{E} N_E \cdot E,$$

where E is the energy lost by each electron and N_E is the number of electrons losing that amount of energy. It is therefore possible to compute the absorbed dose, and as shown by Jones (1965) the agreement with theory is satisfactory. Jones also discusses electronic circuits which will perform the weighting operation.

2 Direct current mode

Pulse counting techniques can be used for dose-rates up to around 0.1 r/min., the upper limit depending upon the size of the detector and the speed of the electronics; above this limit the counting-rates become excessive and use is made of D.C. techniques.

When the semiconductor is exposed to radiation the minority carrier density will be increased owing to the generation of charge carriers, resulting in an increase in the current flowing across the junction. These carriers may be produced in either the depletion or diffusion regions and by measuring the difference between the current with and without radiation the exposure can be estimated. Figure 4 illustrates results obtained using a surface barrier

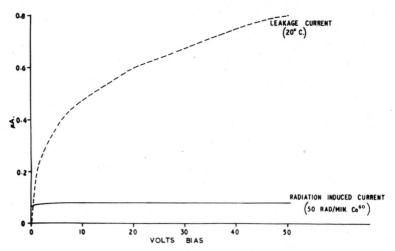

FIGURE 4 Current versus applied bias characteristic. (Parker and Morley, 1967)

detector when irradiated by 50 rad/min. ^{60}Co γ-rays. It can be seen that whilst the leakage current, in the absence of radiation, increases with bias the radiation induced current is independent of bias except at the beginning of its characteristic. This is because the diffusion length was comparable with the detector dimensions in this particular case.

Practical difficulties are experienced owing to variations in the leakage current with temperature and time and the method is only satisfactory at high dose-rates. Kuckuck, Bernescut, Zatzick and Jupiter (1966) report on its use with a flash X-ray machine, where radiation induced currents up to 48 amps were observed. However, at zero applied bias the signal/noise ratio is at a maximum and since the leakage current is zero no difficulty is experienced owing to drift.

This is the *photovoltaic* mode of operation, the photovoltage being set up in a forward direction so as to counteract the natural flow of carriers in the backward direction due to diffusion. The characteristics with respect to sensitivity, temperature dependence and dose-rate response are functions of the load resistance (see, for example, Scharf, 1967) and the following is a simplified treatment of the problem.

If V is the voltage set up across the junction then the current density J_i will be given by Shockley's equation:

$$J_i = K[\exp(eV/kT) - 1],$$

where T is the absolute temperature, e the electronic charge, k Boltzmann's constant and K a constant characteristic of the diode. The radiation induced current density, J_r, will be given by

$$J_r = eR(L_p + L_n + D),$$

where R is the rate of production of charge carriers per cm^2 per sec and is therefore proportional to the exposure rate. L_p and L_n are the diffusion lengths in the p- and n-type material whilst D is the depletion depth.

The resulting current density J will therefore be given by

$$J = K[\exp(eV/kT) - 1] - eR(L_p + L_n + D).$$

If measurements are made under short circuit conditions using a meter of low input impedence then $V \simeq 0$ and

$$J_{sc} = -eR(L_p + L_n + d),$$

indicating a linear dependence of the short-circuit current J_{sc} with dose-rate. This is found in practice (Fig. 5). Alternatively a high input impedence voltmeter may be used giving rise to a more complicated expression which indicates an approximately linear dose-rate dependence at low dose-rates, becoming logarithmic at high dose-rates; this is shown by the experimental results illustrated in Fig. 6. At very high dose-rates, when the photo-voltage becomes comparable with the natural potential existing across the junction, a flattening of response is indicated (Fig. 7).

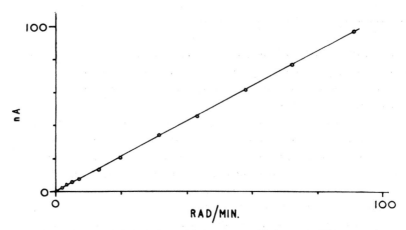

FIGURE 5   Variation of short-circuit current with dose-rate (^{60}Co γ-rays)
(Parker and Morley, 1967)

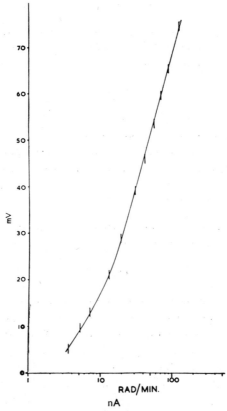

FIGURE 6   Variation of open-circuit voltage with dose-rate (^{60}Co γ-rays)
(Parker and Morley, 1967)

Both theory and experiment show that the sensitivity in the short-circuit mode is independent of ambient temperature, whilst in the open-circuit mode the response is severely temperature dependent.

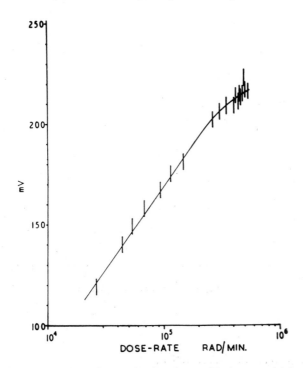

FIGURE 7   Variation of open-circuit voltage with dose-rate in the pulse
(6 MeV linear accelerator). (Parker and Morley, 1967)

For most applications a linear dose-rate response, independent of temperature, is preferable and measurements of the short-circuit current have been found to be convenient and reproducible. By the use of long lifetime material sensitive volumes up to 2 mm in thickness can be achieved which are comparable in sensitivity to many of the more expensive Li-drifted devices. Their sensitivity and simplicity makes them particularly suitable for monitoring applications.

We will now consider the response of the system to photons of different energies. The atomic number of Si is 14, close to that of compact bone (13.8) whilst the electron density is the same as that of bone (3.0×10^{23} elec-

25*

trons/gm). Thus silicon is approximately bone, not air, equivalent and as such considerable wavelength dependence is observed for radiation less than 200 keV in energy (see Fig. 8).

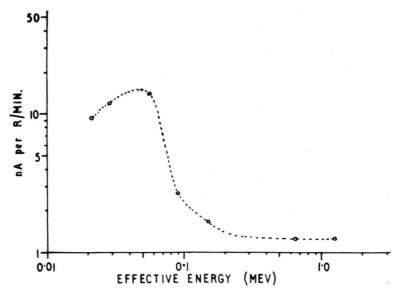

FIGURE 8   Variation of measured energy response per roentgen with energy for needle probe. (Parker and Morley, 1967)

CHARGED PARTICLE DOSIMETRY

Although semiconductor junction detectors have been used a great deal for charged particle spectrometry (see Dearnaley and Northrop, 1966) relatively little work has been carried out on their application to the dosimetry of charged particles.

In a series of papers Baily and Hilbert (1965, 1966a, 1966b) describe the use of Li-drifted detectors to the dosimetry of β-emitters ranging in maximum energy from [32]P (1.70 MeV) to [35]S (0.168 MeV). Use was made of both counting methods and the determination of the open-circuit voltage, which was directly proportional to dose-rate over most of the range of interest.

For plane sources of ^{32}P and [204]Tl these authors studied the ratio of the open circuit voltage to the surface absorbed dose-rate as a function of the distance from the source; the ratio showed less variation as the detector area was decreased and remained essentially constant after a certain minimum source-detector distance was reached (Fig. 9). This distance is about 10 cm, suggesting application as a dose-rate monitor of a health physics nature.

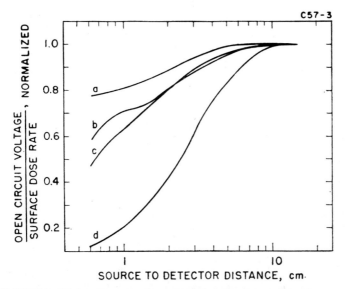

FIGURE 9   Ratio of generated open-circuit voltage to surface dose-rate as a function of source-detector distance. The curves are for a thick ^{204}Tl source of area 1.04 cm^2. Curves (a), (b), (c) and (d) are for detector areas of 0.04, 0.24, 1.0 and 11.9 cm^2 respectively. (Baily and Hilbert, 1965)

With pulse-counting the sensitivity is considerably increased but otherwise the behaviour is similar to that observed in the open-circuit voltage studies. For low energy β-emitters such as ^{35}S no constant ratio is observed between detector response and surface absorbed dose-rate due to energy absorbed in the air between the detector and the source. Nevertheless, the variation is small enough to permit application as a survey meter.

If the range of the particles is less than the thickness of the detector then a determination of the energy distribution (E) can be made. Alternatively, a detector whose thickness is small compared with the particle range will measure the rate of energy loss (dE/dx or LET_∞). A combination of these measurements provides information of value in calculating dose distributions for mixed radiation fields and heavy particle studies. Raju (1967) describes their use with high energy α- and p-beams and has also utilised small silicon diodes for determining beam profiles (Raju, 1966). Similar diodes have been used by Koehler (1967) for employing depth-dose distributions in a water phantom irradiated with small, well-collimated beams of 160 MeV protons. Thick Li-drifted detectors have been of use in examining the characteristics of π-beams in the energy range 50–365 MeV in connection with radiobiological studies (Raju, 1965).

Owing to their good energy resolution semiconductor detectors are also used for measuring neutron spectra via charged particle reactions. The subject has been reviewed by Watt (1966) who also considers other solid state methods of neutron dosimetry. Practical limitations are imposed due to the onset of radiation damage and other lectures in this Summer School are dealing with this type of dosimetry.

RADIATION DAMAGE

When silicon is exposed to β- or γ-radiation greater than about 300 keV in energy, or heavy particles of all practical energies, radiation damage will ensue. With γ-radiation the damage will be uniformly distributed throughout the volume as Frenkel defects which may combine with other impurity centres. In this way energy levels are introduced into the band gap, causing both the majority carrier concentration and the minority carrier lifetime to decrease. The former leads to higher resistivity and thus increased depletion depth at a given bias whilst the latter results in increased reverse current and noise and decreased radiation-induced current and open circuit voltage.

Parker and Morley (1967) studied the effect of ^{60}Co γ-radiation on surface-barrier detectors constructed from 2 msec minority carrier lifetime high-resistivity material. Their measurements suggest that whilst radiation doses of less than 10^3 rad cause measurable effects the damage is unlikely to cause appreciable variations in sensitivity below 10^4 rad. Jones (1962b) studied both p–n junction counters and Li-drift detectors of unspecified carrier lifetime, monitoring both the noise and the γ-sensitivity. No deterioration was observed intil a dose of 10^6 roentgens was reached.

It therefore appears that the devices are usable for the dose range usually encountered in medicine or health physics. It is interesting to note that it is possible to "pre-irradiate" material so as to minimise the effect of damage. Thus Koehler (1967) pre-exposed his detectors to 2×10^6 rads of 160 MeV protons; a further 10^5 rads then altered the sensitivity by only 1%.

CONCLUSIONS

The devices described here possess the usual attributes of a solid state dosimeter, such as ruggedness, stopping power and small size. Compared to most other types of solid state dosimeter the major advantage of the semi-conductor junction device is its ability to measure dose-rate rather than integrated dose. By using different types of associated electronic, equipment a very wide range of dose-rates can be determined, extending from 10^{-5} rad/min to greater than 10^5 rad/min for a detector whose sensitive volume is only 0.04 ml.

The reproducibility is good provided the effect of radiation damage is negligible and the fast response ($\rightarrow 10$ nanoseconds) can be important in connection with pulsed beams. The main disadvantages are wavelength dependence and noise, and the developments reported above in respect to internally amplifying devices are likely to prove an important advance.

Semiconductors junction detectors are finding uses in many areas of radiation measurement. Their technology is advancing rapidly and their suitability for high-resolution spectrometry will be increasingly exploited in the future.

Acknowledgements

I am grateful to the International Atomic Energy Agency and the publishers of "Physics in Medicine and Biology" for permission to reproduce diagrams used in this paper.

References

Attix, F. H., (1962) U.S. Naval Research Laboratory Report No. 5777.
Baily, N. A. and J. W. Hilbert, (1965) *Phys. Med. Biol.* **10** 41.
Baily, N. A. and J. W. Hilbert, (1966a) *Phys. Med. Biol.* **11** 75.
Baily, N. A. and J. W. Hilbert, (1966b) *Health Phys.* **12** 705.
Baily, N. A. and G. Kramer, (1964) *Rad. Res.* **22** 53.
Blanc, D., J. Casanovas, A. M. Chapuis, and G. Soudain, (1965) *Nucl. Instrum. Meth.* **37** 90.
Dearnaley, G. and D. C. Northrop, (1966) *Semiconductor Counters for Nuclear Radiations*, Spon, London (2nd Edn.).
Fowler, J. F., (1963) *Phys. Med. Biol.* **8** 1.
Gibbons, P. E. and D. C. Northrop, (1962) *Proc. Phys. Soc.* **80** 276.
Goulding, F. S. and W. L. Hansen, (1961) *Nucl. Instrum. Meth.* **12** 249.
Gunnersen, E. M., (1967) *Rep. Prog. Physics*, Pr. 1, p. 21.
Guttman, F. and L. E. Lyons, (1967) *Organic Semiconductors*, John Wiley, New York.
Huth, G. C., (1966) *I.E.E.E. Trans. Nucl. Sci.* **NS-13**, 36.
Jones, A. R., (1962a) *Health Physics* **8** 1.
Jones, A. R., (1962b) A.E.C.L. Report No. CRRD-1102.

Jones, A. R., (1963) *Phys. Med. Biol.* **8** 451.

Jones, A. R., (1965) A.E.C.L.-2252.

Jones, A. R., (1967) A.E.C.L.-2637.

Koehler, A. M., (1967) *Rad. Res. Suppl.* **7**, 53.

Kuckuck, R. W., R. Bernescut, M. R. Zatzick, and C. P. Jupiter, (1966) *I.E.E.E. Trans. Nucl. Sci.* **NS-13** 111.

Mayer, J. W., (1967) *J. Appl. Phys.* **38** 296.

Mayer, J. W. and B. R. Gossick, (1956) *Rev. Sci. Instrum.* **27** 407.

McKay, K. G., (1949) *Phys. Rev.* **76** 1537.

Moncaster, M. E., D. C. Northrop, and J. A. Raines, (1963) *Nucl. Instrum. Meth.* **22** 157.

Northrop, D. C., (1960) *Nature* **187** 405.

Parker, R. P., (1967) *Proc. I.A.E.A. Conf. on "Solid State and Chemical Radiation Dosimetry in Biology and Medicine"*, p. 437.

Parker, R. P. and B. J. Morley, (1967) *ibid.* p. 167.

Pell, E. M., (1960) *J. Appl. Phys.* **31** 291.

Raju, M. R., (1965) *Nucl. Instrum. Meth.* **37** 152.

Raju, M. R., (1966) *Phys. Med. Biol.* **11** 371.

Raju, M. R., (1967) *Rad. Res. Suppl.* **7**, 43.

Scharf, K., (1967) *Health Phys.* **13** 575.

Walter, F. J. and D. D. Bates, (1966) *I.E.E.E. Trans. Nucl. Sci.* **NS-13** 231.

Watt, D. E., (1966) U.K.A.E.A. PG Rep. 711 (CC).

CHAPTER III–3

Charged particle tracks in insulating solids

J. MORY

Centre d'Etudes Nucléaires de Fontenay-aux-Roses (France)

A   GENERALITIES

I   Introduction

During the last few years it has been found that in many insulating solids (crystals, glasses, plastics) heavy charged particles produce fine tracks when passing through the material. In 1959 Silks and Barnes[1] reported on electron

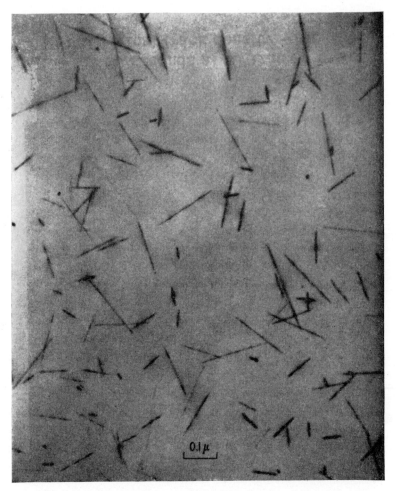

FIGURE 1   Fission fragment tracks in synthetic fluor-phlogopite mica
observed in the electron microscope (after Ref. 4)
(a) before etching; track density $\sim 9 \times 10^9$ cm^{-2};

microscopic observations of small damaged regions of about 100 Å diameter in mica specimens heavily irradiated with fission fragments (Fig. 1). In
1961 Fleisher *et al.* continued this work, with a view to stabilize these tracks
and to improve their observation, but especially to explore their utility in
nuclear physics with respect to the study of cosmic rays.

Their first result was the discovery of the technique of development of

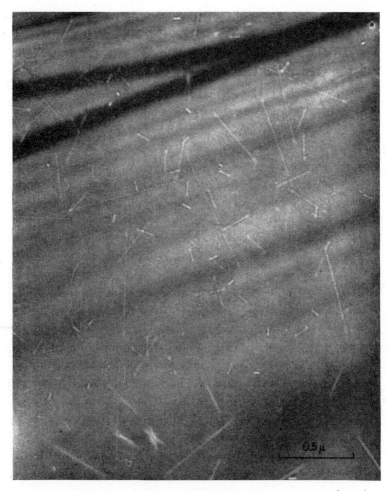

(b) after etching (10 seconds at 20°C in HF 20%); track density $\sim 10^9$ cm^{-2}.
The tracks are hollow channels

tracks in mica by means of etching. They also showed that mica is selective, i.e. it only records particles with mass larger than a given value. Afterwards this study was extended to a larger number of insulators, for which they found new development techniques and determined the sensitivity varying from one insulator to another.

Passing from the essentially qualitative and experimental field to a more quantitative and theoretical treatment, they investigated with Hubbard the formation mechanism of the tracks. They introduced the notion of "ionic explosion spike" and the information criteria for tracks with respect to the "critical energy loss rate" and, more recently, with respect to the "primary ionization rate."

Among the other authors who have participated in this elaboration, one can mention Childs and Slifkin, who developed a technique of decoration of tracks is silver chloride single crystals.[2] Although this technique is valuable for this special case; it is unfortunately not applicable to the majority of other insulating solids.

In the next chapters we will review the different fundamental aspects of this phenomenon of recording charged particles in insulating solids. For this purpose we shall follow an almost chronologic order.

1 Development of tracks

The first investigations of charged particle tracks in mica have been made by electron microscopic observation.[1,3] Although this mode of observation was very interesting for the examination of the structure of the tracks, it became soon clear that serious disadvantages strongly limit its use:

only very thin samples (a few hundreds of Ångströms), which are not easily obtained, can be used.

very small observation surface, hence necessity of very high track densities (10^8–10^9 cm^{-2}).

it is difficult to see a track at full length (i.e. of the order of 10 μ);

in some cases the tracks are annihilated upon the impact of electrons.

Fortunately in 1962 Price and Walker discovered the technique of revealing traces by etching.[4] Under the influence of an appropriate solvent, the track grows larger and becomes visible in the optical microscope. This is explained by the fact that generally a damaged region is chemically more reactive that the bulk material, because of the important free energy associated with a disordered structure. When an insulator containing tracks is dipped into a solvent, the damaged regions which reach the surface are preferentially etched (Fig. 2). On the other hand the internal tracks are not developed. This is a fundamental difference with the nuclear emulsions, where all tracks are revealed, even if they are entirely lying in the bulk of the detector.

In Table 1 the most typical etching conditions for some commonly used insulators are reviewed. We have also mentioned in this table the lightest ion detectable by each material (after).[5]

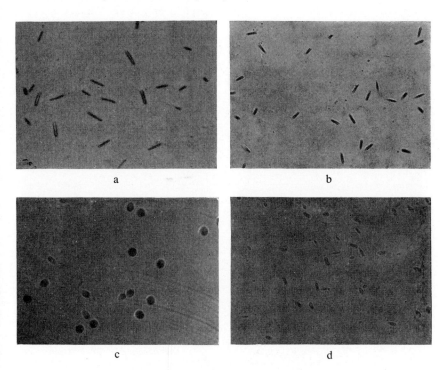

FIGURE 2   Tracks in different materials

(a) Fission fragment tracks in muscovite mica; etching 2 hours at 25°C in HF 40%; (b) Fission fragment tracks in phosphate glass; etching: 45 minutes at 25°C in HF 40%; (c) Fission fragment tracks in ordinary glass; etching: 4 seconds at 25°C in HF 40%; (d) α-particle tracks in cellulose nitrate; etching 2 minutes at 55°C in NaOH–6 N

The track development by etching shows two important characteristics:

after an incubation period necessary for the penetration of the solvent, the transverse dimensions of the tracks vary linearly with time (Fig. 3).

the track length does not increase during etching.

In fact this length tends to decrease as a consequence of surface erosion of the insulator. It has indeed been shown[6] that the condition for visibility of the tracks after etching is that the tracks have to form an angle with the normal, which is smaller than $\theta_c = \cos^{-1}(V_g/V_T)$, where V_g is the etching rate perpendicular to the surface, and V_T is the etching rate along the track. In the case of mica, where $V_g \ll V_T$, this angle is very large, and all tracks are revealed. On the other hand, in some glasses, θ_c is of the order of 40° and the recording efficiency is much poorer. This recording efficiency, which is equal to $\cos^2 \theta_c$, varies from 100% for mica and most plastics, to 40% for some glasses provided of course the particle is detectable.

TABLE I   Track revelation conditions in some commonly used insulators (after Ref. 5)

Solids	Etching conditions			Lightest detectable particle
Glasses				
P_2O_5	HF 40%	45 min	25°C	
	or			
	NaOH 6N	2 h	25°C	S
NaCa	HF 40%	3 sec	25°C	
Quartz	Sol KOH	10 min	210°C	
Micas	HF 40%	3 sec – 40 min	25°C	Ne
Plastics				
Mylar	NaOH 6N	10 min	70°C	He
Lexan (or Makrofol)	NaOH 6N	8 min	70°C	He
Cellulosenitrate	NaOH 6N	2 min	60°C	H
	or			
	NaOK 6N	2–4 h	25°C	

The working conditions of etching largely influence the revelation of the tracks. Generally an increase in temperature or in concentration of the solvent yields an accelerated effect.[4] It seems however that the best results are obtained with slow treatment, i.e. by lowering the concentration (e.g. in glasses) or by lowering temperature (e.g. in cellulose nitrate).[5] The use of ultra-sounds also increases the etching rate.[7]

Although general rules of etching seem to be well established at the present time, it will remain an art rather than exact science, in which some undefined skill of the user is required.[5]

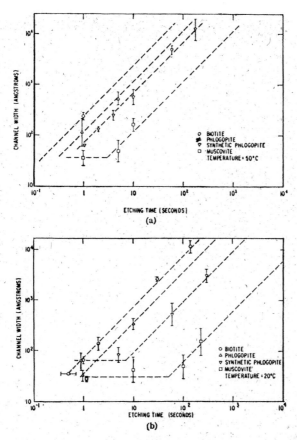

FIGURE 3   Etching rates in several micas in HF 20% (after Ref. 4) at 50°C and 20°C

II   Track counting

The most commonly used method at the present time is counting tracks in the optical microscope. This method is still most useful and time saving if one chooses a magnification appropriate to the size and the density of the tracks. However, apart from the fact that this method is tedious a large number of samples is to be examined, a good and precise counting becomes impossible in the case of low track densities ($<100 \text{ cm}^{-2}$). Among the attempts to realize automatic counting devices we can mention the following.

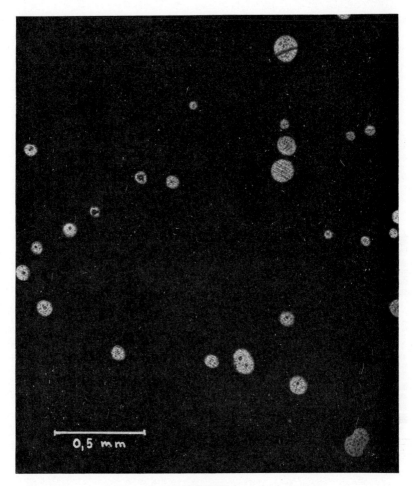

FIGURE 4

The apparatus set up by Debeauvais[8] is based upon a continuous displacement of the microscope table and an automatic photographic camera. Track counting is performed easily by projection of the film. As well as the high cost of the apparatus, counting at very low track densities remains difficult.

The use of micro-densitometer for measuring the variation of the optical density of light transmitted by an irradiated sample as a function of the number of tracks.[9] This method seems to be quite accurate and very fast, but it

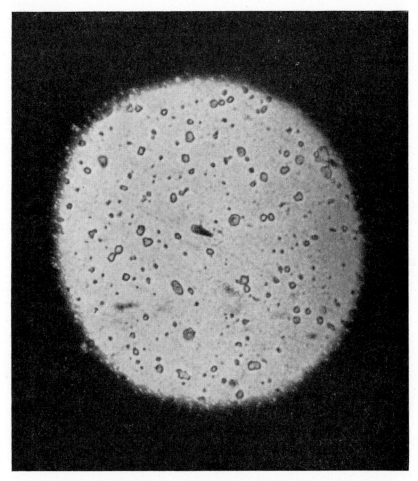

FIGURE 4   Spots created by etching fission fragment tracks in metallized mylar (after Ref. 12)

only covers a narrow useful range of densities (from about 10^5 to about 10^6 cm^{-2}).

The measurement of the electrical resistivity of a membrane traversed by the recorded particles. One measures the electrical resistivity of a cell composed by an electrolyte on both sides of the membrane. This resistance should be a function of the number of tracks and their size. Promising experiments in this field have been performed on mica;[10] on the other hand the experiments on makrofol[11,12] have been less conclusive.

For the measurement of very low densities (1 to 100 cm^{-2} or less), one has thought of using metallized plastic.[5,12,13] For this purpose a plastic plate is metallized (usually with aluminium) on one side. After irradiation the sample is etched on the non-metallized side. The etching agent (e.g. sodium hydroxide) penetrates the channels, traverses the membrane and dissolves the aluminium. The etching rate of aluminium being much larger than the one of the plastic, a spot without metal is obtained after a certain etching time, having a diameter of 50 to 100 times larger than the corresponding track. This spot is then visible with the naked eye (Fig. 4). Consequently this enables counting of extremely low track densities. This procedure is likely to be used in many cases, for measurement of very low neutron fluxes, as well as for the measurement of doses of low radioactive elements or for the detection of heavy particles in cosmic rays.

III Characteristics of insulating detectors

Almost all the insulating solids are likely to record charged particles: inorganic crystals, glasses or plastics. It is therefore possible to choose the detecting material as a function of the investigation which is planned, taking into account both the particle to be recorded and the experimental conditions. Hence it is possible to build ones own detector, e.g. a glass containing as an impurity the material of which the nuclear characteristics are investigated (fission cross section, potential barrier height, etc.)

1 *Effects of environment factors*

Most of the mineral insulators and glasses are relatively insensitive to severe working conditions. Large hydrostatic pressures have few effect.[14] At liquid nitrogen temperature (77°K) the tracks are generally perfectly formed and detectable. Tracks are stable before etching up to 500°C in mica and up to 200°C in most of the glasses. In the higher plastics (e.g. hexan or makrofol), tracks are stable up to about 180°C. On the other hand, in the more sensible plastics (e.g. cellulose nitrate) the external conditions have a more pronounced influence: the tracks are only stable at temperatures up to 85°C and they do not seem to be recorded in the absence of oxygen (experiments have been performed under a vacuum of the order of 10^{-6} torr, under nitrogen atmosphere and at liquid nitrogen temperature).[5] Contrary to the higher plastics, glasses and inorganic crystals, the cellulose nitrate is very sensitive up to destruction to weakly ionizing radiation (γ-rays or UV-light).[5]

The greatest advantage of solid track detectors is the stability in time of tracks before etching. Irradiated samples may therefore be stocked for a very long time without special precautions before they are studied, and without affecting the results. Experiments on zircon have shown e.g. that tracks in this material are expected to remain stable for 10^{39} years at room temperature. In the case of mica this stability is of the order of 10^{16} years. After etching this stability becomes almost infinite. In glass e.g. the etched tracks remain visible and countable with unchanged efficiency even after annealing for several hours at 400°C. (This temperature being close to the softening point.)[15]

2 Formation mechanism of tracks "ionic explosion spikes"

When a charged particle traverses a material, it loses energy, up to immobilization, following several mechanisms:

energy loss by ionization: a particle passing close to an atom can pull out an electron and correspondingly create a positive ion either by capture of the electron or by ejection into the lattice. At each of such electronic interactions the particle loses a part of its energy. This phenomenon especially occurs at high energy.

energy loss by atomic collisions; in this case the particle enters into direct collision with the atom as a whole, and is able to eject it from its lattice site. The energy exchange is much larger, especially if the masses of the particle and the atom are not too different. On the other hand the probability of such an interaction is very small at high energy and increases when the energy of the particle decreases, since the atomic collision cross section is inversely proportional to the energy. The "displacement spike" as introduced by Brinkman[16,17] is associated with this kind of interaction.

There are two arguments which point towards the almost exclusive contribution of ionization in the formation of tracks in insulators:

tracks are observed practically at full length, whereas atomic collisions principally occur at the end of the path;

no tracks are found in conductors or semiconductors, where only atomic collisions are able to produce stable defects. In these solids ionization is indeed a typical transient phenomenon since the number of free electrons is large enough to compensate very quickly an electronic defect.

Starting from these considerations, Walker *et al.* have introduced the notion of ionic explosion spike.[5,18] * These authors state that the charged particle ionizes a large number of atoms along its trajectory by ejection of the electrons into the lattice, thus creating a channel containing a large concentration of positively charged ions. Since the material is an insulator, there are only few free electrons available for neutralizing these ions; hence the ions are subject to a strong Coulomb repulsion which ejects them from their site. This yields a channel of large vacancy concentrations surrounded by a region containing many interstitials (Fig. 5). The preferential etching of

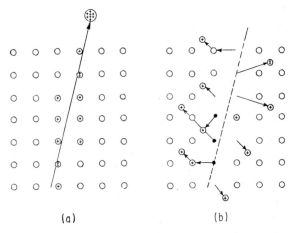

(a)   (b)

FIGURE 5   Formation of a track in a simple crystal
(a) the charged particle has ionized a large number of atoms; (b) mutual repulsion has separated the ions which are ejected in the lattice (after Ref. 18)

t
racks is then explained by the fact that their path is strongly disturbed and hence shows up a much greater chemical reactivity than the bulk material. In fact this model is a generalization of the Varley mechanism for the creation of interstitials in ionic crystals.

If this theory can be applied to all insulators, for plastics another physico-chemical phenomenon may occur. The electrons ejected by ionization (primary electron) as well as the secondary electrons (those ejected by the primaries, sometimes called δ-rays) may break the polymeric chains and

* We review this theory in spite of the fact that it has recently been questioned by some authors (L. T. Chadderton, *Sol. State Comm.* **4**, 391 (1966).

give rise to free radicals, and the degradation of the polymeric.[19] The damaged region thus consists of polymeric chains with a mean molecular weight which is smaller than in the original polymeric. Since the reactivity and the behaviour of a polymeric with respect to a solvent usually vary with the inverse of its molecular weight, the preferential etching of radiation-damaged regions in explained.

It should finally be emphasized that the formation of tracks in polymerics is not only to be explained on the basis of damage by δ-rays. It is probable that both the ionic explosion spike mechanism and the rupture of polymeric chains are playing a role. This should also account for the greater radiation sensitivity of polymerics compared with glasses and inorganic solids.

3 Sensitivity

The question whether the conditions by which a particle could or could not be recorded in a given material, has been unsolved for a long time.

The first hypothesis was that the particle should possess, at its entry in the detector, an energy and a mass such that its energy loss rate dE/dx is larger than some critical value $(dE/dx)_{crit.}$ which is characteristic for each of the materials used.[20] Unfortunately this hypothesis, although attractive in the beginning, was soon destroyed by unexplainable contradictions.

He^4-ions of 1.2 MeV and $dE/dx = 3$ MeV mg^{-1} cm^{-2} e.g. are not detected in makrofol, whereas the same ions with energy of 0.2 MeV but with $dE/dx = 1.5$ MeV mg^{-1} cm^2 are detected. Recent experiments have on the other hand shown that the relativistic ions of iron ($E = 84.000$ MeV) are not detected in cellulose nitrate, which is in contradiction with theory.[21]

Starting from the idea that tracks are only produced by ionization (ionic explosion spike), a new track formation criterion has been studied, namely the criterion of primary ionization rate.[22]

This investigation consists of two parts:

an experimental part, where the insulator is hit by different kinds of ions accelerated to a given energy. The recording efficiency (the ratio of the number of tracks to the number of ions which hit the target) is determined by counting the tracks. Also the quality of the tracks are examined, e.g. their length.

a purely theoretical part, where the variation of the primary ionization rate is calculated for a given insulator and a given ion, as a function of the ion energy.

Afterwards the experimental data are plotted. One finds, for each of the investigated solids, a critical value of *dJ/dx*, above which the tracks are perfectly etched, and recorded with a 100% efficiency. Beneath this value no tracks are observed. A very narrow region surrounds this critical value, where the tracks are often reduced to points with a recording efficiency smaller than one (Fig. 6, 7, 8).

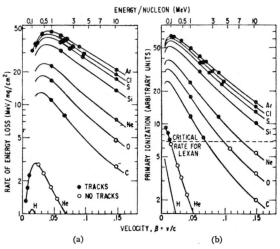

Particle recording characteristics as a function of energy (after Ref. 22)
FIGURE 6   Muscovite mica

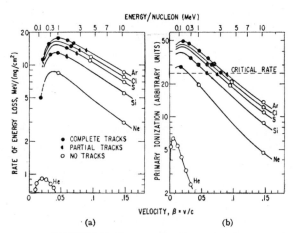

FIGURE 7   Lexan polycarbonate resin

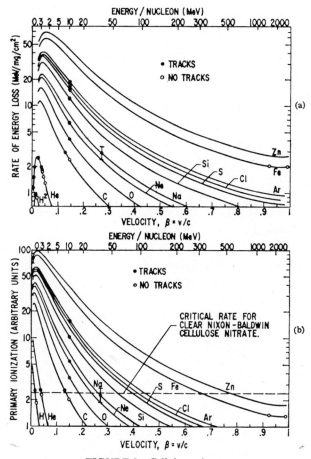

FIGURE 8   Cellulose nitrate

The *dJ/dx*–curves have been established from the Bethe equation:

$$\frac{dJ}{dx} = (\alpha Z_e^2/I_0\beta^2)\,[\ln\{2mc^2\beta^2/(1-\beta^2)\,I_0\} - \beta^2 + 3.04],$$

where

dJ/dx = the number of ion pairs formed per unit length,

Z_e = the effective charge of the ionizing particle,

β = the relative velocity of this particle,

m = the electron mass,

I_0 = the ionization energy of the pheripheric electron of the material,

α = a constant depending on the material,

Z_e is given by an empirical relation of the form

$$Z_e = Z[1 - \exp{(-125\,\beta/Z^{2/3})}]$$

which is valid for velocities $\beta \geq 0.25 \times 10^{-2}Z^{213}$ and for ions with atomic masses between 2 and 20.

For mica the ionization energy is assumed to be 13 eV. It is taken much smaller in plastics; in this case one should indeed take into account not only the ionization of the atoms met on the path, but also the rupture of the polymeric chains. The latter, do considerably sensitive the plastics during etching. The ionization energy is therefore taken equal to 2 eV.

Once more the etching conditions are very important, especially for particles having a (dJ/dx) close to $(dJ/dx)_{\text{crit}}$. In this case tracks which are hardly discernable as points after normal etching, may grow to full tracks after more extended etchings.

Although this theory is not to be considered as completely satisfactory at the present time, and although it will probably be subject to detail improvement, it has the advantage of accounting for the experimental data which are available up till now.

The most striking practical consequence of the criterion of "critical primary ionization rate" is that, for a given insulator, an ion can be recorded if it has

a minimum mass

an energy between two extreme energies E_{min} and E_{max}.

The lightest ion which can e.g. be recorded in mica is Ne^{20} with energy between 2 and 3 MeV[*]. In the polycarbonate lexan (or makrofol) one can record He^4 ions with energy between 0.1 and 0.2 MeV. In cellulose nitrate, which is the most sensitive insulator studied up till now, He^4 ions are detected with energies between 0.2 and 0.5 MeV and 3 to 4 MeV (these limits depend upon the origin of the plastic), and even certain H^1 ions.

It is clear now that these plastics are very useful when one is concerned with a complex radiation. One can then use several insulators, the most sensible one recording all the particles, the least sensible one only recording

---

[*] It should nevertheless be mentioned that massive α doses ($\geq 10^{13}$ α/cm^2) may produce stable defects in mica, under the form of "pleochroic haloes". These haloes occur in the neighborhood of strongly radioactive inclusions (Sm, U, Th and their daughters) and have been observed a long time ago (Michel-Lévy, C. R. *Acad. Sci. Paris* **94**, 1196 (1882) and explained since 1907 (Joly, *Phil. Mag.*, **13**, 381).

the heaviest particles. In this way the different particles can at least be qualitatively identified by subtraction. This can be the case when studying reactor fuel elements (emission of α and fission fragments or cosmic rays, from protons up to iron ions).

Conclusions

Insulators as track detectors have become a very useful tool in different branches of physics. This technique is similar to the technique of nuclear emulsions, but presents several advantages with respect to the latter. Among these one can mention:

low cost

good insensitivity to weakly ionizing radiation

possibility of operation at normal conditions (no need of dark-room work, and revelation of the tracks with products currently available in each laboratory)

absence of heavy elements (or only very small amounts)

stability in time of the tracks (very long before etching, almost infinite afterwards)

possibility of use under severe environmental conditions (temperature, pressure)

possibility to obtain tracks (or even holes) of the diameter wanted.

Since this technique is only five years old, there still remains a lot of work to be done. The most important problem is concerned with counting of the tracks. The few attempts in the field of automatic counting still remain high-priced, of little practical interest, or almost inefficient.

The development of tracks is another aspect which should still be improved. The chemical development has been of great value for the technique of track detection, but in the future other methods will probably be worked out in order to improve the sensitivity of insulators, to observe the tracks at full length, or to obtain tracks in solids which are not sensitive up till now.

B NEUTRON DOSIMETRY

Introduction

In the previous chapter it has been shown that insulators are able to detect and to record charged particles, as far as these particles meet a few conditions of mass and energy. It has also been shown that these conditions almost depend upon the insulator only.

In a general way it can be stated that insulators are insensitive to weakly ionizing radiation (γ-rays, light) and to uncharged particles (neutrons). Although neutrons cannot be detected directly, one can use the nuclear reactions they induce. In neutron dosimetry the most commonly used reactions are the (n, α) and (n, f) reactions. To detect the α-particles one mostly uses cellulose nitrate, which is the most sensitive insulator studied up till now. For the detection of fission fragments the majority of the insulators are convenient: mica, glasses, higher plastics (poly-carbonate, poly-terephtalates, etc.)

The present method is generally of safer and simpler use than the methods used before. Most of the neutron flux measurements are made by radio-chemical activation. This implies a certain number of corrections due to geometry and radioactive decay, and also an elaborated counting device. Some of these disadvantages are avoided by the use of track detection in insulators: the emitted particles are recorded under the form of tracks which remain stable for a considerably long time. The counting of the tracks, although generally not automatic, is performed in a very simple way, especially in the case of sufficiently large track densities (10^4–5×10^6 cm^{-2}), i.e. when a large number of tracks can be observed in only a few ranges under the optical microscope. An experienced observer is generally able to count 400 tracks at a density of 10^5 cm^{-2} in about 15 minutes.

1 *Usual equations*

When a particle converter charged with a neutron is placed in a neutron flux in the presence of an insulator, the number of tracks induced in the insulator is related to the flux by one of the following equations:

$$D = K_1 N_0 t \int_{E_0}^{E_1} \sigma(E)\,\Phi(E) \cdot dE \tag{1}$$

in the case of a thin source (i.e. when the thickness is much smaller than the particle range in the source element)

$$D = K_1 K_2 N_1 R_0 t \int_{E_0}^{E_1} \sigma(E)\,\Phi(E)\,dE \tag{2}$$

in the case of a thick source (i.e. when the thickness is much larger than the particle range in the source element);

$$D = K_1 K_3 N_2 R_1 t \int_{E_0}^{E_1} \sigma(E)\, \Phi(E)\, dE \tag{3}$$

in the case of a source incorporated as a solvent in the detector.

In the Eq. (1)

K_1 is a geometrical factor depending upon the number of particles emitted per reaction; it is equal to 1 if fission fragments are recorded, and equal to $1/2$ for α-particles.

N_0 is the number of atoms undergoing the reaction per surface unit of the source.

In the Eq. (2)

$K_2 = \frac{1}{2}$ (solid angle)

N_1 is the number of atoms undergoing the reaction per volume unit of the source.

R_0 is the particle range in the source element.

In the Eq. (3)

K_3 is a coefficient depending upon the way of observation of the trackes; it is equal to 1 if the tracks are counted on a plane internal to the detector, and equal to $\frac{1}{2}$ if the tracks are counted on a plane external to the detector;

N_2 is the number of atoms undergoing the reaction per volume unit of the detector.

R_1 is the particle range in the detector.

In any case one has also to take into account the recording efficiency. We have seen that this efficiency is 1 for fission fragments in mica, most common plastics and phosphatic glasses. It is of the order of 0.4 to 0.8 in the other glasses. It is almost equal to 1 for α particles with energy smaller than 3 MeV in cellulose nitrate.

To simplify things one can say that for a given assembly (thin or thick source; external or internal to the detector, nature of the detector), the track density is proportional to the neutron flux by the equation

$$D = K \int_{E_0}^{E_1} \sigma \Phi t\, dE.$$

In most cases it will be sufficient to irradiate a standard, which yields

$$D_1 = K \int_{E_0}^{E_1} \sigma(\Phi t)_1 \, dE;$$

all other fluxes are then determined by the equation

$$\int_{E_0}^{E_1} \sigma t \Phi(E) \, dE = \frac{D}{D_1} \int_{E_0}^{E_1} \sigma t_1 \Phi_1(E) \, dE = kD. \tag{4}$$

In practice it seems that the use of very thin sources is not to be recommended, because of the difficulties to prepare and especially to control such sources. Their thickness must indeed be known to an accuracy of at least 1 % in order to avoid additional errors.

Thick sources are more commonly used, since the thickness is of no importance if it is larger than a certain value. On the other hand one has to take into account the flux depression in the source, which is not negligible for sources with a large cross section.

Sources incorporated in the detector are by far the most practical. It is indeed easy to incorporate almost very element in a plastic or a glass.

In this way one can prepare detectors which contain, in a very homogeneous and reproducible way, fissionable elements (uranium or thorium) or elements undergoing the (n, α) reaction (boron, lithium). The detection of fission fragments is generally done on an internal plane (after fracture); the detection of α-particles on a cellulose nitrate detector joined to the glass during irradiation.

2 *Thermal neutron dosimetry*

In the case of a normally thermalized neutron flux, equation (4) of the previous chapter becomes particularly simple, since

$$\Phi t = kD,$$

where k is the track production rate (number of neutrons required for the production of a track); k may be determined by a preliminar irradiation. It will be shown that in this case about ten different glasses containing boron or uranium as a solvent, are sufficient to measure thermal neutron fluxes in the range 10^6 to 10^{20} n/cm^{-2}.

A certain number of studies has been made on the basis of this principle. Debeauvais et al.[23] have measured thermal neutron fluxes by recording fission fragments from a thin natural uranium source in mica. The main result is that they have shown that the recording efficiency of fission fragments is 100% in mica and in makrofol. Since however, as we have seen before, the use of thin sources is disadvantageous, this method has been abandoned.

Walker et al.[24,25] were the first to use tracks produced in thin plates of common glass (microscope sample holders) for the measurement of thermal neutron fluxes. These plates, containing about $4 \cdot 10^{-7}$ wt of uranium, allow an easy measurement in the range of 10^{15} to 10^{19} cm^{-2}. A simultaneous radiochemical measurement of the flux by Ba^{140} and Mo^{99} produced in a uranium wire, to determine the absolute value of the flux, has shown that reproducibility is in favour of the glass, together with the advantages already mentioned. In the same papers the authors have investigated the flux distribution in a reactor hole. The method seems to be very satisfactory.

Prevo et al.[26] and the present author[12] have measured thermal neutron fluxes of tracks induced by uranium impurities included in mica. The flux ranges which were covered are 10^{15} to 10^{19} cm^{-2} for reference 26, and 3×10^{16} to 10^{21} for Ref. 12. The contribution of non-thermalized neutrons is of the order of 3% (0.5% for the fission by fast neutrons of U^{238}, 2.5% for the fission by epithermal neutrons of U^{235}). The disadvantages of this method are the inhomogeneity and the non-reproducibility of the uranium concentration in mica[12] (Fig. 9).

Becker[15] uses tracks in dosimeter glasses to measure thermal neutron fluxes of the order of 10^8 cm^{-2}. The source of fission fragments is a thick layer (about 30 μ) of U^{235}. This irradiation by thermal neutrons does not affect the efficiency of the dosimeter. In this way one may simultaneously obtain γ-rays doses and thermal neutron doses. It is even possible to have an additional measurement of fast neutrons if a threshold detector (thorium or neptunium) is joined.

More recently Maurette and Mory[27] have developed reproducible detectors which are particularly useful for non specialized laboratories. The glass detectors allow to cover a flux range from 10^6 to 10^{21} cm^{-2}. Two main types of glasses are used, containing boron and uranium.

Low fluxes: three types of boron glasses are used. Boron is subject to the (n, α) reaction, but since the α-particles are not detected in glass, it is necessary to detect them by means of an additional sheet of cellulose ni-

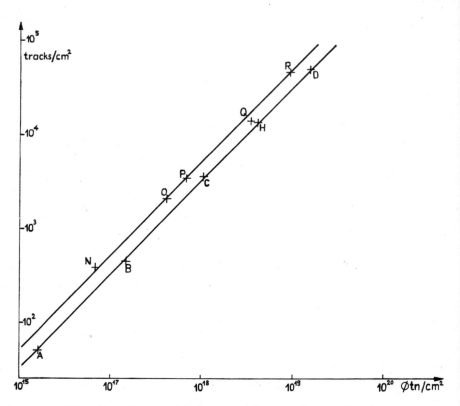

FIGURE 9   Density of fission tracks in natural muscovite mica as a
function of total thermal neutron flux (after Ref. 12)

trate. The emitted α-particles are directly recorded since their energy is
1.47 MeV, and the recording efficiency is nearly 100%. These three glasses
allow measurements with 10% precision in the range 10^6 to 10^{10} cm^{-2}.

Medium fluxes: five types of uranium glasses are used. The induced
fission tracks are counted in the bulk of the glasses after fracture, or an
auxiliary detector joined to the glass and of which the uranium impurity
concentration is very small with respect to the concentration in the glass.
This allows to cover a flux range from 10^7 to 10^{17} cm^{-2}.

High fluxes: three types of glasses containing a very low concentration
of uranium ($\leq 10^{-8}$ at) allow measurements from 10^{17} to 10^{22} n.cm^{-2}. They
are molten quartz or optical glasses. For the very high fluxes ($\geq 10^{20}$ n.cm^{-2})

two problems occur: the induced radioactivity in the detector, and the depletion of uranium. The use of very small samples (a few milligrams) and waiting a few days may solve the first problem. One can take the second one into account by calculation.

We may conclude that the use of two types of detectors (cellulose nitrate and glass) and two types of reactions $((n, \alpha)$ and $(n, f))$ allow measurements in a range of 10^6 to 10^{21} n.cm^{-2}, which is significantly wider than all methods known before.

One may of course imagine an infinite number of solutions, and everybody may develop his own dosimeter for the measurement in the flux range he is interested in. Among the simplest ones, we mention cellulose nitrate itself: it contains oxygen, particularly the isotope 17, which undergoes the (n, α) reaction; since the α-particles have an energy of 1.42 MeV they are directly detectable in cellulose nitrate. By performing a series of irradiations we have been able to show that fluxes in the range of 10^{12} to 3×10^{15} n.cm^{-2} are easily measured in this way.[5,28]

3 Fast neutron dosimetry

Fast neutron dosimetry is not as simple as thermal neutron dosimetry, since in this case the exact energy spectrum is not always known, and since one has to work with a complex spectrum of fast, epithermal and thermal neutrons. The thermal neutrons are almost completely eliminated when the detector is covered with cadmium or boron, but the problem remains to discriminate the two other kinds of neutrons.

On the other hand there are only few nuclear reactions with epithermal or fast neutrons yielding charged particles like the one needed for the present purposes (e.g. α-particles); furthermore these reactions have very low cross sections (of the order of a few millibarns). This means that only (n, f) reactions with fissionable elements like U^{235}, U^{238}, Th^{232}, Np^{237} or Pu^{239} are of interest.

Walker et al.[24] and Prevo et al.[26] have studied the possibility of using uranium, either as an impurity in mica or as an external convertor, for fast neutron dosimetry.

We have investigated the usefulnes of thorium in a thick layer.[12] After a certain number of irradiations by means of a Pu–Be neutron source, we have shown that the track density varies linearly with dose. This dosimeter allows the measurement of doses from 30 to 10^5 rems, for track densities between 10^2 and 5×10^6 cm^{-2} (Fig. 10).

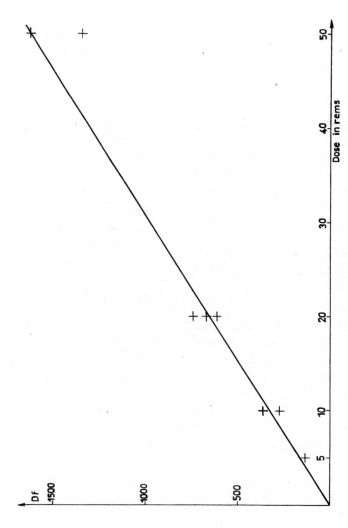

FIGURE 10   Density of fission tracks induced in mica by a thick source of Th^{232} as a function of fast neutron dose (after Ref. 12)

On the other hand Kerr and Stickel[29] have performed experiments of the same nature with plutonium covered with boron, neptunium and uranium 238 as threshold detectors.

In order to account for the essential points of these phenomena, we shall rely on the work performed by Baumgartner and Brakenbush[30] which is at this moment the most recent and complete one.

The authors who studied the development of a new personal dosimeter, (also used for thermal neutrons) state that three conditions are to be fulfilled:

1) the fast neutron energy threshold has to be lower than the one of the *NTA* films used before, which is of the order of 0.7 to 0.8 MeV;

2) the response has to be proportional to dose, and independant of the neutron energy;

3) the dosimeter must measure fast and thermal neutron doses, and give information about the intermediate neutrons.

Figure 11 shows the fission cross sections for the considered nuclides. It is clear that no nuclide gives complete satisfaction.

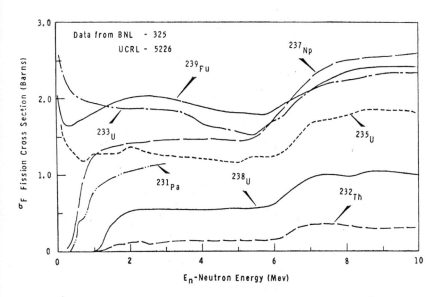

FIGURE 11   Fission cross section as a function of neutron energy for a few fissionable materials (after Ref. 30)

27   Amelinckx (1347)

Uranium 238 has a threshold of 1 MeV, and will not be able to detect the intermediate neutrons. Furthermore it is impossible to obtain U^{238} completely free of U^{235}, but only depleted.

Thorium 237 has a threshold of 1.2 MeV and it cross section is even smaller than in the case of U^{238}.

Uranium 235 and plutonium 239 are very sensitive to thermal and epithermal neutrons. Furthermore, Pu^{239} must be treated in gloveboxes.

Neptunium has obviously the best characteristics for fast neutron dosimetry, with a threshold of 0.4 MeV. However, it is absolutely unstable in the air, and oxydizes spontaneously. Furthermore, its activity is not negligible. It has nevertheless been chosen to form the basis of the new dosimeter, after fixation in a plastic matrix, which makes it more easy to handle.

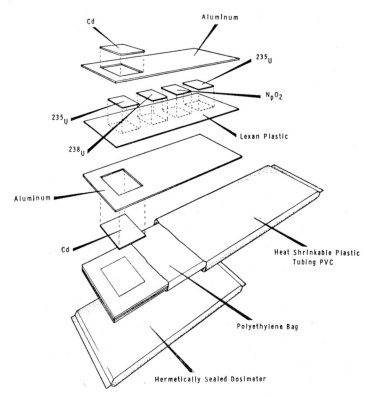

FIGURE 12   Prototype of a neutron dosimeter based upon the recording of fission tracks in insulators (after Ref. 30)

The actual dosimeter built by the authors consists of four parts:

1) a naked sheet of U^{235} (93%) of 0.2 to 0.5 mm thickness;

2) a sheet of U^{235} (93%) of 0.2 to 0.5 mm thickness between two cadmium sheets of 1 mm thickness.

3) a sheet of U^{238} (20 times depleted) of 0.2 to 0.5 mm thickness;

4) a sheet of $^{237}NpO_2$ incorporated in a polyester, of 2.5 mm thickness (i.e. 35 mg.cm^{-2} of $^{237}NpO_2$).

The fission tracks are recorded in a sheet of polycarbonate (Lexan). The whole is placed in a common double plastic holder (Fig. 12).

The calibration of the dosimeter is performed in known neutron fluxes, by means of an ion accelerator and of Pu–Be and PuF_4 sources. Figure 13 shows the track/neutron sensibility for each of the used elements.

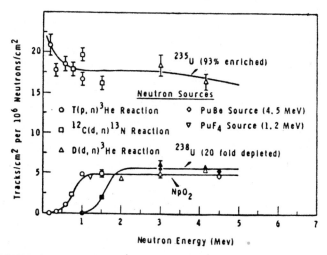

FIGURE 13   Sensibilities of various fissionable elements used in the dosimeter in Fig. 12 (after Ref. 30)

By using this calibration, and by comparing the track densities obtained with each of the detectors placed in any flux; it becomes possible to measure doses in five energy ranges:

1) $E < 0.5$ eV (thermal and slow neutrons), comparison between naked U^{235} and Cd-covered U^{235};

2) 0.5 eV $< E <$ 0.4 MeV (intermediate neutrons): comparison between Cd-covered U^{235} and Np^{237};

3) 0.4 MeV $< E <$ 1.3 MeV (fast neutrons): comparison between Np^{237} and U^{238}.

4) $E >$ 1.3 MeV: comparison between U^{238} and naked U^{235};

5) $E >$ 0.4 MeV: tracks obtained from Np^{237}.

The dosimeter described above allows the measurement of thermal neutron doses from 0.1 mrem; and fast neutron doses up to 150 mrem. The use of metallized plastic would certainly permit accelerating of the analysis of the results and lowering the of cost of the dosimeter. In this way the dosimeter would become clearly lower-priced than the actually used *NTA* dosimeter. On the other hand a β and γ irradiation of 1000 rads has no unfluence upon the results.

The main disadvantage of this dosimeter, as it is actually conceived, is its own activity. This activity is almost due to the neptunium, which yields a dose output of 15 mR/h. This value is inadmissable for a personal dosimeter. Investigations are on hand in order to lower this activity, namely by making the neptunium containing plastic sheet thinner, and by shielding the dosimeter with lead and copper. In this way the authors hope to obtain an admissable output of 1 mR/h.

There still remains much work to be done, especially in the field of dosimetry of high fluxes of fast neutrons. Although thorium and uranium are the easiest elements to handle, neptunium gives the best results. One could easily imagine the use of alloys and glasses with very low neptunium concentration: a concentration of 10^{-6} at. of neptunium in an aluminium sheet or a glass plate should allow an easy measurement of fast fluxes of the order of 10^{17} cm^{-2}.

4   *Flux distribution in a fuel element*

We mention here the experiments which have permitted the determination of the flux distribution in the interior of fuel elements.[31,32] The principle consists of the insertion of a thin detecting insulator (mica, glass or makrofol) between two fuel elements before irradiation. The tracks obtained from the fission of the fuel are detected and counted as a function of radial position. The variation of their density gives the value of the flux decrease caused by internal absorption in the rods (Fig. 14). This method is much simpler to elaborate than the usual method which consists in the recuperation of fission products in aluminium sheets and radiochemical dose measurements, and the results are at least as satisfactory.

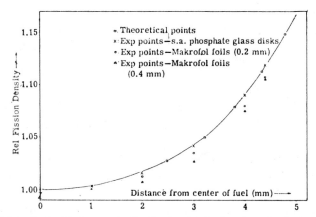

FIGURE 14   Fission track distribution in the interior of a fuel element
(after Ref. 32)

Conclusion

Although neutron dosimetry for fission tracks in insulators has not yet been frequently used, it has seriously progressed. It will become more and more competitive in the future because of low cost, simple use, precision and reproducibility. On one hand the problems of thermal neutron dosimetry are almost solved by the use of commonly obtainable glass. On the other hand the fast neutron dosimetry still requires to be studied and improved. The latter indeed requires the use of peculiar elements which are not found in nature, such as neptunium, an instable and rather radioactive by-product of nuclear reactors.

One may finally predict the detection of protons from (n, p) reactions, as far as plastics will be found which are more sensitive than cellulose nitrate. This would probably facilitate the dosimetry in the range of doses which are of biological interest, but this will not be the case for higher fluxes since these plastics will be very sensitive to γ-radiation, and therefore they will be rapidly damaged.

C   OTHER APPLICATIONS

Besides the applications in neutronics, the discoverey of fission tracks in insulators has become a useful technique in other branches of physics, metallurgy and even medicine.

In nuclear physics this new technique has namely made possible the measurement of very small fission cross sections (down to 10^{-11} barns), of potential barrier heights inaccesible before, of very large or very small radioactive periods. Along the same line age measurements of terrestrial or extra-terrestrial minerals have been performed. Associated with the exploitation of artificial satellites and to the study of meteorites, the study of cosmic rays takes also advantage of the track detection techniques.

In solid state physics the insulators have been used in the study of crystal defects. In metallurgy the technique has been useful for the determination of some elements with very small concentration, and for the study of solid state diffusion.

In neutronics, besides the neutron dosimetry itself, it has been possible to make reactor flux measurements at places which were almost inaccessible before.

Finally in medicine, the realization of micro-porous blood filters will allow one to know better (and maybe to cure) cancer.

In all of these applications, two main characteristics are in favour of the use of insulators as charged particle detectors:

their simple use and their resistance, which allow them to be used even in heavy duty conditions;

their selectivity, which enables to differentiate radiation and to eliminate the radiations which are of no interest. This makes possible the use of the most appropriate detector for the conditions of each experiment.

I Nuclear physics

The insulators have been most frequently used in nuclear physics. The results obtained with this technique are such that its essential neccesity is now a well established fact. Several types of experiments have been done, which will be described hereafter.

1 *Study of fission and spallation*

Two types of 4π-detectors are used:

a detecting insulator with the studied element present in its interior in a convenient concentration

a sandwich detector-element-detector.

During a study of fission by means of 3 GeV protons, the number of parasite tracks occuring in the detector is generally very small (4×10^{-6} in lexan, 3×10^{-9} in mica with iron impurities, and down to 10^{-12} in the less sensitive crystals such as olivine or hyperstene).[5,33] Such low densities of parasite tracks, which cannot be obtained in nuclear emulsions, allow the measurement with good accuracy of real low densities.

Maurette and Stephan[34,35] have been able to measure by the sandwich method, fission cross sections by 156 MeV protons of elements from bismuth to cadmium. The values obtained reach 3×10^{-4} barns with an incertainty of 50%.

Following the same principle, Debeauvais and Cuer[36] have studied the kinematics of fission and spallation fragments emitted by uranium, lead, gold, silver and chromium, under 3 and 18 GeV protons. Their method is based upon the proportions of tracks emitted in forward and backward directions, and upon the relative densities of simple, double and triple tracks.

Fleisher *et al.*[37] have also studied the ternary fission of very heavy compound nuclei. Mica charged with lead, and uranium glasses have been irradiated by means of different heavy ions, in order to investigate the variation of the ratio of the densities of triple to double traces. Their ratio increases with Z^2/A, to become about equal to 1/25 for (Ar + U). In this experiment, performed with argon ions of 414 MeV (not recorded in glass), 125 triple tracks have been observed for a total of about 3000 fissions. This yields the following cross sections:

$-\sigma_d = (3 \pm 0.4)$ barns for double fission,

$-\sigma_{d+t} = (3.1 \pm 0.4)$ barns for double and triple fissions.

Such an experiment would not have been possible with the same precision with electronic counters, because of the intensity of the noise level produced by the argon ions.

Sikkeland[5] has been able to determine the cross section and the angular distribution of fission fragments of light compound nuclei, such as (O + Ho). He suspended the target element in the middle of a circular chamber covered with solid detectors. The same device has permitted Soldatov *et al.*[38] to measure the angular distribution of fragments below the photofission threshold of U^{238}.

Burnett *et al.*[39] used mica for the measurement of the cross section of the compound nucleus of Tl^{201} by means of the reaction ($He^4 + Au^{197}$). The variation of the cross section as a function of energy, which covers ten orders of magnitude, enables one to determine the height of the potential barriers of Tl^{201}, namely 22.5 ± 1.5 MeV; the width of the barrier is of the order of 2 MeV. Other potential barriers have been determined since then following the same method.

2 *Measurement of the half life of instable elements*

The first study performed in this field concerns the measurement of the spontaneous fission of U^{238}. This measurement is of interest in the age determination of terrestrial and extra-terrestrial minerals (see the following chapter). Fleisher and Price[40] have observed the track densities in mica which have been in contact for six months with a thin sheet of natural uranium, and with a glass enriched with uranium of which the date of origin was known. The result, compared with the one obtained by other methods, yields the value $\lambda_f = (6.85 \pm 0.20) \times 10^{-17}$ year^{-1}.

Glass detectors have enabled Flerov et al.[41] to measure the half life of the element 104, which undergoes spontaneous fission. This element is obtained from the reaction (Ne + Pu). The detectors were placed on a mobile belt and the half life, about 0.3 sec, was determined from the belt velocity and the variations of track density along the detector.

A similar device was used by Linov et al.[42] for the measurement of the half life of the isomere with spontaneous fission obtained from the reaction $Am^{243}(n, 2n)$ Am^{242}. Modulation of the neutron beam enabled the authors to separate the spontaneous fission from the fission induced in $Am.^{243}$ The half life measured in this way is about 13 msec.

Several series of experiments[43,44] have permitted to determine a maximum value of 5×10^{-6} sec for the half life of heavy nuclei formed from the action of oxygen ions at 150 MeV, argon ions at 414 MeV and 3 GeV protons upon lead atoms included in thin mica sheets. The samples were studied in the electron microscope.

It would be also of interest to measure the half life of the isotope 10 of beryllium obtained from the reaction $B^{11}(p, \alpha)$ $Be^8(\alpha)$ He^4 (Ref. 5), by means of a detector consisting of cellulose nitrate doped with boron. This must be a possible experiment since previous investigations predict a half life between 4×10^{-15} sec and 1.2×10^{-16} sec. This study could also be achieved with the help of an electron microscope.

The assembly of techniques described, all of them based upon the recording of charged particles in different insulators, has thus enabled the investigators to measure the spontaneous fission periods in a range of 5×10^{-16} sec to 10^{16} years, i.e. 40 orders of magnitude.

II Measurement of age of terrestrial and extra-terrestrial minerals

1 *Terrestrial minerals*

Since their formation all materials existing on earth contain the simple elements in some proportion, and particularly uranium. Recent measurements have shown that concentrations of 10^{-2} to 10^{-12} at/at are detectable, and that uranium is present in all the minerals studied.

As we have seen, uranium 238 is subject to spontaneous fission with a probability of $\lambda_f = (6.85 \pm 0.20) \times 10^{-17}$ year^{-1}. Hence tracks are formed since its origin in the mineral in which the uranium is present as an impurity. It is clear that counting of these tracks is a technique for the determination of the minerals age.[45]

The principle of the method is the following. First of all the tracks formed by the spontaneous fission of uranium 238 are counted (the so-called fossil tracks). This value is equal to:

$$D_f = \frac{\lambda_f}{\lambda_t} N_0 C_u R_0 \left(\exp\left(\lambda_t T\right) - 1\right), \qquad (5)$$

where

λ_f = spontaneous fission constant of U^{238}

λ_t = total radioactive decay constant of U^{238}

N_0 = total number of atoms per cm^3 mineral

C_u = atomic concentration of U^{238}

R_0 = range of the fission fragments in the mineral

T = age of the mineral.

But in this equation C_u is unknown and R_0 is not always well known. These two parameters are eliminated by irradiating the sample with thermal neutrons. This gives rise to the fission of U^{235}, and the track density is then

$$D_i = N_0 C_u I R_0 \sigma_f \Phi_t \qquad (6)$$

where

I = the actual isotopic proportion of U^{235}

σ_f = the fission cross section of U^{235}

Φ_t = the total thermal neutron flux.

From (5) and (6) the age of the mineral is obtained by

$$T = \frac{1}{\lambda_t} \left[\ln \left(\frac{D_f}{D_i} \cdot \frac{\lambda_t}{\lambda_f} I\sigma_f \Phi_t \right) + 1 \right], \tag{7}$$

In this equation λ_t, λ_f, I and σ_f are known constants, and Φ_t, D_f and D_i are to be measured.

A simplified equation, applied if $\lambda_i T$ is very small, is the following

$$T = \frac{1}{\lambda_f} \frac{D_f}{D_i} I\sigma_f \Phi_t . \tag{8}$$

This method is very simple and has been applied to numerous samples of all kinds, the age of which was already determined (Ar/K, Sr/Rb or Pb/Pb methods) and found to be between 0.5 year and 1.4×10^9 years. Up to 10^8 years the track methods yield comparable results with respect to the other methods: this is the case for glass manufactured by men,[46] for natural glass (ages between 0.5 year and 3.5×10^7 years),[47] for mica[45] (ages between 3×10^7 and 10^8 years), and for zircons[48] (ages between 8×10^7 and 1.25×10^8 years).

On the other hand the reproducibility is less good for values above 10^8 years. In mica, where the correct age was up to 1.4×10^9 years, the track method gave too small a value. A sample of apatite was dated at 2.5×10^8 years as compared to 10^9 by the other methods. The most important results are summarized in Fig. 15.

These errors may possibly be explained by several phenomena:

periods of heating (the tracks disappear above a given temperature)

terrestrial movements;

infiltration of uranium in the mica (diffusion from uranium minerals in the neighbourhood).

Notwithstanding this error tendency for the most ancient minerals, the track method has a great number of applications in geology and archeology. Its main advantage is simplicity, no need for considerable apparatus, and the fact that only very small samples are required (a few milligrammes may be enough for dating). The method can thus be successfully applied by small laboratories which should, strictly speaking, only have an optical microscope. They should however have access to a nuclear reactor, which is nowadays not a major obstacle.

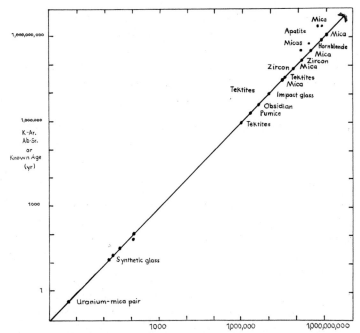

FIGURE 15 Comparison of ages of several minerals as obtained from the fission track method and by radiochemical means

2   *Extra-terrestrial minerals (meteorites)*

There is no question here to measure the age of the meteorites since it is the same as the age of the solar system (the meteorites have been formed during the nucleosynthesis, i.e. about 4.5×10^9 year ago). On the other hand it is of interest to investigate the period of cooling which succeeded their formation.

Tracks in meteorites may have several origins:[5]

spontaneous fission of U^{238}

spontaneous fission of Pu^{244}

fission of heavy elements (Pb, Th) induced by charged particles with high energy from cosmic rays;

spallation reactions of heavy or medium elements by cosmic rays;

heavy ions from cosmic rays,

cosmic mesons with high energy

Dirac's magnetic monopoles (at moment hypothetic particles).

The Pu^{244} isotope has a total period of 7.6×10^7 years and a spontaneous fission period which is 4×10^5 times smaller than the one of U^{238}. If the ratio C_v/C_{pu} of the concentrations of U^{238} and Pu^{244} at the end of the nucleosynthesis is known—i.e. about 45—it is possible to calculate the cooling period T_0 by means of an equation given in Ref. 62.

This equation is obtained from the following considerations:

the spontaneous fission tracks of U^{238} and Pu^{244} are longer (but identical between themselves) than the ones from other origin, and furthermore they are isotropic)

Pu^{244} has completely disappeared from meteorites

the density of tracks yielded by U^{238} only is obtained by a thermal neutron irradiation, since the total age of the meteorite is known (4.5×10^9 years) the fission of U^{235} gives the concentration of U^{238} at the end of the nucleosynthesis, hence the contribution of the spontaneous fission tracks of both nuclides U^{238} and Pu^{244}.

The observation of the other tracks (short tracks, V-form tracks) may yield interesting information about their origin, namely about the nature of cosmic rays, about the original dimensions of the meteorites which have lost material on their path through the atmosphere and which have exploded by the impact on earth.

III   Use of the trace technique in metallurgy : microanalysis

In the chapter on dosimetry we have seen that the density of tracks in a thick sample is related to the concentration of the element producing one or several charged particles (noted P later on) when irradiated by neutrons, by the relation

$$D = kN_0 C R_0 \sigma \Phi t = K C \Phi_t.$$

In this equation

D = density of tracks per unit surface

N_0 = total number of atoms per unit volume,

C = concentration of atoms undergoing the (n, p) reaction,

R_0 = range of the charged particle emitted in the material under consideration,

σ = cross section of the (n, p) reaction;

Φ_t = total neutron flux.

Up till now the measurement of D, allowed to determine the neutron flux to which the sample was submitted, provided that the other characteristics of the material are known.

If on the other hand the flux itself is known, it is possible to determine C by counting the number of tracks. This method is applicable for the analysis of small concentrations of elements undergoing the (n, P) reaction, i.e. in particular:

the elements undergoing the (n, α) reaction, such as boron or lithium;

the elements undergoing the (n, f) reaction, such as uranium or plutonium.

The method described is extremely sensitive. The usual methods are almost limited to concentrations above 10^{-7} at/at (chemical analysis, microprobe). The track method has theoretically no lower limit, since one might in definitely increase the neutron flux requested to obtain a suitable track density. Nevertheless the method is limited in practice by the

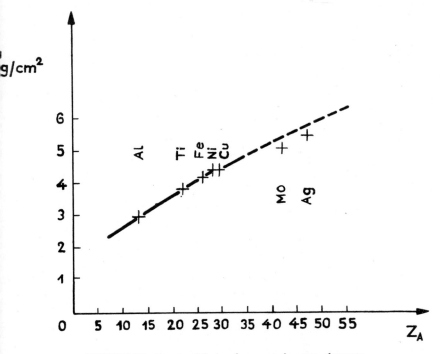

FIGURE 16   Range of fission fragments in some elements

appearance of background tracks produced by impurities in the detector itself, (if an auxiliary detector is used). If one wants to measure a concentration in the detector itself, this lower limit really does not exist except for the influence of the induced radioactivity, which might become too strong in this case).

In this case a new problem, which we have not yet treated up till now, is appearing. It concerns the mean range R_0 of the fission fragments. It is generally unknown as it has only been measured in a small number of materials (Al, Au, mica). Even in these cases one has to be careful is the fission fragments are not recorded along the whole length of their path in the insulator, yielding an observed range which is smaller than the real one. For this reason we have performed a series of experiments in different materials, which enabled us to measure the range with a good precision[50] (Fig. 16).

Note: we will call alphagraphy the radiography by α traces, and fissiography the radiography by fission fragments.

1   *Microanalysis by fissiography*

In metallurgy the use of radioactive tracks for the analysis of elements is a well known technique. If an element has been artificially activated before being added as an impurity in a matrix, its concentration is given by electronic counting and its distribution is obtained by autoradiography on a nuclear emulsion.

This method is particularly useful in the case of elements with a reasonable period (neither too short, nor too long) in order to have a suitable activity at the time of the measurement. This is the case for the β-emitters and the α emitters such as Pu^{239}. But the method is not useful for natural uranium since here long counting and exposure times are required, of the order of several weeks or months. On the other hand the time is considerably reduced if one records the fission fragments emitted by uranium during an in-pile irradiation.

It can be shown[51] that for equal uranium concentration and track density, and using U^{234} (a good α-emitter) for alphagraphy and natural uranium for fissiography, a one week alphagraphic exposure corresponds to a total neutron flux of 6×10^{15} cm^{-2} (i.e. a few minutes in a reactor). If 90% enriched U^{235} is used for fissiography, the same neutron flux corresponds to 140 weeks of alphagraphic exposure.

The recording of fission tracks has obviously been used first for the measurement of the concentration of uranium in mica.[52] In this work Price and Walker have measured concentrations down to 10^{-11} at/at (phlogopite) and 5×10^{-10} at/at (muscovite).

These authors have been able to measure by the same method the concentration of uranium in ancient glasses,[53] in fossil bones[54] and in meteorites.[49]

In order to verify the validity of the method, we have studied[12] two Mg–U alloys for which the analysis had been performed previously by chemical means. The results are compatible within experimental error.

Another interesting application of analysis by fissiography is the study of solid state diffusion at very small concentration, practically at infinite dilution. For this purpose two samples of the elements A and B are firmly pressed together and heated to a suitable temperature for some time. After this thermal treatment the progression of each element (or one of them) into the other is observed. The variation of the concentration C of the element A in the element B as a function of the distance to the interface is a solution of Fick's law $\partial C/\partial x = D(\partial^2 C/\partial t^2)$; where t is the duration of the thermal treatment and D the diffusion coefficient which is characteristic for the diffusion speed of A into B. It is generally expressed in $cm^2 s^{-1}$.

If the element A is fissionable the advantages of the method are again its rapidity and its sensitivity. By fissiography it is possible to measure with in a reasonable time diffusion coefficients corresponding to very small concentrations of fissionable elements. The only limitation is due to background tracks, not only tracks appearing in the detector, but also tracks from uranium impurities in the sample itself. If a sufficiently pure element B is used, it is nevertheless easy to measure concentrations of A as small as 10^{-8} at/at.

Fissiography is performed as follows. The sample A–B (which is called a diffusion couple) is cut perpendicularly to the interface after thermal treatment. This face is pressed to an insulating detector (generally mica), and the whole assembly is irradiated. After development the tracks are counted in strips perpendicular to the interface, and their variation yields the coefficient D.

Our first application of this method concerned the diffusion of plutonium into magnesium.[12] The value of the diffusion coefficient we obtained, $D_0 = 1.5 \times 10^{-10}$ $cm^{-2} s^{-1}$, is in good agreement with the one obtained by other methods: $D_0 = 1.9 \times 10^{-10}$ $cm^{-2} s^{-1}$.

This study has also been performed and worked out by de Keroulas[51,55] in the case of the diffusion at practically infinite dilution of uranium in titanium, iron and steel. These experiments have enabled study of this diffusion in the pure state since concentrations of the order of 10^{-8} at/at are used, compared to 10^{-3} before. Figure 17 shows the fissiography of a

FIGURE 17   Fissiography of a quenched titanium–uraniumdiffusion couple (after Ref. 51)

Ti–U couple, and Fig. 18 gives the variation of the number of tracks in the titanium. In addition it has been possible to display another phenomenon which is hardly accessible by other means: Figure 19 shows the fissiography of a slowly cooled Ti–U couple; a phenomenon of uranium segregation in the titanium during cooling is observed. It is related to the martensitic transformation of titanium, during which the (uranium) impurities are dragged by the $\beta - \alpha$ transformation surfaces. This phenomenon does not occur if the sample has been rapidly cooled by quenching (this in the case of Fig. 17), since the transformation face then moves too rapidly.

It is clear that it is possible to visualize easily certain phenomena which are hardly accessible by other means. At the present time experiments are

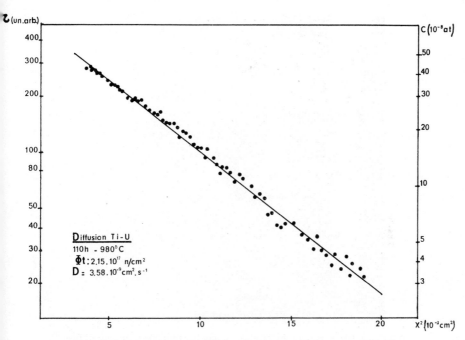

FIGURE 18   Variation of the density of fission tracks as a function of
the square of the distance to the interface according to a fissiography of the
type of Fig. 17 (after Ref. 51)

performed[56] in order to follow the purification of titanium, using the
following principle: the uranium is introduced homogeneously in a titanium
sample; by fissiography the displacement of uranium atoms (and probably
of all the impurities) is observed during different thermal treatment in a
gradient furnace.

2   Microanalysis by alphagraphy

The same procedure may be applied to elements undergoing the (n, α) reaction, such as boron and lithium. The principle is the same as the one used
in neutron dosimetry by boron glasses, and has already been applied to the
analysis of boron in austenitic steels.[57] In this case the method has more
limitations than in the case of fissiongraphy, by the appearance of alpha
tracks coming from the (n, α) reaction on O^{17} of cellulose nitrate (see the
chapter on thermal neutron dosimetry). Hence only elements either with a

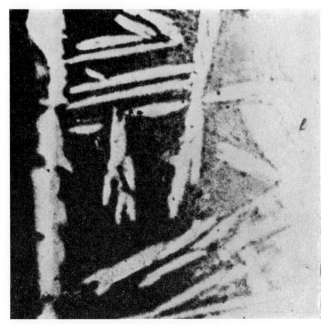

FIGURE 19   Fissiography of a slowly cooled titanium–uranium diffusion
couple, showing uranium segregation (after Ref. 51)

large cross section or being relatively abundant will be detectable. The limit
is 10^{-6} at/at for boron.

On the other hand alphagraphy is extremely useful in nuclear metallurgy.
As we have seen Pu^{239} is a good α-emitter, and the (relative) insensitivity
of cellulose nitrate to β and γ rays makes it essential in glove boxes. It is
by this means possible to autoradiograph fuel elements at their exit of the
reactor, in order to observe the distribution of plutonium in the elements and
its diffusion in the cladding. This method has already been used by Davies
and Darmitzel[58] and it will soon become an essential tool in all radio-
metallurgy laboratories.

IV   Solid state physics

Alphagraphy has been very useful in solid state physics, namely by the
application of the so-called "channeling" effect. We will first briefly describe
this phenomenon.

We consider a perfect crystal in which four close packed atomic rows
form a prism or "channel", the axis of which being a privileged trajectory

for an incoming particle. A particle arriving under a small angle ($<1°$) with the axis is maintained by the atoms along the channel: the particle is said to be channeled. Its energy loss rate is then much smaller than in the case of any other trajectory; consequently its range is longer and the created damage smaller. This channeling effect is now established theoretically[59] and experimentally.[60]

The most favourable channeling directions are, in decreasing order of efficiency:

f.c.c. structure: [011], [001]
b.c.c. structure: [111], [001], [011].

Inversely one might expect that each change or defect of the crystal affecting channeling, will be detectable by means of the transmission of particles through the crystal lattice. Among others alphagraphy is one of the methods by which this transmission may be studied. The α-particles may be easily obtained from small laboratory sources of Pu^{239} and Am^{241}. The very simple device is shown in Fig. 20: S is the α-source, F is the sample considered, the thickness of which being of the order of the α-range, R is the cellulose nitrate detector. The particle flux is here isotropic.

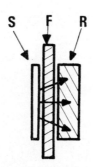

FIGURE 20 α-particle irradiation device. S = particle source; F = filter (i.e. the sample studied); R = detector (after Ref. 62)

Up till now the most important defects are grain boundaries, stacking faults, deformation bands, dislocation loops, etc.

1 *Effect of orientation and grand boundaries*

A series of alphagraphies performed on a platinum platelet of 7 microns, shows that the transmission increases with the annealing intensity, and decreases when the crystal is again cold-worked[61] (Fig. 21). This extremely

28*

FIGURE 21   Alphagraphies showing the influence of crystal structure on
α-particle transmission in platinum (after Ref. 61)

(a) after laminating; (b) after 1 hour annealing at 600°C; (c) after 1 hour
annealing at 900°C; (d) the same, cold-worked by a corrugated cylinder

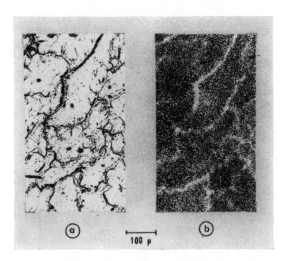

FIGURE 22   Influence of grain boundaries on α-particle transmission in
gold (after Ref. 62)

(a) micrography; (b) corresponding alphagraphy

important phenomenon is explained by the fact that the grain boundaries are almost opaque for α-particles, as shown in Fig. 22, where a micrograph and an alphagraph of a gold sheet of 7μ are compared. During annealing the dimensions of the grain increase, which decreases the relative importance of the grain boundaries. Furthermore the track density is different from one grain to another, by the fact that the grains have an orientation more or less close to a channeling axis.[62]

2 Effect of stacking faults

A more quantitative study has enabled one to investigate the effect of stacking faults in gold.[62] For this purpose a gold sheet of 7μ is quenched from

FIGURE 23 (a) Stacking fault tetrahedra in gold quenched from 1000°C, and subsequently annealed for 10 minutes at 60°C;

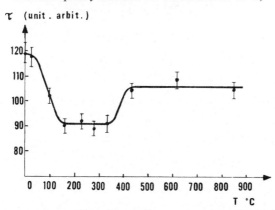

(b) influence of formation and annihilation of stacking fault tetrahedra on α-particle transmission in quenched gold. These tetrahedra are stable between 150° and 350°C (after Ref. 62)

1000°C in water. Afterwards the gold is subject to a series of isochronal annealings at different temperature. The track density after each annealing varies as shown in Fig. 23 b. By quenching the gold sample a large number of vacancies is introduced. By annealing between 20°C and 150°C these vacancies are coagulating in stacking fault tetrahedrons (Fig. 23 a) which may obstruct a large number of channels, and hence decreased the transmission. These tetrahedrons, which are first stable (constant transmission) disappear at high temperature (increasing transmission).

3 *Effect of dislocations*

In a sheet of aluminium (20 microns), quenched in water from 640°C, the quenched-in vacancies coagulate into dislocation loops by annealing at 60°C. These loops are annihilated by self-diffusion above 150°C, and it is possible to observe their annihilation during a series of isothermic anneal-

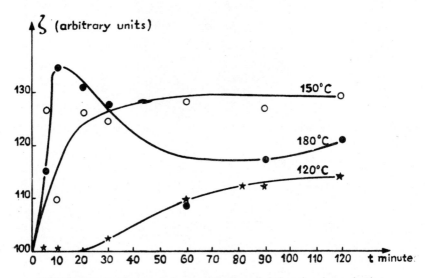

FIGURE 24   Influence of the annihilation of dislocation loops by isothermic annealing in quenched aluminium

ings, using the same device as before (Fig. 24). One sees indeed that transmission increases by annealing, the more rapidly when temperature is higher. On the other hand it is difficult to explain transmission decrease after 20 min at 180°C, the dispersion of the experimental points being too uncertain.

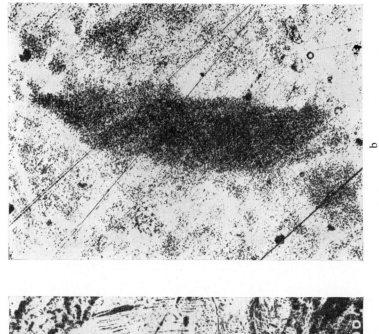

FIGURE 25   Showing a deformation band in a large grain in gold (after Ref. 63)
(a) micrography; (b) alphagraphy

4   *Effect of deformation band*

Figure 25 shows the influence of a deformation band in a gold sheet:[63] probably the grain as a whole has a [100] orientation, whereas the [110] orientation of the deformation band is more favourable for transmission.

This phenomenon of obstruction of α-particle transmission by crystal defects is almost general, and has been observed in numerous materials (Ag, W, Mo, etc.). It is also very useful in the study of the effect of impurities. At the present time experiments are performed concerning the effect of carbon interstitials in iron, and hydrogen in palladium. These examples are of course not limitative, and it is to be expected that many studies will be undertaken by this method. Probably a number of unsolved questions in solid state physics will become clear in this way.

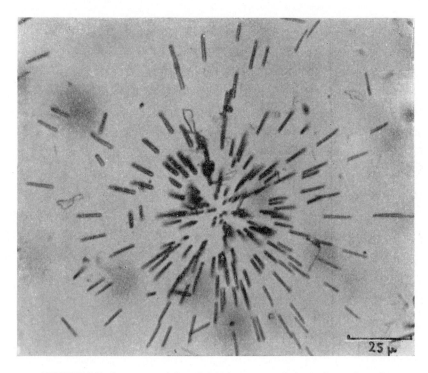

FIGURE 26   Star created by thermal neutron fission of uranium in atmospheric dust on a mica sheet (after Ref. 12)

V   Some other applications

The recording of charged particle tracks has become a useful tool in quite
a large number of very different fields.

    With respect to the protection of personnel working in contaminable
regions, we mention the work of Brackenbush and Baumgartner[64] who
have studied the detection of plutonium in urine. The use of nuclear emulsions permitted the detection of quantities of plutonium corresponding to
an α-activity of at least 0.5 desintegrations per minute. The use of fission

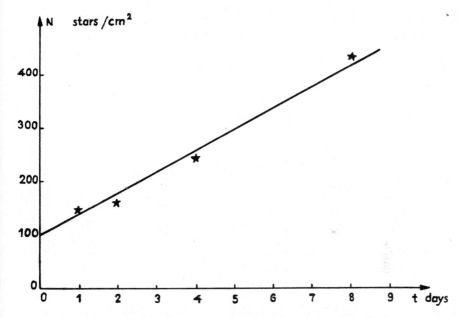

FIGURE 27   Density of stars as a function of exposure time of mica
samples in a laboratory (after Ref. 12)

tracks in makrofol has reduced this limit to 0.1 des.min^{-1}. The precision
of the measurement is at least as good and the results are obtained in a
much smaller time. On the other hand, the extreme sensitivity of the method
requires to work in conditions of absolute cleanliness, since the smallest
amount of atmospheric dust might perturbate the result.

    The influence of atmospheric dust has been the subject of experiments
undertaken by the same authors (and by us.[12] Figure 26 shows the fissio-
graph of dust collected in a laboratory, with its characteristic star shape.

Figure 27 shows the variation of the density of these stars on mica samples exposed for different times in the same laboratory.

In medicine, thin sheets of polycarbonate in which holes of 1 to 20 microns are obtained by etching fission fragment damage, have allowed one to filter blood cells.[65] The free cancerous cells are held up by the filter (the healthy cells are smaller and they traverse), can be coloured in situ and easily examined.

Conclusion

By its sensitivity and its flexibility the recording of tracks in insulators has become a first-class tool. It is to be expected that many of the present applications will soon leave the stage of laboratory scale to become of current use. This new technique may certainly still considerably be improved, and it is to be hoped that this will not only be the case for the fields in which it is already used, but also for other branches of science.

References

1. E. C. H. Silk and R. S. Barnes, *Phil. Mag.* **4**, 970 (1959).
2. C. Childs and L. Slifkkin, *Phys. Rev. Letters*, **9**, 354 (1962).
3. P. B. Price and R. M. Walker, *J. Appl. Phys.* **33**, 3400 (1962).
4. P. B. Price and R. M. Walker, *ibid.* **33**, 3407 (1962).
5. R. L. Fleisher, P. B. Price, and R. M. Walker, *Ann. Rev. Nucl. Sci.* **15**, 1 (1965).
6. R. L. Fleisher and P. B. Price, *J. Geophys. Res.* **69**, 331 (1964).
7. M. Maurette, Thesis, Paris (1965).
8. M. Debeauvais, (private communication).
9. J. W. N. Tuyn, *Nuclear Appl.* **3**, 372 (1967).
10. C. P. Bean, M. V. Doyle, and G. Entine, (unpublished results).
11. J. Mory and R. M. Walker, *Fifth Int. Conf. on Nuclear Photography*, CERN, Geneva (1964).
12. J. Mory, C.E.A.-Report 2846 (1965).
13. R. L. Fleisher, P. B. Price, and R. M. Walker, *Rev. Sci. Instr.* **37**, 525 (1966).
14. Idem, *J. Geophys. Res.* **70**, 1497 (1965).
15. K. Becker, USNRDL-Report TR-904 (1965).
16. J. A. Brinkman, *Ann. J. Phys.* **24**, 246 (1956).
17. Genthon, Thesis, Paris (1967).
18. R. L. Fleisher, P. B. Price, and R. M. Walker, *J. Appl. Phys.* **36**, 3654 (1965).
19. R. Pfohl, M. Monnin, and M. Debeuavais, *C. R. Accad. Sci. Paris* **261**, 2216 (1965).
20. R. L. Fleisher, *et al.*, *Phys. Rev.* **133**, A 1443 (1964).
21. R. L. Fleisher *et al.*, *Science* **155**, 187 (1967).
22. R. L. Fleisher *et al.*, *Phys. Rev.*, **156**, 353 (1967).
23. M. Debeauvais *et al.*, *Int. J. Appl. Rad. Isotopes* **15**, 289 (1964).

24. R. M. Walker, P. B. Price, and R. L. Fleisher, *Appl. Phys. Letters* 3, 28 (1963).
25. R. L. Fleisher, P. B. Price, and R. M. Walker, *Nucl. Sci. Eng.* 22, 153 (1965).
26. P. Prevo, R. E. Dahl, and H. H. Yoshikawa, *J. Appl. Phys.* 35, 2636 (1964).
27. M. Maurette and J. Mory, *Rev. Phys. Appl.* 3, 209 (1968).
28. J. Mory, (unpublished results).
29. G. D. Kerr and T. D. Strickel, *Health Physics* 12, 1141 (1966).
30. M. V. Baumgartner and L. W. Brakenbush, BNWL-332 (1966).
31. M. DeCoster, Rousseau, and J. Mory, (unpublished results).
32. J. W. N. Tuyn, *Nucl. Phys.* 3, 372 (1967).
33. M. Maurette and R. M. Walker, *J. Phys.* 25, 43 (1964).
34. M. Maurette and C. Stephan, *Phys. Chem. of Fission*, IAEA, Vienna (1965).
35. C. Stephan, Thesis Paris (1965).
36. M. Debeauvais and P. Cüer, *C. R. Acad. Sci. Paris* 261, 2633 (1965).
37. R. L. Fleisher *et al.*, *Proc. 3rd Conf. Reaction Complex Nuclei* 332 (1963).
38. A. S. Soldatov *et al.*, *Physics Letters* 14, 217 (1965).
39. D. S. Burnett *et al.*, *Phys. Rev.* 134, B 952 (1964).
40. R. L. Fleisher and P. B. Price, *ibid.* 133, B 63 (1964).
41. G. N. Flerov *et al.*, *Physics Letters* 13, 73 (1964).
42. A. F. Linev *et al.*, (cited after Ref. 5).
43. P. B. Price and R. M. Walker, *Proc. 5th Int. Conf. on Electron Microscopy*, paper G. 4 (1962).
44. R. L. Fleisher, P. B. Price, and R. M. Walker, *Science* 149, 383 (1965).
45. M. Maurette, P. Pellas, and R. M. Walker, *Bull. Soc. Franç. Min. Crist.* 87, 6 (1964).
46. R. H. Brill *et al.*, *J. Glass studies* 6, 151 (1964).
47. R. L. Fleisher and P. B. Price, *Geochim. Cosmochim. Acta* 28, 755 (1964).
48. R. L. Fleisher, P. B. Price, and R. M. Walker, *J. Geophys. Res.* 69, 4885 (1964).
49. Idem, *ibidem.* 70, 2703 (1965).
50. J. Mory, *Rev. Phys. Appl.* 3, 387 (1968).
51. F. de Keroulas, J. Mory, and Y. Quéré, *J. Nucl. Mat.* 22, 276 (1967).
52. P. B. Price and R. M. Walker, *Appl. Phys. Letters* 2, 23 (1963).
53. R. L. Fleisher and P. B. Price, *Science* 144, 841 (1964).
54. R. L. Fleisher, P. B. Price, and R. M. Walker, *7th Int. Glass Cong.*, Brussels, (1965).
55. F. de Keroulas, Thesis Paris (1967).
56. C. Weinberg, (private communication).
57. J. S. Armijo and H. S. Rosenbaum, *J. Appl. Phys.* 38, 2064 (1967).
58. J. H. Davies and R. W. Darmitzel, *Nucleonics* 23, 86 (1965).
59. D. K. Holmes, *Interaction of Radiation with Solids* (Editors R. Strumane *et al.*) p. 33. North Holland Publ. Cy (1964).
60. R. S. Nelson and M. Thompson, *Phil. Mag.* 8, 1677 (1963).
61. Y. Quéré, Thesis, Paris 1968.
62. Y. Quéré, J. C. Resneau, and J. Mory, *C. R. Acad. Sci. Paris* 262, 1528 (1966).
63. J. Mory *et al.*, *5th Int. Conf. on Corpuscular Photography*, Firenze (1966).
64. L. W. Brakenbush and W. V. Baumgartner, BNWL-SA-58 (1965).
65. S. H. Seal, *Cancer* 17, 637 (1964).

Radiation-induced electrical resistivity in pure metals

J. NIHOUL and L. STALS

Solid State Physics Department, S.C.K.-C.E.N. Mol (Belgium)

1 INTRODUCTION

Among the physical properties that are affected in metals by neutron irradiation, the electrical resistivity is no doubt the most frequently and extensively investigated one. A first reason is that this type of measurement allows a very high precision to be achieved by means of a rather simple equipment. Another reason is to be found in the fact that a simple relation is usually assumed to exist between the resistivity increment and the concentration of radiation-induced defects.

Although the latter assumption requires serious reserve, the electrical resistivity method has, in the past years, set up for a most successful tool for the research on structural defects in metals. In the field of neutron dosimetry, however, this method has found until now very little application.

The aim of this contribution is to set forth some general principles and some background information which have to be taken into account for a possible use of resistometric neutron dosimetry.

2 DEFECT-INDUCED RESISTIVITY INCREMENTS

2.1 Theoretical and experimental results

The theoretical calculation of the electrical resistivity of perfect metals is qualitatively well in hand but for quantitative estimates one still needs experimental data such as phonon spectra.[1] The same is true for the evaluation of the electrical resistivity due to impurities and structural defects. In recent years much effort has been paid to this subject.[2-7] Interstitials and vacancies can be considered effectively as positive respectively negative point charges, screened by an electric field, which disturbs the periodicity of the lattice and thus gives rise to an increased electrical resistivity. Whereas the early work was mainly based on the model of free or quasi-free electrons and spherical energy surfaces, more recently somewhat more realistic energy surfaces and better wave functions were used.[8]

For copper it has been estimated along these lines that the electrical resistivities of vacancies ($\Delta\varrho_v$) and of interstitials ($\Delta\varrho_i$) amount to:[8]

$$\Delta\varrho_v \simeq 1.6 \ \mu\Omega\text{cm/at.}\%,$$

$$\Delta\varrho_i \simeq 0.9 \ \mu\Omega\text{cm/at.}\%.$$

This means that the presence of 1 at. % Frenkel pairs in the lattice (a tremendously high concentration) would induce an extra electrical resistivity $\Delta\varrho_F$ of about 2.5 $\mu\Omega$cm, which is of the same order of magnitude as the resistivity of annealed copper at room temperature. This result is in fair agreement with the experimental values obtained by Meechan and Sosin[9] ($\Delta\varrho_F = 3.0 \ \mu\Omega\text{cm/at.}\%$) and by Nilan and Granato[10] ($\Delta\varrho_F = 2.1 \ \mu\Omega\text{cm}$), who combined electrical resistivity measurements with stored energy measurements, thereby assuming a theoretical stored energy value of 4 eV per Frenkel pair. Similar theoretical results are also available for a few other face-centred cubic metals (Ni, Ag, Au, Al)[11,12] but not e.g. for body-centred cubic or hexagonal close packed metals.

For a number of metals, however, an empirical rule has been presented by Lucasson and Walker.[13] Starting from electron irradiation experiments these authors were able to derive Frenkel pair resistivities $\Delta\varrho_F$ for the metals listed in table I. These values are within a factor of 2 in agreement with the theo-

TABLE I

metal	structure	$\Delta\varrho_F$ ($\mu\Omega$ cm/at. %)	$\varrho_{0\,°C}$ ($\mu\Omega$ cm)
Al	f.c.c.	3.4	2.6
Ni		3.2	6.1
Cu		1.3	1.7
Ag		1.4	1.5
Fe	b.c.c.	12.5	10
Mo		4.5	5.2
Ti	h.c.p.	42	43

retically-calculated values, as far as available. A remarkable feature of these results is that they show a linear relationship between the induced resistivity per Frenkel pair and the resistivity of the annealed metal at room temperature. It turns out that a very practical rule of thumb can be formulated as follows: the resistivity induced by 1 % Frenkel pairs is roughly equal to the resistivity of the given metal at the ice point.*

It should be mentioned, however, that all these estimates only apply for the case of mutually independent point defects, as produced e.g. by electron bombardment to a low dose. Fundamental investigations, indeed, of radiation-induced structural defects are preferably performed with electron bombardment. In this case one can use energetic particles of a well-chosen energy (about 1 MeV) so as to create one Frenkel pair per collision. On the other hand, in the case of fast neutron irradiation defects are produced mainly in cascades, so that it is very hard to make reliable

---

* Analogous estimates have been made also for other types of structural defects, see e.g. ref. 20.

theoretical estimates. Within the cascate, the probability of mutual interaction, recombination or association of the defects is very high, which
effect certainly affects the resultant induced resistivity.[14] After high enough
doses, the cascades themselves are no longer interindependent but interfere
with each other, resulting in the bending off and eventual saturation of $\Delta\varrho$
as a function of dose. In view of the many unknown factors which are
involved here, it is clear that, on theoretical grounds, no direct relation can
be established as yet between neutron dose and electrical resistivity.

2.2 Temperature effect: Matthiessen's law

It has been assumed for a long time that Matthiessen's law[15] holds for the
electrical resistivity of defects, which implies that the resistivity increment
per defect is independent of temperature. The partial resistivity contributions
of structural defects (ϱ_s), impurities (ϱ_i) and phonons (ϱ_{ph}) are then considered
to be simply additive, so that at a temperature T the total resistivity is given
by:

$$\varrho(T) = \sum \varrho_j = \varrho_s + \varrho_i + \varrho_{ph}(T). \tag{1}$$

At low temperatures the temperature-dependent electrical resistivity,
ϱ_{ph}, due to phonon-electron interactions, is approximately proportional to
T^5 for the majority of pure metals, whereas at higher temperatures it increases
linearly with temperature. This behaviour is expressed in a Debye-model
according to the formula of Grüneisen–Bloch:

$$\varrho_{ph}(T) = A\left(\frac{T}{\Theta}\right)^5 \int\limits_0^{\theta/T} \frac{x^5 dx}{(e^x - 1)(1 - e^{-x})} \tag{2}$$

where A is a material constant defining the strength of the phononelectron
interaction. The electrical resistivity data for a large number of metals all
lie on the same curve, if they are plotted in a resistivity-temperature diagram, the T-axis being reduced with respect to the Debye-temperature θ.
This is shown in Fig. 1. According to Matthiessen's law, the extra-resistivity
$\Delta\varrho(= \varrho_s + \varrho_i)$ due to defects and impurities is the same for all temperatures,
which means that the resistivity-temperature curve of a metal results from
the corresponding curve of the perfect metal by a vertical displacement over
the same amount at all temperatures, as illustrated in Fig. 2.

Rather important deviations, however, from Matthiessen's law have
been reported as well for point defects,[11] as for dislocation lines.[16,17] For

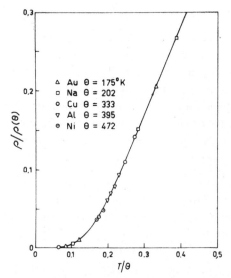

FIGURE 1 The electrical resistivity of various metals plotted as a function of reduced temperature, showing the validity of teh Grüneisen–Bloch equation (after J. Bardeen, *J. Appl. Phys.* **11**, 88 (1940)

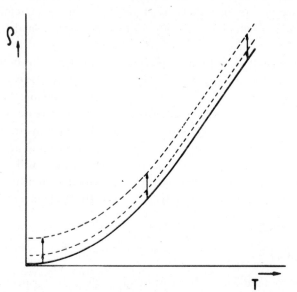

FIGURE 2 Illustration of Matthiessen's rule. The full line represents schematically the resistivity of a pure metal. Dotted lines show corresponding curves for increasing defect concentrations

the present purpose, however, these deviations can be neglected provided that the resistivity measurements are always carried out at the same reference temperature as can be derived from Eq. (1). Since it is well-known that defects are increasingly mobile with increasing temperature, the temperature at which the resistivity measurements are performed must not exceed the irradiation temperature, if it is aimed to preserve as much as possible defects in the specimen. Apart from these considerations a few other factors make it advisable to perform the measurements at a low temperature even if the irradiation temperature is rather high. These factors are:

1   At these low temperatures as e.g. the boiling point of liquid hydrogen (20°K) or helium (4.2°K) the temperature dependent part of the electrical resistivity is negligible small, so that the otherwise difficult problem of temperature stabilization is eliminated. Practically only the temperature independent "residual resistivity" is left over.

2   For the same reason, the fraction of the induced resistivity with respect to the total resistivity is much larger than at higher temperatures.

The latter point may be illustrated as follows. Suppose a pure metal is irradiated having an initial electrical resistivity at room temperature of $5 \,\mu\Omega$cm and a residual resistivity ϱ_0 which is $1000 \times$ smaller (a typical factor for pure metals): $\varrho_0 = 5 \times 10^{-3} \,\mu\Omega$cm. Suppose further an atomic concentration of 0.01% Frenkel pairs are created by the bombardment, resulting in a resistivity increment of $5 \times 10^{-2} \,\mu\Omega$cm (according to the above-mentioned rule of Lucasson and Walker). Assuming Matthiessen's law to be valid, one will measure the same resistivity increase, whatever the temperature at which the measurement is performed (in so far, of course, as the defects considered are not annealing out upon warming up). After irradiation, the electrical resistivity at room temperature will be $5 + 0.05 = 5.05 \,\mu\Omega$cm, (increase by 1%) whereas at liquid helium temperature it will amount to $5 \times 10^{-3} + 5 \times 10^{-2} = 55 \times 10^{-3} \,\mu\Omega$cm, i.e. an increase by a factor 11.

2.3   Size effect

The specimens used for studying irradiation effects by means of resistivity measurements are often in the form of thin wires or foils, in order to increase the electrical resistance and hence the sensitivity of the measurements. One disadvantage of the use of very thin specimens is to be found in the fact that the resistivity per defect becomes a function of the size and also of the concentration of the defects. It has been shown theoretically by Sond-heimer[18] that the resistivity of a thin foil ϱ_f is given by:

$$\varrho_f = \varrho_b \phi\left(\frac{a}{l}\right)\bigg/\frac{a}{l}, \tag{3}$$

where ϱ_b is the resistivity of the bulk material, a the foil thickness, l the mean free path of the conduction electrons and Φ a rather complicated function of the ratio a/l and of the probability for diffuse scattering of the electrons at the foil surface. Starting from this equation Dworschak *et al.*[19] have computed the ratio $d\varrho_f/d\varrho_b$ as a function of a/l, as plotted in Fig. 3. They also found experimental evidence for this phenomenon by simultane-ously irradiating to various doses two aluminium foils of different thickness (40 μ and 5.6 μ). As shown in Fig. 4 the calculated curve is in good agree-ment with the experimental data. It results that for thin foils (e.g. $a < 10$ μ) the resistivity increment per unit defect concentration can easily be too large by a factor 2 as compared with the bulk material.

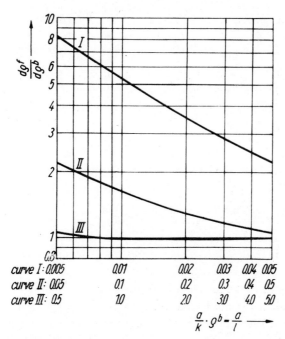

FIGURE 3   Calculated size effect correction for resistivity increments measured in thin foils (after F. Dworschak *et al.*[19]

In order to avoid the complications related to this size effect it is advisable to use specimens the thickness of which is larger than a few times the mean free path of the electrons.

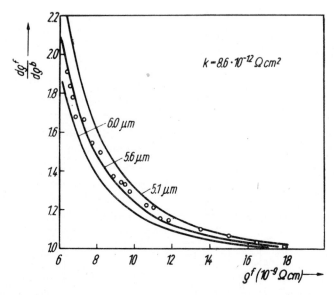

FIGURE 4   Experimental evidence for the necessity of size effect correction for the resistivity increments in thin foils, obtained by simultaneous irradiation of a 40 and a 5.6 μ thick Al foil. The full curves are theoretical (after F. Dworschak *et al.*[19])

3   RESISTOMETRIC DATA ON NEUTRON-IRRADIATED METALS

3.1   Damage production

The electrical resistivity of pure metals is known to increase upon irradiation with fast particles.[20] Since it was soon observed that the induced resistivity annealed out at rather low temperatures, these irradiations are often performed at very low temperatures. It was hoped in that way to retain all the defects produced in the metal. A beautiful example of early experiments on some noble metals is illustrated in Fig. 5. It shows the resistivity measurements performed by Cooper *et al.*[21] on gold, silver and copper, as a function of deuteron dose. Blewitt and coworkers[22] published similar results for various metals and alloys after neutron bombardment (see Fig. 6).

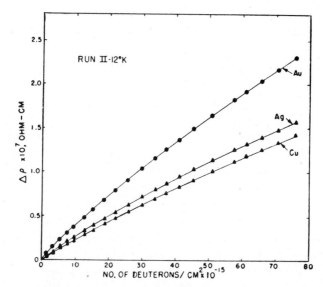

FIGURE 5   Resistivity increase in noble metals as a function of integrated deuteron flux (after H. G. Cooper *et al.*[21])

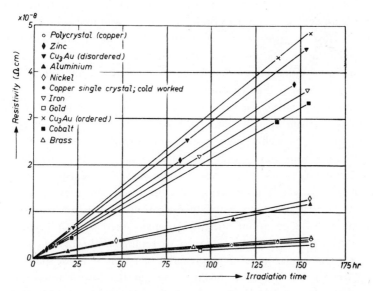

FIGURE 6   Resistivity increase of several metals exposed to neutron bombardment in the ORNL graphite reactor at 18°K (after Blewitt *et al.*[22])

When a metal is irradiated in a nuclear reactor it is subjected to a wide spectrum of neutrons. The threshold energies for direct displacements E_d in most metals are to be found in the range from 20 eV to 50 eV. As the maximum transferred energy is given by the relation:

$$T_{max} = 4\frac{Mm}{(M + m)^2}E \qquad (4)$$

which is derived from the laws of conservation of energy and momentum and where M represents the mass of the target atoms, m the mass of the incident neutrons and E their energy, the neutrons must have energies of the order of 1 keV to exceed the displacement energy E_d.

Therefore, at first sight it looks as if only fast neutrons ($E > 1$ keV) would be effective for radiation damage. In fact also thermal neutrons may play an important role, due to the γ-ray emission upon capture of a thermal neutron by the nucleus. These energetic γ-rays can cause many types of atoms to recoil with sufficient energy to produce one or more Frenkel pairs.[26] The relative amounts of each type of damage are proportional to the ratio of thermal to fast flux and to the ratio of the cross sections for thermal neutron capture and for fast neutron scattering.

Oak Ridge people have paid considerable effort in studying thermal neutron damage in a number of metals, using suitable screens so as to reduce the fast neutron flux to less than 0.1 % of the thermal neutron flux. In normal reactor circumstances the damage produced by fast neutrons will usually be much larger than the thermal neutron damage, except for elements having very high capture cross sections.

Another contribution to resistivity increase upon capture of a thermal neutron arises from the fact that a fraction of neutron captures may produce transmutations. A well-known case is the formation of ^{198}Hg in gold. These foreign atoms act as impurities or chemical defects in the matrix and will consequently give rise to a resistivity increase. These aspects of thermal neutron damage will not be further developed here, but they have certainly to be taken into account in possible investigations on resistometric dosimetry.

As the knowledge about structural defects increased, it became clear that no temperature was low enough to retain *all* the defects produced. Seeger's suggestion[23] that an appreciable fraction of close pairs formed during irradiation might be unstable even at the lowest temperature, is now widely accepted.[24,25] As a result the advantage of bombarding at very low temperatures in order to study radiation damage is somewhat decreased. In view of dosimetric applications, systematic investigations of resistivity increments upon neutron bombardment at reactor temperatures are necessary. A major condition for such investigations is to choose metals in which at least a substantial fraction of the defects are stable at the irradiation temperature. This leads us to the problem of the recovery of defects in metals, which will be discussed briefly in the next section.

3.2 Recovery of defects

A typical recovery curve of a pure metal after irradiation is shown in Fig. 7. Such a curve is the result of a number of electrical resistivity measurements performed at constant temperature (usually 4.2°K) after an annealing pulse of a constant time ("isochronal annealing") at subsequently higher annealing temperatures. After van Bueren[27] five main recovery stages are distin-

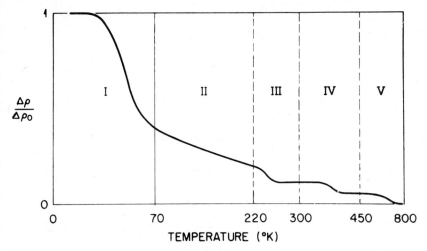

FIGURE 7 Schematic isochronal recovery of the electrical resistivity of neutron-irradiated pure metals as a function of the annealing temperature

guished, labelled from I to V. Whereas the position of the first stage seems to be related with the lattice constant and the Debye temperature of the metal[28,29] all the other recovery stages seem to be related with the melting, point. As a very crude rule it may be formulated that for the majority of pure f.c.c. metals until now investigated, these stages are situated as follows (T_m standing for the melting point): stage II around $0.1\ T_m$, stage III

$\sim 0.2\ T_m$, stage IV $\sim 0.3\ T_m$ and stage V $\sim 0.5\ T_m$. For b.c.c. metals a similar relationship seems to hold,[30,31,32] the homologous temperatures being somewhat lower though (stage III $\sim 0.15\ T_m$, stage V $\sim 0.35\ T_m$).

We will not discuss here the various and often controversial interpretations of these recovery stages, for which the reader is referred to the literature.[20,25] What may be considered as firmly established is that stage I is for a great part to be associated with the recombination of close Frenkel pairs, stage IV with free vacancy migration and stage V with the annihilation of more complex defects such as depleted zones, defect clusters, dislocation loops etc. On the other hand, much controversy still exists about stages II and III and, more particularly, about the question whether the normal interstitials migrate in stage III or already in the higher temperature part of stage I.

4 A POSSIBLE APPLICATION: RESISTOMETRIC NEUTRON DOSIMETRY

4.1 Choice of the metal

As pointed out in sections 3.1 and 3.2 already, the use of a metallic specimen for resistometric neutron dosimetry implies that a substantial fraction of induced defects are stable at the irradiation temperature. Defects annihilating in stage I and II are not of practical importance in this connection since for all metals these stages occur below (or a about) 0°C, i.e. far below the normal operating reactor temperatures. Since, on the other hand, stages IV and V are relatively small after neutron irradiation, it is obvious to look for metals whose stage III occurs at sufficiently high temperature (at least $> 100°C$). Following the rough rule that this stage occurs at temperatures of about $1/6$ to $1/5$ of the melting point (in °K), one may eliminate all metals having melting points below about 2500°C. The main remaining metals are then the body-centred cubic metals niobium, molybdenum, tantalum and tungsten and the hexagonal close packed metals osmium and rhenium. From these, only the b.c.c. metals have been studied to some extend as yet. Furthermore, the results on stage III recovery in niobium and tantalum are most controversial as a result of the influence of gaseous impurities in these metals.[33] The remaining elements molybdenum and tungsten show stage III recovery around 180°C and 350°C respectively (see next section), so that these metals are potentially suitable for resistometric neutron dosimetry in environments at some hundred degrees centigrade below these temperatures.

4.2 Experimental irradiation data for molybdenum and tungsten

The increase of the electrical resistivity of molybdenum and tungsten as a function of neutron dose has been investigated by Kinchin and Thompson[34] and (for tungsten alone) by Perriot and coworkers.[35,36] Their results are in excellent agreement as illustrated in Fig. 8, where the relative resistivity

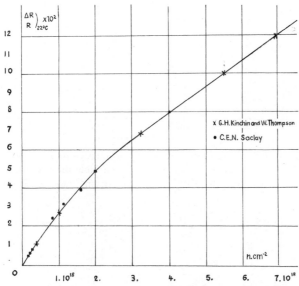

FIGURE 8   Relative resistance increment $\left(\dfrac{\Delta R}{R} \times 10^2\right)$ of tungsten as a function of fast neutron dose up to 7×10^{18} n.cm^{-2} as measured at room temperature (after J. Blons *et al.*[35])

increment as measured at room temperature, is plotted versus the integrated neutron flux above 10 keV. As a typical value it may be noted that the electrical resistivity at room temperature increases by 10% after a fast neutron dose of about 5×10^{18} n cm^{-2}. Such an effect can easily be measured with 1% precision or better by means of a standard equipment. Figure 9 shows a damage production curve in tungsten up to 4×10^{19} n cm^{-2}.

Typical recovery curves for molybdenum and tungsten after neutron irradiation are presented in Fig. 10 and 11 showing the pronounced recovery stages III mentioned in section 4.1, followed by relatively less important recovery stages at higher temperatures.

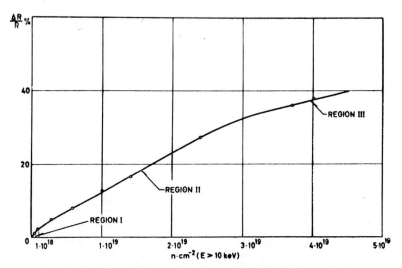

FIGURE 9   Relative resistance increment of tungsten measured at room temperature as a function of fast neutron dose. Note the bending of the curve around the doses 1×10^{18} and 3×10^{19} n cm^{-2} (after G. Perriot[36])

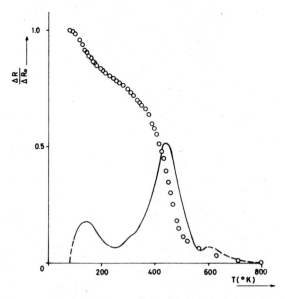

FIGURE 10   Isochronal recovery of the electrical resistivity increment of molybdenum after neutron irradiation at 78°K (after J. Nihoul[30])

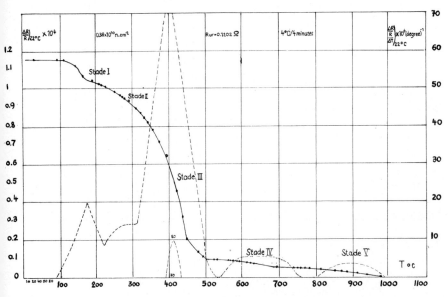

FIGURE 11   Isochronal recovery of the electrical resistivity increment of tungsten after neutron irradiation at about 100°C (after J. Blons *et al.*[35])

4.3   Practical aspects of resistometric neutron dosimetry and concluding remarks

Until now only very few data are available concerning the practical elaboration and use of resistometric neutron dosimetry. This problem has been investigated most extensively by Perriot,[36] who achieved a practical dosimeter, as illustrated in Fig. 12. It consists of a tungsten wire sealed under vacuum in a quartz tube and provided with two current and two potential leads, thus allowing electrical resistivity measurements to be made following simple classical methods. As already mentioned, these measurements should always be performed at the same temperature e.g. at the ice point, although the senistivity is considerably increased if a very low temperature, e.g. 4.2°K, the boiling point of liquid helium, can be used.

Since the results may depend on the energy spectrum of the neutrons and certainly on the ambient temperature of the irradiation, a major practical problem will be the elaboration of suitable correction terms (or a set of calibration curves) for various conditions. For some more details we refer to the work of the Saclay group.[36]

The main advantage of this type of dosimeter would be to yield values of fast neutron doses by means of one single and very simple measurement. Disadvantages of this prototype are its rather important size and the fragility of the quartz envelope. It must not be excluded, however, that in this age of amazing miniaturization these disadvantages will be eliminated one day.

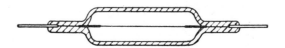

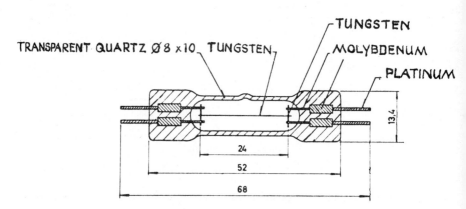

FIGURE 12   Resistometric neutron dosimeter as developed by
G. Perriot[36]

References

1. N. Wiser, *Phys. Rev.*, **143**, 393 (1966).
2. K. Huang, *Proc. Phys. Soc.*, **60**, 161 (1948).
3. J. Friedel, Thèse, Université de Paris, Masson et Cie, Paris (1954).
4. P. Jongenburger, *Appl. Sc. Res.*, **B3**, 237 (1953).
5. J. Friedel, *J. Physique Rad.*, **15**, 433 (1954).
6. A. Seeger and H. Bross, *Z. Physik*, **145**, 161 (1956).
7. H. Stehle, Thesis, T.H. Stuttgart, Stuttgart, (1957).
8. A. Seeger, *J. Phys. Rad.*, **23**, 616 (1962).
9. C. J. Meechan and A. L. Sosin, *Phys. Rev.*, **113**, 424 (1959).
10. T. G. Nilan and A. V. Granato, *Phys. Rev. Letters*, **6**, 171 (1961).
11. A. Seeger and H. Stehle, *Z. Phys.*, **146**, 242 (1956).
12. J. Friedel, The Interaction of Radiation with Solids, Proc. of the Int. Summer School on Solid State Physics, Mol 1963, p. 114 (North-Holland Publ. Company, Amsterdam).

13. P. G. Lucasson and R. M. Walker, *Phys. Rev.*, **127**, 485 and 1130 (1962).
14. A. Babcenco and A. Corciovei, I.F.A. Report FT/51, Bucharest (1964).
15. W. Matthiessen and C. Vogt, *Pogg. Ann.* **122**, 47 (1864).
16. E. Krautz and H. Schultz, *Z. Naturf.*, A9, 125 (1954).
17. Z. S. Basinski, J. S. Dugdale, and A. Whowie, *Phil. Mag.*, **18**, 1989 (1963).
18. E. H. Sondheimer, *Adv. Phys.* **1**, 1 (1952).
19. F. Dworschak, H. Schuster, H. Wollenberg, and J. Wurm, *Phys. stat. sol.* **21**, 471 (1967).
20. H. G. Van Bueren, *Imperfections in Crystals*, North-Holland Publishing Company, Amsterdam (1960).
21. H. G. Cooper, J. S. Koehler, and J. W. Marx, *Phys. Rev.*, **97**, 599 (1955).
22. T. H. Blewitt, R. R. Coltman, D. K. Holmes, and T. S. Noggle in *Dislocations and the mechanical properties of crystals* (Wiley, New York p. 603 (1957).
23. A. Seeger, *Proc. Int. Conf. Geneva II*, paper 961.
24. J. S. Koehler and G. Leibfried, *J. Phys. Soc. Japan* **18**, Suppl. III, 266 (1963).
25. D. K. Holmes, The Interaction of Radiation with Solids, Proc. of the Int. Summer School on Solid State Physics, Mol 1963, p. 147 (North-Holland Publ. Company, Amsterdam).
26. R. R. Coltman, C. E. Klabunde and J. K. Redman, *Phys. Rev.*, **156**, 715 (1967).
27. H. G. Van Bueren, *Z. Metallk.*, **46**, 272 (1955).
28. G. Burger, K. Isebeck, R. Kesler, J. Völkl, H. Wenzl, H. H. Kuhlmann, and H. Schultz, *Phys. Letters*, **20**, 470 (1966).
29. R. Pichon, C. Minnier-Casseyre, V. Hivert, and P. Moser, *Phys. stat. sol.*, **17**, K33 (1966).
30. J. Nihoul, *Phys. stat. sol.* **2**, 308 (1962).
31. J. Moteff and J. P. Smith, ASTM Symp. on Flow and Fracture Behaviour of Metals in Nuclear Environments (1964).
32. L. Stals and J. Nihoul, *Phys. stat. sol.*, **8**, 785 (1965).
33. F. Schlät and A. Köthe, Reinststoffprobleme Bd. III, Ed. E. Rexer, Akademie Verlag Berlin p. 629 (1967).
34. G. H. Kinchin and M. W. Thompson, *J. Nucl. Energy* **6**, 275 (1958).
35. J. Blons, P. Imbert, G. Perriot and G. Tourand, *Colloque sur les effets des irradiations dans les cristaux*, Saclay (1960).
36. G. Perriot in *Neutron Dosimetry* Vol. II, A.E.A. Vienna p. 433 (1963).

Some experiments and difficulties on relating radiation damage to neutron dose in solids

A. VAN DEN BOSCH

Solid State Physics Department, SCK, Mol (Belgium)

1 INTRODUCTION

"When irradiated in a nuclear reactor, a single crystal of lithium fluoride becomes at first yellow, then reddish-brown and finally black". This statement is a very qualitative one. It relates vaguely radiation induced effects in LiF to radiation dose. When one likes to predict more precisely what will happen to a sample on irradiation or to know the quantity of radiation used in an experiment, a more quantitative expression should be found. This is obvious, however it is hard to realize as nature turned out to be complex. On the one hand "radiation" is the collective name for all jets of different kinds of particles;[1] on the other hand lots of structural defects caused by the interaction of radiation with matter are detected in solids.

In the world of radiation, a special place is taken by the neutrons. These elementary particles, together with the protons, are the building stones of the nuclei. However, because the neutrons are neutral, they are not repulsed by the electric charge of the protons and consequently they easily penetrate into the nuclei. The compounds so formed have a neutron–proton ratio which is often too high to be stable. In a few isotopes the absorption of the neutron is followed by fission of the composite nucleus. At this event, in some cases, more neutrons are released, which, on their turn, can be used for producing new fissions. So people were able to construct experimental set up's wherein a chain-reaction is going on. In these nuclear reactors, besides the neutrons, also other kinds of radiation occur. The composition of the radiation depends on the type of the reactor and on the situation of the moment (e.g. the burn-up). Although variation exists an order in magnitude for the mean total energy per fission for each kind of radiation can be given as follows: fission fragments $\simeq 162$ MeV; γ's $\simeq 24$ MeV; β's $\simeq 8$ MeV and neutrons about 5 MeV. The interaction of the radiation with matter causes most of its energy to be converted into heat. Such heat sources are now used for power plants. As a consequence of the industrialization of the nuclear reactors the occurance of radiation tremendously extends and "man" has to manage this. The trouble is that the radiation energy does not convert for a hundred per cent into heat. A small percentage of this energy may induce large structural changes, as well in living matter as in non living constructional materials. In the hope to become able to prevent, or at least to delay awry effects, people should try to gain an understanding of the processes which cause radiation damage. More favourable aspects of the interaction of radiation with matter do also exist; e.g. its use for dosimetry. Discussing some neutron detectors of this kind is our aim now.

2 THE LiF THERMAL NEUTRON DETECTOR

2.1 F-center absorption

In a few cases radiation induced damage in solids is found to be simply related to the radiation dose. The claim for a simple relation between damage and dose implies a sinple situation in the solid. However, we noticed before that lots of structural defects are reported to exist in matter. Consequently, in order to keep things simple a variety of constraints is needed to be introduced in the experiments. These limitations of use will be discussed now for the measurements of F-center absorption in lithium fluoride.

Already some years ago, single crystals of LiF were available in an optical pure form. Their transparency for light with a wavelength between 0.11 and 6 μm and their stability in a normal atmosphere, favoured their use in infra-red and ultra-violet optics. In this pure material no interaction of radiation induced defects with impurities will be considered. The structure of LiF is the same as that of sodium chloride. The lithium and fluorine ions are each situated on the points of separate face-centered cubic lattices which are interleaved with each other.

When a colourless limpid single crystal of LiF, about 0.03 cm thick, was irradiated at room temperature to, say, a neutron dose of about 1.5×10^{12} neutrons per square centimeter, an optical absorption-band appears at about 0.25 μm. This is the *F*-band. It is due to isolated anion-vacancies each of which trapped an electron. The *F*-centers are thought to be created by the following reaction:

$$F^- \xrightarrow{\ h\nu\ } \boxed{e^-} + \textcircled{F}$$

wherein F$^-$ designates an ion of fluorine on a normal lattice site and $\boxed{e^-}$ stands for an F-center. $\textcircled{F}$ indicates a neutral fluorine atom on an interstitial place. Fluorine molecules, constituted by two neutron atoms, were detected with the aid of nuclear magnetic resonance techniques by Ring *et al.*[2] The latter structure defects however do not show an absorption-band in the region covered by currently used spectrometers. The Beckman DK1 spectro-photometer covers the wavelength region between 0.2 μm (u.V.) and 3.5 μm (I.R.).

In the cation sublattice also damage may occur. In single crystals which were neutron irradiated at about 78°K Farge *et al.*[3] found an optical active center due to interstitial lithium. The absorption-band however does not interfere optically with the F-band. It is situated at about 0.55 μm. More, the efficiency of formation is very low as compared to that of the F-band. Its presence was not detected in our crystals which were irradiated above room temperature.

At lower irradiation doses the specific detection of the F-band helps to keep things simple. At higher doses the difficulties arise. The samples become very dense under the F-band and one gets in trouble measuring, in the apparatus mentioned, the feeble transmission of a manageable specimen, the thickness of which as at least 0.1 mm. Although more elaborate techniques may avoid this difficulty it is of no use as the structure defect system itself becomes very complicated. At high doses F-centers coagulate and new absorption bands occur. The first appearing is the M-center, formed by two F-centers on adjacent sublattice sites. This center also absorbs in the F-band region. In principle one can take this effect in account. At 1×10^{15} n.cm^{-2} the situation becomes awful as new bands appear overlapping with the existing ones.

In the dose region wherein the F-center absorption can be determined, Smoluchowski et al.,[4] in their work on electron irradiation of LiF, pointed out that the efficiency of the band-formation depends on the temperature at which the irradiation was carried out. A broad maximum appears between $-63°C$ and $0°C$. A decrease in efficiency of 15% was found at 100°C and an even larger deviation occurs at $-196°C$, at least in irradiations which lasted about 15 hours. At the temperatures mentioned the *F*-centers are supposed to be stable. One knows the defects start to anneal out at temperatures higher than 150°C.[5] Consequently, in order to obtain reproducible results the temperature at the irradiation should be controlled and kept some ten degrees below 150°C.

Some less controllable parameters also influence the reproducibility of the results. For one kind of material and for a neutron dose about 5×10^{12} thermal neutrons per cm^2 a change in the efficiency of *F*-band formation was found to depend on the thickness of some specimens which were annealed for the effects of a previous irradiation.[6] For crystals from the same mother crystal, but as grown, it was possible to predict the optical absorption to better than 5%. It seems that in the thicker specimens the annealing was only partial although from the point of view of *F*-band absorption it was complete. Structural defects may influence the efficiency of the *F*-band formation as impurities do.[7] Consequently, as long as the introduction of such defects and (or) impurities is not under control manufacturing LiF for dosimetrical use, one should work with specimens which have an identical history. The efficiency of each batch should then be determined. This should not sound too bad as these conditions are identical for photographic emulsions, and see, to-day nobody thinks about when he is making a picture.

The former exposition situated the problem from the point of view of the radiation induced structural defects in single crystals of lithium fluoride. A more quantitative expression for what is called the F-band absorption has to be given now. It can be done on the hand of the area under the absorption curve. The latter is obtained by plotting the absorption-coefficient μ_a versus the energy E of the monochromatic light used:

$$\left[\mu_a = \ln \frac{I_0}{I} / D\right]_E. \tag{1}$$

For the F-band in LiF, E is practically situated between 4 and 6 eV. The intensity of a monochromatic lightbeam transmitted by the unirradiated crystal is I_0; and I is the intensity of the beam transmitted by the irradiated crystal. The light in both cases needs to come from identical sources and is supposed to follow the normal to the surface of a planparallel LiF crystal plate of thickness D. Because some changes in the background occur during irradiation, the $I_0(E)$ values are obtained by extrapolating the $I(E)$ values measured at the low energy side of the optical absorption-band.

In the case where the optical density at the maximum is too high to be measured easily in, say, a Beckman DK1 spectrophotometer, the μ values can be estimated by extrapolating them from the experimental points on the band-sides. Such a calculation was carried out for one sample of a thickness of 0.0375 cm which received a thermal neutron dose about 8.8×10^{13} n.cm^{-2}. The μ distribution was assumed to be Gaussian.[8] Figure 1 shows the absorption curve so obtained. The area is calculated to be 196 eV.cm^{-1}. However, for such a technique the precision of the measurement quickly goes down for increasing optical density because the matching of the densities on the sides of the band does not work too well.

On a theoretical base[9] the area

$$A = \int \mu_a(E)\, dE, \tag{2}$$

is shown to be proportional to the number of F-centers per unit volume:

$$N_F = K.A \tag{3}$$

However, theory is not subtle enough to propose an accurate proportionality factor K. A calibration experiment has been carried out by Bate et al.[10] with the assumption that N_F can be determined from the magnetic measurements.

The foregoing discussion demonstrated that the radiation-damage, in some cases, can be quantitatively expressed. Other techniques than the discussed one may also suit the purpose. In principle, in this case of LiF,

30*

electron paramagnetic resonance—or static magnetic susceptibility measurements lead to the same results because the F-centers are paramagnetic. The choice of the technique used leans on different arguments among which "easiness" settles often the matter.

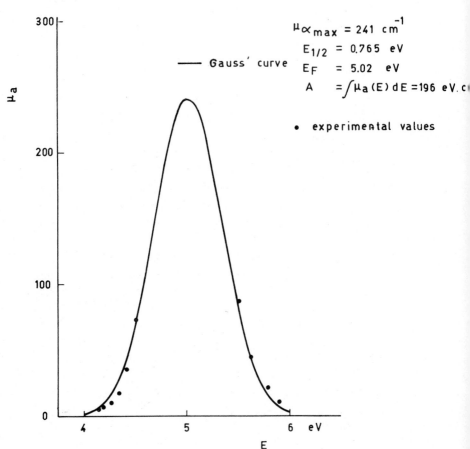

FIGURE 1   The estimation of the μ values at the maximum of an optical dense F-band from experimental points on the band-sides.

2.2   Thermal neutron absorption

In the following an example of a quantitative treatment of a radiation dose will be given. We are going to discuss the irradiation of plates of LiF with thermal neutrons in a graphite reactor. Again this example has been chosen on account of its simplicity. How is it possible that simple situations can occur while we claime that the radiation in a nuclear reactor is complex? A selection between charged and uncharged particles can be made on the base of their penetration depth in matter; the range of the charged particle of the same energy being relatively the smallent. By shielding the specimen with moderator material, the β-ray intensity can be kept rather low at the sample place. The highly ionized fission fragments are even more easily stopped. Practically, only neutral particles are allowed to reach the sample. Remains to differentiate for the neutrons and the γ's. Here the choice of the detector material itself comes into play. In order to minimize the interaction of the γ's with matter the constituting elements are taken among the lightest out of the table of Mendeljeff. The underlying idea is: the lighter the element the less electrons for interacting with the γ's. In contrast to the forementioned situation, the probability for neutrons to interact with these ligther elements should be as high as possible. From this point of view natural lithium is a good choice. The absorption cross-section of the ^{6}Li isotope is very high for thermal neutrons. Moreover, the absorption is followed by fission

$$^6Li(n, \alpha) \; ^3H + Q$$

the energy of which mostly is spent in the sample. The high stopping power of matter for ionized fission particles keeps the range in LiF crystals of the α's, respectively the ^{3}H, to about 4 μm and 27 μm. These lengths can be chosen to be shorter than the dimensions of the sample. The latter can easily be taken about 0.5 cm by 0.5 cm by 0.03 cm. Consequently surface effects are neglected and calculation of the radiation induced energy in the crystal is taken to be Q (4.8 MeV) times the number of fissions in the specimen. One more point is favourable for keeping high the ratio of the effects of the neutrons to these of the γ's. In LiF the efficiency for F-center formation is relatively higher in the n- than in the γ-case; i.e. less energy per F-center is needed by the former—than by the latter—radiation.[11] In fact not only use is made of the difference in the penetration depth of the different kinds of radiation, but also, although to a small extend, on the specificity of the reaction efficiency in the detector material.

The next point in the discussion is a quantitative calculation of the number of fissions in the sample. This number, on the one hand, is related to physical properties of the sample (i.e. to the ability of absorbing neutrons which, on its turn, is related to the cross-section) and, on the other hand to the number of neutrons reaching the sample (i.e. the incoming neutron flux). In pure LiF crystals of natural isotopic aboundance, the number of fissions is practically equal to the number of absorbed neutrons when the specimen is mainly irradiated with thermal neutrons. This is the case when the specimen is situated in the moderator of a graphite reactor. We illustrate, giving the cross-section of respectively ^{6}Li, ^{7}Li and F, for neutrons, the velocity of which is 2.2×10^5 cm.sec^{-1}: $\sigma_{(n,\alpha)}$ ^{6}Li $= 936 \pm 6$ barn (absorption followed by the (n, α) reaction); $\sigma_a 7_{Li} = 0.033$ barn and $\sigma_{aF} = 0.009$ barn. One barn is 1×10^{-24} cm^2. At the forementioned velocity, to better than 0.05%:

$$\sigma_{(n,\alpha)} 6_{Li} \cdot \varepsilon_{6Li} = \sum_i \sigma_{ai} \cdot \varepsilon_i. \tag{4}$$

In this equation ε_i is the isotopical aboundance of the isotope i in its natural element; for ^{6}Li this amounts to 0.0747. The subscript i indicates separately the ^{6}Li, ^{7}Li and F isotopes in the sample. The relatively large absorption cross-section of ^{6}Li, on the one hand, simply relates the number of absorbed thermal neutrons to the number of fissions; on the other hand however it causes the number of incoming neutrons to decrease with the depth in the specimen. This effect of self shielding makes the neutrons to be inhomogeneously distributed in the crystal and consequently complicates the relation between neutron flux and absorption. Nevertheless, in a first approximation this relation can be obtained for specimens of a simple geometry. For plan-parallel plates, the geometry needed in the optical measurements of the F-band, such a relation is derived and the approximations used are discussed. The arrangement under consideration is drawn in Fig. 2.

The neutron flux ϕ is defined by:

$$d\phi = n\mathbf{v} \cdot \mathbf{dS} \tag{5}$$

with $\phi = 0$ when $S = 0$. In this equation n is the number of neutrons per unit volume and $\mathbf{v} \cdot \mathbf{dS}$ is the scalar product of $\mathbf{v}$, the velocity vector of the neutron, with $\mathbf{dS}$, a vector normal to the surface-element and with a length dS.

In the elementary case of a neutron-ray ($dS =$ constant) that passes through an infinitesimal thin layer (of thickness dl) the surface of which is perpendicular to the beam ($|\mathbf{v} \cdot \mathbf{dS}| = v.dS$) one calculates the absorbed fraction of the neutron flux density $\left(= \dfrac{d\phi}{dS} = nv \right)$ from:

$$\frac{d(nv)}{(nv)} = -N \sigma \, dl \tag{6}$$

Herein is $N\sigma dl$ the probability that one neutron is absorbed by the infinitesimal layer. $N.dl$ is the number of ^{6}Li atoms per unit area ($= 1$ cm^2) wherein N is the number of ^{6}Li atoms per unit volume, and σ is the cross-section of ^{6}Li for the (n, α) reaction. The values of N and σ are given,

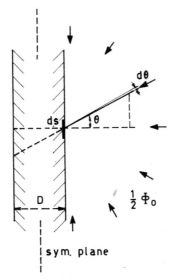

FIGURE 2   The arrangement of a plan parallel plate in an isotropical neutron flux

assuming that only absorption is an important effect in our sample. Indeed, scattering is less probable because most of the scattering cross-sections known are one order in magnitude smaller than the mean absorption cross-section of the LiF considered. In short, radiation softening, due to moderation of the neutrons in the sample is neglected.

The absorption formulation in a macroscopic system is obtained by integrating equation (6) from $l = 0$ (the surface of the sample) to $l = l$ (the penetration depth considered). N is a constant in an homogeneous absorption material. In the case of neutrons which all have the same velocity, σ is a constant too and one obtains:

$$(n_a)_v = (n_i)_v = (n_l)_v = (n_i)_v \cdot (1 - e^{-N\sigma_v l}) \tag{7}$$

wherein $(n_i)_v$ and $(n_l)_v$ are the neutron densities at respectively the surface and the depth l. This equation shows that, when σ depends on the velocity of the neutrons, the outcoming neutron-velocity-distribution differs from the incoming one when we are not restricted to the case of one single velocity. The $\sigma(n, \alpha)$ of ^{6}Li is larger for smaller neutron velocities, consequently the faster neutrons are relatively less absorbed. This radiation hardening however is neglected too in the further discussion. This approximation is acceptable because, in the neutron-spectrum considered, most of the neutron velocities are not too different from the mean and only a small fraction of the neutrons is relatively slow.

Neglecting radiation hardening (in the $+$ or in the $-$direction) results in assuming that the velocity distribution of the neutrons is constant; or in other words that keeping the mean velocity constant in the calculations, is reasonable. This is equivalent in saying that a constant mean cross-section $\bar{\sigma}$, can be used. A value for $\bar{\sigma}$ should now be looked for.

In ^{6}Li $_{(\sigma_{n,\alpha})}$ obeys the $1/v$ law. The law holds for neutron energies up to 1 keV which limit is high compared to the mean energy of thermal neutrons ($\simeq 0.03$ eV). As a consequence of this law, the product of the cross-section with its related velocity does not depend on the velocity anymore:

$$\sigma \cdot v = \frac{c}{v} \cdot v = C, \tag{8}$$

with $C = $ constant. This is the reason why the mean cross-section times the mean velocity, in any distribution, in a constant too:

$$\bar{\sigma} \cdot \bar{v} = \sigma_{\text{ref}} \cdot v_{\text{ref}} = C. \tag{9}$$

The reference, σ_{ref}, is that cross-section which has been measured with neutrons of a certain velocity, v_{ref}. In order to obtain from this relation $\bar{\sigma}$, $\bar{v}$ must be related to v_{ref} for which σ is known. The mean velocity depends on the velocity distribution. For thermal neutrons in the moderator of a graphite reactor, this practically follows the Maxwell-distribution in accordance with $T + 50$ degrees Kelvin.[12] Here T is the temperature of the graphite and the term $+50$ corrects for the fact that the neutrons are not able to become in full equilibrium with the host lattice as they are absorbed before.

The reference velocity, 2.2×10^5 cm $\cdot$ s^{-1}, was chosen because it is the most probable velocity in a Maxwell distribution of a neutron-temperature 293.6°K. It is $\dfrac{\sqrt{\pi}}{2}$ times the mean velocity in the same distribution. Further can be shown[13] that the mean velocity in a Maxwell distribution is proportional to the square root of the neutron temperature. So one obtains:

$$\bar{\sigma} = \frac{\sqrt{\pi}}{2} \cdot \sqrt{\frac{293 \cdot 6}{T + 50}} \cdot \sigma_{2.2 \times 10^5 \, cm \, s^{-1}} \cdot \tag{10}$$

For ^6Li, $\bar{\sigma}$ is 745 barn at a reactor temperature of 40°C.

Passing to the absorption formulation in a more realistic spatial distribution, a new approximation is introduced. The situation is idealized, assuming the specimen to be positioned in an isotropical flux-distribution. This may be done for small samples in a large sized moderator of a reactor, when mainly thermal neutrons are the constituent parts of the radiation.

With the forementioned approximations in mind, one can now formulate the absorbed flux in a plate with surface S and thickness D of an homogeneous absorbing LiF crystal by:

$$\phi_a = 2 \cdot \frac{\int\limits_0^S \int\limits_0^{\pi/2} 2\pi \sin\theta \cdot \tfrac{1}{2} nv \cos\theta \cdot dS(1 - e^{-\frac{N\bar{\sigma} \, dl}{\cos\theta}})d\theta}{\int\limits_0^{\pi/2} 2\pi \sin\theta \, d\theta}. \tag{11}$$

In this equation θ is the angle between the incident neutron ray and the normal to the surface. The penetration depth l became $D/\cos\theta$. On other approximation concerns dS, which is thought to be practically independent of θ. This means that the calculation is carried out as if all surface elements of the crystal considered are in an identical situation.

The foregoing equation then leads to

$$\phi_a = \phi_0 \cdot F(W) \tag{12}$$

wherein $\phi_0 = nvS$ which is the incident flux; and

$$F(W) = \int\limits_0^{\pi/2} \sin\theta \cdot \cos\theta(1 - e^{-\frac{W}{\cos\theta}})d\theta \tag{13}$$

$$= \frac{1}{2}\left\{1 - e^{-W} \cdot (1 - W) + W^2\left(\zeta + \ln W - W + \frac{W^2}{2 \cdot 2!} - \frac{W^3}{3 \cdot 3!} + ...\right)\right\}$$

with $W = N\bar{\sigma}D = \bar{\Sigma}D$; and $\zeta = 0.577...$ the Euler constant. In infinitely thin specimens the absorbed fraction of the flux is

$$\left(\frac{\phi_a}{\phi_0}\right)_{D\to 0} = \lim_{D\to 0} F(W) = W. \tag{14}$$

In real specimens $F(W)$ W and the difference is an expression for the effect of self shielding. In the forementioned LiF samples the relative deviation from W when $D = 0.1$ cm is

$$\left(\frac{W - F(W)}{W}\right)_{D=0.1\mathrm{cm}} = 0.36.$$

Neglecting radiation hardening and flux depression causes the calculated relative absorption to be too high. The neglection of the fact that the small

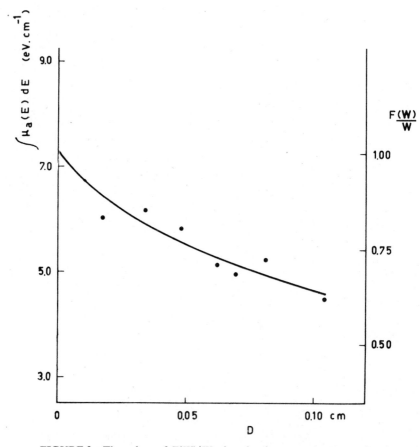

FIGURE 3   The values of $F(W)/W$, given by the curve, are proportional to the number of fissions per unit volume when LiF plates of different thickness are irradiated to the same neutron dose; the dots represent experimental values of A, the absorption under the F-band

lateral faces of the samples are not shielded for neutrons has as a consequence that the later estimation is too low. The effects cancel each other
partially. However, for accurate absorption calculations correction terms
should be added.

The number of absorbed neutrons per unit volume of LiF, N_a, can be
obtained from the absorbed flux. In the simple case wherein during the
irradiation the number of ^{6}Li atoms practically does not change ($N_a \ll N$),
and the flux is constant, one obtains:

$$N_a = t \cdot \frac{\phi_a}{V}, \tag{15}$$

wherein t is the irradiation time and V is the volume of the specimen. The
equation also can be written as:

$$N_a = tnv \frac{SD}{V} \bar{\Sigma} \cdot \frac{F(W)}{W}, \tag{16}$$

or

$$N_a = \bar{\Sigma} \cdot \varphi \cdot \frac{F(W)}{W}, \tag{17}$$

wherein $\varphi = (nvt)$ is the integrated flux; $\bar{\Sigma}$ is the macroscopic cross-section
and $F(W)/W$ is a function of the plate thickness. The latter function is
shown in Fig. 3. In the same figure also experimental F-band absorption
values are plotted.[6]

2.3   Discussion

The energy deliberated per unit volume in a plate detector of lithium
fluoride, when this was exposed to an integrated neutron flux φ is:

$$E_\varphi = Q \cdot N_a = Q \cdot \bar{\Sigma} \frac{F(W)}{W} \cdot \varphi, \tag{18}$$

wherein $Q = 4.8$ MeV; $\bar{\Sigma} = 3.44$ for a sample the isotopic aboundance
of which is the natural one; and $F(W)/W$ is of the order of 1 for thin specimens.

With this formulation one arrives at a point where he knows how to
calculate both, damage and neutron dose. The question arises now how
to relate N_F, the number of F-centers per unit volume, to $E\varphi$, the radiation
energy per unit volume. It has been shown experimentally that the efficiency

of F-center formation

$$F_F = \frac{N_F}{E_\varphi},$$ (19)

is reproducible to better than 5% when (1) φ is constant, and (2) the crystals are taken from a single batch. In crystals of the same batch, when irradiated to a different dose, a different value for e_F is obtained.[6] The ratio of the efficiencies as calculated from an experiment wherein φ_1 and φ_2 were respectively 0.88×10^{14} and 1.63×10^{12} n $\cdot$ cm^{-2} was found to be

$$e_{F\varphi_1}/e_{F\varphi_2} = 0.62.$$

The higher the neutron dose, the smaller the efficiency. In their work on electron irradiation of LiF, Smoluchowski *et al.*[4] came to the same conclusion. This analogy in behaviour indicates that the effect of neutron irradiation is not essentially different from the effects of electron irradiation. The electron irradiating people refined their relation saying that the number of F-centers increases proportionally to the square root of the irradiation time, for concentration of about 2×10^{-4}. In fact, in the neighbourhood of the same concentration, the F-center increase, as determined by magnetic measurements,[14] can also be expressed by the same law. However, at higher doses of course, saturation occurs.

Finally we should discuss here the pros and cons of the considered solid state detector for thermal neutrons. In thermal neutron dosimetry the activation of Co ir often used. This is an indication that the comparison between the two detectors will turn in favour of the Co. It goes this way.

For the ^{59}Co (n, γ) ^{60}Co reaction $\sigma_{2,2 \times 10^5 \text{cm.s}^{-1}}$ equals 33.2 barn.[12] The isotopic abundance of the ^{59}Co isotope in the natural element is 100% so that the product $\sigma_{aCo} \cdot \varepsilon_{Co}$ is of the same order in magnitude as the product $\sigma_{(n,\alpha)}$ ^{6}Li $\cdot \varepsilon_{6Li}$ we mentioned before. Also σ_{aCo} abeys the $1/v$ law, as $\sigma_{(n,\alpha)}$ ^{6}Li does. Consequently, the procedure for calculating N_F and N_{60Co} is the same for both detectors.

In both cases the detecting apparatus can be chosen relatively cheap or expensive, so that in this question money does not settle the matter.

Impurities play a rôle in both detectors. In LiF they may change the efficiency of F-center formation. Also structure defects may introduce the same effect. However, one can calibrate the batch. In the Co, the impurity atoms which were also activated by the neutrons, hamper the measurements.

In most cases it is possible, if necessary, to separate the annoying element. However, in the last decennia so much is known about pure metals that one should not worry too much about this.

One can try to mark in favour of LiF saying that the F-centers are stable in time. However, the half-life of ^{60}Co ($=5.28$ years) is so long that for practical use one can forget about the argument.

The fact that the accurate measurement of the thickness of a LiF plate is more difficult than the determination of a weight in usual situations, is in favour of the Co detector. Moreover, a metal does not break easily and, if by accident the plate was bent it can be flattened and used again. Measurement on LiF powder are relatively difficult. In short, the Co detector is "easier" to handle.

The point that settles the matter in favour of Co is the fact that the saturation of the F-band occurs at much a lower dose than the saturation in the Co activation do. That for high doses the Co detectors become too radioactive is no longer an argument against Co since the element can be diluted homogeneously in aluminium.[15]

In the Co detector, the measured physical property is practically proportional to the integrated neutron flux whilst in the LiF detector it is proportional to φ^b which an exponent $b < 1$.

In the earlier times of the reactor the solid state research workers obtained reproducible measurements for samples irradiated in one single reactor location. When the latter changed the results, for the same reported neutron dose, also became different, although reproducible again. So solid state specialists started suspecting dosimetry people to neglect major changing parameters. This time seems to be over. Thermal neutron dosimetry became refined and allows solid state people to unravel the complex way their materials behave.

3 THE QUARTZ FAST NEUTRON DETECTOR

The fast neutron dose determination seems to evolve in the sense the integrated thermal neutron flux determination did. Once more, solid state people obtain very reproducible results on samples which are irradiated in one single reactor location. However, matching these results to those from specimens irradiated in an other reactor, is not always easy. The parallelum between the proceeding for relating damage to dose, on the hand in the quartz fast neutron detector and, on the other hand in the lithium fluoride thermal neutron detector, will be discussed briefly here.

When quartz is irradiated with fast neutrons it undergoes a profound structural change and gradually vitrificates.[16] The interactions of high energetic neutrons with the constituting elements of the detector material results in knock-on atoms, or ions, which quickly are stopped in matter. At these events small volume elements in the crystal may disorder. The disordering of the cristalline structure is associated with a density decrease. This topic has been the subject of many investigations. Recently a precise comparison between densities and doses as obtained from Fe activation analyses, has been made by Moret *et al.*[17] This author used a density gradient column[18] in which a smooth and fairly linear increase of density, going from top to bottom, is obtained in a liquid. Immersed in this liquid, the mean density of which was chosen property, the samples of different densities reach different equilibrium positions in height in the column. Standards have been calibrated by the float method as described by Spaepen.[19] The apparatus is simple and accurate. The final accuracy on the measurements is better than 5×10^{-5} g $\cdot$ cm^{-3}. In the dosimetry experiments Moret used natural quartz. A batch of 100 samples was made out of one single crystal. As a consequence of this precaution, the initial densities showed only a slight scattering. The deviations from the mean were smaller than $\pm 6 \times 10^{-5}$ g $\cdot$ cm^{-3}. The spread is about five times less than in the case wherein crystals of different batches were considered. The quantitative expression of the radiation damage under discussion is found in the density decrease of the quartz sample. The relative decrease reaches values of about 15% saturating at this point. It seems that, for samples irradiated in BR2 in a dose region between 1×10^{19} and 6×10^{19} n $\cdot$ cm^{-2}, the density could be related to the fast neutron dose with an accuracy of the order of ± 0.1%.

Discussing radiation now, the reproducibility of the relation between damage and dose indicates that there exist a reproducible situation in the reactor. In the case of quartz, as in that of LiF, a selection between different kinds of radiation in the reactor, is obtained by the use of the difference in penetration depth of charged and uncharged particles in solid matter. Fission fragments of the fuel elements are not allowed to penetrate into the sample. From the penetrating radiation the fast neutrons show a specific effect, at least to a certain degree; the contribution of the β's, γ's[11] and thermal neutrons being negligible in pure quartz.

The spectra of the fast neutrons have been studied for the case wherein they are obtained directly from the fissions. The velocity distributions can be expressed by relative simple mathematical equations.[20] In order to facilitate the calculations one should irradiate in a fission spectrum which should be as pure as possible. The detectors should be located near the fuel elements. The moderating effect of material enveloping the sample should be kept as low as possible. Eventually one should try to correct for the remaining effect.

In quartz, as in LiF, the relation between the neutron flux and the primary events can be calculated with the aid of the interaction cross-section of the nuclei. However, in the energy region considered, the scattering cross-section mostly is not a simple function of the neutron velocity. Consequently, machine computation become the obvious mean to get an answer to the problem. All primary knock-on atoms have not eough energy to produce an effect. The threshold energy should be estimated and brought into the calculations. Finally the density decrease in quartz should be compared to the number of energetic primary events which is related to the absorbed fast neutron dose*.

Comparing now the solid state detector to the activation detectors, also in the case of fast neutron irradiations, the discussion turns out in favour of the latter.

The worst point against, the solid, once more, is the early saturation of the density change, restricting the measurements to a dose region which is much too narrow for practical use in material testing reactors.

An other point in favour of activation detectors is the varity of elements with a different known threshold energy for the neutron detection reaction. This difference allows dosimetry people to estimate changes in fast neutron spectra.

4 CONCLUSION

Radiation damage in solids, in some cases, can be related to the neutron dose the sample received. However, in general, for high doses saturation effects will occur and the dose region wherein the relation holds is too restricted for a practical use in reactor technology. This does not exclude the use of solid state detectors in some special cases; one of which may be the use of fission tracks in insulating solids.

---

* The damage study, from the point of view of solid state physics, will be published elsewhere.

References

1. D. H. Frisch and A. Thorndike, *Elementary Particles*, Van Nostrand Inc., N.Y. (1964).
2. P. J. Ring, J. G. O'Keefe, and P. J. Bray, *Phys. Rev. Letters* **1**, 453 (1958).
3. Y. Farge and M. Lambert, *Compt. Rend.* **258**, 5199 (1964).
4. P. Durand, Y. Farge, M. Lambert, and R. Smoluchowsky, *Colloque sur les centres colorés*, Saclay-16–18 Mar. 1967, France.
5. A. Van den Bosch, *Meded. BNV*, Ser. IV, 30 (1964).
6. A. Van den Bosch, *Meded. BNV*, Ser. IV, 332 (1965).
7. H. W. Eetzel and J. G. Allard, *Phys. Rev. Letters* **2**, 452 (1959).
8. D. W. Compton and H. Rabin, *Solid State Physics*, Ed. F. Seitz and D. Turnbull **16** (1965).
9. D. L. Dexter, Solid State Physics, Ed. F. Seitz and D. Turnbull, **6**, 371 (1958).
10. R. T. Bate and C. V. Heer, *J. Phys. Chem. Solids* **7**, 14 (1958).
11. A. Van den Bosch, *Meded. BNV*, Ser. V, 263 (1967).
12. N. K. Taylor and J. K. Linacre, United Kingdom Atomic Energy Authority, AERE-R4111 (1964).
13. A. J. Rutgers, *Physical Chemistry* Intersciences Publ. (1957).
14. A. Van den Bosch, *J. Phys. Chem. Solids* **25**, 1293 (1964).
15. J. Van Audenhove and J. Joyeux, *J. Nucl. Mat.* **19**, 97 (1966).
16. R. Comes, M. Lambert and A. Guinier, *Interaction of Radiation with Solids*, Ed. A. Bishay, Plenum Press, N.Y. (1967).
17. H. Moret, private communication.
18. H. Moret, *Rev. Sci. Instr.*, **32**, 1157 (1961).
19. J. Spaepen, *Meded. K.V.A.W.B.* **19**, n° 5 (1957).
20. K. H. Beckurts and K. Wirtz, *Neutron Physics*, Springer Verlag (1964).

PART IV

The practice of radiation dosimetry

CHAPTER IV–I

Health physics requirements for dosimetry in nuclear establishments

W. A. Langmead

A.E.R.E., Harwell (U. K.)

**A   EXTERNAL RADIATION DOSIMETRY PRACTICE IN THE U.K.A.E.A.
    —FILM DOSIMETRY AND ITS APPLICATIONS**

1   Introduction

The three lectures to be included under the general title "External radiation
dosimetry practice in the U.K.A.E.A." are designed to outline the philosophy, objectives and general practice of personnel dosimetry as used in the
Authority. The place of film badges, thermoluminescent techniques and other
dosimetry methods using solid state phenomena will be discussed in relation
to an integrated system for personnel monitoring in the Authority's nuclear
establishments. In this first lecture, emphasis will be placed on film dosimetry; however it may be of interest if first the wider problem of personnel
monitoring in the United Kingdom as a whole is considered, if only to
place the Authority's problems in perspective.

2   Personnel monitoring in the United Kingdom

Apart from the Authority, the chief users of radiation are the hospitals,
universities and industry. Approximately 14,000 individuals in the hospitals
and medical schools of the United Kingdom, another 16,000 individuals
employed in general industry and about 20,000 individuals in the U.K.A.E.A.
are regularly monitored with film badges. Thus, in all about 50,000 people

in the United Kingdom wear film badges, representing nearly 1 in every 500 men and women employed.

The hospitals in the British National Health Service arrange for their own personnel dosimetry services, and until recently there has been little co-ordination of the various systems in use. There is a tendency for each film badge practitioner to leave his own imprint on the procedures and equipment he uses, with the result that hospital physics departments have been operating a large number of different personnel monitoring systems.

Most radiation users in industry make use of the facilities provided by the Radiological Protection Service. This organization, which is run by the Ministry of Health and the Medical Research Council, provides a film badge service at a nominal charge, the films being transmitted to and from the user by post. In this way the small user of radiation is provided with a service which would be uneconomic and inefficient if it had to be provided by himself. Virtually no privately-owned commercial film badge services exist in the United Kingdom.

3   Development of personnel monitoring philosophy[1]

The main objectives of a personal monitoring programme may be summarised as follows:

i) to demonstrate compliance with regulations or, more generally, with the recommendations of the International Commission on Radiological Protection (I.C.R.P.);

ii) to assist in making estimates of doses to the bodies or critical organs of individuals who have suffered acute irradiation under accident conditions;

iii) to enable information on personal doses to be fed back to management at various levels in order that appropriate operational control may be exercised and strengthened when found to be inadequate.

Before considering the relative merits of different dosimetry systems, it is important to be clear as to the dose information necessary to satisfy these objectives. The basic requirement of a dosemeter system for personnel monitoring is, of course, that it should register the dose received at the position of measurement with reasonable accuracy over the whole range of radiations and energies and of dose and dose rates likely to be experienced under both normal and abnormal conditions. In many situations this requirement is difficult to meet in toto but it should be approached as nearly as is possible. Additionally the dosemeter may be required to provide information about the type and energy of the incident radiation; whether this need is essential for some purposes or not has been debated at more than one international meeting[2,3] and has generated considerable heat among those holding opposing points of view.

The philosophy underlying personnel monitoring procedures has changed considerably over the last forty years or so and these changes are related to changes in the form of the maximum permissible doses recommended by national and international bodies. In the early days of radiology, a simple piece of X-ray film clipped to the breast pocket gave a qualitative picture of the stray radiation reaching the wearer from clinical radium sources and the rather poorly-protected X-ray equipment then available. In 1928, however, the International Protection Committee, to become in later years the International Commission on Radiological Protection, defined the roentgen, the first international unit of X-ray quantity. This unit, based on ionization in air, led to much activity in the design of ionization chambers for the measurement of X- and γ-rays, with the result that considerable expertise was built up among the few physicists engaged in this work. By contrast, film dosimetry in Britain had lagged behind—although not so in Germany[4,5]—partly because the large number of variables in the chain of events leading to a photographic record and the variable energy response characteristics of all films gave rise to a genuine belief that the accuracy of the photographic method was not high.

It was not surprising, therefore, in the days before the war, that most hospitals[6,7] relief on the pocket ionization chamber for the measurement of personal exposure of their staff. The method is accurate, the energy response characteristic of the ion chamber could be made reasonably flat and, for the measurement of personal doses of a small number of workers, the procedure is reasonably practicable. However, the ion chamber is an expensive instrument and one not improved by laundering when left forgotten in laboratory coats! Some workers[8] therefore persevered with the film badge, and although its shortcomings as an accurate dosemeter were admitted, it was generally considered[9] that high accuracy in personnel dosimetry was not required. Furthermore, until 1948, the recommendations of the British X-Ray and Radium Protection Committee[10] relating to the "tolerance dose", referred only to the exposure of the person. This was usually interpreted as surface dose to the front of the trunk and some effort was expended by film users to improve the energy response characteristic of the film badges by means of thin metallic foils which were arranged to sandwich the wrapped film. It must be emphasized that the purpose of these foils was not to provide energy discrimination but, on the contrary, to flatten the energy response of the film. The decision in 1948 to use film badges of this type at the recently inaugurated Atomic Energy Research Establishment, to be followed subsequently by similar decisions at other establishments of the United Kingdom atomic energy industry, meant that a majority of the radiation workers in Britain were being monitored by means of film badges.

In 1954, ICRP for the first time introduced into their Recommendations[11] the concept of critical organs. The organs considered particularly vulnerable from the point of view of irradiation were stated to be: skin, bloodforming organs, the gonads (with respect to impaired fertility) and the eyes (with respect to cataracts).

Furthermore, different maximum permissible weekly doses were recommended for the different critical organs, and for the purposes of dose calculation, effective depths for the critical organs were suggested. Finally, RBE values or Quality Factors as they are now called, for different types of radiation were recommended, in most eases implying the separate measurement of these radiations, the permissible doses being expressed in the new unit, the rem.

Following the 1954 Report of ICRP, a further change in the approach to personnel dosimetry became apparent. Although more accurate methods of dose measurement by means of film badges were described in the literature, there has been increased emphasis on these improvements being coupled with methods for determining the type and energy of the incident radiation[12,13]. This is partly due to the fact that the accuracy of the assessment of *dose* by the film method depends on the availability of such data; however, these data are also helpful in enabling estimates to be made of the doses to those critical organs which are below the surface of the body.[14]

It should be emphasized that in the U.K. more than 90% of all routine personnel dose measurements, i.e. about 45,000 films per annum, record less than that fraction of the permissible dose appropriate to the film issue period and no attempt is made to estimate organ doses from these film data. In fact, it is only in satisfying objective (ii) referred to earlier, that is personnel dosimetry following accidental irradiation, that the additional information relating to type and energy of the radiation may sometimes be helpful in the reconstruction of accident situations and the estimation, albeit approximate, of doses to irradiated body organs.

The more recent recommendations of ICRP issued in 1959[15] and 1964[16] have re-emphasized that the maximum permissible doses relate to critical organs and no less than twelve separate organs are now specified in five or six different permissible dose categories. This diversity of basic radiation norms gave rise to some difficulties in the drafting of legislation in the U.K. and to avoid such complications, the Ionising Radiations (Sealed Sources) Regulations, 1961, of the Factories Acts[17] define maximum permissible doses at or near the surface of the body. The doses specified follow the recommendations of ICRP, but safety factors are automatically introduced since the skin almost always receives a larger radiation dose from external radiation than do the subcutaneous critical organs, e.g. the blood-forming organs, thyroid, bone, etc.

Although the specification of maximum permissible doses at accessible points simplifies dose measurement, the use of an energy-independent device such as a simple ionization chamber for such measurements is ruled out, since it is mandatory to record separately the doses from different categories of radiation types, e.g. X- and γ-rays; X-rays, γ-rays, β particles, electrons and positrons; and the latter group but excluding β radiation of energy not exceeding 2.5 MeV. Thus these Regulations give legal support to the concept that a personnel monitoring device must be a simple spectrometer as well as a dosemeter. Since many establishments of the Authority are factories as defined in this legislation, the terms of these Regulations materially affected the choice of personnel dosemeter available to us. Although the legislation calls only for a "suitable film or films to be worn in an appropriate holder or holders obtained from an approved laboratory", the approval of the dosimetry practice rests with the Chief Inspector of Factories. In this way control remains with the latter, without the detailed specification of procedures which would tend to be restrictive regarding the introduction of new methods.

Research establishments are not covered by the Factories Acts, and at present most of the activities undertaken at Harwell are not subject to statutory regulations. However, a Code of Practice for the Protection of Persons exposed to ionizing radiations in Research and Teaching was issued in 1964.[18] The requirements of the Code are similar in respect of personnel dosimetry in that the wearing of a film badge is specified, supplemented where necessary by an ionisation chamber for short term dose control. However, the interpretation of the readings of the dosemeter are not specified in terms of types and energies of the incident radiations as is the case in the Factories legislation.

4 Film badges used in the U.K.A.E.A.

4.1 *Metal holder*

Prior to 1963 a simple metal film holder, shown in Fig. 1, was used throughout the Authority.[19] It was designed to provide filtered and unfiltered areas on both sides of Ilford PM1 or PM3 film, the dose-density characteristics of which are shown in Fig. 2. The filtered area of the holder was divided into halves containing separate cadmium and tin filters for the measurement respectively of slow neutrons by the (n, γ) reaction in cadmium and the γ-ray dose for energies of 100 keV and above. The energy dependence of PM1 film in the holder is shown in Fig. 3.

Although it is possible to derive some information about the effective energy of the incident X- and γ-radiation from an examination of the small areas of the film covered by the tin-plate case of the holder, this badge suffers from the shortcoming that it cannot be used to measure doses due to exposure to radiation below an effective energy of about 100 keV unless the effective energy is known from other data. Even greater difficulties arise if a mixture of X- and β-radiation are incident on the film. Of course, no substantial difficulty arises in estimating the maximum incident dose which could give rise to any particular blackening pattern. However, over-estimates of the true dose by an order of magnitude could arise in this way, and the new plastic badge has been designed to obviate some of these difficulties.

4.2 *Plastics holder*

The plastics film holder, designed jointly by A.E.R.E. and the Radiobiological Protection Service[20] for use with Kodak R. M. film, is shown in Fig. 4. Since high sensitivity (the ability to detect a minimum dose of at most 10 millirads of 1 MeV gamma radiation) and wide dose range (up to 100 rads of 1 MeV gamma radiation) are required, this is most easily achieved by the use of a fast and a slow emulsion coated on opposite sides of the film base.

The choice of the fast emulsion, which faces the front of the film packet, was decided by the maximum attainable sensitivity which is about 7 millirads of 1 MeV gamma radiation per increase in density of 0.01. It reaches a density of 4.0 with about 6 rads of 1 MeV gamma radiation. When the density has reached the measurement limit, the fast emulsion can be removed by washing in warm water and measurements may then be made on the slow emulsion.

Ideally the slow emulsion should have the same energy dependence as the fast emulsion (so that the same filters will be appropriate for both emulsion),

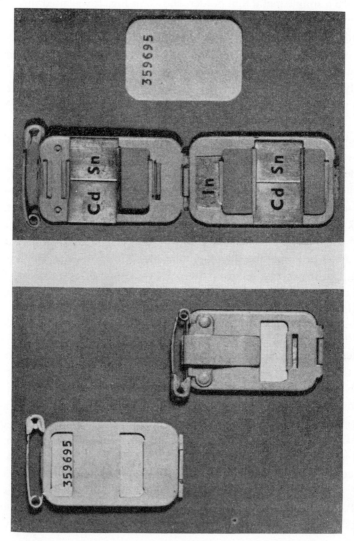

FIGURE 1 Metal film holder used in U.K.A.E.A. until 1962. Left: open view showing filters. Right: closed dosemeter showing pocket clip

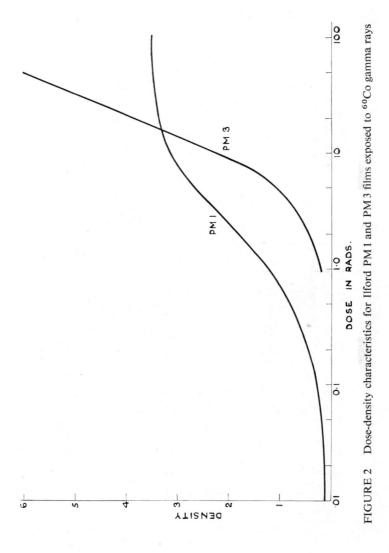

FIGURE 2   Dose-density characteristics for Ilford PM1 and PM3 films exposed to ^{60}Co gamma rays

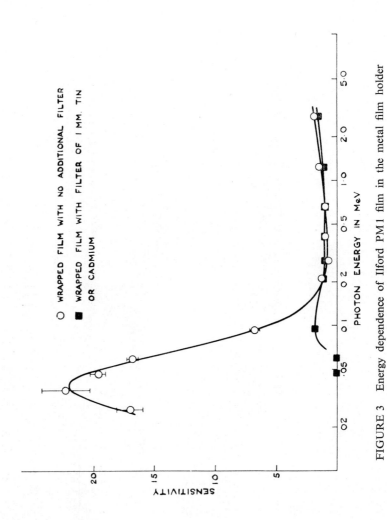

FIGURE 3   Energy dependence of Ilford PM1 film in the metal film holder

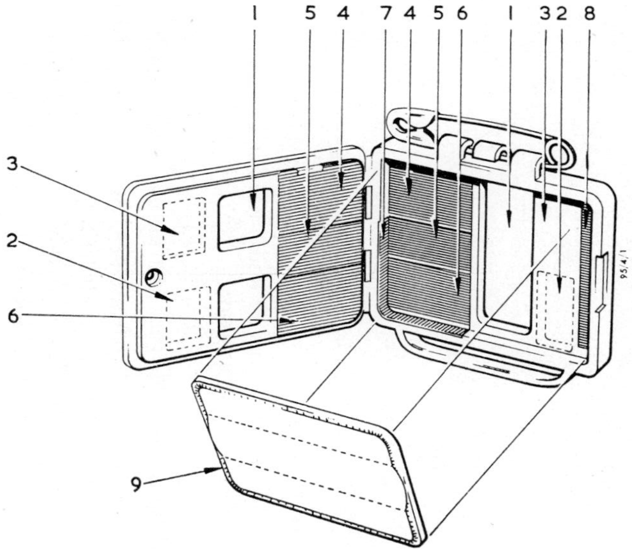

Filter Types

1 Window
2 Thin plastics
3 Thick plastics
4 0·040″ Dural
5 0·028″ Cd + 0·012″ Pb
6 0·028″ Sn + 0·012″ Pb
7 0·012″ Pb edge shielding
8 0·4 gm of indium
9 Kodak R.M. Film

FILM HOLDER TYPE ERP 30

(moulded in polypropylene)

AERE R 4669

The holder employs an integral hinge and is held closed by an internal snap fastening

FIGURE 4   New A.E.R.E./R.P.S. plastics film holder

should have a measurable response for a dose of 5 rads (so that there is an overlap with measurements made on the fast emulsion) and should only reach a density of 4.0 at doses in excess of 1000 rads. The Kodak slow emulsion only approximately fulfils these requirements. The dose overlap is only just achieved and the density at a dose of 1000 rads is 6.0 (Fig. 5). However, no difficulty arises in the measurement of densities up to this value using the Baldwin Radiological Densitometer.

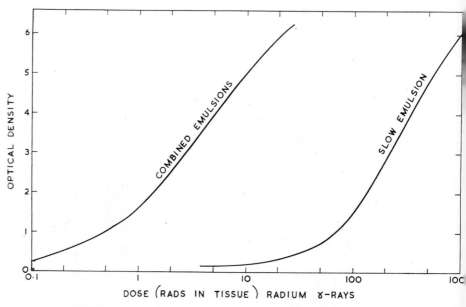

FIGURE 5   Dose-density characteristics for Kodak RM film exposed to radium gamma rays

The holder is moulded in polypropylene and has six filtered areas. An open window is required together with two thicknesses of plastics for the separation of photon and beta effects and the interpretation of beta exposure. Slow neutron dosimetry requires a cadmium filter and the two remaining areas are assigned for photon dosimetry.

The general function of the filters is as follows:

1) The open window allows all incident radiation which can penetrate the packet to interact with the film. The window is slightly wider than would otherwise be necessary to accommodate the film serial number.

2) The thin plastics filter (0.020 in., 0.51 mm, thick) provides essentially the same photon response as the window but attenuates beta radiation by an amount on the beta energy.

3) The thick plastics filter (0.110 in., 2.9 mm, thick) transmits all but the lowest energy photons and absorbs all but the highest energy beta radiation.

4) The thickness of the dural filter (aluminium copper alloy Spec. B. S. L 72) is such (0.040 in., 1.00 mm) that the ratio of the plastics filter response to the dural filter response changes continuously from 65 keV (the energy at which the tin-lead filter response commences to fall significantly) down to 15 keV, where the dural filter response is zero.

5) The thickness of the tin-lead filter (0.028 in., 0.71 mm, tin + 0.012 in., 0.30 mm, lead) is chosen so that the response is almost independent of energy over a wide range of energies—75 keV to 2 MeV.

6) The cadmium-lead filter matches the tin-lead filter as to photon radiation response. With slow neutron exposures, the capture gamma radiation which is produced will blacken the film and provide means of dose estimation. This is a standard method of evaluating thermal neutron exposures.

When calculating the optimum filter thicknesses a value must be assumed for the effective angle of incidence of the radiation. This is often taken to be 45° though it is sometimes not considered at all. Discussions with operational health physicists suggest that radiation exposure comes predominantly from the front and within an angle of $\pm 60°$ to the normal. A film oscillating through this angle at a constant rate was found to yield the same response as that of a static film at an angle of 35° to the normal. This latter angle has been assumed in deciding filter thicknesses in this holder.

If a densitometer aperture of 3 mm diameter is to be used, the separate film areas should not be less than 1 cm square in the case of the window and the plastics filters in order to minimise edge effects. The metal filters should be rather larger and in this case it is the leakage of low energy radiation which is important. If low energy photons can reach the film areas sandwiched by the tin-lead or cadmium-lead filters without passing through them, a serious error will be introduced. This possibility has been largely eliminated by arranging for these filters to be adjacent in order to provide a large screened area. The two filters are backed by a continuous piece of 0.012 in lead which shields the tin-cadmium joint and is bent up around the two outer edges of the film between these filters to provide edge shielding.

The strip of indium (0.4 gm), which is housed in a recess in the front half of the holder does not form part of the film dosemeter proper but is provided to aid the identification of exposed personnel in a criticality accident. However, it does contribute another useful function. For any radiation energy below 2 MeV the foil shows as a negative image along the top edge of the film provided that the radiation is incident on the front of the holder. This enables flash exposures from front or back to be differentiated.

The photon response curves of the combined emulsion for the various filter thicknesses in the holder are shown in Fig. 6 for radiation incident at an angle of 35° to the normal.[20] The effect of angle of incidence upon the response under the tin filter is shown in Fig. 7. These results are expressed relative to unit response at the energy of cobalt 60 gamma radiation.

The beta responses of the film for the various filter combinations relative to the open window are given in Table 1.

TABLE 1   Dependence of the film response upon the beta energy and the filter used

Beta E max. MeV	Relative Response			
	Window	50 mgm/cm^2	300 mgm/cm^2	Dural
.46	(100)	(8)		
.8	100	33 $\pm$ 2.0	0	0
1.7	100	74 $\pm$ 2.5	12.2 $\pm$ 0.6	0
2.25	100	95 $\pm$ 3.0	30 $\pm$ 2.2	4.5 $\pm$ 0.6
3.6	100	97.5 $\pm$ 1.4	49 $\pm$ 2.0	19 $\pm$ 3

and the variation of film response with energy is given in Table 2.

TABLE 2   Variation of the response of the unfiltered film with beta energy

Maximum Beta Energy MeV	Film Response Relative to Radium Gamma (open window)
0.4	(0.4)
0.8	0.75
1.0	0.85
1.5	1.1
2.0	1.3
2.5	1.5
3.0	1.6
3.5	1.6

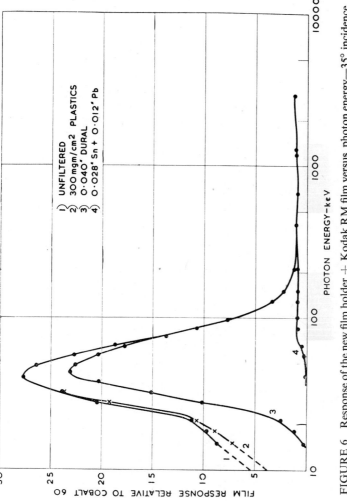

FIGURE 6 Response of the new film holder + Kodak RM film versus photon energy—35° incidence

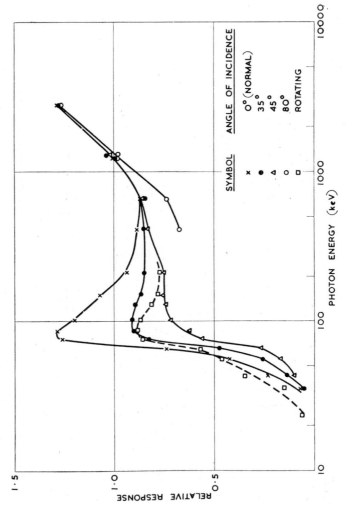

FIGURE 7 Response of Kodak RM film under the tin-lead filter—variation with energy and angle of incidence

5 Dose assessment using plastics holder

Before any calculation of true dose can be undertaken it is necessary to convert the observed film densities to "apparent doses" using a calibration curve constructed from films exposed to various known doses of radium gamma radiation in a standard exposure jig. In general it is not necessary to carry out separate beta or X-ray calibrations. Thus the apparent dose is the equivalent gamma dose, denoted by the symbol D_{filter}, in the area defined by the suffix. One of the aims of the dose assessment system is to derive the various dose estimates from the apparent doses by means of simple calculations which are suitable for automation.

5.1 *Slow neutrons*

In the present holder the cadmium/lead and tin/lead filters have the same attenuation effect on γ-radiation and any difference in the apparent doses beneath these filters results from a thermal neutron exposure. The apparent radium gamma-ray dose under the cadmium/lead filter is produced by the ^{113}Cd (n, γ) ^{114}Cd reaction in the filter and the ^{1}H(n, γ) ^{2}D reaction in the tissues of the individual wearing the badge, as well as by other incident photon-irradiation. The apparent radium gamma-ray dose under the tin/lead filter is produced by ^{113}Cd(n, γ) ^{114}Cd reaction in the adjacent cadmium filter, the ^{1}H(n, γ) ^{2}D reaction in the body and other incident photon radiation. By means of previous experiments[21] in which true incident gamma and neutron doses were derived from ion chamber and gold foil measurements and film measurements in normal holders and holders without cadmium filters, simple equations have been derived which yield the dose-equivalent from routine readings on the film:

$$\text{slow neutron dose-equivalent, } D_n = \frac{1}{3.42} \times (D_{\text{Cd/Pb}} - D_{\text{Sn/Pb}}) \text{ rem}$$
(measured on personnel)

$$\text{gamma dose, } D_\gamma = (D_{\text{Sn/Pb}} - 1.01 D_n) \text{ rad.}$$

For free-air measurements, the numerical constants are somewhat different.

The uncertainties on the measurement of thermal neutron dose-equivalent by this method, based on the instrumental errors in the calibration, is estimated as $\pm 20\%$.

Corrections are sometimes necessary in other filter areas for the effects of thermal neutron exposures. In the method of interpretation of the apparent

32*

doses to be described, the corrections are small except for beta dose estimation. The values of apparent radium gamma dose (rad) per rem of neutrons to be subtracted from the measured values under the various filters are given in Table 3.[21]

TABLE 3   Corrections to be subtracted from apparent doses for slow neutron exposures

Filter Area (exposures on personnel)	Apparent radium gamma dose (rad per rem of neutrons)
Open window	0.77
Thin plastics	0.63
Thick plastics	0.60
Dural	1.23

5.2   *Beta dose assessment*

The beta dose is calculated from the difference in apparent doses under the window and the thick plastics filter. The assumption used is that the value of $(D_{window} - D_{300})$ depends only on beta radiation, the effects of X- and gamma radiation being removed by the subtraction process. This is not strictly true because at energies of less than 20 keV there is some absorption of photons in the plastics filters.

The overall beta correction factor F is derived in two stages. First the derivation of a parameter R, which is characteristic of the beta ray energy, and secondly the application of the appropriate value of F, either from the graph shown in Fig. 8; or, for a simplified dose estimation system, the curve has been transformed into a series of steps given in Table 4.

TABLE 4   Beta correction factors

$\dfrac{D_{window} - D_{300}}{D_{50} - D_{300}} = R$	Correction Factor $= F$
$R \leq 2.2$	1.2
$2.2 < R \leq 3.6$	1.6
$3.6 < R \leq 7.0$	2.1
$R > 7.0$	2.5

The corrected beta dose is then obtained from:

Beta dose $= F.\, x(D_{window} - D_{300})$ rads in tissue.

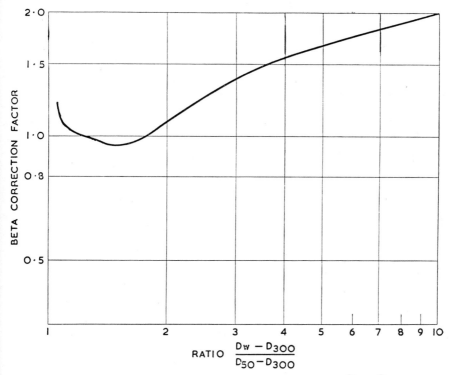

RATIO $\dfrac{D_w - D_{300}}{D_{50} - D_{300}}$

FIGURE 8   Beta correction factor as a function of ratio: $\dfrac{D_w - D_{300}}{D_{50} - D_{300}}$

5.3   *Photon dose assessment*

The photon dose is obtained by summation of fractions of the apparent doses for the tin-lead, dural and thick plastics film areas. Suitable values of the fractions for use with the combined emulsions of the film are given in formula I which is applicable for photons with energies from 20 keV to 2 MeV:

Total photon dose (combined emulsions) =

$$\left[D_{\text{Sn/Pb}} + \frac{D_{\text{dural}}}{50} + \left(\frac{D_{300} - D_{\text{dural}}}{10} \right) \right] \quad \text{rads-in-air.} \qquad \text{(I)}$$

The energy dependence of the three components of formula I are shown separately in Fig. 9 and their sum in Fig. 10. The performance of this expression is quite satisfactory even when it is used to evaluate exposures involving mixtures of radiation energies including beta radiation.

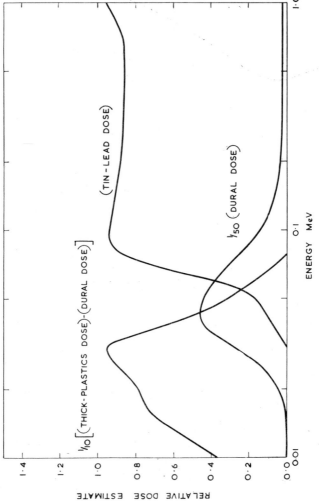

FIGURE 9   The components of Formula I in photon dose assessment, as a function of energy

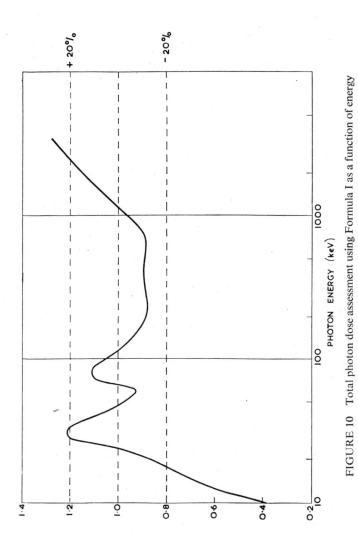

FIGURE 10   Total photon dose assessment using Formula I as a function of energy

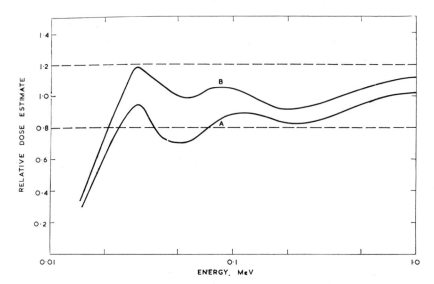

FIGURE 11   Total photon dose assessment (Formulae I and II)— slow emulsion

For dose assessment using the slow emulsion, formula I gives adequate accuracy although the optimum fraction of the apparent doses are those given in formula II, the energy dependence of which is compared with that of formula I in Fig. 11.

Total photon dose (slow emulsion) =

$$1.1 \times \left[D_{\mathrm{Sn/Pb}} + \frac{D_{\mathrm{dural}}}{30} + \left(\frac{D_{300} - D_{\mathrm{dural}}}{10} \right) \right] \quad \text{rads-in-air.} \qquad \text{(II)}$$

5.4   *Assessment of photon doses at energies above 2 MeV*[22]

One of the problems of radiation dosimetry around power reactors cooled by carbon dioxide is the presence of gamma radiation of energies up to 7 MeV. The high energy components in the gamma-ray spectrum arise from the excited states of oxygen-16. In the reactor the oxygen in the primary coolant circuit undergoes an (n, p) reaction and the resultant nitrogen-16 decays with 7.4 second half-life to oxygen-16. The decay of the excited states of ^{16}O gives mainly a 6.1 MeV gamma-ray with about 7% of the disintegrations occurring with the emission of a 7.1 MeV energy photon.

The plastics film holder was not designed for use at energies above 2 MeV and the filters are insufficiently thick to provide secondary electron equi-

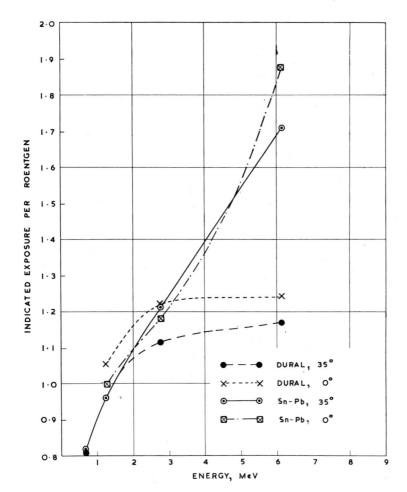

FIGURE 12   Film response curves as a function of high photon energy

librium at these energies. The response of the film therefore depends on conditions outside the film holder and it is often not possible to obtain an unambiguous estimate of exposure. However, if secondary electron equilibrium is established or approached, and low energy radiation, e.g. energies below 300 keV, is not present, a fairly reliable dose estimate may be obtained making use of the ratio of the film response under the tin-lead and dural filters. This ratio decreases from 1.0 to 0.64 as the energy rises from 1 MeV to about 6 MeV. The film response curves as a function of energy are shown in Fig. 12.

5.5 *Other limitations in dose estimation*

The accuracy attainable in the routine use of this film badge will be discussed in detail in lecture No. 3. However, apart from the difficulties which arise in the measurement of photon doses at energies above 2 MeV, it is inevitable that the resolution of different types of radiation becomes increasingly difficult as the energy limits for which the film holder was designed are approached.

One specific area where errors can become significant involves mixtures of low energy photons and high energy beta radiation. Below 20 keV the estimate of photon so falls fairly rapidly and passes the -20% level at 18 keV (see Fig. 10). On the other hand very low energy photons are significantly absorbed in the plastics filter and therefore produce a pseudo-beta exposure. This will more than offset the drop in photon response, where surface dose is to be considered, as shown in Table 5[20].

TABLE 5   Observed doses in exposures involving very low energy photons

Energy keV	Estimated doses per rad true photon dose		
	Photon dose	Pseudo Beta dose	Aggregated dose
30	.97	0	.97
20	.80	.75	1.55
15	.70	1.1	1.80
10	.35	1.3	1.65
6	.02	1.4	1.4

6   Film dosimetry for fast neutrons

The fast neutron film dosemeter used in the U.K. is based on the nuclear emulsion. Proton recoils produced by collision of fast neutrons with the hydrogen of the emulsion, or in material surrounding the emulsion, are visible as tracks in the developed emulsion when examined microscopically (Fig. 13). The tracks counted per unit area of emulsion can be related to neutron dose, either by calibration or calculation.

The dosemeter used in the Authority[23] consists of a sandwich of a sheet of 0.010 in. polythene between two 50 micron glass-based nuclear emulsions (Ilford type K1). The thickness of emulsion and radiator were chosen to give an acceptable relationship between response and rem dose over a range of neutron energies. Since the microscope technique employed affects the minimum length of track which is recognisable, it sets the energy threshold in practice. The response of the dosemeter will also be modified by the presence

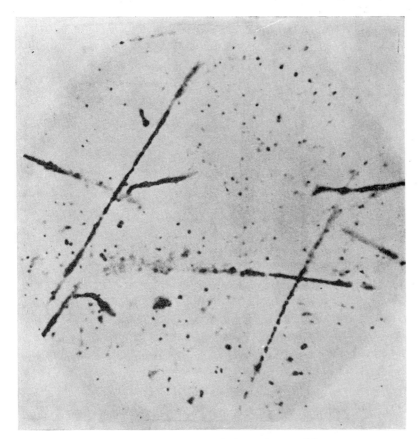

FIGURE 13   Proton tracks in nuclear emulsion

of gamma induced fog which reduces the visibility of the tracks. Another factor which can affect the esponse is the possibility of the latent image fading in the time elapsing between exposure and processing.

Two distinct microscope techniques have been employed:

i) A continuous scanning method used for routine work in which a strip 1.05 cm. long on each plate is scanned on an inclined stage, the field diameter being 95 microns. The sensitivity is 260 tracks per 2 sq. mm. per rem of

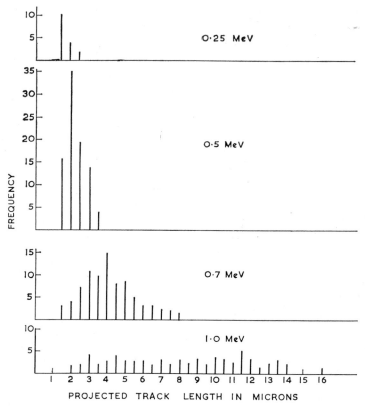

FIGURE 14   Track length distribution as a function of neutron energy
(for equal rem doses)

Pu–Be neutrons, with a background in the range 4–8 tracks per 2 sq. mm. scanned.

ii) A slower but more sensitive and reproducible method involving the inspection of discrete fields. The whole depth of the emulsion is scanned and usually 20 fields would be examined on each of the pair of plates. The Pu–Be calibration is 46 tracks for 40 fields per rem with a background of 1 or less.

The observed variation of efficiency with energy is given in Table 6 where figures are expressed relative to a Pu–Be calibration[24]. The minimum recognisable track length used was 4 grains (1.5 to 2 microns) which sets a fairly high standard for continuous microscope work.

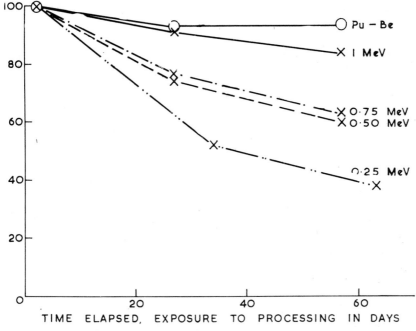

FIGURE 15 Latent image fading of Ilford K1 film

The low energy efficiency is critically dependent on the minimum observable track length. The absolute threshold (i.e. the minimum energy at which any response is observed) rises to about 0.6 MeV if the minimum length rises to 5 microns as it may well do in routine work.

TABLE 6 Variation of dosemeter efficiency with neutron energy
(Discrete field examination, minimum track length 1.5–2.0 microns)

Neutron Energy MeV	Efficiency %
0.25	23
0.5	96
0.7	90
1.0	73
Pu–Be	(100)

Observed projected track length distributions for 45° neutron incidence are shown in Fig. 14. The number of tracks plotted has been scaled so that each distribution corresponds to the same rem dose. The measurements were made under conditions which should make a track length threshold of 3–4 grains attainable.

The photographic latent image regresses with time and the rate of loss varies considerably from one type of emulsion to another. The Ilford emulsions are designed to minimise latent image fading. Loss of developable grains will have a relatively greater effect on the visibility of short tracks and therefore the degree of track loss will depend upon neutron energy. This has been observed, and measurements are shown in Fig. 15. The performance of the Ilford emulsion is quite acceptable for issue periods of one month.

6.1 *Effect of gamma fog*

Nuclear emulsions are relatively insensitive to gamma radiation and the small doses encountered in normal use produce no significant effect. Thus for Pu–Be neutrons, there is about 30% loss of recognisable tracks as a result of 4 rads of gamma irradiation. However, since the shorter, low energy proton tracks are more difficult to see, the effect of gamma radiation on these will be correspondingly greater; 4 rads of gamma radiation produce an 85% loss of recognisable tracks from neutrons of energy 0.25 MeV.

6.2 *Effect of microscope techniques on the efficiency*

The effect of scanning speed on the efficiency of track recognition is not marked for Pu–Be neutrons for which the proton recoils are easily visible. However, for low energy particles, an increase in scanning speed reduces the efficiency considerably, as shown in Table 7.

TABLE 7 Effect of microscope techniques on the efficiency

Neutron energy MeV	Percentage efficiency			
	Discrete Field	Slow scan 8 min/cm	Medium scan $4\frac{1}{2}$ min/cm	Fast scan $2\frac{1}{2}$ min/cm
Pu–Be	100		100	
1.0	73	50	45	41
0.7	90	47	41	35
0.5	96	48	40	32
0.25	23	8	0	0

6.3 *Effect of personal performance of operators*

The recognition of very short tracks is largely subjective and the performance of the microscopists used in the routine service has been assessed for a number of neutron energies by comparing their dose estimates with the actual dose received by the dosemeter. The results of five operators for mono-energetic neutrons incident at 45° are given in Table 8.

TABLE 8   Dependence of operator efficiency on neutron energy (scanning technique)

Operator	$A*$	B	C	D	E	Mean	Mean less A
		Routine emulsion scan dose / Instrument dose					
Neutron energy MeV							
0.25	—	0.00	0.00	0.00	0.03		0.00
0.5	0.51	0.25	0.44	0.48	0.68	0.47	0.46
0.75	0.48	0.23	0.28	0.40	0.43	0.37	0.34
1.0	0.52	0.28	0.29	0.54	0.55	0.44	0.42
2.0	0.70	0.41	0.34	0.61	0.64	0.54	0.50
3.0	0.75	0.39	0.35	0.65	0.53	0.53	0.48
Pu–Be	1.13	0.84	0.66	0.86	0.77	0.85	0.78

* Operator A is more experienced than the other 4 operators.

7   Automation of film dosemeter assessments

7.1 *Track counting*

The advantages of an automatic system to replace the tedious and laborious counting by eye of tracks in a nuclear emulsion are obvious. Instruments to carry out this task have been described by Becker[25] and Narath and Koeppe.[26] The method employed at A.E.R.E. recognises and counts defined nuclear tracks against an optical background of individual blackened silver grains, blobs, scratches, etc. Of the identifiable tracks at least $100/cm^2$ are due to contamination of the emulsion by alpha radioactivity.

The method, which has been developed[27] in conjunction with Southern Instruments Ltd., has concentrated upon optical and mechanical methods

FIGURE 16   The prototype automatic proton track counter

for scanning the emulsion and is basically that of a projection microscope in which the image is swept across a system of slits by means of a rotating mirror drum. The intensity of the light passing through the slits is measured with a photomultiplier and the shape of the signal is analysed electronically to differentiate between tracks and other objects.

The completed prototype instrument which is in use at Harwell, is shown in Fig. 16.

7.2 *Automatic film densitometry*

The development of automatic methods for densitometry at A.E.R.E. has proceeded in two stages. Semi-automatic densitometers, based largely upon commercially available components, have been in use since the beginning of 1963 and have been described by Peirson.[28] Films are handled singly and film handling and identification are manual but reading of density and conversion to apparent dose are automatic. The output is in the dual form of printed doses (radium gamma equivalents) and of punched cards or tape for input to a computer for the calculation of true dose. A general view of this instrument is shown in Fig. 17.

The prototype fully automatic densitometer handles processed films which have been stacked in a cassette whence they are moved automatically to a position where the identification code is read and to a second position where the densities are measured. Normally films are numbered with an arabic decimal number which is read and recorded by the densitometer operator. To eliminate visual reading of the number, an additional coded number is provided which can be interpreted by the automatic instrument. This is achieved by printing a coded number along one edge of the film by exposure to low kilovoltage X-rays through a coding shutter.

After the code has been read, the film densities are compared with an optical wedge in the form of a rotating disc in a split beam densitometer. The output is provided in a form suitable for dose assessment by a computer unless the film is rejected due to the number code proving unreadable or the densities being excessive or the film being incorrectly orientated. The average reading time per film is 12–15 seconds with two films being handled simultaneously.

At present the number of film processing laboratories handling the 20,000 routine film badges in the Authority has been reduced to four by the use of these automated techniques. When the fully automatic densitometer equipments, based on the prototype, become available it is expected that only one

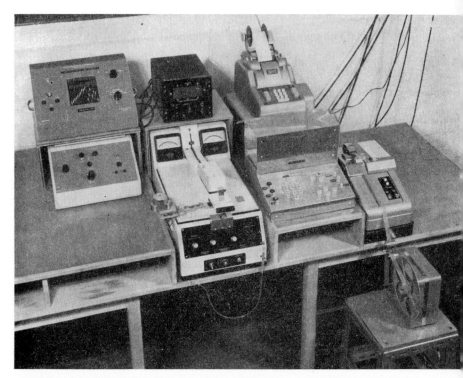

FIGURE 17   General view of the A.E.R.E. semi-automatic densitometer

routine processing laboratory will be required to handle all the Authority's routine films. A similar automated scheme for reading and recording the films used by the Central Electricity Generating Board has been proposed.[29]

8   The operational use of film dosemeters

Although close liaison exists between the health physics laboratories of the several establishments of the Authority, the personnel dosimetry practice employed in each establishment is decided locally. However, the differences in the methods used are of minor importance.

In the Authority, film badges are issued to all staff working with radiation, almost irrespective of the average dose level received. However, in circumstances where adequate containment and/or shielding can be guaranteed, local practice may not require the routine issue of film badges. Most establishments issue routine films on a monthly or four-week schedule. Where dose rates tend regularly to be such that there is a significant chance of operators exceeding 1.5 rem/year, weekly or fortnightly issues are made, and for special jobs involving high dose rates, an additional film badge may be issued for the period of the job. An extra film badge is also worn on the forehead if there is a possibility that the eye lenses are likely to be preferentially exposed, and until recently wrist films were worn if there was a special risk of exposure to the hands. Thermoluminescent dosimetry is now the method of choice for this purpose. Before the introduction of TLD methods finger films were used at some establishments where control of the dose to the finger tips of workers presented special problems. Owing to the difficulty of attaching such films satisfactorily to the fingers and to pressure blackening arising in use, these methods were never satisfactory and have been completely replaced by TLD.

Renewal films are mostly issued direct to individuals or in batches to supervisors for issue to their staff, who change their own films and return those exposed to the film laboratory. However, two laboratories prefer to collect the exposed films in the badges and to monitor the badges for possible contamination before fitting the renewal films and returning the badges to the staff. Those establishments not collecting the badges routinely claim that contamination is easily spotted photographically and the badges concerned may then be called in for decontamination. The two systems appear to be equally efficient as regards the number of lost films, the average percentage of films irrevocably lost being approximately 0.5 per cent.

As for nuclear track plates, about 300 of these packs are issued at Harwell for monthly periods. The doses measured are usually very small; rarely are doses greater than 0.3 rem recorded, and this dose represents a track density only about four times the natural background for the emulsion.

Around power reactors, it is the Authority's policy to carry out detailed area monitoring and to supplement this with a limited issue of nuclear track plate personnel dosimeters. Few of these plates worn by staff operating Calder Hall type reactors have shown detectable doses.

9 Results of film badge monitoring in U.K.A.E.A.

Table 9 shows in summary form the results of body monitoring films relating to recent years.

Some reductions have occurred in the numbers of film wearers consequent on the recommendation by ICRP that for workers whose annual dose is "most unlikely" to exceed 1.5 rems individual monitoring is not required.

33*

TABLE 9   Results of body monitoring films assessed for gamma radiation

	1957	1959	1961	1963	1965	1966
Number of film wearers	10,160	16,374	19,900	19,454	19,003	17,899
Total dose (man-rads)	5,655	6,843	8,540	7,643	9,620	10,020
Average dose per film wearer (rads/year)	0.56	0.42	0.43	0.39	0.51	0.56
Number of times 3 rads/13-week limit was exceeded	54	14	8	4	7	4
Annual doses over 5 rads	237	43	41	22	64	111

Although there has been an increase in recent years in the number of individuals whose annual body dose has extended 5 rems, no individual has received a body dose in excess of the cumulative total given by the formula 5 (N-18) rems, where N is the age above 18 in years.[16]

B   EXTERNAL RADIATION DOSIMETRY PRACTICE IN THE U.K.A.E.A—THE USES OF LUMINESCENCE DOSIMETRY

1   Introduction

Although the film badge has many advantages as a personnel dosemeter, it suffers from the drawback that the dose received can only be determined after the film has been processed. The feedback of dose information to assist in the control of personal dose in the working area is therefore slow. In many situations, particularly in areas where the dose rate is high and varies rapidly from point to point, a more rapid feedback of information is essential.

In some situations the physical size of the film badge precludes its use, e.g. for the measurement of the doses to the hands and fingers. Finger films have been used for this purpose but it is impractical to incorporate into such a dosemeter an elaborate set of filters similar to that used in the plastics film holder for the assessment of body doses. A single filter has therefore been used and consequently there is no unique relationship between the film blackening and the dose.

There are many other circumstances where film dosimetry is not the method of choice. However, this is not to suggest that the relative merits of photographic film and other forms of personnel dosemeter should be assessed in any absolute sense. The requirements of a personal dosemeter should be considered for each individual application and the relative merits of the various types of dosemeter examined in the light of these requirements. It is our purpose in this paper to consider the circumstances in which luminescence techniques are the methods of choice.

2 Extremity dosimetry

2.1 *Outline of method*

For the estimation of doses to the fingers in the handling of radioactive materials, the TLD system has already become the method of choice in many establishments of the Authority and has largely superseded the use of wrist or finger photographic film dosemeters for this purpose.

The reasons for the preference for TLD in this application can be summarized as follows:

a) The compactness and simplicity of the dosemeter;

b) uniformity of response with radiation energy;

c) linearity of response with dose over a very wide range;

d) high sensitivity;

e) rapidity of dose read-out.

Most of the development work in this field has been carried out at the Authority's establishment at Winfried Heath in Dorset and the system in use has been described in the literature.[30,31]

Lithium fluoride powder was chosen for this application because its response to radiation is almost tissue-equivalent. Other materials which have been widely discussed are calcium fluoride and calcium sulphate but although these materials have some attractive properties, their thermoluminescent response per unit dose is energy dependent which rules them out for this work.

Preliminary measurements[30] showed that 30 mg of powder spread thinly over an area of about 1 cm^2 would be optimum for exposure and read-out. Ideally the powder should be contained in thin, approximately tissue-equivalent material. For ease of manufacture and durability in use polyvinyl

FIGURE 18   P.V.C. dosemeter sachets

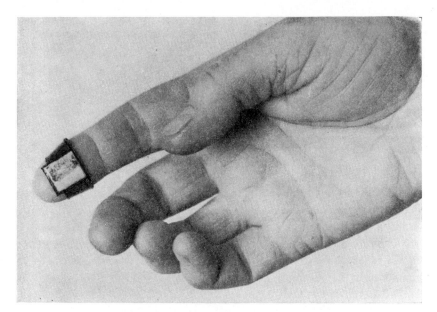

FIGURE 19   LiF dosemeter worn on the finger

chloride (P.V.C.) is preferable despite the distortion of the overall response by the chlorine present ($Z = 17$) which, however, is not unacceptable.

The final design of the sachet is shown in Fig. 18; it can be moulded from black (graphite-loaded), or transparent P.V.C. Black P.V.C. was used initially because of the reported light sensitivity of LiF but this effect was found to be negligible in normal use. The front surface facing the incident radiation is now made of transparent P.V.C. with a nominal thickness of 14 mg/cm^2 which is moulded on to a back surface of black P.V.C. 28 mg/cm^2 thick. This combination makes the powder easily visible, thus giving a visual check of the quantity and distribution of the powder. A sachet worn on the finger is shown in Fig. 19. It is fixed to the finger or other surfaces by adhesive tape, or can be made self-adhesive.

Conrad ^{7}LiF is used routinely in this application at Winfrith, although other types of LiF powder are also used in other work both at Winfrith and other Authority establishments. The powder is annealed before use at 400°C for one hour followed by 20 hours at 80°C. It is then sieved and particles in the size range 75–150 μm (100 to 200 mesh B.S.S.) are dispensed in 30 mg ($\sigma = 0.6$ mg) quantities by means of a vibratory dispenser. The filled sachet is then sealed with a simple heat-sealer. After irradiation the sachet is opened and the powder is shaken out on to the electrically-treated read-out tray. Some powder inevitably remains in the sachet and a 2% error results; the total dispensing and recovery errors amount to 3% and all observations are normalised to 30 mg of powder.

The read-out system integrates the light output between preselected tray temperatures of about 150° and 280°C thus ensuring that only the main stable peak of the glow curve is used. This, together with pre-annealing and the use of a nitrogen atmosphere during read-out, eliminates unwanted and unstable light peaks and reduces to insignificance the effects of ultra-violet and visible light, fading and non-linearity of response.

The sensitivity of the read-out system is checked against small standard radioactive light sources placed beneath the photomultiplier tube. The stability is such that the light output from 30 mg of powder irradiated to 1 rad or more is measured with $\sigma = 1\%$. The standard deviation increases below 1 rad because of variations equivalent to 3 to 5 millirads caused by fluctuations in the photomultiplier dark current. For doses of 100 mrad, the standard deviation is about 4%.

2.2   *Energy response of ^7LiF in P.V.C. sachets*

Measurements have been made at Winfrith[32] of the response of the Conrad ^{7}LiF powder in the 28 mg/cm² thick P.V.C. sachets. For photon radiation the response is flat to within $\pm 5\%$ for gamma energies in the range 80 keV to 1.25 MeV. If the response curve is normalised at the latter energy, the curve rises to a peak of 1.40 at 28 keV and falls again to unity at 15 keV and 0.71 at 10 keV. Thus in the energy range 10–80 keV doses may be overestimated by a maximum of 40% or underestimated by 30%.

For a front sachet wall of 14 mg/cm² P.V.C. the response at 10 keV is 0.98 and doses are always overestimated by a maximum of 43%, based on unit response for radium-226 calibration. The response values are summarised in Table 10.

The response of the powder in the 14 mg/cm² sachet to beta irradiation has been measured and by extrapolation the effective thickness of the bare powder has been found to be about 13 mg/cm². Thus, the measured beta dose corresponds to the dose at a tissue depth of about 27 mg/cm². Relative to rads in soft tissue at a depth of 7 mg/cm² (which is conventionally taken as the base of the epidermis), the beta response of the dosemeter falls off rapidly at low energies due to absorption in the P.V.C. and self-absorption in the powder, as shown in Table 11.

TABLE 10   Photon responses of ^{7}LiF in sachet

Energy keV	Measured response per rad in soft tissue 28 mg/cm² P.V.C.	Calculated response per rad in soft tissue 14 mg/cm² P.V.C.
10	0.71	0.98
15	1.00	1.12
20	1.20	1.26
27.5	1.40	1.43
40	1.31	1.32
50	1.24	1.24
1000	1.00	1.00

TABLE 11   Beta ray response of ^{7}LiF in sachet (14 mg/cm²)

Max. energy (MeV)	Response per rad in soft tissue at depth of 7 mg/cm²
2.5	0.95
2.0	0.93
1.5	0.88
1.0	0.75
0.77	0.64
0.22	0.028

However, the thickness of the epidermal layer of the palmar surfaces of the fingers and hands is certainly greater than 7 mg/cm², and 20–30 mg/cm² may well be nearer the true thickness. The dosemeter therefore gives a substantially realistic estimate of the beta dose to the basal layer of the epidermic in the most critical areas.

More than 3000 dosemeters of this type had been issued at Winfrith alone up to the beginning of 1967 and have provided a convenience, accuracy, reliability and rapidity not available by any other method.

2.3   *Read-out equipment*

The read-out equipment which is used in most establishments of the Authority is shown in Fig. 20. This equipment, which is now available commercially in a simplified form, was originally developed to investigate the potentialities of the LiF type of dosemeter. At that time the available commercial instruments were limited in flexibility and did not readily permit the addition of equipment for obtaining glow curves.

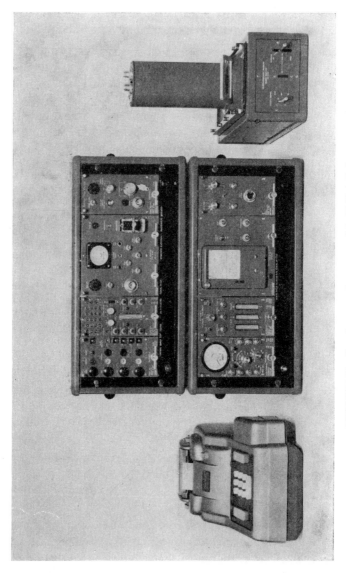

FIGURE 20   Read-out equipment used in U.K.A.E.A.

An important feature of the equipment is the temperature control of the counting system which provides digital read-out. By means of a thermo-couple welded to the underside of the heating tray, a temperature-controlled voltage is applied to a D.C. amplifier which incorporates two relay-operating circuits which are independently set to operate at any desired temperature. The lower temperature operating-relay effectively starts a scaler and the higher temperature relay effectively switches it off. Thus, the counts recorded on the scaler is an integration of the light output between the two defined temperature limits. In this way the variable light output obtained from low temperature peaks in the glow curve may be avoided with consequent avoidance of "fading" and resulting lower accuracy.

2.4   *Other systems*

The dosemeter has one main disadvantage in its present form, namely that the powder is in loose form and has to be poured out of the sachet for the read-out process. There are dangers of losing the powder due to damage to the sachet whilst being worn or of losing some when pouring it into the read-out tray. There is also the danger of mixing powders from different batches—and hence different sensitivities.

The use of thin, flexible, solid dosemeters would clearly avoid some of these difficulties provided that other disadvantages were not thereby introduced. Conrad have produced LiF powder incorporated in a matrix of polytetrafluoroethylene (p.t.f.e.). In the form of circular discs, 13 mm diameter and 0.4 mm thick, these devices can conveniently be used as finger and hand dosemeters. They tend to develop a soiled appearance after repeated use but this does not seem to affect their response. However, the lowest dose that can be measured with these dosemeters is approximately three times greater than with corresponding amounts of the powder, due presumably to loss of light in the material. Great care must be exercised in the read-out procedure to ensure good thermal contact in the reader tray. Poor contact can give rise to apparent variations in response up to a factor of two between different discs.

3   Short-term dose control

In many circumstances the dose rate levels in working areas may be so high that the period of time allowed for work in such areas must be restricted. This is often accomplished by means of short term dose measurements made with personal dosemeters which may be read by the wearer at any time during the work. Quartz fibre electrometers are often used for this purpose although they have a number of limitations among which the limited dose range and poor energy response characteristic are the more serious.

Of course, the nead for such instruments to be worn for a particular job often depends on the results of area monitoring carried out in advance. If dose rates are high but not too variable, the work can proceed on the basis of a working-time calculated from the area monitoring results. In these circumstances a second film badge, additional to the routine body film, is often worn, the dose assessment being made as soon as possible after the exposure. However, there is usually some considerable delay before the dose is evaluated and for short-term dose control this can be inconvenient; also the cost in operator time in processing small numbers of films and carrying out the subsequent dose assessments is an important factor to be borne in mind when considering possible alternatives to the film.

For this type of work the TLD method has many advantages, particularly in areas where mixed beta and gamma radiation exists, and where the ratio of beta to gamma dose-rates is high and variable in time or space. Speed in dose evaluation is important and a rugged, portable—or easily transportable—reader is desirable, suitable for use in or near the area where the work is being carried out.

Lithium fluoride dosemeters, in the form of sachets of ^{7}LiF powder, are being used increasingly at several Authority establishments for short term dose control, the routine body film badge being also worn. A "standard" sachet has been produced at Harwell to meet the increasing demand and over 60,000 were supplied last year to users both in the Authority and elsewhere in the U.K. These sachets are now available commercially at about £8 per 1000.

Other thermoluminescent devices used for short term dose control in the Authority include the LiF-teflon discs and the M.B.L.E. CaF_2 dosemeters. The latter have been used at Aldermaston for a limited number of applications but the poor photon energy response characteristic below about 60 keV and negligible beta response do restrict its usefulness despite the dosemeter's many other advantages.

4 Routine personnel monitoring

The relative merits of film and thermoluminescent dosemeters for routine body monitoring have been discussed widely.[3] The advantages of the film badge are the diagnostic information that can be derived from the processed film as to the nature of the irradiation in the event of significant exposure of an individual, and the comparative readiness with which artefacts or unusual radiation conditions can be recognised. The main advantage of TLD is that the period of issue of the body dosemeter could be extended, possibly to one year; some would also consider the directness with which the total dose is available on read-out an advantage. However for this application at least two TL dosemeters would be required, one enclosed in a filter for the measurement of photon dose and one unfiltered to measure total dose including that from beta irradiation.

A possible alternative to using *either* the film badge *or* TLD for this application is to use film badges for personnel who are expected to receive significant doses and for whom, therefore, diagnostic information on the nature of the irradiation is most likely to be required, and to use TLD for those likely to receive relatively low doses. At least one large establishment in the U.S. has adopted this system[33] employing two LiF–teflon discs, one shielded and one unshielded, incorporated into a conventional plastics badge. Although these flexible discs are adequate for this application, a rigid cheap dosemeter would be more suitable, and this has yet to be developed.

Apart from a consideration of the relative dosimetric performance of the two methods for this application, a comparison of the overall merits of the two systems must take account of the economic factors involved in terms of staff requirements, capital investment in equipment and running costs. The film badge systems now available enable large numbers of films to be handled quickly and cheaply; most TLD installations are on a laboratory scale and until the results and costs of systems involving a high degree of automation are available it is unrealistic to make critical comparison of the two systems.

5   Personnel monitoring for neutrons

As we mentioned before, the use of nuclear track emulsions for personnel monitoring for fast neutrons has severe limitations as the neutron energy—and consequently the energy of the "knock-on" proton—falls below about 500 keV. The possibility of employing thermoluminescent effects for this purpose using ^{7}LiF (to minimise the effects of thermal neutrons on lithium-6) has been reported[34] but the sensitivity of the method is low even if the powder is suspended in alcohol to increase the hydrogeneous environment. The sensitivity is also strongly dependent on neutron energy.

A method making use of the moderating effect of the body on fast neutrons incident thereon has been discussed by Becker[35] and subsequently examined experimentally by Mejdahl.[36] The method appeared promising in certain limited situations and has been developed at Winfrith[37] as a practical neutron dosimetry system for use in such situations. If the body is placed in a field of neutrons, a flux of emergent thermal neutrons is produced of magnitude dependent on the energy of the incident neutrons. For incident thermal neutrons, 80% of the flux will re-emerge from the body whereas for incident 1 MeV neutrons, the flux of emergent thermal neutrons will be about 10% of the total incident flux. By measuring the flux of thermal neutrons leaving the body it is possible to calculate the dose due to the incident neutrons provided that the energy spectrum of the incident neutrons is known, or can be considered constant and a calibration factor has been established by means of a rem-meter.

In principle the measurements can be made with a film badge making use of the $^{113}Cd(n, \gamma)$ ^{114}Cd reaction in the cadmium filter, but the sensitivity is poor. However, ^6LiF is so very sensitive to thermal neutrons that it can be used for measuring the low flux of thermal neutrons leaving the body in practice.

The main component of the neutron dosemeter consists of a sachet of 30 mg ^6LiF shielded from incident thermal neutrons by a piece of cadmium. However, owing to the very high sensitivity of this device for thermal neutrons, reflected thermals arising from even a small incident flux of thermal neutrons introduces a large error and must be corrected for. This is achieved by means of a second ^6LiF dosemeter mounted on the front side of the cadmium shield. It has been found that about 40% of the thermal flux incident on the unshielded dosemeter is reflected and affects the first dosemeter. A correction of 40% of the neutron reading of the unshielded dosemeter is therefore subtracted from the neutron reading of the shielded dosemeter in order to derive the response due to neutrons other than thermal. If there is also an appreciable flux of gamma rays, a third dosemeter incorporating ^7LiF is used and both readings of the ^6LiF dosemeters are corrected before the neutron doses are evaluated. All three dosemeters, together with the cadmium shield, may be conveniently incorporated into a cylindrical plastic holder.

Dosemeters of this type are in use at several Authority establishments to measure neutron doses in reactor environments where the neutron energy spectrum remains fairly constant. Phantom measurements have established a linear relationship between response of the shielded dosemeter and true dose to the body due to epithermal and fast neutrons. This work will shortly be published.

6   Development of lithium borate

The use of lithium borate as a dosimetric material has been described by Schulman *et al.*[38,39] It has many properties in common with lithium fluoride but has the great advantage over that material in being cheap. Primarily for this

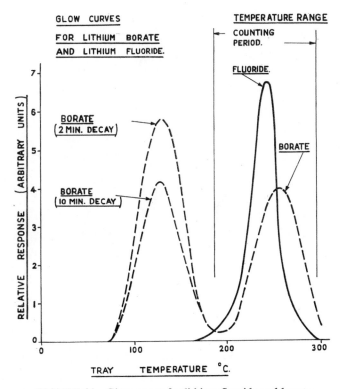

FIGURE 21   Glow curves for lithium fluoride and borate

reason, the Authority establishment at Windscale[49] has developed the material for certain health physics purposes. Owing to the presence of both ^6Li and ^{10}B in the natural material, lithium borate has a particularly high response to thermal neutrons and may therefore be used in the application described in Sec. 5. It may also be used as a substitute for lithium fluoride in neutron free areas.

The TL sensitivity of the borate is about the same as the fluoride. The glow curves for the two materials are shown in Fig. 21, and it appears that the stable borate peak is produced at about 255°C which is slightly higher

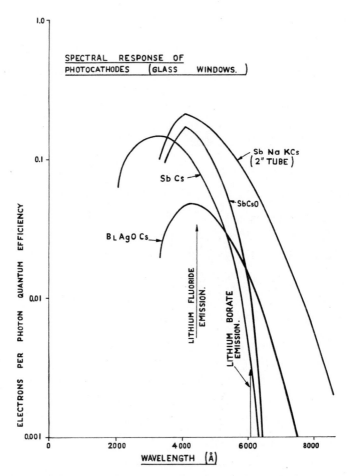

FIGURE 22   Spectral response of P.M. photocathodes

than the stable fluoride peak. The low temperature peak, which is not measured in practice, appears at about 120°C and decays quite rapidly.

However, the sensitivity of both materials is very dependent on the impurities introduced and the method of manufacture. The most sensitive borate produced at Windscale is as good as Conrad LiF and the background reading from unirradiated powder is equivalent to about 40 millirads when measured in read out equipment primarily designed for LiF.

The thermoluminescent emission from lithium borate is orange in colour (6050 Å) unlike the fluoride which emits light of wavelength 4400 Å. The type of photomultiplier used in the read-out instrument is therefore important for maximum sensitivity. Figure 22 shows the spectral responses of four photocathodes which have been investigated. Although the Bi.AgO.Cs and Sb.Na.K.Cs photocathodes measure the borate emission with increased efficiency relative to the other types of photocathode, the high dark currents associated with these more efficient photocathodes give rise to background signals equivalent to several hundred millirads. For general use the Sb.CsO photocathode gives the best compromise between high sensitivity and high background and leads to the equal read-out sensitivity of fluoride and borate referred to earlier.

Lithium borate has an interesting photon energy response characteristic in that at low energies it is about 20% less sensitive than for hard gamma radiation whereas lithium fluoride has a rising energy response at low energies up to 40% greater than for hard γ-radiation. This has some advantage if it is necessary to irradiate the borate powder in a container having an effective atomic number greater than that of tissue. One final point—the 30 mg samples of borate used in the dosemeter are cheap enough to throw away after use.

7 Radiophotoluminescent glass dosimetry

Recent advances in radiophotoluminescent glass dosimetry arising from the production of low-Z glass[41] have improved the potential of this method of personnel dosimetry. Higher sensitivity, lower background luminescence, reduced energy dependence, improved fading stability are all features of the new glass and, with special care, small gamma exposures in the range 50–100 millirads become measurable with good accuracy. In a very comprehensive review article on this subject, Becker[42] has summarised the advantages and disadvantages of the RLPD method compared with film dosimetry and thermoluminescence. Although the advantages of glass have been stated with considerable enthusiasm by other workers,[43] it is difficult to see how glass dosemeters can be seriously considered as a general replacement for well-designed film badges in view of their poor response to photons of energy below about 45 keV and their insignificant response to beta radiation.

The measurement of low energy, scattered photon radiation and beta radiation is essential for the control of skin doses to workers in plant areas where, for example, fission product contamination is present as in high activity caves where irradiated fuel elements are handled, in cooling pond areas and in effluent treatment plant. The measurement of low energy photon radiation is also most important in plutonium areas due to the predominant X-ray emissions at 13, 17 and 20 keV. In fact, in such areas as well as in laboratories handling pure beta emitters, the disadvantages of RPL glass dosimetry mentioned above are overwhelming.

It is possible that at some time in the future the film badge will cease to be the primary personal dosemeter used in the U.K. If and when that day comes, I think the replacement for film dosimetry is much more likely to be TLD than RPLD primarily on the grounds of its energy independence. Such a change would probably follow a change in measurement philosophy with more emphasis on the determination of surface dose and less on radiation spectrometry and the assessment of organ dose.

There remains one field of work where RPL glass is used for personnel dosimetry in the U.K. Atomic Energy Authority. There are certain plant areas where the use of the film badge is precluded because the ambient temperature of the working environment is too high. This is particularly true in the vicinity of the uranium gaseous diffusion plant at our Capenhurst establishment. Although the containment and low radiation background in these areas in any case makes the wearing of a routine personal dosemeter unnecessary, there is a remote possibility of a criticality accident producing high level gamma irradiation and to cover such an eventuality RPL glass dosemeters are issued to workers in these areas.

The dosemeter used has been described by Peirson.[44] It consists of a block (12 × 12 × 6 mm) of phosphate glass containing about 8 % by weight of silver metaphosphate. Owing to the relatively poor energy characteristic of the unshielded glass, each block is surrounded by a cylindrical lead filter 1.25 mm thick into which a number of small holes are punched to improve the response to low energy photons. The energy response of the assembled dosemeter is reasonably flat above about 50 keV. The device is not sensitive to beta irradiation.

In practice these devices are issued for periods of two years and give little trouble.

C EXTERNAL RADIATION DOSIMETRY PRACTICE IN THE U.K.A.E.A.—ACCURACY REQUIRED AND ATTAINABLE USING PERSONAL DOSEMETERS

1 Introduction

At the present time the film "badge" dosemeter is the device most widely used throughout the world by nuclear establishments, indeed by establishments of all kinds using radiation, to monitor the radiation exposure of their staff. From time to time the performance of the film dosemeter relative to other types of dosemeter is challenged[45,46] and, as we have seen, periodic reappraisal of the worth of the film badge as a radiation protection monitoring device is made leading to controversy at international meetings.

In assessing the accuracy attainable using a particular type of a dosemeter it is important to consider separately the inherent reproducibility of a given response from the dosimetric material, e.g. film, lithium fluoride, glass, etc., and secondly the inaccuracies introduced by the circumstances of the irradiation of the material and the subsequent read-out and dose assessment. All too frequently one hears statements regarding the relative accuracy attainable with the film badge and thermoluminescence for personnel dosimetry without any qualification as to the design of film badge and method of dose assessment being considered in the comparison or, for example, how (if at all) fading is being avoided in the TL read out technique.

The second general point we would like to stress has already been touched on before. It is not enough to consider in isolation the accuracy of a particular system of dosimetry. It is important also to consider the total information provided by the method, the ease and speed with which a result may be obtained, the permanence of the dose effect produced and the ability to re-determine the dose; all these may be important, possibly more important, than the simple accuracy limits on dose determinations made by the method considered.

As was mentioned before, prior to the introduction of the plastics A.E.R.E./R.P.S. multi-filter badge, the eight major establishments of the U.K.A.E.A., as well as many other institutions in the United Kingdom, monitored the radiation exposure of their staff by means of the tin-plate film holders shown in Fig. 1, used with either Ilford Type PM1 or PM3 film, or Kodak R.M. film. Before the metal badge was taken out of routine service, it seemed profitable to investigate the accuracy attainable with the dosimetry system then employed. The information so obtained would be

34*

useful in estimating the reliability of dose records obtained in the past and would also provide an index against which the expected improved performance of the new plastics badge could be compared.

Accordingly an experiment was carried out in 1961 to test the performance of the routine film badge service then available. The eight establishments of the Authority taking part in the exercise were tested "blind", that is to say without prior knowledge by the laboratories concerned of the doses and types of radiation used. The method employed and the results obtained are relevant in considering the attainable accuracy, and are therefore discussed in some detail.

2   Organisation of the 1961 experiment[47]

The metal film holder, constructed of 0.015 in. thick tin-plate has two pairs of opposing metal filters which sandwich the film and a pair of opposing open windows. The filter pairs are 1 mm. tin and 1 mm. cadmium thick respectively.

The Ilford PM1 film in conjunction with 1 mm. tin filters has a characteristic response which is constant within $\pm 50\%$ over the photon energy range 70 keV to 3.0 MeV, and within $\pm 20\%$ over the energy range 150 keV to 1.5 MeV.[19] (See Fig. 3).

Ilford PM3 was developed for use in monitoring personnel exposed to diagnostic X-rays for which purpose the blackening of the unfiltered part of the film is usually evaluated. The response of this part of the film varies by only $\pm 10\%$ for X-rays generated at voltages in the range 55–150 kV.[48]

The energy dependence of the Kodak film in conjunction with 1 mm. tin filters is greater than for Ilford PM1 film but less than for PM3. A pronounced peak in the response curve occurs for photon energies about 100 keV. This peak disappears with filters of (0.7 mm. tin +0.3 mm. lead) used in the new plastics badge and emphasizes the importance of designing the film holder in relation to the characteristics of the monitoring film to be used in the holder.

The experiment was initiated in November, 1961. Each establishment was asked to send to the Radiological Protection Division of the Authority Health and Safety Branch at Harwell, twelve badges containing unexposed films of the type used routinely in the establishment, together with an additional set of twelve films to be used as controls.

The badges containing the experimental films were then irradiated with various doses of X-, γ- and β-radiation and mixtures of these radiations which were known only to the authors. Eleven of the twelve badges were given doses not exceeding 3 rads in air; the twelfth film was given a larger dose of gamma radiation not exceeding 200 rads in air.

After irradiation the sets of twelve films, together with the unexposed control films were returned to the establishments for processing and dose evaluation. Special emphasis was placed on the use by establishments of the normal routine procedure for film processing densitometry and assessment of the doses, and they were asked that no special arrangements, e.g. the preparation of additional calibration films, should be undertaken to improve the accuracy of the dose evaluation. Only under such conditions would the experiment enable an estimate of the accuracy attainable *in routine practice* to be made.

3   Irradiation conditions used

3.1   *Combinations of radiations used*

Data on the irradiations of the twelve dosemeters provided by each establishment are listed in Table 12.

TABLE 12   Doses and radiation combinations used in the first experiment

Irradiation ref. no.	Radiation	Total dose (rad-in-air)
1	^{60}Co γ-rays	0.096
2	^{60}Co γ-rays	0.34
3	^{60}Co γ-rays	1.75
4	29 keV X-rays	0.030
5	29 keV X-rays	0.114
6	29 keV X-rays	0.48
7	^{204}Tl β-rays	0.145
8	^{204}Tl β-rays	0.37
9	^{204}Tl β-rays	1.05
10	^{60}Co γ-rays	0.43
	+29 keV X-rays	+0.043
		i.e. (0.47) Total
11	^{60}Co γ-rays	0.68
	+29 keV X-rays	+0.030
		i.e. (0.71) Total
12	^{60}Co γ-rays	89.4

The irradiations were carried out at perpendicular incidence and, except for the β-ray exposures, were effectively without backscatter.

3.2 *Gamma irradiations*

For simultaneous exposure to gamma rays, all the film badges to be given the same dose were clipped on to a horizontal perspex arc, radius 28 cm, centred on the 190 mCi cobalt-60 source. The arrangement is shown in Fig. 19. The source was one metre above the floor and the nearest wall was at least three metres from the source.

The exposure dose rate along the arc measured with calibrated ionisation chambers was 2.95 ± 0.03 R/hr.

3.3 *X-irradiations*

X-rays for the experiment were produced using a constant potential generator (Siemens 250 kVp "Stabilipan" unit) and a Siemens oil-cooled X-ray tube. The operating conditions for the irradiations are given in Table 13.

TABLE 13   X-ray operating conditions and beam quality

kV (const. potential)	75
filtration	2 mm Al
first h.v.t.	2.20 mm Al
$\dfrac{\text{second n.v.t.}}{\text{first h.v.t.}}$	1.56
Effective energy[49] (keV)	29

For the X-ray exposures the collimated beam was horizontal. The film badges were clipped on to a light vertical aluminium frame (Fig. 20), the centre of which was one metre above the floor and 110 cm. from the X-ray tube target. The nearest wall was four metres from the frame.

All the films to receive the same dose were exposed together. The frame was shaped to give a uniform dose-rate within $\pm 1\%$, measured with five calibrated ionisation chambers, over the 25×25 cm area used; the exposure dose-rate was about 60 R/hr.

3.4 *Beta irradiations*

The beta source consisted of thallium-204 ($E_{max.}$ 0.76 MeV), bonded in silver and covered in pure silver to a thickness of 25 mg/cm^2. The disc source was 3 cm in diameter and its activity was 5 mCi.

The area uniformly irradiated by this source was small so that it was necessary to expose the film badges individually. Each film badge was clipped in turn on to a perspex plate, 3/16 in. thick, which completely covered the back of the badge and held it at a known distance on the axis of the source (Fig. 21).

The exposure times used ranged from 75–150 seconds and were controlled by a thick perspex shutter. Source film distance of about 10 cm and 16 cm were used giving dose-rates at the film of 22 and 8.4 rad/hr.-in-air measured using an extrapolation chamber.

3.5 *Accuracy of radiation doses*

One of the Type 1120 ionisation chambers which was used in both the X- and γ-ray irradiations had been calibrated in roentgens by the National Physical Laboratory at X-ray energies from 34 to 124 keV. This chamber was used as the standard for the X-irradiations. The other chambers had been calibrated,[50] using a standardised radium source, and were found to have equal sensitivities within $\pm 0.25\%$; these were used as the standards for the ^{60}Co irradiations.

It should be noted that the doses have been expressed in the somewhat unusual unit, rad-in-air. This is because the maximum permissible doses specified in the U.K. factory legislation[17] are at present also expressed in this unit. A conversion factor of 0.88 rad-in-air/R[51] was used to interpret the readings of the A.E.R.E. Type 1120 ion chambers to obtain the X- and γ-ray doses which are listed in Table 12. The β-dose rates, expressed initially in esu/cm^3 hr for air at N.T.P., were also converted numerically to rad-in-air/hr by multiplying by 0.88.

For the X- and γ-irradiations, the nominally equal doses are believed to differ by no more than $\pm 1.5\%$; for the β-irradiations the variations may be $\pm 2\%$. The stated values of the doses may have errors within about $\pm 3\%$ for X- and γ-exposures and within about $\pm 5\%$ for the β-ray exposures.

4   Results of dose assessments

The detailed results of this experiment will be presented later in this lecture in order to allow comparisons to be made with the results of a second experiment involving the plastics badge. Summarising, 109 individual dose assessments were made in the experiment and all but 25 of these assessments were within $\pm 40\%$ of the correct dose. Almost all the gamma dose assessments were within $\pm 20\%$, the larger deviations being due to the use of a calibration convention different from that used by the majority.

The assessments of the X-ray doses suffer from the difficulty of X-ray energy determination with the metal badge. This, together with the rapid variation of film sensitivity with photon energy below 100 keV, makes high accuracy in X-ray dose assessment improbable. It is possible to obtain some information as to the quality of the incident radiation from the ratio of the apparent radium gamma doses in the open window and in the tin-filtered areas of the film provided, of course, that beta irradiation has not also occurred. If such an energy estimate is not attempted, the apparent dose of radium gamma radiation in the tin-filtered area alone can represent a very large range of true dose values depending on the unknown incident radiation energy.

Although the experiment highlighted known deficiencies in the metal badge design, it also brought to light the effects on accuracy of different techniques of film calibration, processing, densitometry and dose assessment used in the various Authority establishments. Apart from the design of the new plastics badge, which was in progress before the conclusion of this experiment, one of the main consequences of the experiment was the setting up of a Working Party to attempt the standardisation of various aspects of film dosimetry in the Authority.

The recommendations of the Working Party, which were unanimously adopted as part of the routine practice at all Authority establishments, have been published[52] and provide guidance on the size and type of film calibration source, the range of calibration exposures to be covered and the design of an exposure jig to achieve reproducibility of calibration data. In addition to the necessary calibration films, it is recommended that a number of standard films be exposed to known doses under defined conditions. These films are used to adjust the dose-density curve obtained from the calibration films where this is shown to be necessary as a result of changes in film emulsion sensitivity.

Further recommendations relate to the type, use and replacement of developer, development temperature, methods of mixing, etc. With regard to densitometry, the illuminating aperture size and range of densities measurable to a defined accuracy are also the subject of recommendations, as is the preferred method of specification of the lowest dose to be recorded.

5 The 1965 experiment

5.1 *General arrangements*

In 1965 a similar experiment to that already described was undertaken but on this occasion all the establishments taking part were using routinely the new A.E.R.E./R.P.S. plastics holder containing Kodak R.M. film. Also since the date of the first experiment, the recommendations of the Working Party on Film Dosimetry referred to above had been implemented and all establishments were using standard film calibration, processing, densitometry and dose assessment methods. Since the basic design of the plastics film badge allows photon energy determination and discrimination between photon and beta radiation, it was to be expected that improved accuracy would be achieved in dose evaluation.

Although the second experiment followed the general pattern of the first, a number of refinements were introduced. A larger batch of eighteen badges were requested for irradiation with an appropriate number of additional controls. Twelve badges from each batch were exposed to radiation types and doses similar to but not identical with those used in the first experiment. The additional six badges were exposed to mixtures of radiations chosen to provide a more stringent test of the capabilities of the new plastics badge.

Data on the irradiations of the sets of 18 dosemeters provided are listed in Table 14.

TABLE 14   Doses and radiation combinations used in the second experiment

Irradiation reference number	γ-rays			X-rays		β-rays		Total dose (rad-in-air)
	Nuclide	Photon dose	Assoc. electron dose	Energy	Dose	Nuclide	Dose	
1	^{60}Co	0.042	0.008					0.050
2	^{60}Co	0.515	0.095					0.61
3	^{60}Co	0.995	0.187					1.18
4				38 keV	0.023			0.023
5				38 keV	0.206			0.206
6				38 keV	1.00			1.00
7						^{204}Tl	0.119	0.119
8						^{204}Tl	0.357	0.357
9						^{204}Tl	1.34	1.34
10	^{60}Co	0.293	0.055	56 keV	0.053			0.401
11	^{60}Co	0.465	0.088	56 keV	0.025			0.578
12	^{60}Co	63.0	11.9					74.9
13	^{60}Co	5.88	1.12	91 keV	1.70			8.70
14	^{60}Co	24.1	4.5	38 keV	1.00			29.6
15						^{204}Tl	1.16	
						$+^{90}$Y	0.44	1.60
16	^{60}Co	0.187	0.035	56 keV	0.139	^{204}Tl	0.209	0.570
17				38 keV	0.723	^{90}Y	0.521	1.24
18				38 keV	0.053	^{90}Y	0.521	0.574

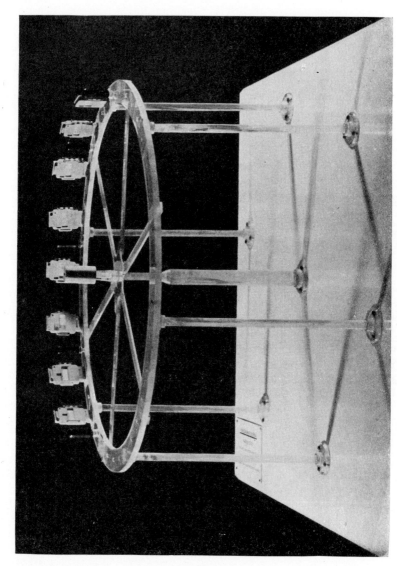

FIGURE 23 Gamma-radiation exposure jig (Second experiment)

5.2 *Gamma irradiations*

As in the previous experiment, the dose-rate employed for the gamma irradiations was measured with ionisation chambers having wall thickness of -300 mg/cm^2. The ionisation produced in these chambers is due largely to secondary electrons liberated in their walls; low energy electrons originating outside the chamber will not therefore produce ionisation therein

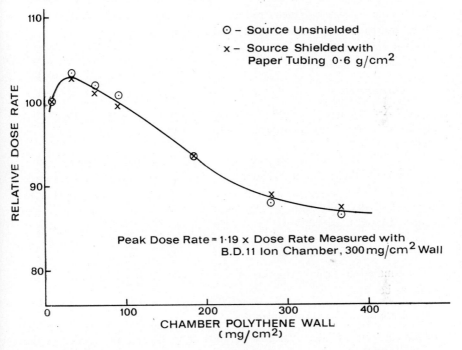

FIGURE 24   Relative dose rates measured by shallow ion chamber 30 cm from ^{60}Co source

unless their range is greater than the wall thickness. Consequently, the dose rate produced by the excess secondary electron flux density at the perspex ring, (shown in Fig. 23) over that in equilibrium with the gamma-ray flux density there is largely unmeasured by the chambers but is partially measured by the unfiltered area of the film.

It was therefore necessary to measure this proportion of the true dose-rate excluded by the chamber walls. In this experiment a shallow disc-shaped ionisation chamber was used, which was supported on the perspex ring with its front window facing the source. The rear electrode of this chamber was of graphite and provided full backscatter for electrons. The front window was 7 mg/cm² thick metallised plastics, and plastics filters were placed close to this window, and between the window and the source, in order to measure the change of dose rate with absorber thickness.

The results obtained are shown in Fig. 24 which indicates that the maximum doserate (which occurs for an absorber 30 mg/cm² thick) is 19% greater than the dose rate measured for an absorber thickness of 300 mg/cm². Therefore, each γ-ray exposure was taken to be accompanied by an additional electron or "β-ray" dose amounting to 19% of the dose measured by the Type 1120 chambers.

5.3 *X-irradiations*

For the X-ray exposures similar arrangements were made as for the earlier experiment. The X-ray qualities are listed in Table 14.

5.4 *β-irradiations*

In addition to the thallium-204 source used previously, an yttrium-90 source ($E_{max.}$ 2.26 MeV) was used. Its method of construction, size and activity were identical to the ²⁰⁴Tl source; the irradiation times used were somewhat longer in this experiment.

5.5 *Accuracy of radiation doses*

The estimated accuracy achieved in the second experiment was about the same as before.

5.6 *Methods of dose assessment*

In the earlier experiment various methods of evaluating and recording the doses received by the films were employed by the eight establishments taking part and in some eases this caused difficulty in converting the dose assessments into a form which permitted intercomparison with other establishments.

In the 1965 experiment all establishments taking part used the methods of dose assessment described in the first lecture.

6 Results of dose assessments

The detailed results obtained in the two experiments are compared in Figs. 25–29. Each figure shows the ratios of assessed dose to true dose for the eight establishments. Figure 25 shows results for the four different levels

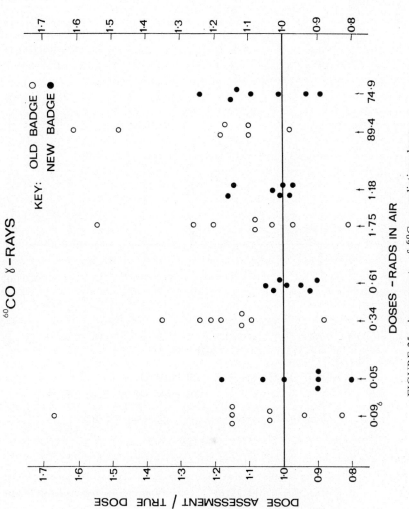

FIGURE 25 Assessments of ^{60}Co γ-radiation doses

of ^{60}Co gamma irradiation. Clearly doses in the range 0.05–100 rad of medium energy γ-radiation can be measured with errors no greater than ±20% using a multi-filter badge. It is of interest that almost all the assess-

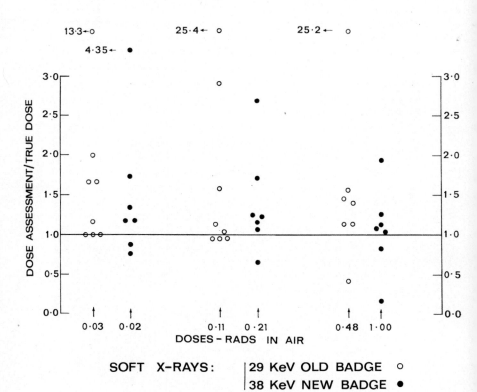

FIGURE 26   Assessments of soft X-radiation doses

ments in experiment No. 2 reported the presence of additional so-called "beta" doses of magnitude approximately 20% of the γ-dose levels. These doses are, of course, due to the extra secondary electrons referred to in the section on γ-ray irradiations.

Figure 25 shows the assessments for the three different dose levels of low voltage X-rays. The second experiment shows improved assessments but there is substantially more difficulty in arriving at correct dose evaluation in this energy region. Most assessments showed errors in the range −40 to +100%.

For mixtures of X- and γ-radiation doses, the gamma dose assessments determined the overall accuracy attainable. Figure 27 shows that ±20% is generally possible for such mixtures.

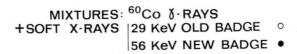

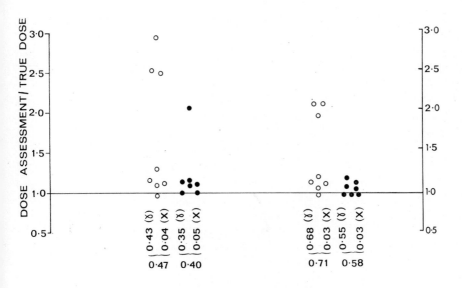

FIGURE 27   Assessments of mixtures of γ- and X-radiation doses

The dose assessments of ^{204}Tl β-irradiations shown in Fig. 28 are capable of misinterpretation. The assessment of β-doses with the simple metal badge is difficult if, as in the experiment, the β-energy is not disclosed. In the absence of such information most laboratories made their assessments using the dose-response curve for radium γ-rays, a procedure which generally gives rise to large errors. However, the dose-response curve for ^{204}Tl β-radiation is very similar to that for radium γ-rays; fortuitiously therefore accurate results were obtained. The assessments with the plastics badge were made using a generalised method,[20] the accuracy of which is

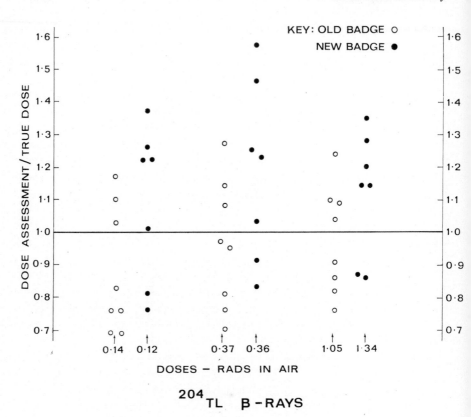

FIGURE 28   Assessments of [204]Tl β-radiation doses

similar for all β-energies. In the dose range used (0.10–1.5 rad), errors of
−25 to +60 % may occur.

Finally, the results of the assessments of the six additional exposures of
mixed radiations which were included in the second experiment as more
stringent tests of the performance of the new plastics badge are shown in
Fig. 29. For one or more of the following reasons these exposures were
expected to be unusually difficult to determine accurately:

a) the doses fall in the region of overlap of the dose-density characteristics
for the combined emulsions and the slow emulsion and are not accurately
measurable on either;

b) 91 keV X-rays are near the K-absorption edge for lead and dose estimates
for this radiation are especially sensitive to angle of incidence of the radiation;

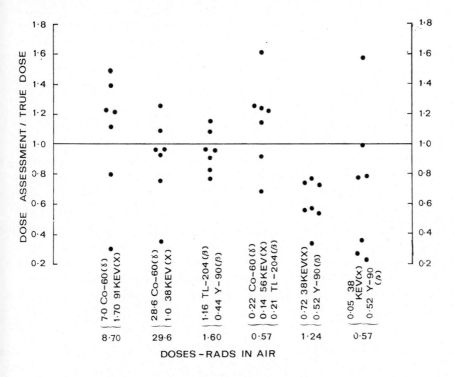

MIXED RADIATIONS – NEW BADGE

FIGURE 29   Assessments of additional mixtures of radiations with the new film badge

c) some exposures required part of the assessment to be made with the combined emulsions and part after removal of the sensitive emulsion;

d) ^{90}Y beta rays are transmitted in part through the dural filter and may therefore be indistinguishable from soft X-rays. The much greater sensitivity of the film to low energy X-rays than to beta rays makes difficult the detection of ^{90}Y beta rays in the presence of 38 keV X-rays leading to underestimates of total dose.

7   Conclusions from experiments

In drawing conclusions from these experiments it is important to bear in mind that the irradiations employed were deliberately selected to include all the radiation types (except neutrons) to which the dosemeters respond and to cover a large part of the measurable dose range. They are, however, by no means representative of the types of irradiations or magnitudes of personal doses routinely experienced in operational practice. Indeed, most of the experimental irradiations were of a type more likely to have been encountered under accident conditions and which therefore would at least have merited follow-up enquiries if not detailed investigations. The lack of opportunity for these has undoubtedly made the dose assessments more difficult.

However, considered as a whole the dose assessments show satisfactory accuracy and those in the second experiment indicate a good over-all performance by the A.E.R.E./R.P.S. dosemeter. When the results of the two experiments are compared, the improvement in accuracy attained, largely by the introduction of the plastics dosemeter but also partly from the improved performance by all laboratories as a result of the adoption of standardised procedures, is marked. Table shows, in summary form, the results of the two experiments for the comparable irradiations. Particularly noteworthy is the elimination of the extreme values seen in the first experiment. These arose largely from the need to avoid underestimating personal doses when faced with ambiguous patterns of film blackening resulting from the use of the simpler dosemeter.

TABLE 15   Summary of accuracy attained in the two experiments

Range of accuracy ($\pm\%$)	1961 Experiment pressed tin-plate dosemeter (% of 94 assessments)	1965 Experiment A.E.R.E./R.P.S. dosemeter (% of 84 assessments)
0–20	63	70
21–40	16	19
>40	21	11

8   Accuracy required in routine personnel monitoring

The two experiments described above have shown how the accuracy attained in routine personnel monitoring may be increased by improvements in the design of the dosemeters and by attention to detail in the practice of personal dosimetry. The results obtained in the second experiment compare favourably with those obtained in similar experiments reported in the literature.[53,54,55] Since other systems of personnel dosimetry have been claimed to have a superior performance to that of the film badge,[42] it is necessary to consider whether the accuracy attainable by means of the film badge is adequate for routine monitoring of personnel exposed to radiation or whether we should consider using an alternative system on grounds of accuracy alone notwithstanding other merits of the systems being compared.

Recently Committee 4 of ICRP has set up a Task Group to consider the general principles of monitoring for radiation protection of workers. Although the Report of the Task Group has not yet been accepted by the Commission, it is possible to state[56] that the accuracy considered by the Task Group as necessary for routine monitoring should be such that the uncertainty in assessing the annual dose measured by the dosemeter should not exceed 50% of the recorded dose, or 1 rem, whichever is the larger. This uncertainty is intended to cover systematic bias as well as random variations in the dosemeter readings.

Larson *et al.*[57] has suggested that the dose evaluated by a film badge, D_e, may be expressed in terms of the true dose delivered, D_d, by a relationship:

$$D_e = a + b\,D_d + \delta$$

where a and b are systematic bias parameters, and δ is a random variable with a mean equal to zero and a variance, σ^2, dependent on the exposure level D_d. The relationship found for a series of U.S. film processing laboratories was approximately:

$$\sigma^2 = \gamma\,D_d, \quad \text{where}$$

$$\gamma = \text{a constant}$$

$$D_d = \text{true dose delivered.}$$

At the 95% confidence level, the relative percentage error may be expressed as:

$$\text{R.E.} = \frac{2\sigma}{D_d} \times 100 = 200\sqrt{\frac{\gamma}{D_d}}.$$

If the true dose delivered is taken to be 5 rems—the maximum permissible annual dose for uniform whole body exposure—and the relative error is taken to be 50%, then the constant $\gamma = {}^5/_{16}$. If one assumes that the life-time maximum aggregate dose limit for the whole body accumulated over 47 (age 18 to age 65) annual intervals is 235 rems, then assuming no bias in the dose measurements, the relative error at the 95% confidence level will be:

$$\text{R.E.} = 200\sqrt{\frac{5}{16 \times 235}} = 7\%.$$

35*

Similarly, if the dose of 5 rems is determined with a relative error of 50 % at the 95 % confidence level with no bias, then the variation in each of twelve monthly dose measurements (of approximately equal value) would be:

$$\text{R.E.} = 200 \sqrt{\frac{5 \times 12}{16 \times 5}} = 173 \%.$$

Thus, each monthly dose need only be determined with a precision of $\pm 173 \%$ to achieve an accuracy of $\pm 50 \%$ in the annual dose, which in turn leads to an accuracy of $\pm 7 \%$, in the lifetime dose, all at the 95 % confidence limit.

Of course, if one makes the assumption that the annual whole body dose is less than 2 rems (and therefore the fixed upper limit of uncertainty of 1 rem proposed by the Task Group becomes operative), an increasing value of relative percentage error is permissible depending on the dose level assumed.

9 Conclusions

It is clear from the above analysis that the accuracy attainable by means of film badge dosimetry can be adequate for the purposes of personnel monitoring. Whether it is so depends on the design of the badge and the care expended in film processing and dose assessment.

The accuracy attainable by thermoluminescent techniques in the measurement of absorbed dose at the position occupied by the dosemeter is clearly more than adequate for the purposes of personal protection. The accuracy achieved by RPLD methods depends on the type of radiation required to be measured. If this is gamma radiation, the method is more than adequate; if it is beta radiation, the method is decidedly inadequate.

In the light of the above, the choice between film and TLD is unlikely to be decided on grounds of accuracy but on the many other factors, mostly administrative, which were discussed in the introductory sections.

Acknowledgements

I should like to thank my many colleagues in the U.K. Atomic Energy Authority who have contributed material and ideas to the substance of this paper. Some of these have been acknowledged in the list of references; to the others, not mentioned by name, acknowledgement of their help is gratefully recorded.

References

1. Langmead, W. A., "External radiation dosimetry practice in the united Kingdom atomic Energy Authority." *Proc. Symp. Personal Dosimetry Techniques for External Radiation*, Madrid, 1963, E.N.E.A.
2. Langmead, W. A. "The place of luminescence dosimetry in the control of occupational hazards of ionizing radiations" *Proc. International Conference of Luminescence Dosimetry*, Stanford, 1965, U.S.A.E.C.
3. *Proc. Symp. on Radiation Dose Measurements*, Stockholm, 1967, E.N.E.A. (in press).
4. Dorneich, M., and Schaeffer, H., "On the measurement of radiation in Roentgens by the photographic method", *Phys. Zeit.* **43**, 390 (1942).
5. Franke, H., *Fortschr. Roentgenstr.* **38**, 22 (1928); and **44**, 691 (1931).
6. Grimmett, L. G., and Read, J., "Protection problems associated with use of a 5-gm radium unit", *Brit. J. Rad.* **9**, 712 (1936).
7. Wilson, C. W., "Protection in radium Teletherapy at Westminster hospital", *Brit. J. Rad.* **13**, 105 (1940).
8. Clark, L. H., and Jones, D. E. A., "Some results of the photographic estimation of stray *x*-radiation received by hospital *x*-ray Personnel", *Brit. J. Rad.* **16**, 166–168 (1943).
9. Maynford, W. V., "Some problems of radiation protection", Silvanus Thompson Memorial Lecture, *Brit. J. Rad.* **24**, 525–37 (1951).
10. *Recommendations of the British X-ray and Radium Protection Committee*, Sixth Revised Report (Feb. 1943).
11. Recommendations of the International Commission on Radiological Protection (Revised Dec. 1954), *Brit. J. Rad.*, Suppl. 6 (1955).
12. Langendorff, H. and Wachsmann, F., "Radiation protection, using the film blackening method, of persons working with radioactive materials", *Atomkernenergie*, **3**, 60–64 (1958). AERE-Trans-830.
13. Soole, B. W., "Photographic badges for the estimation of the quality of x- and γ-radiation", *Brit. J. Rad.*, 29, 450–54 (Aug. 1956).
14. Adams, N., "The derivation of absorbed tissue doses from the results of personnel dosimetry techniques", in *Proc. Symp. on Personal Dosimetry Techniques for External Radiation*, Madrid, 1963, E.N.E.A.
15. *Recommendations of the International Commission on Radiological Protection*, **1959**, Pergamon Press (1959).
16. *Recommendations of the International Commission on Radiological Protection*, **1965**, ICRP Publication 9, Pergamon Press, 1966.
17. *Ionising Radiations (Sealed Sources) Regulations*, S.I. No. 1470, H.M.S.O. (1961).
18. *Code of Practice for the protection of persons exposed to Ionising Radiations in Research and Teaching. Ministry of Labour* H.M.S.O. (1964).
19. Heard, M. J., Cook, J. E. and Holt, P. D. *Photographic Emulsion Dosimetry and the A.E.R.E. Film Dosimeter* AERE-R 3300 H.M.S.O. (1960).
20. Heard, M. J. and Jones, B. E., "A new film holder for personnel dosimetry" in *Proc. Symp. on Personnel Dosimetry Techniques for External Radiation*, Madrid, E.N.E.A. (1963).
21. Boot, S. J. and Dennis, J. A., *The Slow Neutron Calibration of Film and other Gamma Dosimeters* AERE-R 4960 H.M.S.O. (1965).

22. Holt, P. D. and Gibson, J. A. B., *High Energy Gamma Ray Dosimetry: Experimental measurements at a nuclear power station*, AERE-R 4451 (1964).
23. Cook, J. E., *Fast Neutron Dosimetry using Nuclear Emulsions* AERE HP/R 2744 (1958).
24. Douglas, J. A. and Heard, M. J., *The Performance of Nuclear Emulsions used as Fast Neutron Dosimeters in the vicinity of Nuclear Reactors* AERE-R 5367 (1967).
25. Becker, S., Automatic nuclear emulsion scanner, *Health Physics*, **4** (1960), 164.
26. Narath, A. and Koeppe, P., "An automatic scanner for nuclear emulsions", *in Proc. I.A.E.A. Symposium on Neutron Detection, Dosimetry and Standardisation*, Harwell, 1962. I.A.E.A.
27. Heard, M. J., "Report on the progress of automation of photographic dosimetry, April, 1964", *J. photogr. Sci.*, **13**, 32 (1965).
28. Peirson, D. H., "Progress in the automation of photographic dosimetry" in *Proc. Symposium on Personnel Dosimetry Techniques for External Radiation*, Madrid (1963) E.N.E.A.
29. Hill, M. J., *Film Badges in the C.E.G.B.—A scheme for their reading with a new instrument and record keeping with a computer*" RD/B/N 441 C.E.G.B. (1965).
30. Perry, K. E. G. and George, E., *An experimental system for thermoluminescent dosimetry* AEEW-R 411 H.M.S.O. (1965).
31. Johns, T. F., "Measurement and assessment of radiation doses from the handling of reactor fuels," in *Proc. International Symp. on Dosimetry of Irradiations from External Sources*, Paris (1964).
32. Peabody, C. O. and Preston, H. E., *A plastic sachet dosemeter containing lithium fluoride powder for surface and finger-tip dosimetry*, AEEW-R 497 H.M.S.O. (1967).
33. Cusimano, J. P. and Cipperley, F. V., *Personnel dosimetry, using thermoluminescent lithium fluoride-teflon dosimeters* (in press).
34. Wingate, Catherine L., Tochilin, E. and Goldstein, N., "Response of lithium fluoride to neutrons and charged particles" in *Proc. International Conf. on Luminescence Dosimetry*, Stanford Univ. U.S.A.E.C. (1965).
35. Becker, K. H. and Tuyn, J. W. N., "Some recent studies in neutron glass dosimetry" in *Proc. International Conf. on Luminescence Dosimetry* U.S.A.E.C. (1965).
36. Mejdahl, V., "Thermoluminescence dosimetry in fast-neutron personnel monitoring using body moderation" in *Proc. Symp. on Neutron Monitoring*, Vienna I.A.E.A. (1967).
37. Johns, T. F., Personal communication (to be published).
38. Schulman, J. H., Kirk, R. D. and West, E. J., "The use of lithium borate for thermoluminescence dosimetry" in *Proc. International Conf. on Luminescence Dosimetry*, Stanford Univ. U.S.A.E.C. (1965).
39. Kirk, R. D., Schulman, J. H., West, E. J. and Nash, A. E., "Studies on thermoluminescent lithium borate for dosimetry" in *Proc. Symp. on Solid-State and Chemical Radiation Dosimetry in Medicine and Biology*, Vienna, I.A.E.A (1966).
40. Brunskill, R. T., Personal communication (to be published).
41. Yokota, R. and Nakajima, S., "Improved fluoroglass dosimeter as personnel monitoring dosimeter and microdosimeter" *Health Physics*, **11** (1965), 241.

42. Becker, K., "Radiophotoluminescent dosimetry", *I.A.E.A. Atomic Energy Rev.*, **5**, No. 1, 43 (1967).

43. Kiefer, H., Maushart, R. and Piesch, E., "Results with phosphate glass dosemeters in personnel dosimetry" *Atompraxis*, **11**, 88 (1965), also *AERE-Trans.* 1046 H.M.S.O. (1965).

44. Peirson, D. H., *The Phosphate glass dosimeter* AERE EL/R 2590 H.M.S.O. (1958).

45. Becker, K., "Photographic, glass or thermoluminescent dosimetry?", *Health Physics*, 12, 955 (1966).

46. Newell, R. R., Editorial—"The film badge" *Radiology*, 77 (1961) 995.

47. Langmead, W. A. and Adams, N., "Investigations of the accuracy attained in routine film badge dosimetry" *Health Physics*, **13**, (1967) 167.

48. Stephenson, S. K., "Christie Hospital metal film badges for use with Ilford PM 1 and PM 3 films" in *Proc. Symp. on Film Badge Dosimetry, Harwell*, 1961 AHSB (RP) R 19 (1962) H.M.S.O.

49. Grodstein, G. W., *X-ray attenuation coefficients from 10 keV to 100 MeV*, N.B.S. Circular 583 and supplement. U.S. Govt. Printing Office (1957).

50. Holt, P. D., Personal communication.

51. *Report of the International Commission on Radiological Units and Measurements* (ICRU), N.B.S., Washington D.C. (1959).

52. Adams, N., Heard, M. J. and Holt, P. D., "Film dosimetry practice with the A.E.R.E/R.P.S. film holder: a collection of experimental data." AERE-R 4669 H.M.S.O. (1965).

53. Bingo, K. and Miyanaga, I., "Detection limit and precision in photographic dosimetry." *J. nucl. Sci. Technol.*, **2**, No. 1, 24 (1965).

54. Gorson, R. O., Suntharalingam, N. and Thomas, J. W., "Results of a film-badge reliability study." *Radiology*, **84**, No. 2, 333 (1965).

55. Barber, D. E., "Measurement of the performance of film badge services." *Am. industr. Hyg. Ass. J.*, **27**, No. 3, 243 (1966).

56. Dunster, H. J., Personal communication.

57. Larson, H. V., Unruh, C. M., Beetle, T. M. and Keene, A. R., "Factors involved in establishing film dosemeter performance criteria" in *Proc. Symp. on Radiation Dose Measurements*, Stockholm, E.N.E.A. (in the press) (1967).

Personnel monitoring with radiophotoluminescent dosimeters*

R. MAUSHART†

Kernforschungszentrum Karlsruhe
Radiation Monitoring Service
Federal Republic of Germany

1   INTRODUCTION

In this paper it shall not be dealt with the physical and chemical properties of the various types of silver-activated metaphosphate glasses, but with their use as routine dosimeters for radiation protection purposes.

---

* This paper is a shortened version of the Chapter IV "Radiophotoluminescent glass dosimeters" by R. Maushart and E. Piesch, in Technical Guide-Book on Personnel Dosimeter Systems for External Radiation Exposures, IAEA Vienna.

† Present adress: Labor Prof. Dr. Berthold, Wildbad-Schwarzwald, Federal Republic of Germany.

RPL glasses are manufactured commercially today which can measure the low-level long-term exposures experienced in occupational radiation protection, have a linear dose sensitivity over a large dose range, show no appreciable fading over fairly long periods and whose indicated dose value is only slightly dependent on radiation energy and practically completely independent of the dose rate. Another useful property of these glasses for routine personnel monitoring is that the measured value is not erased by the measuring procedure and the measurement can be repeated at will so that in addition to intermediate readings, the dosimeter can add up even small doses over very long periods (long-term dosimeter). Silver-activated metaphosphate glasses are, therefore, used to an increasing extent as personnel monitors.

However to come out with a serviceable dosimeter, it is not sufficient to consider the glass independently. Indeed it is only one part of a three-component system that consists of the glass, the casing and the reader. Furthermore, this system must not only be optimized for its dose-indicating properties, but also for its practicability in handling and wearing the dosimeter and in evaluating its results. Several designs exist already, and more are probably to come yet, so at the end of this lecture we will not have arrived at the blueprint of the ideal RPL dosimeter. But we will have seen several examples of dosimeters in use, and we will hopefully have a feeling where the trends are going.

2 PRACTICAL USE OF GLASS DOSIMETERS

2.1 General considerations

In the design of casings for dosimeter glasses and the practical use of glasses for personnel monitoring, the following technical and administrative requirements must be kept in mind:

a) The dosimeter assembly (glass and casing) should give a dose response which is energy-independent and direction-independent;

b) The over-sensitivity of the glass to thermal neutrons should be reduced;

c) The casing should protect the glass from exposure to ultraviolet light;

d) The casing should protect the glass from mechanical damage (scratching of surfaces etc.), soiling and radioactive contamination; it should be possible to wash the glass before measurement;

e) It should be possible to heat the glass to about 400°C for re-use (erasing of measured value);

f) The glass should be clearly identifiable. When firmly attached to the capsule, the casing should be clearly identifiable.

2.2 Energy compensation methods

Dosimeter systems with one or more glasses can be used to compensate for energy dependence. A single dosimeter, which is energy-independent as well as direction-independent over a limited energy range is preferable in routine dosimetry, since the amount of dose is indicated directly without the need for making a correction for radiation quality and for separating other radiation components. This can be done with one-layer filters in the energy range above 80 keV and with differentiated, e.g. perforated, filters in the energy range above 30–40 keV. In the energy range below 30 keV two glasses with different filters must be used for dose determination in all cases. There are dosimeter assemblies which use a combined double dosimeter for dose determination in the energy range even below 80 keV. The determination of two measured values however not only involves twice the amount of work in measuring but also doubles the measuring error and, through the additional effects of the varying energy-dependence and direction-dependence of both glasses, also leads to further errors in evaluation.

It should also be borne in mind that the experimentally-determined energy-dependence of dose response is strongly dependent on the direction of incidence of the radiation. The direction-dependence which results from the shape of the glass is in many cases made worse by the combination of filters used. The alteration in the direction of incidence of radiation leads, depending on the effective thickness of the filter, to a change in energy compensation.

For routine dosimetry, it is thus necessary to know the energy dependence at least for radiation incidence directions with maximum and minimum dose indication. Most of the references to energy-dependence in the literature relate to a frontal radiation-incidence direction.

Double or multiple dosimeters can be used to separate dose components of different energy ranges or different types of radiation (γ-radiation, thermal neutrons). An idea of the radiation quality (X- and gamma radiation) is also obtained from the ratio of measured values.

To a large extent, the following filter techniques, which are used in photographic film dosimetry, have also been used for energy-compensation in

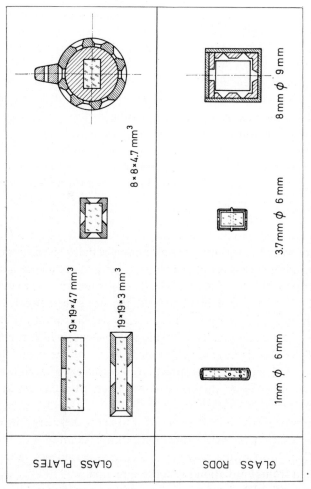

FIGURE 1   Diagram showing various dosimeter casings for phosphate glasses of various sizes for gamma energy compensation

phosphate glass dosimetry: (1) Use of one-layer homogeneous filters (Al, Cu, Sn, Cd, Pb); (2) use of an inhomogeneous one-layer filter, which brings about a multiple-layer filter effect by means of a tapered bore or a perforated foil; and (3) use of several glasses with different filters. Instead of flat filter foils in homogeneous, bored or perforated form, which are put on both sides of the film, cubical, cylindrical or spherical filters with the same design characteristics are now used for glasses of various designs (see Fig. 1).

2.3 Routine dosimeter for *X*- and gamma radiation

2.3.1 *Energy range from a few MeV to 40 keV*

One-layer filters (e.g. 1.2 nm Sn or 1 mm Cd or 0.5 mm Pb) lead to an energy-independent dose indication only above 80 keV. A 1-mm Cd-capsule with conically perforated lateral surfaces also measures low energy quantum radiation up to 40 keV.[3] This capsule does not, however, fulfil the requirements with regard to cleanness of the glass and dose-equivalence response

FIGURE 2   The spherical dosimeter casing for Yokota glass (8 × 8 × 4.7 mm³)

for thermal neutrons, and thus has not been used in practice. In a special spherical casing with tapered holes (2 mm Sn with 15% hole) optimum energy independence is achieved with a $8 \times 8 \times 4.7$ mm^3 Yokota glass in the energy range from 45 keV to 1.2 MeV within $\pm 8\%$ for one direction of incidence of the radiation and within $\pm 18\%$ for all directions of incidence of the radiation.[4] The glass is also protected by a plastic inlay against ultraviolet light, contamination, soiling and mechanical damage (see Fig. 2). A boron admixture in the plastic inlay reduces the detection sensitivity of the glass to thermal neutrons. Thus the total dose from quantum radiation and thermal neutrons is recorded in terms of dose equivalence with a single glass. So far most practical experience has been gained with this combined spherical dosimeter.[5]

Figure 3 shows the energy dependence of dose response for this dosimeter; this has been determined for radiation incidence directions with maximum and minimum measured value indication (see Table 1). The direction-dependence for various quantum energies is shown in Fig. 4.

TABLE 1   Energy and direction dependence of different capsule

	glass 1 mm Cd	glass 1 mm Cd conical holes	glass plastic sphere 2 mm Sn conical holes
Average energy dependence			
above 45 keV	—	$\pm 29\%$	$\pm 8\%$
87 keV	$\pm 32\%$	$\pm 10\%$	$\pm 6\%$
Direction dependence			
at 45 keV	—	$\pm 37\%$	$\pm 14\%$
87 keV	$\pm 24\%$	$\pm 30\%$	$\pm 8\%$
150 keV	$\pm 10\%$	$\pm 16\%$	$\pm 3\%$
Energy and direction dependence			
above 45 keV	—	$\pm 56\%$	$\pm 18\%$
87 keV	$\pm 42\%$	$\pm 30\%$	$\pm 8\%$

The spherical dosimeter may be changed to give a reading directly proportional to the absorbed dose in various critical organs by changing the energy-compensation filters. Such a spherical dosimeter (1.2 mm Sn and 85% covered surface) in conjunction with an Alderson man-phantom,

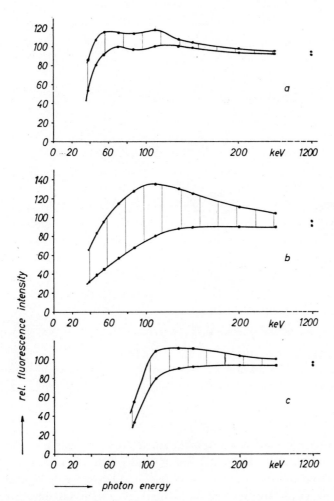

FIGURE 3. The dependence of the relative fluorescence intensity of the Yokota glass (8 × 8 × 4.7 mm³) in various dosimeter casings upon gamma radiation energy for radiation-incidence direction with maximum and minimum dose indication   (a) spherical casing   (b) right-angled casing of 1 mm Cd with conical holes   (c) casing made of 1 mm Cd

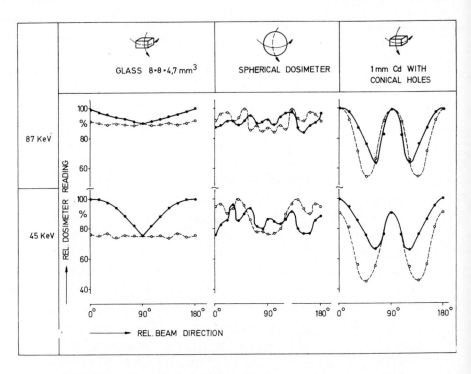

FIGURE 4 The dependence on radiation incidence of the relative fluorescence indication of a Yokota glass ($8 \times 8 \times 4.7$ mm³) in various casings and exposed to quantum radiation of energy 45 keV and 87 keV

measures directly—for at least frontal radiation incidence from the forward half of room—the absorbed dose in the gonads and bone marrow independent (within $\pm 15\%$) of energy in the energy range from 50 keV to 1.2 MeV.[6] (Fig. 5). From the dosimeter reading one can derive the desired absorbed dose in the testes, ovaries and bone marrow considering an energy-independent conversion factor.

A combined double dosimeter (2-mm Sn or 2-mm plastic filter) achieves with the total measured value of both glasses ($F_{Sn} + 0.15F_P$) within $\pm 20\%$.[7] An improvement in measuring technique has led to an energy-independence in the range above 40 keV, within less than $\pm 5\%$.[8]

The energy independence and direction independence achieved so far seems to be adequate in the entire energy range for the purpose of practical radiation protection.

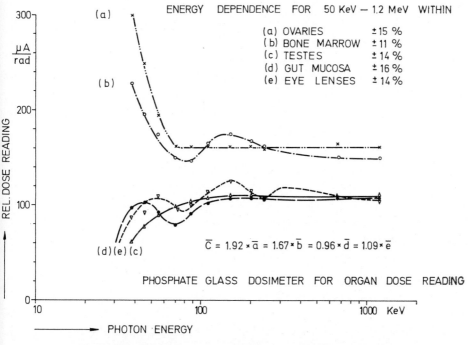

FIGURE 5   Phosphate glass dosimeter for organ dose reading

2.3.2   *Energy range under 40 keV*

A combined double dosimeter with 1-mm plastic and 0.06 mm Cu[15] achieves an energy independence of within $\pm 20\%$ for low energy quantum radiation in the range 15 to 40 keV, when the difference in measured values ($F_P -$ $1.1F_{Cu}$) is used (see Fig. 6). In this case the component of dose from high energy quantum radiation and the possible component of dose from beta radiation or thermal neutrons resulting from the difference are not taken into account. The dose measurement is practically direction independent for directions of incidence of $\pm 60°$ (in relation to the normal from dosimeter axis). The distance between both glasses and the attachment of the glasses to the casing are such as to facilitate semi-automatic evaluation (see Fig. 7). Measurement of measured value difference has the advantage of determining the dose independent of radiation energy and of determining the component of dose from quantum radiation with energy below 40 keV. In combination with the spherical dosimeter the radiation quality can also be ascertained (see Fig. 8).

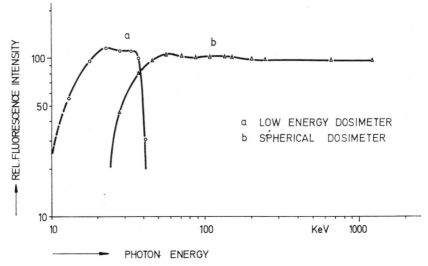

FIGURE 6 The energy dependence of a double dosimeter for low-energy X-radiation measurement (double dosimeter measured value 0.8) F_P — 1.1 F_{Cu} (b) spherical dosimeter. F_P — Fluorescence intensity of a Yokota glass in a 1 mm plastic filter F_{Cu} — Fluorescence intensity of a Yokota glass in 0.06 mm copper filter

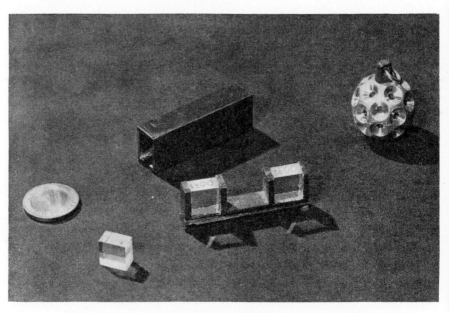

FIGURE 7 The double dosimeter arrangement for measurement of low-energy X-radiation

A combined multiple-dosimeter (three glasses with Sn, Al and plastic filters) achieves energy-independence of within $\pm 15\%$ in the energy range 25 keV to 1.2 MeV.[8]

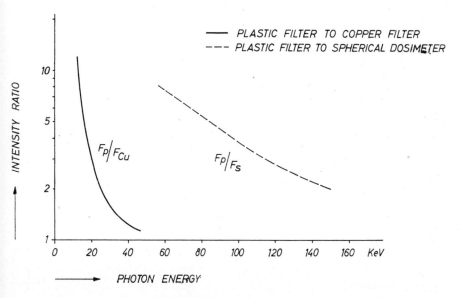

FIGURE 8   The determination of radiation quality from the fluorescence intensities of three glasses which are carried in a combined triple dosimeter (spherical dosimeter and double dosimeter) F_S — glass in spherical casing F_P — glass in plastic filter F_{Cu} — glass in Cu filter (0.06 mm)

2.3.3   *Accident dosimeter for quantum radiation*

The requirements which a dosimeter has to fulfil in the special conditions of an accident are some what different from those in routine monitoring. In this case, the lower detection limit can be higher and the energy range to be detected can be above 80 keV. The directional dependence of single casings can also be greater. For rapid and more reliable use, only single dosimeters can be considered in practice. For military and civil defence purposes several casings have been developed, some of which have air-tight locks, a magnetic lock aperture together with identification marks. In many cases these dosimeters are carried as supplementary dosimeters for film badges. In particular, small glass rods are used in simply designed casings. The first major

36*

accident dosimeter developed by the US Naval Research Laboratory (Type BP-60 Size $19 \times 19 \times 4.7 \text{ mm}^3$) has a lead filter with a central hole to compensate for energy dependence above 80 keV. Developments in other countries led to similar glasses and casings. The casing consists of, for example, a lead filter 1.4 mm thick with tapered apertures on all sides and achieves energy independence within $\pm 20\%$ above about 70 keV.[9]

An accident dosimeter with small glass rods (1 mm diameter and 6 mm long) of the type carried in the Oak Ridge badge dosimeter has copper, lead and teflon filters. For quantum energies above 115 keV the energy dependence of the dosimeter amounts to $\pm 30\%$.[10] With a glass rod in a 0.25 mm thick gold casing, an energy-independence of within $\pm 15\%$ is achieved in the energy range from 70 keV to 1.2 MeV; with additional apertures of 0.4 mm diameter, an energy-independence of within $\pm 5\%$ is achieved in the energy range from 47 keV to 1.2 MeV.[8]

If the glasses are not marked, routine evaluation of large numbers of micro-rods is more difficult. Furthermore, non-reproducible positioning of the micro-rods when measuring floirexcence also leads to rather serious measuring errors (about $\pm 6\%$).

Larger glass rods (French glass, 3.7 mm diameter and 6 mm long) are inserted on cylindrical tantalum casings, whose metal halves have a symmetrical cylindrical aperture and have holes bored in the front surfaces.[11,12] Such a dosimeter is energy-independent within $\pm 20\%$ in the energy range above 50 keV.

A dosimeter with a Yokota glass ($15 \times 6 \times 1.5 \text{ mm}^3$) designed for civil defence application, is combined with an identification tag to which it is always attached even during measurement. The glass is sealed in a casing which is air-tight and dust-proof and has a magnetic lock.[13]

The special accident dosimeters described above have been used so far to supplement other dosimeters which are not able to measure large doses. It is, of course, unnecessary to carry such accident dosimeters in routine personnel monitors containing glass dosimeters because of the high range (up to 3000 R) already provided by the glass dosimeters.

2.4 Evaluation equipment

2.4.1 *Measuring methods*

The evaluation instruments essentially contain the optical fluorescence, electronic amplification and indication components. The optical component consists of (a) the ultra-violet light source (usually a high-pressure mercury lamp); (b) the measurement chamber with the glass in its holder and lens combinations for optical filtering and dispersion of the stimulating and fluorescent light; and (c) the photomultiplier for detection of fluorescent light (see Fig. 9).

The optical light-path of the stimulating light is arranged, with advantage, vertically in relation to the optical light-path of the fluorescent light to be measured. This offers various possibilities, according to the shape of the glass, for mounting the glass and stimulating fluorescence.

Several measuring instruments have been developed commercially, each designed for a particular type and size of glass and for the special application for which the dosimeter is to be used. Early measuring instruments were designed exclusively for measuring high exposures above 10 R and were therefore insensitive and of rather simple design. Instruments have also been developed for the micro-dosimeters which are used as accident dosimeters in routine personnel monitors. Battery-operated evaluation instruments for major-accident dosimeters use arc-discharge tubes or flash tubes instead of a mercury lamp. The development of Yokota glass with a low preliminary dose and high sensitivity required more sensitive evaluation equipment. Such equipment was made by the firm Toshiba, Japan, and has been improved in the course of the years; it is now available in various designs. One may hope that the increasing use of phosphate glasses for routine personnel monitoring may lead to various new and improved instruments which may also be suitable for semi-automatic evaluation.

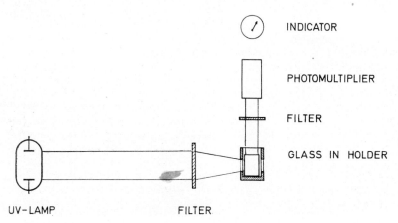

INDICATOR

PHOTOMULTIPLIER

FILTER

GLASS IN HOLDER

UV-LAMP   FILTER

FIGURE 9   Schematic diagram for evaluation equipment for phosphate
glass dosimeters

2.4.2 *Low-dose evaluation equipment*

The measurement of low doses gives rise to special requirements with regard to the design of the glass mounting, the reproducibility of the position of the glass in the stimulating light and the filtering out of the fluorescent light in the optical light-path.

The stimulating light is collimated by a lens and baffle combination in such a way that it impinges only on the glass and thus produces no scattered radiation in the glass mounting (see Fig. 7). To secure slight light scattering and good measuring sensitivity, it is desirable that the glass be in a position in the stimulated light which leads to a low surface-volume ratio for the part of the glass which is stimulated to fluorescence. Special care must be taken for the stabilization of the photomultiplier high voltage and the voltage of the mercury lamp. The need to measure low currents makes it necessary to compensate for the dark current in the photomultiplier by an additional voltage. With the first Toshiba instruments, this could be done only with a

FIGURE 10 The double dosimeter arrangement for measurement of low-energy quantum radiation

battery-voltage, but with the newer types of instruments it is possible with mains-powered direct voltage.

The first evaluation instruments were improved by various users, particularly with regard to voltage stabilization, measuring sensitivity and the mechanical control of the glass mounting in the measurement chamber (see, for example, Ref. 14).

Instead of a direct measurement of the anode current, a zero balance by means of a potentiometer in the entire dose range offers, with the new type of instruments, the advantage of uniform accuracy in readings. Long-term variations in voltage, changes in the candle-power of the mercury lamp and changes in photomultiplier amplification are compensated for by calibration with reference glasses. In all these instruments the measuring chamber and the manual glass inlet are similar in design. In measuring, the individual glass must be inserted manually into the holder and introduced into the measuring chamber together with the holder (see Fig. 10).

2.4.3 *High-dose measuring instruments*

The sensitive Toshiba instrument is also suitable for high-dose measurements; with a different glass mounting, glass of different dimensions ($6 \times 6 \times 3$ mm^3 or 1 mm diameter $\times 6$ mm) can be measured. For individual dosimetry, several small mains-operated and battery-operated evaluation instruments are offered at prices between \$400 and \$2000 (see Table 2). They were developed specially for the Schulman glass DT-60/PD or for micro-rods (1 mm diameter and 6 mm long). The best evaluation instruments of this kind make it possible to determine exposures above 1 R.

2.4.4 *Automatic evaluation equipment*

Up to now no commercial instruments have been made available which can semi-automatically or automatically evaluate a large number of sensitive or intensive glass dosimeters. The measuring chambers are not so suitable for the insertion of a semi-automatic glass inlet in the available evaluation instruments because of their design.

The operating process could be made automatic by:

a) Automatically opening the capsule before measuring or sealing if after measuring;

b) Automatically inserting the glass in the measuring position; and

c) Automatically recording the dose test value and, if possible, the glass marking with printed or magnetic tape storage.

TABLE 2 Commercially available glass dosimeter readers (21)

No.	Manufacturer	Type Name	Main Application	Glass Sort	Dose Range (R gamma)	Reading	Power Supply	Price
1	Bausch and Lomb Rochester, N. Y.	Microdosimeter Reader	Biological Dosimetry	Fluorods 1 × 6 rods (15 × 6 × 1.55 mm)	$10-10^4$	Pointer Instrum.	Mains	DM 7400 $ 1230
2	Carbonisation Entreprise et Ceramique, Montrouge/Seine		Military Dosimetry	C.E.C. Glass	about $1-10^3$	Pointer Instrum.	Battery	about DM 2000
3	Speciality Electronics, Developm. Corp., Syosset, N. Y.	Dosimeter Reader 95 A	Military and Civil Defense Dosimetry	Schulman Glass DT-60 B/PD	10-600	Pointer Instrum.	Mains	DM 3630
4	Speciality Electronics, Developm. Corp., Syosset, N. Y.	Computer-Indicator CP-263/PD	Military and Civil Defense Dosimetry	Schulman Glass DT-60/B/PD	10-600	Pointer Instrum.	Battery	
5	R. A. Stephen and Co. Mitcham, Engl.	Dosimeter Reader	Military and Civil Defense Dosimetry	Schulman Glass DT-60 B/PD	$10-10^3$	Pointer Instrum.	Mains	about DM 5000
6	Tokyo Shibaura Electr. Co. (Toshiba) Tokyo, Japan	Fluoro-Glass Dosimeter FD-5	Pers. Dosimetry, special application	Yokota Glasses of different dimensions	$0.01-10^4$	Pointer Instrum.	Mains	about DM 15000
7	Total KG, Ladenburg, Germany		Milit. and Civil Defense, Dosim.	Yokota or C.E.C. Glass	about $1-10^3$	Pointer Instrum.	Battery	
8	G. K. Turner, Assoc. Palo Alto, Calif.	Radiation Dosim. Reader	Biological Dosimetry	Fluorods 1 × 6 rods (15 × 6 × 1,5mm)	$10-10^4$	Pointer Instrum.	Mains	$ 1160

For this purpose, casings are particularly suitable in which the previously washed glass is hermetically sealed (elimination of the washing process). The reading of the glass marking can be carried out on a part of the casing which is connected with the glass substructure.[15] If the measuring process were automatic, it would permit the rapid evaluation of a large number of glasses, the simultaneous measurement of two or more glasses and the automatic reading of the test-value difference or the test-value ratio.

2.4.5 *Reference standards*

Reference glasses are used to calibrate the evaluation equipment. These are phosphate glasses with the same base in which, however, the silver has been replaced by manganese or samarium. With ultra-violet stimulation such glasses show the same fluorescent light distribution as irradiated silver-activated metaphosphate glasses. With reference glasses, the fluorescence intensity is not altered by moisture, temperature or external radiation. They can therefore be used as a calibration standard over fairly long periods of time.

2.4.6 *Outlook*

A new evaluation method[22] seems to make it possible to measure depth dose distribution, radiation energy and radiation incidence direction with a single phosphate glass. Fluorescence intensity is measured as a function of the space coordinates in the glass brick by means of a continuously scanning device.

Another development may lead to the possibility of evaluating doses as low as 1 mR. By excitation of the fluorescence with very short light pulses, one is able to measure the decay time of the fluorescence flash. It has been shown[23] that the decay of the radiation induced fluorescence is much longer (3 μsec) than that of the predose or the dirt components (0,3 μsec).

Thus, these components can be separated by suitable electronic pulse shape discrimination. The result is the measurement of very low doses without even the necessity of washing the glasses.

2.5 Dose evaluation

2.5.1 *Washing the glass*

For measuring purposes the dosimeter glass must be completely clean. Fingerprints, dust, moisture or oil or detergent residue on the surface of the glass can, during evaluation, lead to additional fluorescence radiation through stimulation or scattering or reduce the UV light through absorption. This can falsify in an irreproducible manner the measurement of the pre-dose and the actual dose and, above all with low doses, lead to serious errors in measurement. The glass should therefore be washed before use as a matter of routine. In addition to the glass, the glass holder and baffles in the evaluation equipment must be clean and should only be handled with forceps.

During washing, the dirt is removed from the surface with grease solvents (chemical washing agents, detergents), the washing agent is washed off and the glass is thoroughly dried. Accordingly, it is necessary to clean the glass in three stages with acetone, distilled water and alcohol.[16-18] The glass can also be treated for a short time in a washing agent solution with ultrasonics and then rinsed out with distilled water and alcohol. When the glass is very dirty, it must be treated for a rather long time (about 24 hours) with detergents or chromosulphuric acid, and then rinsed in running water. In this case it is desirable to examine the surface visually with a magnifying glass or under microscope in order to determine whether the washing has been effective. In difficult cases, it is advisable to dab or wipe off the surface with a cloth soaked in the washing agent.

In the case of a large number of glasses, the washing process must also be fast, effective and reproducible; for this reason it is essential to select the best possible combination of washing and rinsing agents. The ability of small residues of the washing agent left on the glass surface to produce fluorescence and thus to affect the measurement of the pre-dose or of low doses, has been investigated for many washing agents by means of their fluorescence spectrum and the dose measurement.[18] Watery solutions of detergents are in fact found to have a much higher degree of self-fluorescence, but they clean the soiled areas more effectively and can be more easily removed from the surface after the actual washing than chemical cleansing agents. For rinsing ethyl-alcohol is preferable to methanol. An example of a standard washing process for the routine evaluation of a large number of glasses is given below:

1) Ultrasonics treatment in 1 % solution of detergents (2 minutes);

2) Rinsing in running water (2 minutes);

3) Noistening in distilled water ($\frac{1}{2}$ minute); and

4) Moistening in alcohol ($\frac{1}{2}$ minute) and subsequent drying of glasses in dust-free surroundings.

This washing process should also be followed in the order mentioned when new glasses or glasses which appear to be clean but have been in storage for a rather long time, are to be measured. After washing, care must be taken to ensure that the glasses to be measured do not get dusty.

For routine operation, it is desirable to have washing racks for about every 100 glasses. The glasses should be placed in the racks at some distance from one another so that they are not scratched during washing (see Fig. 11). For washing or drying the glasses, semi-automatic equipment employing vacuum or air-flow can be used.[17] During washing or drying the glasses,

FIGURE 11   Frame for simultaneously washing of about 100 glasses

particular care should be taken to ensure that the glass surfaces through which the stimulating light enters or the fluorescent light emerges do not touch any surface. The orientation of the glass during washing should be selected according to the orientation of the glass in the evaluation equipment (see Fig. 12).

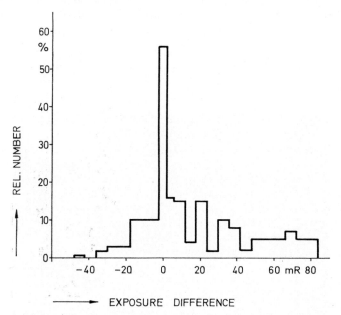

FIGURE 12   The measured value difference with 120 glasses when during the second measurement of the same glass, a residue of washing agents appears on the inlet and outlet surfaces as a result of wrong arrangement of the glass during washing

2.5.2   *Measurement*

The term "measurement" comprise all those working processes ranging from insertion of the glass in the holder to recording the result of the measurement, i.e. insertion of the glass in the holder, introduction of the holder into the light-path of the reader, observation of the scale reading, recording the data in prescribed forms, removal of the holder from the instrument and removal of the glass from the holder. These working processes are simplified, depending on the design of the evaluation equipment or the possibility of semi-automatic evaluation.

The instrument may give the fluorescence intensity F as a scale reading or as current measured in microamperes and the dose may be obtained from a calibration curve relating fluorescence intensity and dose ($D = aF$) or the instrument may be calibrated to give the dose directly.

In either case the original calibration must be made with irradiated standard glasses. A continuous secondary calibration of the reader, reproducible over fairly long periods, may be made using reference glasses which indicate a known measured value, since the reference glasses do not add up any radiation dose or change their measured value over long periods and their measured value cannot be erased (see Sec. 2.4.5).

Such a check with reference glasses should be carried out before commencing measurements and from time to time during use of the instrument. This check should include verification of zero-balance (dark current compensation) with the glass holder but without glass and adjustment of the

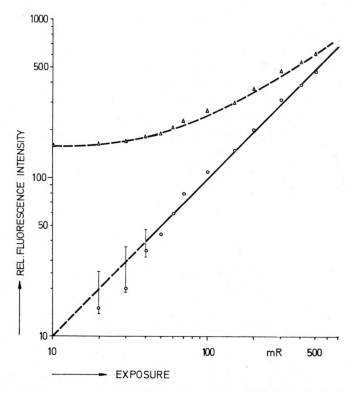

FIGURE 13   The variation of the fluorescence intensity of Yokota glass with exposure in the range below 1 R   *Δ-Δ-Δ-Δ-Δ* measured value incl. predose   0-0-0-0-0 measured value after subtracting predose

photomultiplier working-point for a specified measured value within the measurement range.

For routine evaluation, it is advantageous to measure glasses first of all in the sensitive measuring range (e.g. exposures from 10 mR to 1 R); the few glasses with higher measured values can be measured later in the less sensitive measuring range after appropriate calibration. In the case of evaluation after an accident, this procedure may be reversed.

To detect low doses, the pre-dose must be substracted from the post-irradiation measured value (see Fig. 13). For this purpose the glass must be marked with identification markings after the pre-dose is measured and recorded.

2.5.3   *Identification of glasses*

The glasses and/or the casings in which they are used must have suitable identification markings for proper assignment of doses to monitored individuals. The marking should be legible and should not be destroyed during washing. Glasses of adequate size could be marked on a non-polished lateral surface. Combinations of numbers or of letters are suitable for this purpose. For example, on a glass measuring $8 \times 8 \times 4.7 \, mm^3$, four digit numbers can be engraved or written by pencil. If the glass is attached inseparably to a part of the casing, the marking may with advantage be made on the casing. Marking of this kind is essential for automatic evaluation during which the marking and the measured value of the dosimeter are read off and automatically recorded.

2.5.4   *Erasing of measured values and re-use of glasses*

In order to have a lower detection limit of about 40 mR, the measured value must be erased after an accumulated exposure of 1–2 R has been reached, since the measuring error in this range will be about 40 mR. For routine dosimetry, it is desirable that the erasing procedure reproduces the original pre-dose, does not change the dose sensitivity of the glass due to heat treatment and does not produce any visible change in the glass or its surface characteristics.

A short-term temperature increase to 250–400°C leads in all types of glasses to a reduction of the measured value.[20] The extent to which the measured value is erased depends, in a different manner, on the type of glass, the temperature, the period of heat treatment and the amount of dose to be erased. Thus for each type of glass optimum temperature and heat treatment period must be determined experimentally. With Yokota glasses exposed to below 100 R, the measured values are reduced to pre-dose levels after heat treatment at 400°C for about 20 minutes. With a temperature below 350°C, an effective reduction in the measured value is achieved after heat treatment for a few hours but the original pre-dose is no longer obtained. Repeated irradiation of the glass with subsequent erasing of the measured value at 400°C does not lead, even after annealing eight times, to any significant change in dose sensitivity. Thus a heat treatment temperature of 400°C seems desirable in routine dosimetry.

After long periods of heat treatment, i.e., with more frequent erasings, there is generally an increase of about 2 microamperes (equivalent to about 20 mR) for one hour of heat treatment in the case of Yokota glasses. After a longer period of heat treatment (about 15 hours) the surface of the glass may become opalescent.

2.5.5 *Measurement accuracy and relaibility*

2.5.5.1 *Possible sources of error*—The measurement accuracy will depend upon whether the glass dosimeter is used for laboratory measurements, routine monitoring of personnel over a short period of time (e.g. three months) or as a long-term monitor over a period of one year. The influences of the various measuring errors will vary in each case, being smallest when the glass dosimeter is used for laboratory measurements and largest when it is used as a long-term monitor.

When phosphate glasses are used particularly for measurement of low doses, the following sources of error must be recognized and taken into account:
(1) slight differences in dose sensitivity among individual glass dosimeters; (2) the combined error involved in determining the difference between the post-irradiation measured value and the pre-dose; (3) soiling which may give rise to the mistaken impression that small doses are present; (4) the poor measuring accuracy of evaluating instruments in the low dose range; and (5) long-term fading of the RPL and the long-term drift in measuring instruments.

The effects of such errors can, in part, be determined separately for a particular type of glass and a given measuring instrument as follows:

2.5.5.2 *Errors in measuring instrument alone*—This may be determined from the deviations of measured values in multiple measurements with the

Solid state dosimetry

same glass. The accuracy in readings and the short-term fluctuations in measuring instrument caused by voltage fluctuations in the grid or fluctuations in photomultiplier dark current, amount to less than ± 5 mR with the usual measuring instruments. Long-term instability may result from wear and tear of the reference glasses and the glass-holder.

2.5.5.3 *Errors from varying dose sensitivity of different glasses*—Within manufacturing tolerance, variations in dimensions of glass and inhomogeneities within the glass may lead to varying dose sensitivities even when the composition of the glass is uniform. The distribution of measured values of 100 glasses ($8 \times 8 \times 4.7$ mm³) exposed to 1 R, is given in Fig. 14. Table 3 gives the standard deviation of measurements made on glasses irradiated with low doses. In routine personnel monitoring, less favourable values are obtained due to variations in casings and irradiation conditions.

TABLE 3   Standard deviation of $8 \times 8 \times 4.7$ mm³ glass*[8]

Exposure mR	Standard Deviation %
10	4
15	3,5
25	3
50	1,5
>150	1,0

* Laboratory Condition

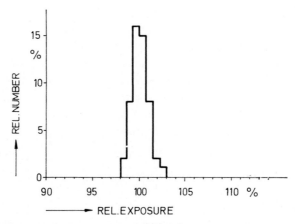

FIGURE 14   Relative accuracy after deduction of predose of 52 Yokota glasses exposed to 1.6 R

2.5.5.4 *Effects of error from soiling*—Unsatisfactory washing or the residues of washing agents on the surfaces of glasses may yield with the same glasses, doses varying in magnitude after repeated washing. The deviation in pre-doses after 100 glasses have been washed and measured twice is given in Fig. 15.

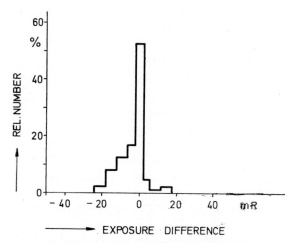

FIGURE 15 Histogram showing the distribution of measured values of 120 Yokota glasses after each glass is washed twice

2.5.5.5 *Effects of errors resulting from use over long periods*—In order to determine the long-term accuracy, several-dosimeters must be used at the same location for a rather long period of time in order to eliminate local heterogeneities in the radiation field. The distribution of measured values in pairs of dosimeters (50 pairs in all) which were set up in the open air to monitor the environment over a period of three months is shown in Fig. 16. Since all the various sources of error are taken into account, these values will indicate the reliability or reproducibility of measurements in the low dose range over long periods of time.

2.5.5.6 *Total error in routine personnel monitoring*—By reproducibility is meant the limit of error in dose measurements arising from all the various sources of error. The reproducibility of dose determination in routine personnel monitoring was ascertained from deviation of measured values of a pair of glasses in spherical casings carried at the same time by the same individual. Although dissimilar irradiation conditions may be shown in different cases, the pairs of dosimeters showed an agreement in measured values within $\pm 5\%$ in about 60% of the cases (Fig. 17).[5] Since different radiation energies and directions of incidence of the radiation were found in these practical tests, a larger number of sources of error were involved

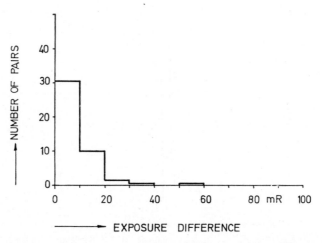

FIGURE 16   Histogram showing the distribution of the difference in measured values of pairs of glasses (50 pairs) exposed in spherical casing at the same location to environmental radiation for a period of three months

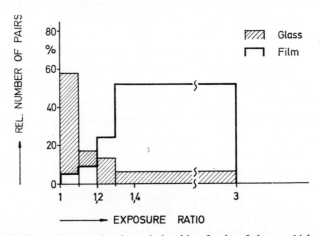

FIGURE 17   Measured value relationship of pairs of glasses which were carried in the spherical casing, together with two film dosimeters, by the same person on the same part of the body in monthly routine monitoring (exposure range 40 mR to 5 R) (measured value after subtraction of predose)

than in laboratory measurements or in environmental monitoring. The results can, therefore, serve as a realistic basis for determining the measuring accuracy which can be achieved during routine personnel monitoring.

2.6 Organization of monitoring service

2.6.1 *General*

Because of the favourable long-term properties of glass, a monitoring period of three months (instead of a shorter period of one month or less) could be introduced. Glass dosimeters whose pre-doses have been determined may be issued to personnel from a central facility at an appropriate time before the end of the monitoring period. The used dosimeters could then be collected and sent to the central facility for dose measurement. The glasses received at the central facility for dose evaluation do not need heat treatment to stabilize the measured value. If the glasses show exposures of the order of a few roentgens, it is necessary to erase the measured value only if the glass is to be used for monitoring exposures over a quarterly period and is not intended to be used as a long-term monitor for a period of one year.

Two glasses can be used in rotation to add doses of the same individual over a number of years. Unused dosimeters may be left in the custody of the individual (or organization) and used only in case of necessity. The central facility could then be informed of the period during which the dosimeter was used. The organization of paper work involved in monitoring (dose indexing and statistical analysis) is greatly facilitated if each user is always provided with the same dosimeter, so that the sequence of names of the monitored individuals and their identification numbers could in general remain unchanged. It is thus desirable, contrary to general practice, that no distinction is made between individuals who are regularly monitored and those who are temporarily monitored. In principle a person can be provided with a dosimeter for a year, even if he is only occasionally engaged in work in a radiation area during each monitoring period.

There may arise some problems in ensuring that the glass is used in the same casing. Confusion can be avoided if the numbers on the glass and the casing are compared during packing and unpacking. The best solution, however, is to ensure that the dosimeter glass and glass casing are firmly connected to each other. It will be of some disadvantage to send the complete dosimeter (instead of simply the glass) because of the additional space and weight in packing them and the higher costs involved in mailing. If a large number of dosimeters is involved, special packing is advisable.

37*

In case of an accident, the glass dosimeters can be evaluated at once on-site with simple portable instruments without adversely affecting more accurate evaluation at the central facility. This will eliminate loss of time resulting from possibility the long period required for sending the dosimeters to the measuring centre and getting back the results.

2.6.2   *Working procedure*

This assessment relates to the routine evaluation with simple laboratory instruments and does not take into account semi-automatic or fully automatic evaluation instruments. The assessment of the automatic dose evaluation involves additional considerations as regards the extent to which it is worthwhile is small measuring centres, the amount of time saved and the saving in personnel.

The evaluation of glass dosimeters requires relatively smaller space and comparatively fewer personnel. In the actual evaluation (excluding indexing and dispatch of the dosimeters) the following procedures must be adopted:

The dosimeters must be arranged on a shelf according to the user or in numerical order;

The glass must be unpacked from the casing and inserted in the washing-frame in the order indicated;

The glass must be washed and then dried;

The glass must be measured in the order indicated (insertion of the glass in the holder and into the evaluation instrument, recording the measured value, removal of the glass);

Dose determination (calibration, conversion, subtraction of pre-dose); and

The glass must be packed in the casing (checking to ensure that the numbering of the glass and casing agree).

The washing can be omitted if the glass is in an airtight and dustproof casing. The period required for measurement, particularly the insertion of the glass, can also be reduced by improving the evaluation equipment.

With the simplest type of evaluation instruments about 100–200 glasses can be measured per hour by trained staff. In routine evaluation the separate jobs can be done by different people who relieve each other several times at short intervals, i.e. during the working day, in accordance with the work-plan.

In the evaluation described, two or three people per evaluation instrument and working day can, for example, evaluate 1000 glasses. The maximum capacity based on the equipment is about 20,000 evaluations per month. To carry out the above tasks properly, including indexing and dispatch, some six workers will be required.

In addition dosimeters which have been carried by individuals engaged in work with open radioactive substances must be checked for contamination. In this case it is recommended that the dosimeter should, while being used, be covered in a polyethylene envelope, which protects the casing itself from contamination and can be checked more easily for surface contamination (beta activity in a methane flow-counter or with an end-window GM counter.)

The glasses should be washed and measured in a dust-free, if possible air-conditioned, draft-free measuring room. The glasses can be dispatched and unpacked in an adjoining room.

2.6.3 *Working period*

In assessing the working period of a centre for evaluating routine dosimeters three different cases are taken into account:

a) The routine evaluation of a large quantity of glasses at the end of the prescribed monitoring period (about 5000–50,000 glasses per month);

b) The evaluation of individual dosimeters following an accident within the monitoring period (minimum period); and

c) The fastest possible evaluation of a large quantity of dosimeters following an accident (maximum capacity and minimum period).

The net working times for individual evaluation and the evaluation of 1000 glasses are shown in Table 4. It is estimated that in a working day 100 glasses can be measured by one person in an hour. Thus in routine evaluation most of the work is devoted to packing and unpacking the glasses and to dose measurement and determination, and a very small amount of time is devoted to washing. A rationalization of the evaluation is achieved when the measuring process leads, through suitable calibration, to a direct dose indication, when the casing is automatically opened (glass combined with capsule), when the glass is semi-automatically measured and when the measured, including the dosimeter number, is automatically recorded.

Thus the working time required for a single measurement is about 7 minutes and for the evaluation of 5000 glasses about 110 hours.

It can be assumed that the fastest possible evaluation of dosimeters following an accident will be made at a maximum rate of about 200 glasses per hour in the case of a single measuring centre employing two persons and using

TABLE 4   Working time for the evaluation of phosphate glass dosimeters

Operation	Time for 1 Glass	Time for 1000 Glasses
Unpacking Arranging, Placing into frames	15 sec	4 h 10 min
Washing		
Ultrason	2 min	
running water	2 min	
Alcohol rinsing	30 sec	1 h
distilled water	30 sec	
drying	60 sec	
Measuring		
Insertion of glass		
Measurement of glass		
Registration of measured value		
Taking glass out of reader	30 sec	10 h
Dose determination	10 sec	3 h
Calibration	—	
Packing	15 sec	4 h
Working Time	ca. 7 min	ca. 22 h

an evaluation instrument. With accident dosimeters, which are already constructed with dust-free casings and a magnetic lock, the glass combined with the identification mark need only be inserted in the measuring instrument for a short time in order to make an evaluation. Thus the maximum capacity per hour and evaluation instrument may then be higher.

2.6.4 *Cost*

In evaluating the costs for a personnel monitoring service using glass dosimeters, local variables such as costs of space and salaries of staff must be taken into account. The following example will serve to illustrate the cost involved in setting up an evaluation centre. The following capital equipment and consumable supplies (amounting to about $5000) will be required: one measuring instrument for routine evaluation, reference glasses for calibration, ultrasonic washing equipment, about 20 frames for washing and drying glasses, one muffle furnace with temperature control for erasing measured values, and expendable supplies such as washing agents etc.

If 33% of the cost of purchasing the above items is written off by the evaluation centre, this will leave a net cost of $0.2 per evaluation with three persons and a monthly capacity of 10,000 glasses. To this must be added the cost of despatch and indexing. The user of the dosimeter service must also pay the cost of two glasses and casings per person monitored plus a 10% supplement. The annual cost of monitoring one person thus amounts to about $3 for monthly evaluation and about $1.6 for three monthly evaluation.

References

1. J. H. Schulman *et al.*, "Dosimetry of *X*-rays by radiophotoluminescence", *J. Appl. Phys.* **22**, p. 1479 (1951). J. H. Schulman and H. W. Etzel, "Small volume dosimeter for *X*-rays and *γ*-rays", *Science* **118**, p. 184 (1953).
2. R. J. Ginther and J. H. Schulman, "New glass dosimetry is less energy independent", *Nucleonics* **11**, p. 52 (1953).
3. K. Becker, "Phosphatglasdosimeter für die Routineüberwachung in kerntechnischen Anlagen", *Nukleonik* **5**, p. 154 (1963).
4. R. Maushart and E. Piesch, "A photoluminescent personnel dosimeter with spherical case for nergy and direction independent dose measurements", Paper No. 21 presented at the Intern Symp. on Dosimetry of Irradiat. from Extern. Sources, Paris (1964).
5. E. Piesch, "Anforderungen an Personendosimeter und deren Zuverlässigkeit für rechtserhebliche Strahlenschutzmessungen" Vortrag ESG-Tagung Jülich (1966).
6. R. Maushart and E. Piesch, "Health physics dosimeter system for the improved measurement of absorbed dose", Paper No. 109 1st Congr. I.R.P.A., Rome, 6–10-September (1966).
7. I. Miyanaga and H. Yamamoto, "Studies on silver-activated metaphosphate glass as a personnel monitoring dosimeter", *Health Physics* **9**, p. 965 (1963).
8. R. Yokota and S. Nakajima, "Recent improvements in radiophotoluminescence dosimetry", Paper presented in *Intern. Symp. Luminesc. Dosimetry*, Stanford (1965).
9. J. H. Schulman, W. Shurcliff, R. J. Ginther and F. H. Attix, "Radiophotoluminescence dosimetry system of the US Navy", *Nucleonics* **11**, p. 52 (1953).
10. W. T. Thornton, D. M. Davis and E. D. Gupton, *"The ORNL badge dosimeter and its personnel monitoring applications"*, ORNL-3126 (1961).
11. H. Francois, Y. Bourbigot, H. A. Grand-Clement, G. Portal, and G. Soudain, "Dosimetrie personelle à fonctions multiples adapté à la dosimetrie des fortes irradiations accidentelles". Personnel dosimetry for radiation accidents. *Proc. of a Symposium of the IAEA, Vienna*, p. 319 (1965).

12. "Les lumidosimetres radiophotoluminescents" (Technical Report of Carbonisation Entreprise et Ceramique, Montrouge/France).
13. H. J. Hardt, "The development of an individual dosimeter for measurement of high level radiation doses" *Proc. of a symposium*, IAEA Vienna, p. 127 (1965).
14. C. K. Menkes, "Modification of the Toshiba FGD-313 glass dosimeter reader to improve accuracy and reproducibility", *Health Physics* **12**, p. 852 (1966).
15. R. Maushart and E. Piesch, "Phosphate glasses as routine personnel dosimeters", Paper presented at the Intern. Conf. Luminescence Dosimetry, Stanford (1965).
16. R. Yokota and S. Nakajima, "The fluoroglass dosimeter with high performance", Toshiba Review 1963 UCRL-Trans-984 (1963).
17. C. K. Menkes, "A glass dosimeter washing technique for improved reproducibility", *Health Physics* **12**, p. 429 (1966).
18. E. Piesch, "*Die Bedeutung des Waschvorganges bei der Fluoreszenzmessung von Phosphatgläsern*", Direct Information 4/66 (1966).
19. R. Maushart and E. Piesch, "Dosimetrische Eigenschaften neuerer Phosphatgläser für die Routinedosimetrie", *Atompraxis* **12**, p. 11 (1966).
20. H. Kiefer, R. Maushart and E. Piesch, "Erfahrungen mit Phosphatglasdosimetern zur Personendosimetrie", *Atompraxis* **11**, p. 88 (1965).
21. K. Becker, "Die gegenwärtige Situation in der militärischen und Zivilschutz-Personendosimetrie", *Zivilschutz* **30**, p. 56 (1966).
22. H. Kiefer and E. Piesch, "Neue Methode zur Ermittlung der Strahlenqualität und der Strahleneinfallsrichtung mit Phosphatglasdosimetern", *Atompraxis* 11/12, Direct (1967).
23. J. Kastner, D. Eggenberger, and A. Longecker, "UV. Laser Excitation for Ultra Sensitive Photoluminescent Dosimetry". *IAEA Symp. Solid-State and Chem. Radiat. Dosimetry in Med. and Biol.* No. SM-78/33, Wien (Oktober 1966).

The technical characteristics of and applications for phosphor-Teflon thermoluminescent dosimeters

BENGT BJARNGARD and DOUGLAS JONES

Controls for Radiation, Inc., Cambridge, Massachusetts USA

Abstract

Phosphor–Teflon dosimeters have been in use now for some three years. This paper describes the production technique and the physical properties of LiF, $CaF_2 : Mn$, $CaSO_4 : Mn$ and $Li_2B_4O_7 : Mn$–Teflon dosimeters. Precision at various dose levels and problems associated with reuse of the dosimeters are discussed together with fading and energy dependence. The wide range of dosimetric characteristics of these dosimeters has allowed their use in almost all branches of radiation dosimetry. Special dosimeters have been developed for application in clinical dosimetry, especially an intracavitary probe and an interstitial needle. LiF–Teflon discs are used for finger dosimetry and for personnel badge dosimetry. Special applications of very thin dosimeters, about 10 microns, illustrate the great versatility of dosimeter shape and size that is a very important capability of the phosphor–Teflon dosimeters.

1 INTRODUCTION

Phosphor–Teflon dosimeters were developed some three years ago.[1] Since this time they have found wide application in many different branches of radiation dosimetry. One of the reasons for this is that the solid and easily handled phosphor–Teflon dosimeters can be manufactured in a variety of sizes and shapes to fit particular and often difficult measuring problems. They can, furthermore, be produced in large batches with the same properties, of course within certain limits. Sensitivity variations among dosimeters of the same production batch can be made so small that individual calibration of the dosimeters is generally unnecessary. The purpose of this paper is to review the characteristics of and applications for these dosimeters and to present results on recent developments in this area.

2 MANUFACTURE

The production technique is based on a thorough mixing of phosphor powder of grain size of about 10 microns with Teflon powder. This mixture is extruded, typically as 1 mm diameter rod, or molded into bars of 5 to 15 mm diameter. The highest as 1 mm diameter rod, or molded into bars of 5 to 15 mm diameter. The highest content of phosphor per dosimeter is about 30% by weight. For higher concentrations, the mechanical properties of the dosimeter deteriorate. Furthermore, concentrations above 10% can be achieved only in a manufacturing based on molding. For extrusion, in order to prevent the extruded rod from breaking or varying in diameter, about 10% is maximum and 4% our standard.

The molded or extruded material is cut into dosimeters of the desired shape. The final step in the manufacturing process is to subject the dosimeters to a heat treatment (annealing) to eliminate possible, mechanically excited thermoluminescence and to normalize glow curves and sensitivities.

The thermoluminescent phosphors LiF, CaF_2 : Mn, $CaSO_4$: Mn and $Li_2B_4O_7$: Mn have been incorporated in Teflon in this way.

Phosphor–Teflon dosimeters have been made and investigated in two basic shapes, discs and rods. However, these have been of various dimensions and content of phosphor, as is described below. Figure 1 shows typical routinely used dosimeters in the shape of rods and discs. In addition, phosphor–Teflon tape has been fabricated by skiving the sides of a bar.

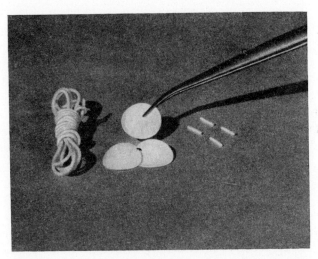

FIGURE 1.   Typical routinely used phosphor-Teflon dosimeters

3   MEASUREMENT OF THERMOLUMINESCENCE

3.1   The readout instrument

All measurements described here have been made with a Controls for Radiation Model 5100 TLD Readout Instrument. For readout in this instrument, the dosimeter is placed in a high-resistivity metal heating element. During the readout cycle, a current passes through and heats the heating element, which in turn heats the dosimeter by conduction. The thermoluminescence then emitted is detected by an EMI 6097S photomultiplier. The anode current from the phototube is integrated during about 14 seconds, starting with the dosimeter at room temperature. The heating current is disconnected about 4 seconds before the end of the integration period.

The anode current has usually been monitored as a function of time on a recorder. This curve will be referred to below as a "glow curve". The automatically integrated value corresponds to the area under the glow curve during the integration period. This value minus the value obtained in the same way in the readout of irradiated dosimeters is the quantity below called "thermoluminescence".

3.2 Heating elements

The method of heating the phosphor–Teflon dosimeters is of prime importance for the results that can be achieved. The ideal heating technique is fast and reproducible with a minimum contribution to the background from incandescence light, emitted by the hot heating element. These requirements necessitate a good thermal contact between the heating element and the dosimeter.

Temperature gradients within the dosimeter volume, while undesirable in studies of exact glow peak temperatures, can to some extent be tolerated in practical dosimetry work. Since they will result in smeared out glow curves, they can only be accepted as long as they do not cause incomplete integration of the thermoluminescence. Because of the low thermal conductivity of Teflon and the possible distortion after use of phosphor–Teflod dosimeters, these conditions become more important than in work with loose powder. Poor and irreproducible thermal contact leads to changes in the shape of the glow curves for identical dosimeters. With a measurement method, based upon the integration of the light between fixed times, this would seriously affect the precision in a group of measurements.

The main requirement on a heating element is therefore that it provides good thermal contact to the dosimeter, so that the dosimeters are heated up fast and in the same way, independent of small individual deviations from the ideal shape.

The flat disc dosimeters are best readout in a heating element which presses the dosimeter to the hot surface. The heating element used by us consists of a Nichrome strip onto which the dosimeter is pressed by a metal screen, fastened to the edges of the Nichrome. The metal screen is perforated with a 60 % open area. Another construction, which reduces the fraction of light absorbed by this cover, has a hole punched in the screen, as reported by Endres[2] for the readout of elliptically shaped LiF–Teflon dosimeters. The dosimeter is then held down along its perimeter. Still another arrangement has been used by Knight[3] who made holes in the Nichrome strip and by applying a suction pump to the underside of the Nichrome strip, held the dosimeters against the not surface. He reported improved results from this method, but it is our opinion that we can achieve similar results by the use of stiffer screen material.

Disc dosimeters of various dimensions are measured with the screen type of heating elements as are flat dosimeters of various shapes, cut from continous tape of the phosphor–Teflon material.

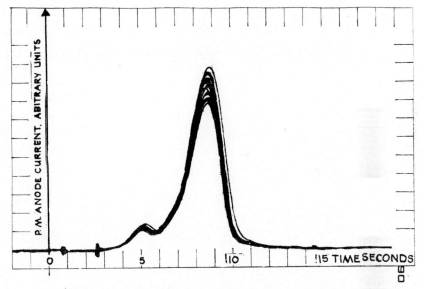

FIGURE 2. Superimposed glow curves of twenty 13 mm × 0.13 mm LiF–Teflon discs

Figure 2 shows superimposed glow curves of twenty 0.13 mm thick by 13 mm diameter LiF–Teflon discs and illustrates the highly reproducible heating cycle for these dosimeters, read out in the screen type heating element.

Dosimeters of the rod type are read out in a heating element, consisting of a strip of Nichrome, onto which are welded two metal bars. The rod dosimeter is pressed down in the space between the bars. Here, it is held in firm contact with the metal since the diameter of the bar is slightly larger and the gap between the bars is slightly narrower than the diameter of the rod dosimeter. This construction yields better results than one based on a depression in the Nichrome strip, covered with a perforated screen, which pressed the dosimeter down in a U-shaped groove.

4 VARIOUS TYPES OF PHOSPHOR–TEFLON DOSIMETERS

The thermoluminescent phosphors that have been incorporated into Teflon are LiF, $Li_2B_4O_7$: Mn, CaF_2 : Mn and $CaSO_4$: Mn. LiF has been most extensively investigated. It has been used as LiF enriched in ^7Li to 99.993 % for reduced sensitivity to thermal neutrons, LiF enriched in ^6Li to 95 % for high sensitivity to thermal neutrons and, of course, LiF with natural abundance of ^6Li (7.5 %) and ^7Li (92.5 %).

TABLE I   Dosimeter types, size and phosphor content

Basic shape	Phosphor	Dimensions (mm)	Phosphor content (% by weight)	Phosphor content (mg)
DISCS	LiF-7	13 × 0,13	28	10
		13 × 0.26	28	20
		13 × 0.4	28	30
		13 × 0.5	28	40
		8 × 0.5	5	3
		6 × 0.02	28	0.04
	CaF_2 : Mn	6 × 0.13	28	2.6
		6 × 0.4	28	8
		6 × 0.02	28	0.04
	$CaSO_4$: Mn	13 × 0.4	28	32
	$Li_2B_4O_7$: Mn	13 × 0.4	30	28
TAPE	LiF	width 25 thickness 0.4	28	23 mg/cm²
RODS	LiF-7	6 × 1	4	0.4
	LiF-6	6 × 1	4	0.4
	$Li_2B_4O_7$: Mn	6 × 1	4	0.4
LONG RODS	LiF	diameter 1	4	0.6 mg/cm
	$Li_2B_4O_7$: Mn	diameter 1	4	0.6 mg/cm

One basic limitation on the size of a dosimeter follows from the requirement that during a fixed time, the entire dosimeter volume shall be heated to a high enough temperature to release the thermoluminescence, without axceeding at the same time the crystalline melting point of Teflon at 327°C in eny part of the dosimeter.

When a phosphor with low glow peak temperature is incorporated in Teflon, the size requirements are quite flexible, since only a relatively small amount of power has to be transferred to the dosimeter to release the light. $CaSO_4$: Mn with a glow peak at only about 100°C can be incorporated into large Teflon dosimeters, and work is in progress to increase the sensitivity of $CaSO_4$: Mn–Teflon dosimeters by using larger dosimeters than the 13 mm diameter discs so far investigated. A phosphor like CaF_2 : Mn with a glow peak at 240°C is more difficult, and we have found that a CaF_2 :$_2$Mn–Teflon disc of diameter 6 mm and thickness of about 0.5 mm is a maximum size for this dosimeter. LiF and $Li_2B_4O_7$: Mn with main glow peaks at 210°C and 220°C can be used in phosphor–Teflon discs of 13 mm diameter and thicknesses up to 0.5 mm. For continuous tape, which is read out in cut pieces, similar restrictions apply.

For rod dosimeters, we have so far limited our experiments to 1 mm diameter and these use of LiF and $Li_2B_4O_7$: Mn. The length of such a 1 mm diameter rod has, in all our experiments, been 6 mm. When longer rods have been used during the irradiation, they are cut up in 6 mm pieces before readout; however, pieces up to at least 10 mm length can be easily read out.

Table I lists the types of dosimeters that have been used so far.

5   FUNDAMENTAL PROPERTIES OF THE DOSIMETERS

5.1   General

The properties of the thermoluminescent phosphors are not changed by the incorporation into Teflon, the chemical inertness of which is well known. The color of the emitted light is unchanged, since Teflon does not have any absorption bands in the region of visible light. The glow curve is retained, although glow peaks are broadened in measurements of thermoluminescence light versus time because of the existence of temperature gradients, partially caused by the low thermal conductivity of Teflon. The important relation between dose and thermoluminescence is also conserved. Tochilin[4] established the dose rate independence of the thermoluminescence of LiF and CaF_2 : Mn powder up to 10^{12} rads/sec. Pinkerton[5] has confirmed that this is true also for CaF_2 : Mn–Teflon dosimeters. For LiF–Teflon, a complete investigation has not yet been made, but no indications have been found of dose rate dependence.

Table II gives a summary of the properties of the phosphors that have been incorporated in Teflon.

TABLE II   Summary of properties of phosphors

	LiF	$Li_2B_4O_7$: Mn	CaF_2 : Mn	$CaSO_4$: Mn	Teflon
Main glow peak, °C	210	220	240	140	none
peak of emission spectrum Å	4000	6050	5000	5000	none
max. measurable dose rads	10^5	3×10^6	10^6	10^4	5×10^6 in air
deviation from linear dose response relationship	superlinear at 10^3	superlinear at 3×10^3	none	none	
dose rate independence rads/s.	up to 10^{12}	not studied	up to 10^{12}	temperature dependent	
density g/cm³	2.64	2.3	3.18	2.61	2.3
effective atomic number	8.2	7.4	16.3	15.3	8.8

5.2   Energy dependence

The energy dependence is only to a minor extent affected by the presence of the Teflon matrix. For very low energy photons, the range of the secondary electrons is such that the ionization is produced by electrons generated within the phosphor grains. For intermediate energy photons, when Compton interactions predominate the mass-energy absorption coefficients of the media involved are so close that the energy dependence of the phosphor is not perturbed by the Teflon matrix. At very high energies and in some intermediate range deviations from the behavior of the phosphor itself may occur. Principles similar to those used by Greening[6] in calculations of the energy dependence of Photographic film could be used for a theoretical analysis. Some measurements of the energy dependence of phosphor–Teflon dosimeters have been made. Endres[7] has measured the energy dependence of LiF–Teflon discs 0.4 mm thick. His results are shown in Fig. 3.

There are three different forms of energy dependence in thermoluminescent dosimetry. The first has already been discussed and involves the ratio of the mass absorption coefficient of the thermoluminescent dosimeter to some standard material so that, for example, after exposing LiF–Teflon dosimeters to 100 R of 23 keV photon radiation we would expect about 40% more thermoluminescence than after exposing the dosimeter to 100 R of Co–60 photon radiation as is shown in Fig. 3. This is simply explained by the difference in the mass absorption coefficient of LiF–Teflon and air at these two energies, since it is the absorbed energy in the dosimeter which will determine the thermoluminescence. A second form for LiF was first reported by Naylor[8] and has been further investigated by several workers.[9,10] Its presence in LiF–Teflon has been confirmed by us. The increased sensitivity

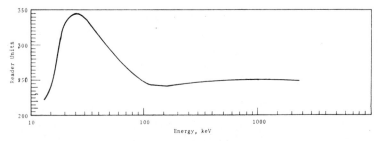

FIGURE 3.   Measured energy dependence of LiF–Teflon discs 13 mm diameter × 0.4 mm thick (reproduced by permission of G. W. R. Endres)

of LiF which occurs at doses above 1000 rads is energy dependent. This means that the slope of the superlinear portion of the dose-response curve as seen in a log–log diagram is energy dependent. It has been the case in reporting these results that the curves at different energies have been normalized so that they coincide in the linear portion.

A third type described by Pinkerton[11] is that the thermoluminescence per rad is energy dependent even on the linear portion of the dose response curve.

TABLE III   Thermoluminescence/rad (carbon) as a function of mean electron energy (reproduced by permission of A. Pinkerton)

Mean electron energy, mean	Relative response per rad (carbon)		
	LiF type 700	LiF-Teflon	CaF$_2$: Mn-Teflon
0.4	1.08	0.985	1.00
2.8	1.045	1.02	1.01
4.7	1.03	1.02	1.00
6.6	1.015	1.00	1.00
8.5	1.025	1.00	1.02
11.4	1.02	0.98	1.005
14.3	1.015	1,005	1.02
16.2	1.00	1.00	1.00

Pinkerton reported an 8% increase in the thermoluminescence per rad of LiF-7 at a mean electron energy of 0.4 MeV compared to 16.3 MeV. This effect was also studied using LiF–Teflon and CaF_2 : Mn–Teflon dosimeters and, in this case, the thermoluminescence/rad was invariable with electron energy. These results are shown in Table III. No explanation has been offered to account for this difference between the phosphor and phosphor–Teflon dosimeters.

This effect has been studied to some extent with $Li_2B_4O_7$: Mn–Teflon dosimeters. For LiF as already stated it is the slope of the superlinear portion of the doseresponse curve which is energy dependent. $Li_2B_4O_7$: Mn–Teflon Micro Rods were irrradiated at different doses from 10^2 to 2×10^4 rads with either 15 MeV electrons or Co–60 gamma rays. Figure 4 shows the integrated

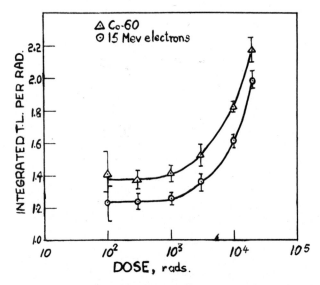

FIGURE 4.   The integrated thermoluminescence of $Li_2B_4O_7$: Mn–Teflon Micro Rods per rad (water) as a function of dose for both 15 MeV electrons and Co-60 gamma irradiations

thermoluminescence per rad as a function of the dose, the most probable reason why those curves do not coincide is that the dosimetry as vased on the Fricke dosimeter and the dose in $Li_2B_4O_7$: Mn–Teflon will be somewhat different at these two energies for the same dose in ferrous sulphate solution. The main purpose of this preliminary study was to see if the dose-

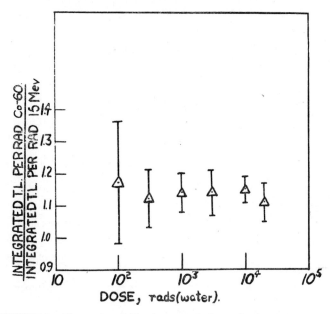

FIGURE 5. The ratio of the integrated thermoluminescence per rad from Co–60 irradiation to 15 MeV electron irradiation

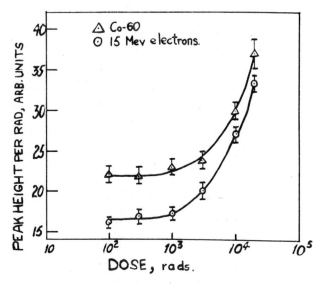

FIGURE 6. The glow peak height of $Li_2B_4O_7$: Mn–Teflon Micro Rods per rad (water) as a function of dose for both 15 MeV electrons and Co–60 irradiations

response relationship was a function of radiation energy. Figure 5 shows that the ratio of the integrated thermoluminescence per rad for Co^{60} gamma and 15 MeV electrons is a constant from 100 to 2×10^4 rads. The glow peak height was also measured in this experiment and using this as the parameter to define the thermoluminescence different results were obtained. Figure 6 shows the peak height per rad as a function of the dose. Here there is a significant difference between the slope of these lines and this shows up clearly in Fig. 7 where the ratio is plotted as a function of the dose.

As already stated, the results reported are preliminary and, in order to obtain a better understanding of the mechanism involved, it will be necessary to make further studies with lower energy radiation. However, it does appear that the peak height and integrated thermoluminescence may not always be considered as congruent parameters in termoluminescence dosimetry.

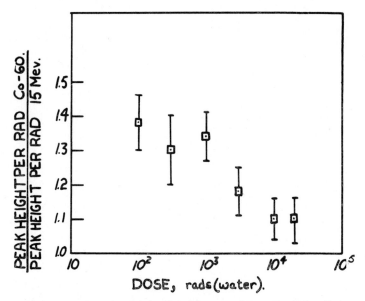

FIGURE 7.   The ratio of the peak height per rad from Co–60 irradiations
to 15 MeV electron irradiation

5.3   Fading

Many studies have been reported on the room temperature fading of thermo-luminescent phosphors. It has been shown that the fading of the thermo-luminescence of LiF at room temperature is around 5% per year following an initial decrease of as much as 15 % in the first day as result of the complete fading of the low temperature peaks in this material.[12,13,14]

Schulman[15] has reported a 10 % fading in 4 weeks of the thermolumines-cent peak height of CaF_2 : Mn phosphor. This was not expected from know-ledge of the relatively high temperature of the glow peak of this material and Schulman (*loc. cit*) attributes this loss of signal to a multiplicity of glow peaks which make up the glow peak seen in TLD measurements with this material.

$CaSO_4$: Mn has a relatively low temperature glow peak and thus the signal fades rapidly, 50 % fading in the first day has been reported.[16]

Phosphor–Teflon dosimeters will behave, with respect to fading, in the same way as the phosphors.

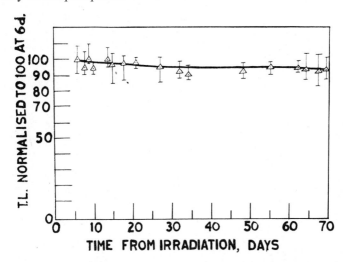

FIGURE 8. Fading of the integrated thermoluminescence from LiF–Teflon Micro Rods from 6 to 70 days at 28°C

A preliminary study of the fading of $Li_2B_4O_7$: Mn has been reported by Christensen.[17] We have studied the fading of LiF and $Li_2B_4O_7$: Mn–Teflon Micro Rods. Figure 8 shows the decrease of the integrated thermolumines-cence from LiF at a temperature of 28°C and Fig. 9 shows the fading of $Li_2B_4O_7$: Mn over a period of from 6 to 70 days. The method employed in these experiments was to irradiate a group of five dosimeters to 600 rads with Sr^{90} beta particles at 10 rads/s on each occasion over this time period and read out all the dosimeters on the same day. As can be seen, the fading

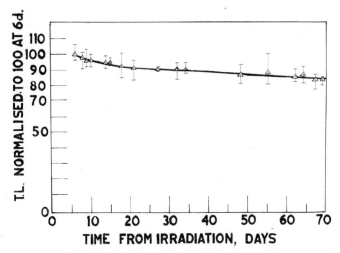

FIGURE 9.   Fading of the integrated thermoluminescence from $Li_2B_4O_7$:
Mn–Teflon Micro Rods from 6 to 70 days at 28°C

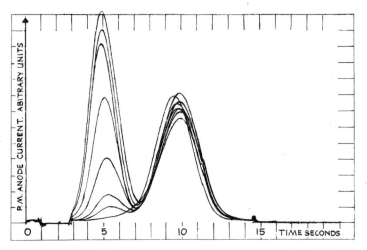

FIGURE 10.   Superimposed glow curves of $Li_2B_4O_7$: Mn–Teflon Micro
Rods. Read out at different times from 30 secs. to 90 mins. following a
radiation exposure

of $Li_2B_4O_7$: Mn is greater than that of LiF even though the main glow peak
is at a slightly higher temperature. This we feel is due to the very broad
trap distribution and not a discreet number of glow peaks which makes up
the glow peak in $Li_2B_4O_7$: Mn as has been established by noting a continu-

ous upward shift in the glow peak temperature in fading studies at 150°C. The initial fading of $Li_2B_4O_7$: Mn is illustrated by Fig. 10 which shows the experimental results taken over a period of from 30 seconds to $1^1/_2$ hours after a dose of 600 rads (Sr^{90} beta particles) at 10 rads/s. As can be seen, the low temperature peak fades rapidly. Attix[18] has reported the retrapping of electrons from shallow traps into deeper traps in LiF. This does not occur in $Li_2B_4O_7$: Mn as can be seen from Fig. 11 which is a plot of the results shown in Fig. 10. The low temperature peak fades almost completely in this time, and the height of the main peak remains a constant.

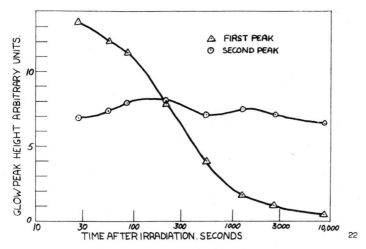

FIGURE 11.   The glow peak height of the 1st and 2nd peaks in $Li_2B_4O_7$: Mn–Teflon Micro Rods as a function of time following irradiation

5.4   Precision and range of measurement

5.4.1   *General*

The factors which limit the precision with which measurements can be made with phosphor–Teflon dosimeters fall in two different groups. One group determines the precision obtainable at low doses where the background constitutes a significant portion of the gross signal. This group consists mainly of the different background components. The second group limits the precision at such doses where the signal is very much greater than the background level and consists of the factors that can cause a variation in the sensitivities of the dosimeters in a batch.

The signal obtained in a thermoluminescence measurement is composed of three components: the radio-thermoluminescence, the light-emission in the readout of unirradiated dosimeters, and the dark current of the photo-multiplier. The first component is the net signal, the two others constitute the background in a readout. Dosimeters of the same production batch will range slightly in sensitivity, for reasons which will be described. This variation is in general characterized by a 3% standard deviation. The variations in the readout value of unirradiated dosimeters may be given in terms of an equivalent mrad signal as may the dark current.

The variance in a series of measurements at any dose level with phosphor–Teflon dosimeters can be described by the following equation:

$$\sigma^2_{\text{TOTAL}} = \left(\frac{P}{100} xD\right)^2 + \sigma^2_{\text{BG}} + \sigma^2_{\text{DC}}$$

σ^2_{TOTAL} is the total variance of the measurements in mrads. P is the percentage standard deviation of measurements when background effects are negligible (sensitivity variations), D is the dose in mrads, σ^2_{BG} is the variance of the readout of unirradiated dosimeters, in equivalent mrads, and σ^2_{CD} is the variance of a dark current measurement, in equivalent mrads.

5.4.2 *Sensitivity variations*

There are, in general, four sources of sensitivity variations within a group of dosimeters.

1. Variations in the amount of phosphor in dosimeters of the same size.
2. Variations in the size of the dosimeters.
3. The variation of the sensitivities due to thermal-annealing effects.
4. Variations in the optical density of the dosimeters, which can be caused by temperature disturbances in various parts of the production process and sometimes also by contamination with foreign material.

To accomplish reproducibility among the dosimeters, the fundamental requirement is that phosphor throughout the Teflon matrix in the molding mixture must be uniform. Any tendency of the phosphor to coalesce during the fabrication process must be prevented. Thorough mixing of the powder eliminates the influence of possible variation of sensitivity within the phosphor itself.

Random fluctuations in the number of grains of phosphor incorporated in each dosimeter of a group must be considered as a possible source of variation although this will not be of any consequence unless the average number of grains per dosimeter is sufficiently small.

LiF and $Li_2B_4O_7$: Mn phosphor powder is prepared by crushing a solid mass of the material. The powder which is used in the production of phosphor–Teflon dosimeters is the fraction that passes a 200 mesh Tyler sieve. The resulting particle size distribution for these phosphors shows an average grain size of 12 microns, while the minimum size is about 2 microns and the maximum size about 70 microns. From this information one can estimate that the LiF and $Li_2B_4O_7$: Mn Micro Rods with 0.4 mg of phosphor contain as few as about 10,000 phosphor particles. Consequently, the statistical distribution could contribute with as much as 1 % standard deviation to the variations in the sensitivities of a group Micro Rod dosimeters.

However, normal disc dosimeters (13 mm diameter by 0.4 mm thick) contain about 29 mg of phosphor. In this case, variations in the number of grains per dosimeter are insignificant. $CaSO_4$: Mn and CaF_2 : Mn are prepared by diffusing the activator into very fine powder. The resulting grain size is smaller than for LiF and $Li_2B_4O_7$: Mn, about 5 micron as an average with a narrow particle size distribution. In this case, the variations in the number of grains per dosimeter will again be insignificant for dosimeters containing more than 0.1 mg phosphor.

In general the variation in the gross weight of a batch of dosimeters is defined by a standard deviation of 2 % of the mean value. However, in the case of the discs, the slicing operation by which the discs are made will produce variations in thickness of ± 0.02 mm. Hence, the percentage variations in the weight of 0.13 mm thick discs are four times greater than in discs 0.5 mm thick. It is possible to correct for the variation in the gross weight of the discs and improvements in the precision of measurements with CaF_2 : Mn–Teflon discs have been obtained by correcting for variations in weight.

As already mentioned, the dosimeters are annealed in the production process. For LiF, variations in the temperature cycle among the dosimeters especially the cooling rate from a high temperature, in this case 300°C, will produce variations in the sensitivities of a group of dosimeters. CaF_2 : Mn, $CaSO_4$: Mn and $Li_2B_4O_7$: Mn are relatively unaffected by variations in the annealing cycle.

Variations in the optical density of a batch of dosimeters will result in variations in the thermoluminescence of dosimeters since the light transmission is affected. Webb[19] reported a correlation between the optical density of LiF–Teflon dosimeters and the measured thermoluminescence. Such variations are small in new dosimeters. As the dosimeters become used, however, discoloration may occur. This partly results from contamination of the surface by foreign matter, which is then burnt into the pores of the Teflon during readout or annealing. Furthermore, at temperatures in excess of 327°C permanent changes occur in the optical characteristics of the Teflon matrix.

5.4.3 *Background*

The background in a readout, i.e. the reading from unirradiated dosimeters is reduced by reading in an inert atmosphere, as shown by McCall[20] for LiF. This is true also for $Li_2B_4O_7 : Mn$. Figure 12 shows the measurement of

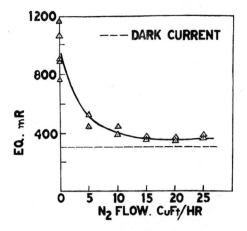

FIGURE 12.   The background reading of $Li_2B_4O_7 : Mn$ disc dosimeters as a function of the flow rate of Nitrogen into the readout chamber

unirradiated $Li_2B_4O_7 : Mn$–Teflon dosimeters in terms of equivalent mR as a function of the flow rate of prepurified dry nitrogen into the readout chamber.

Figure 13 shows the three components in the readout of $Li_2B_4O_7 : Mn$–Teflon discs which have been irradiated to 100 mrads and their contribu-

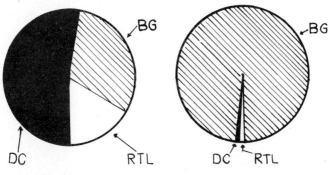

Components of Signal   Variance of Components

RTL = Radio-thermoluminescence
DC = Photomultipler dark current
BG = Non-radiation induced light emission

FIGURE 13.   Components in the readout of $Li_2B_4O_7$: Mn–Teflon discs irradiated to 100 mrads

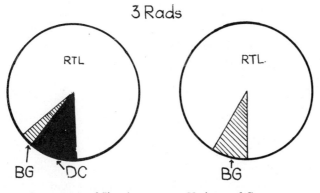

Components of Signal   Variance of Components

RTL = Radio-thermoluminescence
DC = Photomultiplier dark current
BG = Non-radiation induced light emission

FIGURE 14.   Components in the readout of $Li_2B_4O_7$: Mn–Teflon discs irradiated to 3 rads

tions to the variance. The dark current of the photomultiplier is a large proportion of the signal. However, since it is possible to measure it accurately, the variance in the TLD measurement introduced by the dark current is very small. The figure shows quite clearly that it is the signal present in the readout of unirradiated dosimeters which contributes the major portion of the variance at these low exposures. If measurements with LiF–Teflon and $Li_2B_4O_7$: Mn–Teflon are to be extended to lower doses, a technique must be devised for further reducing the spurious thermoluminescence of the phosphors.

Figure 14 shows the components of the signal in the readout of $Li_2B_4O_7$: Mn–Teflon discs irradiated to 3 rads and this shows the transition from a "background effect" dominated variance to one that is limited by the variations in the sensitivities of the dosimeters.

The correlation between measured and calculated precision of $Li_2B_4O_7$: Mn–Teflon discs is illustrated in Table IV.

TABLE IV   Measured and calculated precision which may be obtained with $Li_2B_4O_7$: Mn–Teflon discs

$Li_{\frac{1}{2}}B_4O_7$: Mn–Teflon discs 13 mm × 0.4 mm		
Dose	Measured Standard deviation	Calculated Standard deviation
40 mrads	71%	100%
370 mrads	7.5%	10%
3 rads	2.9%	3%
4.3 rads	3.3%	3%

5.4.4   *Individual calibration*

As already stated, the variation in the sensitivities of dosimeters in a production is typically defined by 3% standard deviation. If one can measure the individual sensitivities of dosimeters in a group and then reuse them without changing the relative sensitivity, a calibration factor can be assigned to each dosimeter and very high precision measurements are possible. This technique is easily applied to CaF_2 : Mn, $CaSO_4$: Mn and $Li_2B_4O_7$: Mn–Teflon dosimeters since those dosimeters do not change their sensitivity after use. Measurements have been made with such disc dosimeters with a precision of less than 1% standard deviation. The method used was to irradiate a group of dosimeters to about 10 rads. Each disc was numbered with a ball point pen, which does not interfere with measurements. The dosimeters were then read out and the relative sensitivity of each dosimeter in the group determined.

Mårtensson[21] reported a technique for maintaining the relative sensitivity of LiF–Teflon dosimeters. As already stated the sensitivity of LiF is particularly sensitive to variations in the cooling rate from a high temperature. It is, therefore, essential to put each dosimeter through the same temperature cycle. This cycle is performed in the readout instrument and Fig. 2 shows the readout of a group of 13 mm discs × 0.13 mm thick LiF–Teflon dosimeters and illustrates the reproducibility of the heating cycle. After readout the dosimeters are allowed to cool in the instrument for 45 seconds. They are then annealed at 80°C for 24 hours. Mårtensson (*loc. cit.*) reported that using this technique the maximum variation in the sensitivity of a dosimeter in 17 such cycles was 3%. We have also made measurements with the LiF–Teflon discs 13 mm diameter by 0.13 mm thick were the standard deviation after calibration was only 0.7% in twenty measurements.

TABLE V   Precision of measurements in the phosphor–Teflon dosimeters

Dose rads	Precision % standard deviation				
	LiF–Teflon Rods 1 × 6 mm	LiF–Teflon discs 13 × 0.4 mm	$Li_2B_4O_7$: Mn discs Teflon 13 × 0.4 mm	CaF_2 : Mn discs Teflon 6 × 0.4 mm	$CaSO_4$: Mn discs Teflon 13 × 0.4 mm
0.0001					20
0.001					5
0.01		20			3
0		7	25		3
1	10	3	4	8	3
10	4	3	3	3	3
100	3	3	3	3	3
1000	3	3	3	3	3

Table V illustrates the precision which may be obtained with phosphor–Teflon dosimeters *without individual* calibration at different dose levels. The precision with individual calibration is in all cases less than 1% standard deviation for doses where background effects are negligible.

5.4.5   *Largest measurable dose*

Since the measurement of thermoluminescence is a secondary standard dosimetry technique, the accuracy of measurements will be defined by the accuracy of the standard measurement plus the accuracy of the comparison. Further, one can expect the accuracy at a particular dose to be related to the rate of change of thermoluminescence with dose. This is well illustrated by Fig. 15 which is a graph of the dose per unit thermoluminescence for $Li_2B_4O_7$: Mn. Observe that the abscissa is the thermoluminescence and not

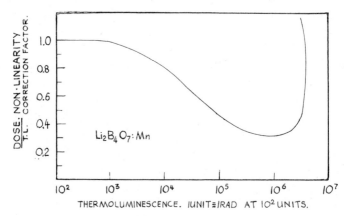

FIGURE 15   The dose per unit thermoluminescence (the non linearity correction factor) as a function of thermoluminescence

as is usually the case, dose. This is a very convenient way of representing the dose-response relationship of a phosphor, since the ordinate can be used as a non-linearity correction factor. Furthermore, plotting this way shows at what dose superlinearity commences and we would suggest that this dose should be defined by a non-linearity correction factor pf 0.95. The non-linearity correction factor is changing rapidly at around 3 Megarads, and this may sensibly be taken as the highest measurable dose for $Li_2B_4O_7$: Mn. The accuracy at this high dose will be limited because of the uncertainty in the correction factor.

5.5   Annealing and re-use

Before thermoluminescent dosimeters are reused after an irradiation and readout process, it is essential that they are heat-treated (annealed). This annealing procedure serves to eliminate the thermoluminescence remaining after the irradiation and the readout process. For some phosphors, like $CaSO_4 : Mn$, $CaF_2 : Mn$ and $Li_2B_4O_7 : Mn$ this is essentially the sole purpose of annealing.

In most practical cases this thermoluminescence is of the order of 1–0.1 % of the original value. Sometimes, one can omit the erasing of this memory, as when the previous dose was small or when the doses in consecutive irradiations are very similar or increasing.

In some phosphors, e.g. LiF, the sensitivity of the phosphor changes with the previously accumulated dose. This effect can most easily be understood by assuming that new traps are created by the radiation. It is desirable to eliminate this kind of memory effect so that the same calibration constants for individual dosimeter with different radiation history may be used. For LiF, it has been shown[22] in order to eliminate these new, radiation–induced traps in a reasonable length of time an annealing temperature of 400°C is necessary. This temperature is, of course, impossible to use with phosphor–Teflon dosimeters, since the melting point of Teflon is about 330°C.

The kinetics for the elimination of the radiation-induced enhanced sensitivity will be a characteristic of the phosphor. Fir LiF this enhanced sensitivity is very stable as already mentioned, 400°C for 1 hour is required and Table VI shows the sensitivity of LiF–Teflon dosimeters after exposure to

TABLE VI   Sensitivity of LiF-Teflon dosimeters following various exposures and annealed at 330°C for 20 hrs. and 300°C for 30 mins.

Previous dose rads	Sensitivity of LiF–Teflon dosimeters Compared to unirradiated dosimeters	
	After annealing at 330°C for 20 hours	After annealing at 300°C for 30 mins.
25	1.01	0.98
100	1.01	1.04
600	1.02	1.02
2,500	1.04	1.83
12,000	1.08	3.10
45,000	1.09	3.30
150,000	1.11	2.85
250,000	1.07	2.75
550,000	0.95	2.50
750,000	0.97	2.3
900,000	1.01	2.0

various doses and annealed at 330°C for 20 hours and 300°C for 30 mins. From this one can see the large increase in sensitivity that will be induced in a dosimeter after a large dose, if only annealed at 300°C for 30 mins. However, 330°C for 20 hours is almost equivalent to the 400°C for one hour which is used for the loose LiF powder. Although, even after this annealing, a dosimeter which had received a previous dose of 150,000 rads was 11% more sensitive than a dosimeter which had only received 25 rads. $Li_2B_4O_7$: Mn–Teflon dosimeter exhibits a superlinear dose response above 3,000 rads as has been shown in Fig. 4. However, the radiation-induced traps which one supposes are responsible for this behavior are unstable and can be annealed away at 300°C for 90 minutes. This is illustrated in Table VII, which shows the sensitivity of $Li_2B_4O_7$: Mn–Teflon disc dosimeter after various doses and annealing at 300°C for 90 mins.

TABLE VI: Sensitivity of $Li_2B_4O_7$: Mn–Teflon dosimeters following various exposures and annealed at 300°C 90 mn

Previous dose rads	Sensitivity of $Li_2B_4O_7$: Mn–Teflon dosimeters Compared to unirradiated dosimeters After annealing at 300°C for 90 minutes
7	0.99
21	0.96
70	0.98
210	0.94
700	0.95
2,100	0.96
7,560	0.95
12,000	0.96
16,000	0.98
56,000	0.97
76,400	1.01
83,000	1.01
117,000	1.01
351,000	0.97
364,000	0.99
621,000	0.97

In conclusion $Li_2B_4O_7$: Mn, $CaSO_4$: Mn–Teflon dosimeters all have relatively simple thermal annealing characteristics and an annealing temperature and time may be chosen to eliminate the memory of a previous exposure. On the other hand, LiF–Teflon dosimeters exhibit complicated thermal annealing effects and if dosimeters have accumulated doses greater than 10^3 rads, the sensitivity will increase. Furthermore, a second stage annealing of 80°C for 24 hours as described by Cameron[23] must be performed to modify the glow curve structure and minimize the low temperature peaks in LiF, the presence of which will interfere with precision dose measurements. A further factor to be considered in the case of LiF is the cooling rate from 300°C to 80°C in the annealing process. If dosimeters are cooled at different rates, this will result in a variation in the sensitivity of the dosimeters. In the manufacturing process the dosimeters are laid out on aluminium plates and annealed at 300°C for 17 hours followed by 80°C for 24 hours. Even though a very close control of the temperature cycle is maintained the precision which may be obtained with LiF–Teflon dosimeters is in general not quite as good as the other phosphor–Teflon dosimeters because of the thermal annealing effects.

6 APPLICATIONS IN MEDICINE

6.1 Intercomparison and calibration of radiation sources and machines

Thermoluminescence dosimetry is well suited for intercomparison of the dosimetry at various institutions. Such intercomparisons are vital in radio-therapy for the interpretation of treatment results at various clinics. The need for a convenient method has been further accentuated since most national laboratories do not yet provide calibration services for electrons or photons with energies above 3 MeV.

From the practical standpoint thermoluminescence dosimeters are of small size and rugged which facilitates exchange by mail. Almond et al.[24] have described the use of LiF powder for intercomparison dosimetry and good results were obtained.

In a previous section of this paper a precalibrating technique has been described to obtain a measurement precision of 1% Standard Deviation with phosphor–Teflon dosimeters, which means these are a very attractive alter-native to the use of loose powder in intercomparison dosimetry. This precision would mean that the average of two readings could be accepted at the 98% confidence level with a precision of $\pm 2\%$. In order that standardiz-ing laboratories should have a unified approach in their calibration services, thermoluminescence dosimeters could be used for the calibration of machi-nes emitting any photon energy. Here the effective energy of the radiation could be determined by the relative thermoluminescence of a pair LiF–

Teflon and CaF_2 : Mn–Teflon discs with little prior knowledge of the beam energy. The use of thermoluminescent phosphors with different mass absorption coefficients to estimate photon energy has been described by Kenny.[25]

6.2 Depth dose distributions

In radiotherapy, after a machine or a source has been calibrated accurately, the next step is to establish depth dose distributions under various conditions. The LiF and $Li_2B_4O_7$: Mn Micro Rods and Discs are very useful tools for this purpose. The small size and good tissue-equivalence of the Micro Rods make them excellent dosimeters for the study of depth doses in homogeneous media as well as in complicated phantoms. Brenner *at al.*[26] have recently described their application in studies of the influence of bone and air cavities in high-energy electron fields.

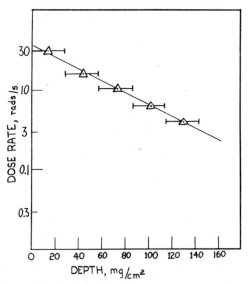

FIGURE 16.   Measured dose rate as a function of depth in LiF–Teflon
from Ra (D + E) eye applicator

LiF–Teflon discs have been sliced with a microtome as thin as 10 microns. Schulz[27] reported the use of these thin dosimeters, in phantom experiments, to determine the dose delivered to the various soft tissues in contact with the craniums of children who were being treated for the disease Tinea Capitis with low energy X-rays.

These applications clearly show the potential of this dosimetry technique. Other applications that have been tried are studies of the dose distribution in the surface of a medium, irradiated with photon radiation.

Thin phosphor–Teflon dosimeters can be applied to complicated beta dosimetry problems and solve them in an elegant and simple way. Figure 16 illustrates this to obtain the depth dose distribution from a Ra(D + E) eye applicator, 0.13 mm thick by 13 mm diameter LiF–Teflon discs were stacked one on top of the other and the beta particle source placed in contact with the top disc and left there for a predetermined time. These discs were then read out and the thermoluminescence compared with that of other discs irradiated to known doses. The line drawn through the experimental points in Fig. 16 was determined by the conventional semi-empirical relationship for beta particle attenuation.[28]

Phosphor–Teflon discs have been used to measure the dose rate from gold rings which were contaminated with radon daugther products. Radiation damage to the fingers of two persons wearing such gold rings has already been reported.[29] The principal radioisotopes present are RaD (Pb[210]) and RaE (Bi[210m]) which emit beta particles of 0.017, 0.063 and 1.17 MeV. Besides the beta particle irradiation to the finger, one can also expect a contribution from bremsstrahlung generated within the gold ring.

FIGURE 17.   LiF and $CaSO_4$: Mn–Teflon discs in position in a phantom finger. (A) Lucite tube, (B) Gold ring, (C) LiF–Teflon discs, (D) $CaSO_4$:Mn-Teflon discs

Figure 17 shows the position of the dosimeters on a phantom finger consisting of a hollow lucite tube. LiF–Teflon dosimeters 0.13 mm thick by 13 mm diameter were stacked and wedged between the ring and the lucite. $CaSO_4$: Mn–Teflon dosimeter 6 mm diameter by 0.4 mm thick were stacked along the center of the hollow tube.

After exposure the thermoluminescence measurements of the LiF–Teflon dosimeters were used to determine the dose rate to the surface layers of the skin and the $CaSO_4$: Mn–Teflon thermoluminescence measurements were used to estimate the dose rate to the finger bone. A through discussion of this experiment will be published elsewhere.

6.3　In vivo dosimeters

In external beam radiation therapy the dose delivered to a diseased organ and the normal tissue at risk is most often computed from isodose curves when the dose rate from the therapy unit gas been accurately established. In a similar way, when interstitial radiation sources are used, the dose to the particular sites are determined from tables based upon radioactive sources loaded in a geometric pattern that more or less simulates actual conditions. Dose computations on this basis rarely conform to the real situation. The difficulties involved in positioning the radiation sources in the body as well as body inhomogenities, bones, air cavities, etc., make the real situation considerably different from the hypothetical model. If these details of the particular treatment case are taken into consideration the problem of computing doses becomes one of formidable complexity. It is, therefore, desirable to actually measure the dose at the points of interest during radiotherapy. This is possible, in many cases, with phosphor-Teflon dosimeters. An *in vivo* dosimeter for such use must be of small size, rugged and able to withstand the temperature and humidity of the body and the rigor of sterilization. It should also be a dosimeter which measure a quantity which is readily translated into medically significant terms. An energy dependence close to that of tissue is, therefore, a highly desirable feature. To be of value in most clinical dosimetry problems the dosimeter must be capable of measuring doses over a range of at least three decades. The response must be independent of the dose rate. A dosimeter which gives a precision of better than 5% is probably adequate for clinical dosimetry.

Various other requirements for an *in vivo* dosimeter have been considered by Roswitt *et al.*[30]

Phosphor–Teflon Micro Rods 1 mm × 6 mm containing LiF or $Li_2B_4O_7$: Mn satisfy all the requirements of an *in vivo* dosimeter. We have used these dosimeters in two specialized *in vivo* dosimeters, an intracavitary probe and an interstitial needle.

The intracavitary probe consists of a thin walled polyethylene catheter 35 mm long which contains 10 LiF–Teflon Micro Rod dosimeters. The dosimeters are interspaced by two plastic spacers and a 1 mm diameter

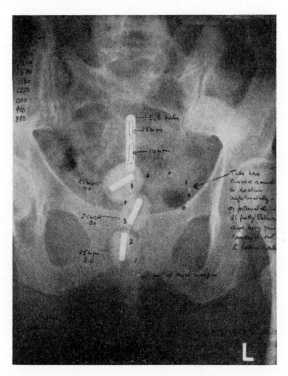

FIGURE 18. Radiograph of intracavitary probe being used to determine the total dose to the rectum of a patient undergoing radium therapy for carcinoma of the Vagina. (Reproduced by permission of Dr. I.G.D. Bell)

lead ball. The resulting sensing length is 15 cms. It is then possible to make a measurement of the dose at 15 mm intervals across a radiation field. The lead balls serve to localize the dosimeters on a radiograph. Figure 18 shows this probe being used in the measurement of the total dose to the rectum of a patient undergoing radium therapy for carcinoma of the vagina. The lead balls are clearly visible in this radiograph. A recent development in the design of this probe has been the substitution of radioopaque polyethylene for the plastic spacers and lead balls. The radio-opaque polyethylene serves to space all the dosimeters at 15 mm intervals and also to localize the dosimeters. Figure 19 is a photograph of this probe being used to measure the dose in the nasopharynx of a patient undergoing external beam radiation therapy for carcinoma. Figure 20 is a radiograph of this same patient and the radio-opaque spacers are clearly visible.

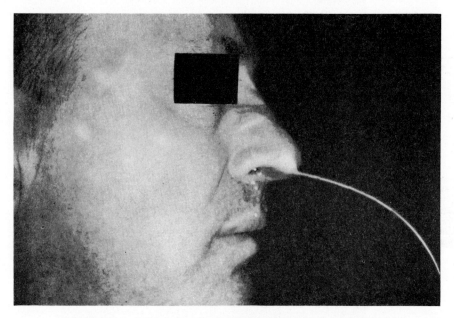

FIGURE 19.   Photograph of intracavitary probe being used to determine the radiation dose to the nasopharynx. (Reproduced by permission of Dr. N. Simon.)

The possibility that the radio-opaque material introduced into these probes would seriously modify the directional independence of the LiF–Teflon Micro Rods was investigated by irradiating three probes contained in the same plane with a radiation beam at various angles to this plane. One of these probes contained no radio-opaque material. The thermoluminescence of the probe containing the radio-opaque material was compared to this probe. Figure 21 illustrates the effect of the lead balls on the directional dependence of the dosimeters contained in the probe. Figure 22 illustrates the effect of the radio-opaque polyethylene spacers on the directional dependence of the dosimeters in the probe. As can be seen from these figures, the radio-opaque material only disturbs the directional independence of the LiF–Teflon dosimeters for a photon energy of less than 30 keV and an incident angle of greater than 70°, two conditions which are rarely met in clinical practice.

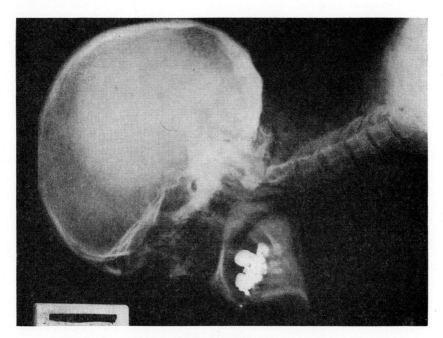

FIGURE 20. Radiograph showing the intracavitary probe being used for dosimetry in the treatment of carcinoma of the nasopharynx with Co–60 gamma radiation. (Reproduced by permission of Dr. N. Simon)

The flexibility and small size of this probe allows it to be used at almost any site in the body. Dose measurements in the oesophagus are an obvious example where the probe could be used to give invaluable data in the treatment of carcinoma of this organ by external beam therapy. Simon[31] has described the use of a similar probe to measure the dose delivered to the liver of a patient being treated with Sr^{90}—Y^{90} micro-spheres.

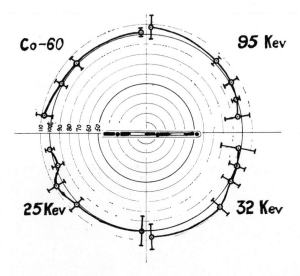

FIGURE 21.   The directional dependence of an intracavitary probe containing lead balls relative to a probe containing no radiographic markers

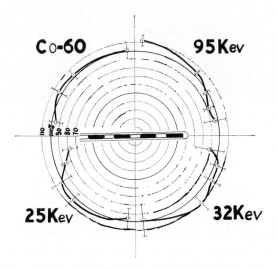

FIGURE 22.   The directional dependence of an intracavitary probe containing radio-opaque plastic spacers relative to a probe containing no radiographic markers

Two sizes of interstitial dosimeters have been produced, one with an overall length of 49 mm containing four LiF–Teflon Micro Rods, the other just 16 mm overall length containing one Micro Rod. The dosimeters are spaced by radio-opaque polyethylene and are contained in a needle shaped, stiff, polypropylene tube. Stainless steel wires are permanently sealed into the needle. The outside diameter of each of the needles is 1.7 mm. Figure 23

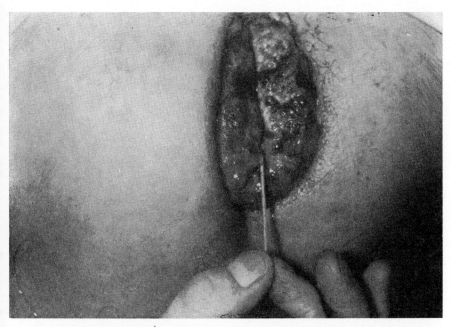

FIGURE 23. The interstitial dosimeter being used to measure the dose delivered to a patient undergoing radiotherapy for carcinoma of the rectum

shows the needle being used to measure the dose delivered to a patient undergoing radiotherapy for carcinoma of the rectum. Figure 24 is a radiograph of a radium needle implant of the urethra. The interstitial dosimeter has been implanted along with the radium needles and the radio-opaque spacers are clearly visible and thus define the position of the dosimeters exactly.

Few interstitial dosimeters have been described previously. This is because of the difficulties in finding a dosimeter capable of satisfying the stringent requirements for this type of dosimetry. The value of knowing the dose delivered to selected sites in a radium implant can not be in doubt, since very often the radiotherapist can estimate the position of "hot" or "cold" spots. By confirming this by actual measurement the dose distribution in the tumour can be subsequently modified and the chance of radiation necrosis and tumour recurrence very much reduced.

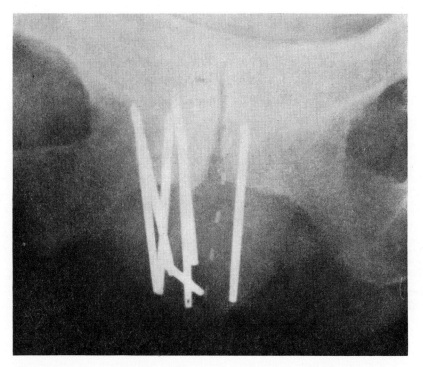

FIGURE 24.   Radiograph of a radium needle implant of the Urethra, the interstitial dosimeter is contained in the implant. (Reproduced by permission of Dr. I. G. D. Bell)

6.4   Exit and entrance dose measurements

Svarcer *et al.*[32] have described the use of LiF for exit dose measurements in external beam therapy of carcinoma of the bronchus and the oesophagus. It was shown that air-filled cavities could cause errors up to $\pm 15\%$ from an estimate of the dose delivered to the tumour, based on isodose curves for unit density material.

Routine entrance and exit dose measurements can serve to check the treatment set-up and to monitor the therapy exposure. This is of special importance in the radiotherapy of the bronchus where, very often, during the treatment session the lung becomes reaerated resulting in an increased transmission of the incident beam and a consequent overexposure.

Lithium fluoride–Teflon Discs 8 mm diameter, 0.5 mm thick have been especially developed for routine entrance and exit dose measurements. These discs are easily taped onto the patient's skin and a single disc could be used to integrate the total dose delivered to the patient during a treatment session. These discs contain 3 mg of LiF which is sufficient for measurements from 10 to 10^5 rads with an accuracy of 3% standard deviation.

7   APPLICATIONS IN HEALTH PHYSICS

7.1   Introduction

Health physics dosimetry consists of a broad spectrum of measurement problems, comprising various aspects of personnel dosimetry and environmental monitoring for different types of ionizing radiation. For these problems a variety of dosimetry techniques are used at present. Ionization chambers and photographic film are the most commonly used detectors but are supplemented with other methods for special purposes. One of the most interesting aspects of thermoluminescence dosimeters is that they can provide a single system for general application in health physics.

7.2   Finger and hand dosimetry

A finger and hand dosimeter has been described by us previously.[33] Recently Knight[3] reported the successful use of such finger and hand dosimeter under actual working conditions.

Finger and hand dose measurements present a serious problem in routine personnel dosimetry. The particular difficulty is that the maximum dose to the hand has to be estimated in an unpredictable radiation field with very steep dose gradients, and that this estimate must be based on a measurement technique which does not interfere with the monitored persons ability to perform delicate manipulations.

To illustrate the type of dose patterns that can occur, we have measured the doses on the hand of a person holding a radium needle inside a plastic tube. As shown in Fig. 25, the maximum dose was 560 mrad on the thumb, while ring and wrist dosimeters showed less than 2% of this. In a similar experiment illustrated in Fig. 26, a plate of natural uranium was placed on a waterfilled glove, simulating a hand. The tips of the fingers in immediate contact with the plate received almost 100% of the dose measured on the surface on the plate, while the ring dosimeters showed less than 0.2%.

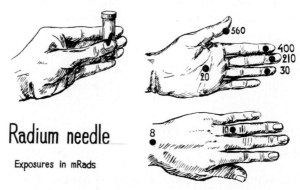

FIGURE 25.   Doses in mrad at various points after holding a one milligram radium needle for five minutes

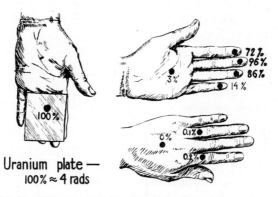

FIGURE 26.   Doses recorded on the hand after holding a plate of natural uranium as shown. The doses are expressed as a % of the dose at the surface of the uranium plate

It is obvious from this experiment that a realistic estimate of the maximum dose to the hand in similar situations can seldom be made unless measurements are actually made where the maximum exposure can be expected, usually on the finger tips.

Consequently the conventional technique for finger and hand dosimetry, i.e., to use photographic film as ring or wrist dosimeters is of little or no value.

The dosimeters used are illustrated by Fig. 27. The radiation sensing component is a disc, 12.5 mm diameter by 0.4 mm thick, consisting of 28 mg of thermoluminescent LiF uniformly incorporated in Teflon. This disc

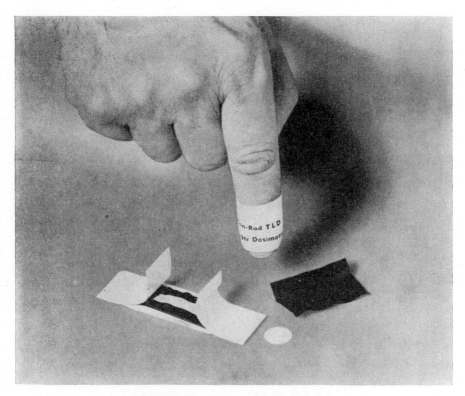

FIGURE 27.   Finger and hand dosimeters

is contained in a light-proof polyethylene pouch, 7 mg/cm² thick. The pouch is in turn fastened to the skin by a strip of adhesive tape. In situations where a minimum cover over the disc is essential, the tape is fastened to the ends of the pouch, and thus the thickness covering the discs is only 7 mg/cm². When a thicker cover can be tolerated, the tape, 30 mg/cm² thick, is allowed to extend over the pouch.

The LiF–Teflon disc responds to the energy deposited by the ionizing radiation within its volume. If the disc is covered with 7 mg/cm² and since it is 90 mg/cm² thick, the response of the disc is a measure of the energy absorbed in a layer at a depth between 7 and 97 mg/cm². The biologically important dose is usually taken to be that to the thin basal layer at 7–10 mg/cm² depth. As long as there is no significant dose gradient between 7 and 97 mg/cm² depth, the measured value in the LiF–Teflon disc will correspond to the dose to the basal layer. This is usually the case for X and gamma radiation. Insufficient electron equilibrium may in certain cases complicate interpretation of measured data, but otherwise the close resemblance in atomic composition of LiF-Teflon and tissue ensures a simple relation between the dosimeter response and the dose to the basal layer.

For beta and other electron radiation, the thickness of the disc is not negligible. 7 mg/cm², the thickness of the radiation insensitive surface layer of the skin as well as of the plastic pouch, corresponds to the maximum range of an electron of about 60 keV energy. Electrons of less energy are therefore hardly of interest. 300 keV electrons have a maximum range corresponding to the thickness of the disc. In the region between these energies, the interpretation of measured values will be difficult and the average dose measured by the discs will be less than the dose to the basal layer. Further calculations are needed to clarify these conditions, as for example were made by Casnati and Breuer for skin contamination.[34]

For still higher electron energies the response will become easier to interpret. In the practically important case of natural uranium the average

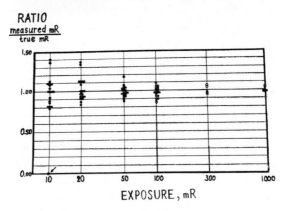

FIGURE 28. The precision of dose measurements using LiF–Teflon discs 13 mm diameter by 0.4 mm thick

dose in the disc is about 80 % of the dose to the basal layer as estimated from previously published data.[1]

The precision of dose measurements with these dosimeters without individual calibration has been measured by exposing a numbe of dosimeters to known doses of Co–60 radiation. The results are shown in Fig. 28, which illustrates that measurements down to 10 mR are possible. Above this exposure the standard deviation decreases with increasing dose.

The sensitivity of the dosimeters to mechanical shock was studied by dropping a hammer onto the LiF–Teflon discs. The results, illustrated in Fig. 29 show that the dosimeters are practically insensitive even under these extreme conditions. The possibility that friction could produce tribo-

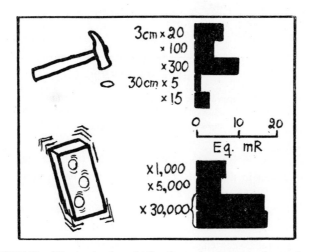

FIGURE 29.   The production of tribo-thermoluminescence by mechanical
shock and friction

thermoluminescence was investigated by violently shaking dosimeters in a black plastic box. The results obtained, also shown in Fig. 29, show a slight response to the shaking. The conclusion must be, however, that the dosimeters are practically insensitive to mechanical disturbance.

Another possible cause for the spurious thermoluminescence is excitation by light, which has been reported previously for LiF.[35,1] Dosimeters exposed to normal fluorescent laboratory light show a definite light sensitivity, Fig. 30. Experiences with ultraviolet radiation suggest that it is this component of the light that is responsible for the excitation. Light is, however, efficiently excluded by the use of the light-proof pouches, into which the LiF–Teflon discs are packed in subdued light. The data in Fig. 30 indicate a slight increase in the signal from dosimeters stored in the dark following the annealing. The reason for this is not known at present.

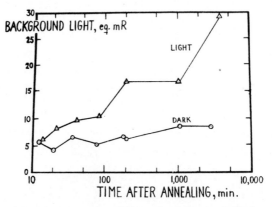

FIGURE 30.   The appearance of thermoluminescence following annealing in LiF–Teflon discs which have been kept in darkness or exposed to normal laboratory fluorescent light

The conclusion of these experiments is that unirradiated dosimeters should be included in any measurement series for background determination.

These dosimeters fulfill practically all the requirements for finger and hand dosimetry. The most serious drawback is associated with the inherent problems in any measurement of beta and electron dose to a very thin layer. Compared to photographic film dosimeters, the dosimeters have the advantages of being capable of at least the same precision, having a vastly superior energy dependence for X and gamma radiation, which leads to better accuracy and allowing the monitored person to wear the dosimeters where meaningful doses will be recorded, i.e., on the finger tips, without interfering with his work. The ease and speed of readout offers possibilities for a flexible monitoring technique.

7.3   Personnel badge dosimetry

The basic characteristics of LiF–Teflon disc dosimeters 13 mm diameter and 0.4 mm thick applied to personnel dosimetry have been thoroughly investigated by Endres[2,7] and Cusimano.[36] Figure 31 shows the reproducibility of LiF–Teflon dosimeters following an exposure of 100 mrem. Cusimano (*loc. cit.*) has also shown that the LiF–Teflon dosimeters will accurately record exposures even if this is delivered at a low dose rate. In this experiment 30 LiF–Teflon discs were irradiated with 5 mrem (radium-

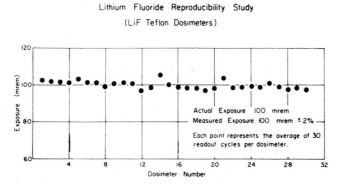

FIGURE 31. Lithium-Fluoride Teflon reproducibility study. (Reproduced by courtesy of J. P. Cusimano)

gamma) twice a week for 13 weeks to a total of 130 mrem. The dosimeter readings average 140 mrem. This is about 8 % higher than the actual irradiation 130 mrem. This is shown in Fig. 32. Note that the lowest reading of a dosimeter was 126 mrem and the highest 157 mrem. From this data it was concluded that a 500 mrem per year exposure accumulation could be

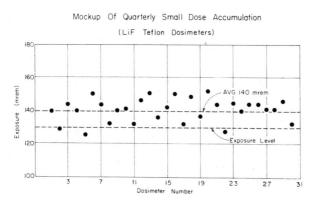

FIGURE 32. Mock up of quarterly small dose accumulation. (Reproduced by courtesy of J. P. Cusimano)

measured with a good accuracy. The response of LiF–Teflon dosimeters to mixed fields of gamma and beta radiation has also been evaluated. Figure 33 shows the results of test exposures of mixed fields compared to the dose equivalent recorded by the dosimeters.

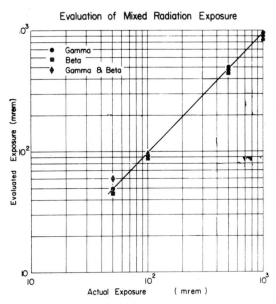

FIGURE 33.   Evaluation of LiF–Teflon disc response to mixed radiation exposures

We have also investigated the application of LiF–Teflon dosimeters to personnel dosimetry and have designed a badge to contain these dosimeters. We have based this design upon the calibration factors for personnel dosimetry proposed by A. R. Jones.[37] The basic tenet of this concept is that since the ICRP[38] defines personnel dosimetry requirements in terms of the maximum permissible dose to certain organs then the ideal dosimeter should give a direct estimate of dose at these sites. For radiation from external sources these critical organs are the skin, gonads, and blood forming organs. Attix[39] and Piesch[40] discussed the application to personnel dosimetry of these principles.

If one is willing to accept certain simplifying assumptions, for example frontal irradiation only, it is possible to modify the response of a LiF–Teflon dosimeter so that the thermoluminescence measurement will indicate the dose at a selected body site. In the case of the gonads we have covered the LiF–Teflon disc with 1 mm aluminium. Calculations of the response of the dosimeter over a range of photon energy from 30 keV to 1.5 MeV have shown that this is nearly the same as that proposed by A. R. Jones for a personnel dosimeter for routine use, which can estimate the dose to the testes to within $\pm 10\%$. We are, at present, working on ways to improve this and also to design a filter and phosphor–Teflon dosimeter combination which will have an energy dependence suitable for an accident dosimeter. In this case the critical organ is the blood-forming bone marrow rather than the gonads (A. R. Jones, *loc. cit*).

FIGURE 34.   The Con-Rad TLD badge

The measurement of skin doses with LiF–Teflon dosimeters has been discussed in detail in the previous section. The results presented there show the excellent capabilities of the LiF–Teflon discs for this purpose.

Figures 34 and 35 show the construction of the TLD badge made by us. There are three main components in this badge. The front cover contains identification information: the wearers name, an identification number, and

40*

this number coded in binary form along one edge by a series of indentations. The second layer contains the filters used to modify the energy-response relationship of the dosimeters. The final layer contains compartments for the phosphor–Teflon discs. One disc is covered by only 7 mg/cm^2 of mylar

FIGURE 35.   The Con-Rad TLD badge. (A) identification plate, (B) filters, (C) dosimeters

and effectively measures the dose to the skin in the same way as the finger dosimeter described. Another disc is covered by the 1 mm aluminium filter already mentioned and therefore measures the gonadal dose.

Our approach to satisfying the legal requirements in personnel dosimetry has been to substantiate the testimony of a competent health physicist with information on the temperature cycle in the readout of the dosimeter. We have built a TLD Readout System in which the badge identification number is sensed from the badge and printed out. The thermoluminescence in the readout is printed and so is the maximum heating element temperature attained in the readout of the dosimeter. Since it can be shown from well established physical principles that a thermoluminescent dosimeter will emit an amount of light proportional to the prior radiation exposure if it is heated to a sufficiently high temperature, the printed evidence on the temperature attained in the readout cycle will support the recorded dose.

As a result of technical and commercial developments, the overal cost of a thermoluminescence personnel dosimetry system is approaching that of the well established methods of film and ionization chamber techniques. Thermoluminescence dosimetry, therefore, has become a serious alternative to conventional dosimetry methods. The question is not so much in our opinion, simply to replace the film badges as to obtain a single system which fulfills the various needs of health physics dosimetry. If this can be achieved with a more direct approach to the personnel dosimetry problem than is provided by film badges, then, of course, a desirable improvement would be accomplis by film badges, then, of course, a desirable improvement would be accomplished. Table VIII shows the cost at present for TLD dosimeters.

TABLE VIII   Present cost of TLD dosimeters

Phosphor		Dosimeter	Present Dosimeter Cost*	Dosimeter Cost per Readout**
LiF	Rod	1.0 mm × 6 mm	$ 0.27	$ 0.014
LiF	Disc	0.4 mm × 13 mm	0.90	0.045
LiF	Disc	0.5 mm × 8 mm	0.37	0.019
CaF_2 : Mn	Disc	0.4 mm × 6 mm	0.27	0.014
$CaSO_4$: Mn	Disc	0.5 mm × 13 mm	0.37	0.019

* Cost based on a lot of 1,000 dosimeters.
** A dosimeter is assumed to be used twenty times.

7.4   Environmental monitoring

Thermoluminescent phosphor–Teflon dosimeters are well suited for environmental monitoring of various types. In nuclear installations, for instance, film badges are frequently used to monitor the radiation levels around the reactor. This can be done with thermoluminescence dosimeters. TLD badges of the type described in the previous section are advantageous because of the simple interpretation of the measured data. Furthermore, phosphor–Teflon dosimeters are insensitive to such environmental factors as high humidity. Climatic temperature variations have no effect on the thermoluminescence response of LiF, CaF_2 : Mn and $Li_2B_4O_7$: Mn– Teflon dosimeters.

The minimum detectable dose with $CaSO_4$: Mn–Teflon dosimeters, at this time, is 100 micro-rads. These dosimeters can be used to map the dose distribution in an environment where the dose rate hardly exceeds the naturally occurring level. Normally, one has to restrict the measuring period with these dosimeters to less than a day because of the fading of the signal. The dosimeters can also be used for measurements of doses when radioactivity is released in air or water.[41]

8 SPECIAL APPLICATIONS FOR THIN DOSIMETERS

One of the most significant advantages of phosphor–Teflon dosimeters over other thermoluminescent dosimeters is their ability to measure the doses deposited in a very thin layer. Phosphor–Teflon dosimeters can be sliced with a microtome as thin as 10 microns.

Such thin discs can be used as simple solid state Bragg–Gray cavity chambers. Work on the behavior of these thin slices has already been reported

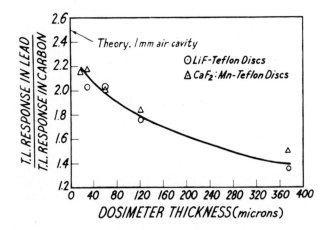

FIGURE 36. The ratio of ^{60}Co gamma dose response in phosphor–Teflon dosimeters measured in lead to that measured in carbon as a function of dosimeter thickness

by us.[42] Measurements were made with discs nominal thicknesses when the discs were irradiated to the same exposure with ^{60}Co gamma rays but sandwiched in different materials. Figure 36 shows the ratio of the signal from discs in lead and discs of the same size in carbon as a function of the thickness of the discs. As the discs are made thinner, the ratio approaches the value predicted by the cavity ionization theory.[43]

CaF_2 : Mn–Teflon discs about 15 micron thick were used to study this ratio as a function of the atomic number of the surrounding material. The

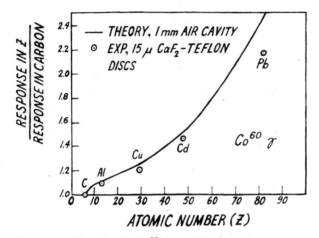

FIGURE 37.   The ratio of the ^{60}Co gamma dose response measured in various materials to that measured in carbon irradiated to the same exposure. Theoretical values for 1 mm air cavity are shown for comparison[39]

results of these measurements are shown in Fig. 37. The solid curve shows values according to cavity ionization theory[43] for a 1 mm air gap. Further work on this technique for dose measurements is in progress, especially for studies of dose distributions at bone-tissue interfaces.

A practical dosimetry problem, where the use of thin phosphor–Teflon dosimeters offered a solution, presented itself in the sterilizing irradiation of meat with low energy electrons. The initial energy of the electrons was about 500 keV but the energy was degraded by scattering and absorption in air. 0.1 and 0.4 mm phosphor–Teflon discs did not give consistent data, but accurate measurements of the dose on any part of the animal carcass were obtained when 15 micron slices were used.

9 CONCLUSION

The inherent properties of Teflon and the flexibility in fabrication techniques allow a wide choice in dosimeter shape and size. The dosimeters are easy to handle and read out, and they are relatively insensitive to disturbances. The absence of an envelope allows continuity between the surrounding medium and the radiation sensing volume, a necessary condition for many applications. In conclusion, dosimeters of thermoluminescent phosphor incorporated in Teflon constitute a highly versatile system, which can be used for simple and convenient routine measurements as well as for the study of sophisticated dosimetry problems.

Acknowledgements

The authors are grateful to Dr. I. G. D. Bell of St. Williams Hospital, Rochester, England, J. P. Cusimano, of the National Reactor Testing Station, Idaho Falls, Idaho, U.S.A., G.W.R. Endres of Battelle Memorial Institute Richland, Washington, U.S.A., A. Pinkerton of the Sloane-Kettering Institute for Cancer Research, New York, U.S.A. and Dr. N. Simon of 945 Fifth Avenue, New York, U.S.A. for supplying material which has been reproduced in this paper.

References

1. B. E. Bjarngard, R. C. McCall, and I. A. Berstein, *Proc. Int'l. Conf. Luminescence Dosimetry*, Stanford, California, 1965. *U.S. Atomic Energy Commission, Conf-65037*, page 308 (1967).
2. G. W. R. Endres, "Performance study on LiF–Teflon thermoluminescent dosimeters". Presented at First Topical Symposium on Personnel Radiation Dosimetry, Chicago, USA, January 1967.
3. G. B. Knight, "Extermity dosimetry with lithium fluoride". Presented at First Topical Symposium on Personnel Radiation Dosimetry, Chicago, USA, January 1967.
4. E. Tochilin and N. Goldstein, *Health Physics* **12**, 1705 (1966).
5. A. Pinkerton (privat communication).
6. J. R. Greening, *Proc. Phys. Soc.* (London) B **64**, 977 (1951).
7. G. W. R. Endres, "Thermoluminescent dosimetry studies." Page 8, report BNWL-339, UC-48 Pacific Northwest Laboratory, Richland, Washington.
8. G. P. Naylor, *Phys. Med. Biol.* **10**, 564 (1965).
9. J. Wagner and J. R. Cameron, *USAEC Rept.* COO-1105-117 (1966).
10. M. Ehrlich, *Proc. Int'l. Cong., IRPA*, Rome (1966). Pergamon Press (in Press).
11. A. Pinkerton, "Comparison of calorimetric and other methods for the determination of absorbed dose," Presented at Conference on High Energy Radiation Therapy Dosimetry. New York Academy of Sciences. New York, June 1967.

12. N. Sunthalingam and J. R. Cameron. Absence of Fading in LiF (TLD-100) (abstract) *Phys. Med. Biol.* **11**, 624 (1966).
13. G. A. M. Webb, *Brit. J. Appl. Phys.* **18**, 7 (1967).
14. R. M. Hall and J. P. LaRocca. "Development and applications of thermoluminescent dosimeters". *Health Phys.* (In Press).
15. J. H. Schulman, *Solid state and chemical radiation dosimetry in medicine and biology*, IAEA, Vienna, STI/PUB/138 p. 3 (1967).
16. B. E. Bjarngard, "The properties of $CaSO_4$: Mn thermoluminescent dosimeters" Report AE-109, *Aktiebologaet Atomenergi*, Stockholm, Sweden (1963).
17. P. Christensen, Danish Atomic Commission, Riso, Report No. 161. August 1967.
18. F. H. Attix, "Thermoluminescence dosimetry", Presented at the Conference on High Energy Radiation Therapy Dosimetry, New York Academy of Sciences. New York, June (1967)
19. G. A. M. Webb, Report No. RD/B/HG 693. Central Electricity Generating Board, Berkeley, Glos., England.
20. R. E. Fix and R. C. McCall, "A sensitive LiF dosimeter for routine beta and gamma personnel monitoring," Presented at Health Physics Society Annual Meeting, Cincinnati (1964).
21. B. Mårtensson. *Proc. Fourth Nordic Meeting on Clinical Physics.*
22. J. R. Cameron and D. W. Zimmerman, USAEC Report COO-1105-102 (1965).
23. J. R. Cameron *et al.*, *Health Physics* **10**, 25 (1964).
24. P. R. Almond and R. J. Shalek, "Solid state and chemical radiation dosimetry in medicine and biology," IAEA, Vienna, STI/PUB/138 p. 149 (1967).
25. G. N. Kenney, *The "Paired TLD" Technique for the Measurement of X-Ray Beam Quality in Vivo*. M.S. Thesis, University of Wisconsin (1965).
26. M. Brenner *et al.*, "The effect of inhomogeneities on dose distributions of high energy electrons," Presented at the Conference on High Energy Radiation Therapy Dosimetry, New York Academy of Sciences, New York, June 1967.
27. R. J. Schulz, "Dose measurements at interfaces using LiF micro discs," (abstract) *Phys. Med. Biol.* **11**, 623 (1966).
28. R. D. Evans, "The atomic nucleus," Chapter 21, page 628. Published by McGraw-Hill, New York (1955).
29. N. Simon & J. Harley, "Skin reactions from gold jewelry contaminated with radon," *J. of American Medical Association* (In Press).
30. B. Roswit *et al.*, "*In vivo* radiation dosimetry for clinical and experimental radiation therapy, "*Progress in Clinical Cancer*, p. 96. Grove & Stratton Inc., New York (1965).
31. N. Simon *et al.*, "Intra-arterial irradiation of carcinoid tumors of the liver". *Am. J. Roentgen, Rad. Therapy and Nuc. Med.* (In Press).
32. V. Svarcer and J. F. Fowler, *Brit. J. Radiol.* **38**, 785 (1965).
33. B. E. Bjarngard and D. Jones, *Proc. Int'l. Congress of IRPA*, Rome 1966. Pergamon Press (In Press).
34. E. Casnati and F. Breuer, *Proc. Conf. on Personnel Dosimetry for Radiation Accidents*, IAEA, Vienna (1965).
35. J. Lippert and V. Mejdahl, *Proc. Int'l. Conf. Luminescence Dosimetry*, Stanford, California (1965). USAEC CONF.-65037 p. 204 (1967).

36. J. Cusimano, *Experimental Observations in Thermoluminescent Dosimetry*. Report TLD-4500. Idaho Operations Office, USAEC, Idaho Falls, Idaho, USA.
37. A. R. Jones, *Health Phys.* **12**, 633 (1966).
38. ICRP. Publication No. 6 (1964) Pergamon Press.
39. F. H. Attix, *Health Phys.* **13**, 219 (1967).
40. E. Piesch, *Health Phys.* **13**, 759 (1967).
41. B. E. Bjarngard, *Proc. Int'l. Conf. Luminescence Dosimetry*, Stanford, California (1965). USAEC, CONF-65037 p. 195 (1967).
42. B. E. Bjarngard and D. Jones, *Solid State and Chemical Radiation Dosimetry in Medicine and Biology*, IAEA, Vienna, STI/PUB/138 p. 99 (1967).
43. V. H. Ritz and F. H. Attix, "A solid state Bragg–Gray cavity chamber," *Selected Topics in Radiation Dosimetry*, IAEA, Vienna (1961) 481.

Field experience with thermoluminescent dosimeters

JOHN P. CUSIMANO, FOSTER V. CIPPERLEY,
JOHN C. CULLEY

Idaho Health Services Laboratory
United States Atomic Energy Commission
Idaho Falls, Idaho

A routine system of personnel dosimetry utilizing the phenomena of thermolumines-cence has been developed at the National Reactor Testing Station. Research in thermo-luminescent application techniques was initiated in 1965 for the purpose of developing a suitable system for long-term monitoring of low-exposure-probability personnel.

The new routine dosimetry system utilizes two lithium floride-teflon disc dosimeters held in a plastic dosimeter retainer that is the same size and shape as a standard film packet placed in the National Reactor Testing Station dosimetry badge. The field ex-perience using the new system since its application in November 1966 is presented.

The search for better methods and materials for the detection and measure-ment of external radiation has gone on constantly since radiation dosimetry came into being some thirty years ago. The most widely accepted method of personnel dosimetry during this period has been the use of photographic film in holders containing various configurations of filter materials. In spite of its many inherent weaknesses, this method has provided yeoman service throughout the atomic industry and has achieved a good degree of reliability.

The Health Services Laboratory of the Idaho Operations Office (ID) furnishes personnel monitoring coverage for approximately 8,000 persons per months at the National Reactor Testing Station (NRTS), which previously involved the processing of some 120,000 routine dosimetry films per year.

The majority of these persons do not come in contact with any radioactive sources nor work in any radiation area and therefore receive little or no radiation exposure. During the period of 1951 through 1965, a total of 22,716 regularly assigned persons were provided coverage with approximately 17,000 or 74% accumulating 500 mrem of exposure or less.

Approximately 10% of the NRTS personnel receive approximately 80% of the total recorded exposure. Most personnel do not require constant surveillance from a health physics standpoint; however, because the facilities at the NRTS are primarily oriented toward experimentation and testing, it is mandatory that a reliable method of monitoring radiation exposure to personnel be maintained for all employees in emergency situations and to provide necessary record-keeping capabilities.

Research in thermoluminescent application techniques was initiated in early 1965 with the aim of developing a suitable system for longterm monitoring of low-exposure-probability personnel. The empirical data obtained on the response characteristics, reliability, reproducibility and accuracy of low-dose accumulation over long periods of time, as well as the effects of ultraviolet and visible light, the effects of annealing, and neutron sensitivity,[1] demonstrated the efficiency and practicability of a lithium fluoride (LiF)–teflon system for routine personnel monitoring. Also the opinion by the AEC ID Office of Chief Counsel, that the dosimeter result recorded in the regular course of business is as admissible as evidence as a processed dosimetry film, eliminated the need for physical retention of the dosimeter. Therefore, the decision was made to utilize LiF–teflon dosimeters for long-term, low-dose accumulation for low-exposure-probability personnel.[2]

At this point we would like to offer a word of caution. LiF–teflon dosimeters are not the final and complete answer to all personnel dosimetry problems. These as well as other TL dosimeters measure an integrated dose and cannot differentiate between low-level x-ray and beta. The response to beta, in our experiments, appears to be approximately 50% of the response to Ra-gamma radiation which makes an accurate evaluation of a mixture of the two impossible unless the ratio of each is known.

In the NRTS system a cadmium filter is used to determine penetrating radiation *vs.* non-penetrating. At the levels we are normally measuring, we have no concern as to the type of radiation being measured and in case of an accident we would be concerned primarily with the penetrating radiation which we can evaluate quite accurately. If spectrometric capabilities are required for type and energy determination and dose evaluation such as

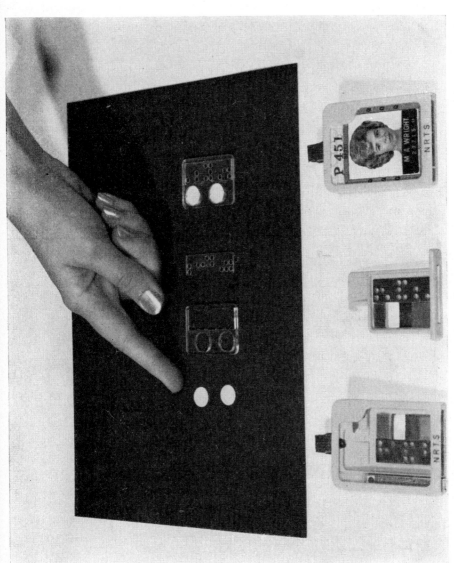

FIGURE 1   NRTS TLD badge

presently provided by multifilter film badges, considerable modification of the NRTS system would be required.

The NRTS personnel presently being monitored using LiF–teflon dosimeters are those who normally receive less than 500 mrem per year total exposure. Except in case of accident or a known exposure the dosimeters are read on a quarterly basis, as compared to the film system of once per month.

If a low-probability-group person is used on a "hot job", the usual internal control procedures apply, and special processing of his TLD is requested (Health Physics Request) to ascertain his exposure for the period to that point.

The TLD system is so designed as to require no modification of the NRTS dosimetry badge. In the field, the appearance of the TLD and the film badge are identical. The system utilizes two LiF–teflon disc dosimeters, one positioned in the open-window area and the other in the cadmium-filter area of the dosimetry badge. They are held in a plastic dosimeter retainer of our own design shown in Fig. 1, the same size and shape as a standard personnel monitoring packet.

The cadmium shielded dosimeter is not normally read, serving as a

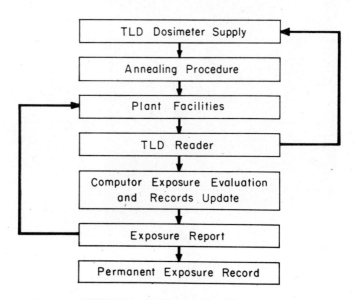

FIGURE 2   TLD operational flow chart

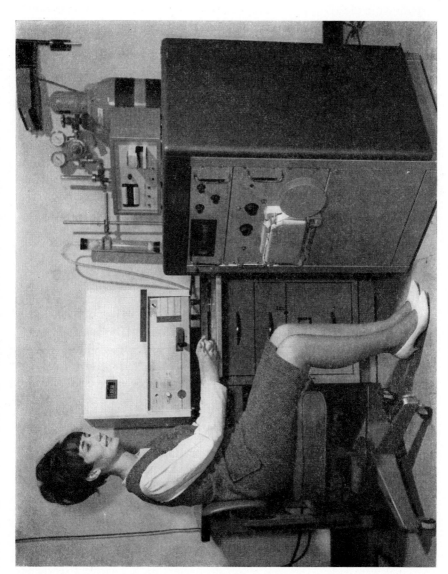

FIGURE 3   TLD read-out system

backup and source of additional data in case of a high exposure. Also incorporated in the ID bagde is a capsule containing sufficient lithium fluoride phosphor for three additional readouts. A duplicate dosimeter retainer system is utilized to allow the exchange of the dosimeters in the field.

A flow chart of the normal operation in routine TLD personnel monitoring is presented in Fig. 2. The TL dosimeters go from storage, through the annealing procedure and then are issued for personnel monitoring at the plant facilities. At the end of the monitoring period the dosimeters are read out and put back into storage. The punched paper tape produced by the TLD reader shown in Fig. 3, is used for input to a computer evaluation program. This program determines the net calibration values, the calibration factor, the net thermoluminescence value of the field dosimeters, and the indicated exposure. The program also performs record updating and prints out an exposure summary report for the current period. The original exposure report is incorporated in the permanent record system by the Dosimetry Branch, and the appropriate number of copies are made available to the plant facility concerned.

Regardless of the satisfactory experimental results, the reliability of any new system must be proven in actual field experience. In November of 1966, some 200 persons were placed on the TLD system at one of the NRTS reactor complexes. One month later, at the end of the year, the dosimeters were exchanged and evaluated. Personnel exposures ranged from zero through 250 mrem. The higher exposures were consistent with the expectations of the plant health physicist. Some 650 personnel in another plant facility were also placed on the TLD system in November. During the early part of December the reactor was shut down. Personnel utilizing the TLD system were used for maintenance and decontamination work due to their low exposure history. The dosimeters of these persons were specially processed at the request of the area health physicist. The exposures ranged from zero through 500 mrem. The plant health physicist indicated that the reported exposures were in line with anticipated exposures based on the work being performed.

The full-scale TLD program for personnel monitoring at the NRTS was initiated in January of 1967. Approximately 52% of the regularly assigned personnel were issued the new teflon dosimeters on a quarterly servicing schedule. Frequency distributions are presented in Table I for the first two quarters of 1966 when monthly film badges were used exclusively and for the first two quarters of 1967 when either monthly film badges or quarterly

TABLE I Quarterly frequency distribution

			First quarter			
Range (rem)		0–0.5	0.5–1.0	1–2	2–3	>3.0
	Total					
1966	5196	4835	264	90	7	0
1967	5167	4732	261	147	27	0
			second quarter			
Range (rem)		0–0.5	0.5–1.0	1–2	2–3	>3.0
	Total					
1966	5023	4531	343	129	20	0
1967	5542	5155	241	140	6	0

TLDs were used. Comparison of the data shows no significant change in accumulated exposure for the corresponding periods. This indicates the capability of the TLDs to accumulate low-exposure doses over extended time periods.

2652 TLDs were processed in the routine servicing of badges covering the first quarter of 1967. Of this total there were four outliers, or questionable readings, and one lost reading. The four outliers were machine-operator errors which were identified and corrected. The lost reading resulted when a painter dropped his badge in the paint and then cleaned it in the field using paint thinner. As a result, the dosimeter discs were covered with dried paint and could not be read.

For the second quarter of 1967, 2762 TLDs were processed. One high-reader was found, two dosimeters were missing and two had been tampered with. The high-reader was due to a machine-operator malfunction and was corrected. One badge had both disc dosimeters missing at the time of servicing. It had apparently been opened in the field during the coverage period. The disc dosimeters in another badge had been scribbled on with heavy black pencil and were not read.

Although the badge is designed to be tamper-proof it can be opened in the field if sufficient effort is applied. All questionable results, lost reading and unusual conditions were investigated, Exposure Questionaires executed and the individuals and their supervisors contacted.

Beginning in January 1967, the off-site as well as the 300 on-site environmental monitoring stations were placed on a semi-annual servicing schedule. Teflon dosimeters are used in the dosimetry badge and are numbered according to their location. Based on preoperational background studies performed in 1948–49 prior to the construction of the NRTS, the natural radiation background level for the particular locale was determined to be 10–12 mR per month or 120–150 mR per year.

The film used in the off-site environmental monitoring program had an assumed lower detection limit of approximately 10 mR. These films were serviced monthly and consistently yielded zero results. For record and reporting purposes these zero results were assigned the minimum detection limit value of 10 mR, or 60 mR total for each semi-annual reporting period. A comparison of results from twelve off-site monitoring stations is presented in Table II. The film results are the accumulated assigned exposures for six monthly servicings while the TLD results are the actual accumulated exposures over a six-month period.

TABLE II   NRTS off-site environmental
program
January–June 1967
Values in mR

Station	TLD	Film
1	35	60
2	45	60
3	50	60
4	50	60
5	45	60
6	45	60
7	45	60
8	70	60
9	40	60
10	50	60
11	55	60
12	40	60

This same situation existed with the on-site monitoring stations except for those adjacent to the Burial Ground. Solid waste is deposited in deep trenches which are backfilled as they reach capacity.

TABLE III Burial ground monitoring
all values in mrem

Station	TLD 1st six months '67	Film 1st six months '66
1	275	170
2	110	250
3	110	150
4	80	190
5	65	145
6	85	180
7	90	290
8	45	945
9	60	280
10	45	2070
11	50	170
12	25	240
13	25	160
14	35	220
15	75	2135
16	100	3210
17	165	290
18	435	325
19	215	560
20	45	285
21	130	390
22	65	570
23	125	530
24	140	460
25	310	370
26	510	410
27	695	540
28	735	780
29	990	1025
30	695	1035
31	1205	1750
32	2410	3880
33	2010	365
34	1070	385
35	585	1165

Variable film results are found depending on the content and physical condition of the trenches. A comparison of radiation exposures is presented in Table III for 35 stations for the first six months of 1966 accumulated by

41*

monthly film badges and the first six months of 1967 accumulated by TLDs exposed over the entire period.

The use of LiF–teflon dosimeters for monitoring low-exposure-probability personnel has been accepted by AEC–ID and all Contractors at the NRTS. Some 3,000 persons, or approximately 60% of the regularly assigned NRTS personnel are presently using the LiF–teflon dosimeters on a quarterly servicing schedule. The new program will provide a significant cost savings in less frequent servicing of the badges with the associated record keeping.

Thermoluminescent phenomena is no longer a laboratory curiosity but a routinely applied reality in health physics dosimetry.

Acknowledgement

Special thanks is given to George J. Ball of the ID Environmental Branch for his assistance in compiling this report.

References

1. J. P. Cusimano, United States Atomic Energy Commission, Idaho Operations Office, Report IDO-12060 (1967).
2. F. V. Cipperley, United States Atomic Energy Commission, Idaho Operations Office, Report IDO-12056 (1966).

CHAPTER IV–5

Properties of different phosphors as used in a packaged TLD system; multiple readings of dose by U.V. light transfer

C. BROOKE

Manufacture Belge de Lampes et de Matériel Electronique, 80, rue des Deux Gares, Bruxelles 7

In this paper the practical properties of different phosphors as used in a "packaged" thermoluminescent dosimetry system will be examined.

In particular we will dwell upon special properties of the M.B.L.E. CaF_2, specially upon the repopulation of thermoluminescent traps by exposure to ultra-violet light. This repopulation renders multiple readings of the accumulated dose possible.

645

DOSIMETRY SYSTEM

The properties of phosphors as given hereunder concern their use in the integrated system developed in our laboratories.

This system has been already described[1,2] and only its main properties will be summarized.

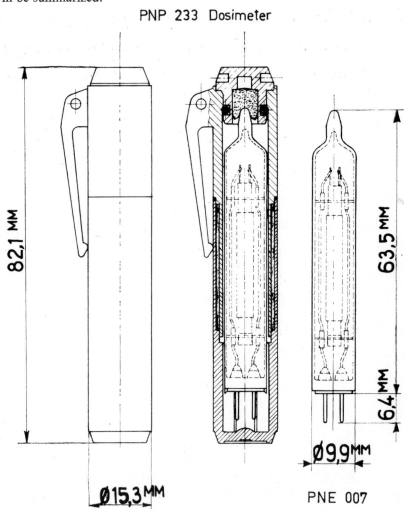

PNP 233 Dosimeter

FIGURE 1　The laboratory dosimeter, which exists in several versions: laboratory and very low dose with M.B.L.E. CaF_2, LiF, etc.

The phosphor is firmly bonded on a small metal tube (cathode) containing a heating filament, the whole being enclosed in an air tight envelope in the shape either of a miniature radio valve or of an electric fuse (Fig. 1 and 2).

PNP 088 Dosimeter

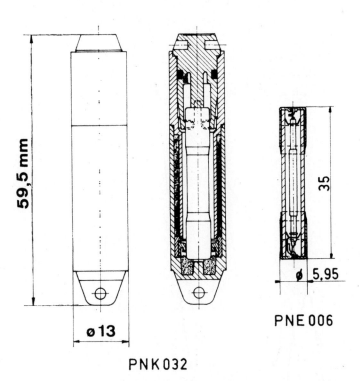

PNE 006

PNK 032

FIGURE 2   The miniature version of the M.B.L.E. CaF$_2$ dosimeter

The reading is very simple, the dosimeter is introduced into a cavity of the reader, the adequate electrical power is applied to the filament for a few seconds, and a photometric system measures the peak height of the main peak of the phosphor used.

Such a packaged system has few drawbacks: the dimensions cannot be made very small, and the structural materials can have a somewhat adverse effect on the energy response.

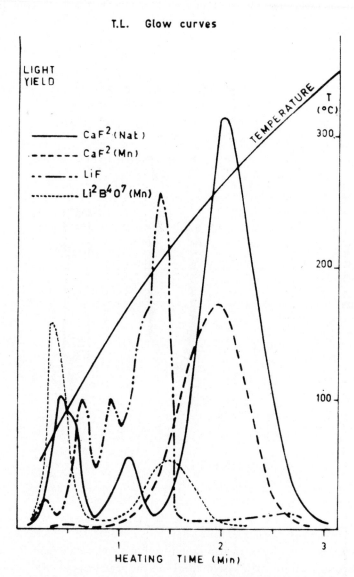

FIGURE 3 Glow curves of most used phosphors, as obtained with
powdered phosphor and slow heating rate. The light yield scale is arbitrary
and gives no indication as to the relative efficiencies of the phosphors

Otherwise there are only advantages:

1 The dosimeter forms a self-contained whole unit, sturdy and permanent, so that each dosimeter can be calibrated individually.

2 It is very easy to read, and the readout could be fully automated; there is no pouring, weighing or positioning of powder.

3 Because the phosphor is firmly bonded onto the cathode and sealed under vacuum or in a controlled atmosphere, there is no so-called triboluminescence nor any alteration in time.

4 Heating with a filament inside a metal tube is particularly efficient and accurate, and the low power needed is easily stabilized to a high degree.

This all means precision and good reproducibility, and allows us to use the peak height method of reading, which is selective (only the main peak is read) and thus gives freedom from low temperature peaks which fade with time, and also entails the best signal to noise ratio.[2]

PROPERTIES OF DIFFERENT PHOSPHORS

The most useful, and most used, phosphors are: $CaF_2(Mn)$, $CaF_2(M.B.L.E.)$, LiF and the recently developed $Li_2B_4O_7$; we shall now examine their properties, especially when used in our TLD systems. We shall leave out $CaSO_4(Mn)$ as this phosphor, though very sensitive, has only a low temperature peak decaying quite rapidly in time.

GLOW CURVES AND DECAY OF INFORMATION

The glow curves of the phosphors are given in Fig. 3, as measured in powdered form with a slow heating rate; it can be seen that they all exhibit an important peak at a sufficiently high temperature, so that no fading of the information should occur.

This is in fact the case for the phosphor based on natural Calcium Fluoride we use, and no fading could be found after 9 months;[3] peaks I + I', corresponding to a temperature of about 80°C fade rapidly as can be seen from Fig. 4 which shows also the decay of peak III at high temperatures, showing that the dosimeter is usable to about 100°C.

For $CaF_2(Mn)$ there is, strangely enough, some decay (see Fig. 5), Schulman has given the explanation (see this volume, page 107), this fading is less when one uses the peak height reading method than with the integral reading method, which explains why the fading showed by $CaF_2(Mn)$ mounted in our type of dosimeters is less than that usually quoted in the literature.

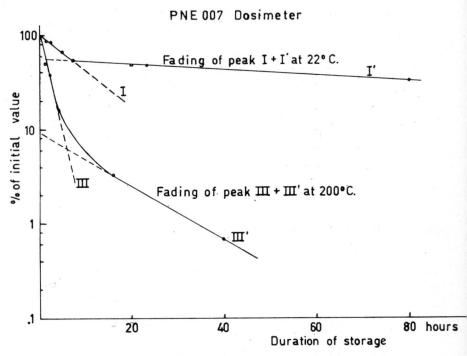

FIGURE 4   The first peak $(I + I')$ of CaF_2 (M.B.L.E.) shows a definite fading at room temperature. Peaks III and III′ are completely stable at room temperature; the curve shows their fading rate at 200°C

Lithium Borate, from preliminary measurements, seems to present no fading (Fig. 6).

For LiF, some contradictory results have been reported in the literature; however, as reported in Cameron's paper, these discrepancies have been explained and there is practically no fading at room temperature.

With the M.B.L.E. type dosimeter, incorporating TLD–100 LiF, bonded with silicone, and measured by the peak height method, there is an effect of prior annealing on the storage properties.

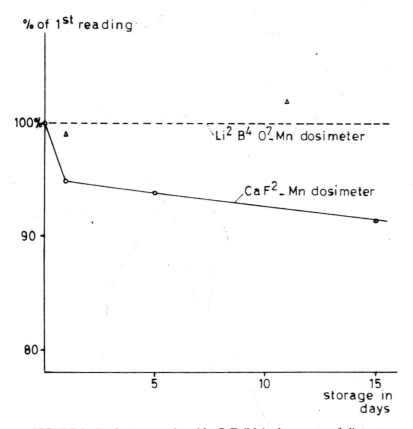

FIGURE 5   Dosimeters made with $CaF_2(Mn)$ show some fading at room temperature, though less than reported in the literature, due to measurement of peak height instead of integral of glow curve. Preliminary measurements on Lithium Borate dosimeters indicate no fading

It is usual to anneal LiF before irradiation (for example 24 hours at 80°C) in order to suppress the low temperature peaks. Figure 6 gives the glow curve of LiF dosimeters with and without annealing. It can be seen that the effect of annealing is not only to reduce the low temperature peaks, but also entails an inversion in the relative heights of the high temperature peaks. This affects the peak height reading.

PNE 010 Dosimeter (LiF)

**Effect of annealing
on the glow curve**

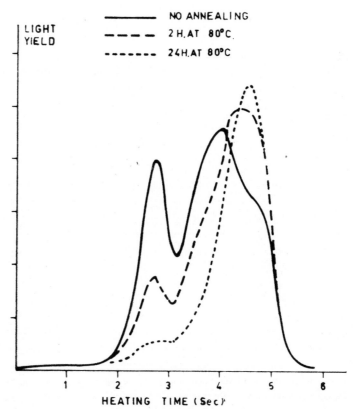

FIGURE 6   Glow curves of LiF (TLD-100) dosimeters after different
annealing treatments

When a dosimeter is irradiated without prior annealing, and stored at room temperature, there is after a few weeks an effect identical to prior annealing, with the effect of giving increased reading by the peak height method.

This room temperature annealing also takes place on unirradiated dosimeters. Figure 7 shows the time needed for annealing as a function of the temperature and confirms the fact that it takes place also at room temperature.

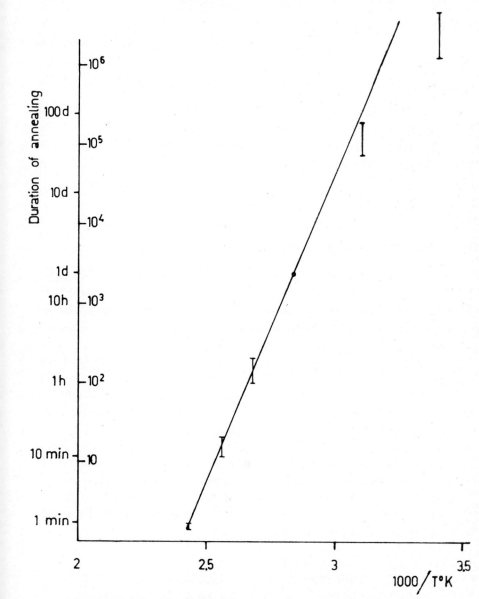

FIGURE 7   Annealing time as a function of temperature for LiF (TLD-100)
dosimeters. The annealing also takes place at room temperature

EFFICIENCY AND SPECTRAL SENSITIVITY

Our laboratory has made some measurements to assess the absolute efficiency of some phosphors.[2,4]

The measurement consisted in counting the photons emitted during the glow curve. This was done with a quartz face E.M.I. 6255 S photomultiplier in geometrical configuration, followed by a very fast amplifier and counting system resolving single photoelectron pulses.

Account is taken of the absorption of light in the phosphor itself by extrapolating the results to zero thickness.

The relative sensitivities for the different phosphors were found to be (expressed in counts per mg of phosphor for a dose of 1R):

CaF_2 (M.B.L.E. Standard)	23,000
Best natural CaF_2	100,000
CaF_2(Mn) from N.R.L.	10,060
LiF (TLD 100)	905

Taking into account the quantum efficiency curve of the photomultiplier tube and the geometrical conditions, we have found for our standard CaF_2 that an energy of 1650 eV is necessary to extract one photoelectron from the photocathode of the P.M. tube under the assumption of total light collection.

The sensitivity of the Lithium Borate we have tried (provided by Dr. Langmead) is about 0.25 of that of TLD 100 using a S 11 type photocathode that is not well suited to its light emission wavelength; it should be possible to reach about the same sensitivity as LiF with a better suited photocathode, such as the EMI "Super S 11".

The lowest detectable dose with a T.L. dosimetry system is of course dependent not only on the intrinsic efficiency, but also on the emission band, its compatibility to available photomultiplier response curves and the possibility of discriminating against heating light by filters.

The main emission wavelengths for the phosphors studied have been investigated by Gorbics[5] and are as follows:

CaF_2 (M.B.L.E.)	3,800 Å
CaF_2 (Mn)	4,950 Å
LiF	4,000 Å
$Li_2B_4O_7$ (Mn)	6,000 Å

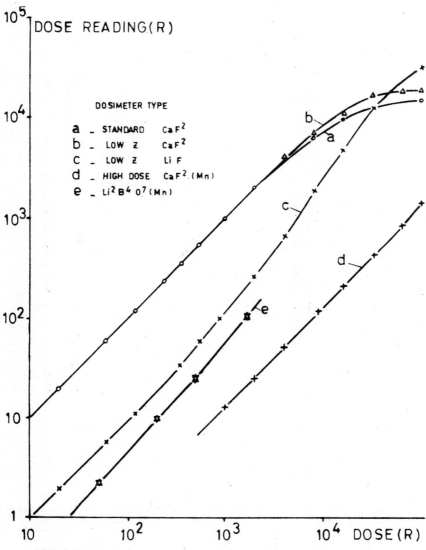

FIGURE 8 Linearity of T.L. dosimeters made with different phosphors

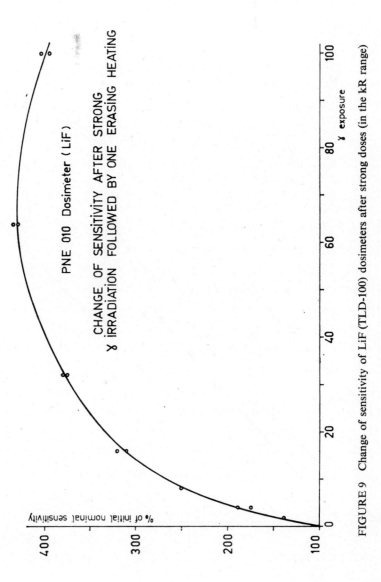

FIGURE 9   Change of sensitivity of LiF (TLD-100) dosimeters after strong doses (in the kR range)

Both our phosphor and LiF emit in the band of best photocathode efficiency while $CaF_2(Mn)$ emits in the green and allows very good separation from the infra-red.

The orange emission of Lithium Borate is awkward both as regards photomultiplier response and separation from heating light.

We have made high sensitivity dosimeters, based on selected and specially treated natural calcium Fluoride that can measure from 100 microroentgen upwards.

LINEARITY AND RADIATION DAMAGE

Another aspect of phosphors is the linearity of their response, their saturation characteristics and resistance to radiation damage.

Figure 8 shows the linearity of dosimeters made with different phosphors in the medium to high dose range.

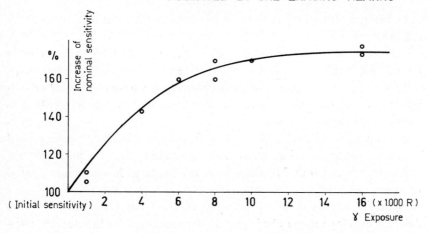

FIGURE 10   Change of sensitivity of CaF_2 (M.B.L.E.) dosimeters after large doses. This change appears only after annealing through heating and thus does not affect the linearity of the first high dose reading

Both types of calcium fluoride are very linear, but whereas natural based CaF_2 shows saturation in the kR range, synthetic $CaF_2(Mn)$ is linear to the Megaroentgen range.

On the other hand, both lithium phosphors show the well reported so-called superlinearity for high doses.

From published results (see Schulman's paper), $CaF_2(Mn)$ is quite impervious to any radiation damage up to very high doses, LiF, on the other hand, is appreciably affected,[6] first by a marked increase in sensitivity (see Fig. 9 for the effect on our dosimeters), followed by a loss in sensitivity.

Our calcium fluoride shows also some increase in sensitivity (Fig. 10) after large doses; however this increase does *not* affect the first reading of that dose, as is borne out by the linearity curve.

The increase in sensitivity appears only after a heat annealing procedure such as is provided by repeated readings of the dosimeter, or a reading followed by an "erasure heating", i.e. a somewhat longer heating (10 instead of 7 seconds) provided on the readers for complete erasure of the dosimeters after large doses.

This increased sensitivity can be brought back to its initial value by a long exposure of the dosimeter to U.V. light.

ENERGY RESPONSE

CaF_2 being a rather high Z material has consequently a rather poor energy response curve.

The response curve obtained with our CaF_2 laboratory dosimeter is given in Fig. 11; it gives a factor of 7 at 50 keV; and so needs correction.

Figure 12 shows the response curve obtained with a tin and lead filter with holes; one can see that it is within 25% from 30 keV upwards, which is adequate for most purposes.

In the case of the LiF dosimeter, as the phosphor itself has quite a good response, the structural materials have a marked effect, in particular the envelope material (our LiF dosimeters are made with aluminium instead of nickel cathodes).

Figure 13 and 14 show the response curve of our LiF dosimeters with different envelope materials; higher Z structures tend to increase the over-shoot and displace it to higher energies, while of course worsening the cut-off energies.

We have as yet no measurements on lithium borate dosimeters.

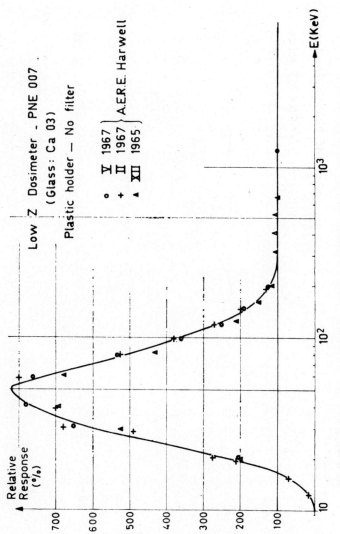

FIGURE 11 Energy response of bare CaF$_2$ (M.B.L.E.) type PNE 007 dosimeter

42*

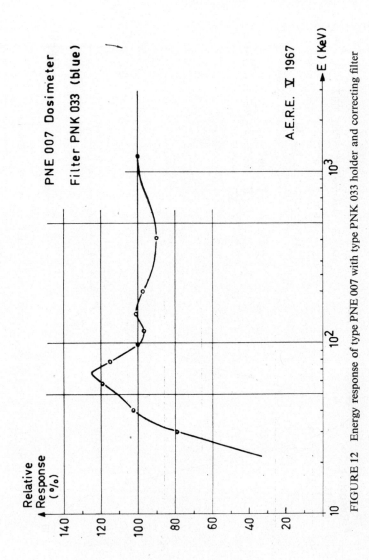

FIGURE 12   Energy response of type PNE 007 with type PNK 033 holder and correcting filter

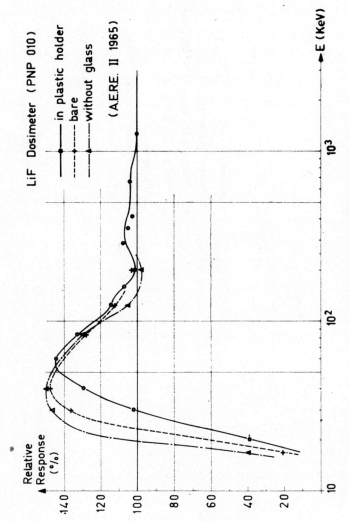

FIGURE 13 Effect of the envelope material of LiF (TLD-100) dosimeters

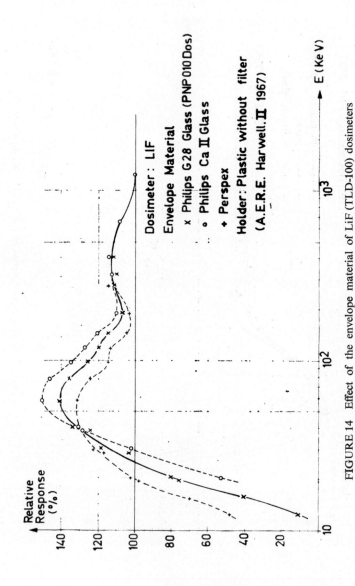

FIGURE 14 Effect of the envelope material of LiF (TLD-100) dosimeters

BETA RESPONSE

We have made some prototype dosimeters with plastic instead of glass envelopes. Preliminary measurements of sensitivity to β rays, made with Mr. Harvey (C.E.G.B. Dos. Lab. Berkeley) give the following results:

Isotopes	$E_{\max}$	Sensitivity = $R_{(Co^{60})}/Rad_{(tissue)}$	
		CaF_2	LiF
^{90}Y	2.27	~0.7	~0.65
^{210m}Bi	1.17	~0.45	~0.3
^{204}TC	0.77	~0.12	—

One can visualize a "badge" containing several small TL dosimeters with different filters and/or different phosphors, adapted to any particular radiation risk and automatically read when needed in a few seconds.

To conclude the first part of this paper, it should be noted that the properties of CaF_2 from different origins may vary greatly as has been reported by Mr. Schayês in Stanford.[4]

Usually one finds the different peaks at the same temperatures, but both their relative importance and their absolute efficiency can vary between wide limits.

Up to now we have been unable to assign accurately the properties of Fluorides with the type of impurities on their concentration.

EFFECT OF EXPOSURE TO LIGHT ON NATURAL BASED CaF$_2$

When an irradiated CaF_2 dosimeter is exposed to light there is a loss of the stored dose (Fig. 15, curve C), which means that the dosimeters must not be unduly exposed to strong light in practical use.

When a new, virgin dosimeter is exposed to light, there is a slight TL build-up to an asymptotic value (Fig. 15, curve A) depending on annealing and other treatments of the phosphor.

If the dosimeter, before exposure to light, has received radiation doses (which have been read and erased), the same asymptotic TL build-up occurs but this build-up bears a linear relationship with the total life dose on the dosimeter. It is obvious that this effect can be used for a repeated reading of the integrated dose on the dosimeter.

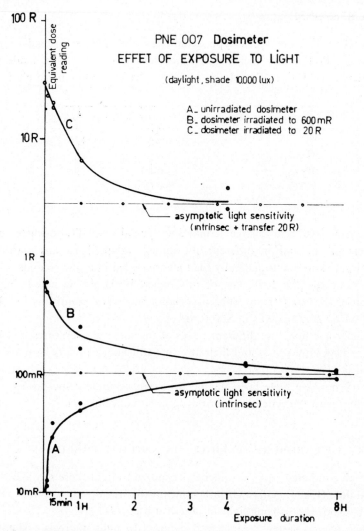

FIGURE 15   Effect of light on PNE 007 CaF$_2$ (M.B.L.E.) dosimeters

We will now consider this repopulation of TL traps by light. The trap structure of CaF$_2$ (M.B.L.E.) is quite complex and some very deep traps exist, giving rise to glow peaks (V, and in some fluorites VI) at high temperatures (550°C for peak V) (Fig. 16).

It is not a practical proposition to read these peaks by heating, because such high temperatures are detrimental to the phosphor, and moreover there is a significant light quenching.

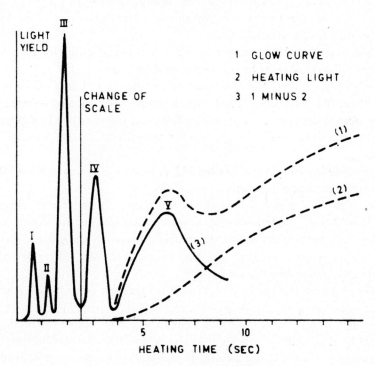

FIGURE 16   Glow curve of CaF_2 (M.B.L.E.) dosimeter under very strong heating to show peak V

Thus the deep traps are never emptied in the course of normal use of the dosimeter, and consequently store and integrate the accumulated life dose on the dosimeter, irrespective of the number of normal TL measurements.

When exposed to light there is a transfer of charge carriers from the deep traps to shallower traps corresponding to the normal TL glow peaks.

If the transferred charge carriers correspond to a small fraction of the available carriers stored in the deep traps, and if the transfer conditions (amount of light, geometry, etc....) remain constant this repopulation can be repeated several times and can represent an accurate measurement of the dose.

It is interesting to note that the carriers are in fact transferred mainly not to the normal principal peak III, but to the neighbouring peak III'. It is also an increase in this peak III' (and not peak III) which is responsible for the increase in sensitivity observed after strong irradiations.

We have no explanation yet for this different behaviour of peaks at nearly equal temperatures.

When exposing the dosimeters to light the loss of dose competes with the repopulation of traps by transfer from deep traps.

The intensity of these two effects depends on the spectral distribution of the light used. We have determined experimentally that shorter wavelengths in the ultra-violet are relatively more effective in transfer than in depopulation of traps and give a better transfer intensity to loss of information ratio.

In practice one cannot use very hard U.V. because of the absorption of the glass envelope of the dosimeters.

Let us finish with practical results of this light transfer memory effect.

Figure 17 gives the transferred amount (expressed in transferred dose reading relative to given dose). In practice, to avoid too great a loss of information at each transfer, it is best to use a transfer corresponding to about 0.5 % of the dose received.

Figure 18 gives the linearity of transfer for medium doses, which is quite good.

For high doses, the transfer is "superlinear" (Fig. 19), this can be explained by the radiation damage (increase in sensitivity) at these doses.

This increase in sensitivity, as already said, does not appear on first reading of the dose, but only after annealing through reading and erasing. Of course the light transfer is only made after erasing, and in fact the transfer is linear if the readings are corrected for the increase in sensitivity.

Another important aspect is the loss of stored information at each transfer. In the conditions adopted, this loss is approximately 20 % after 10 readings (Fig. 20).

There is a threshold for the light transfer, due to some intrinsic light sensitivity and remnants of peaks V not emptied by the treatment given to the phosphor and dosimeter in the course of manufacture.

This threshold, under optimized conditions, is 3 R (equivalent transferred dose) for laboratory dosimeters.

With a calibrated U.V. exposure jig it is possible to obtain a standard deviation of 5 % on the measurement of doses by the light transfer effect.

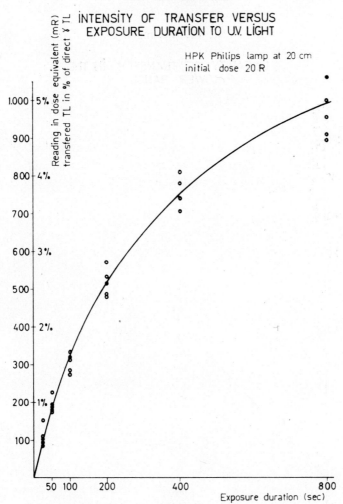

FIGURE 17 Intensity of U.V. light transfer expressed in fraction of
initial dose in function of duration of exposure to U.V.

This possibility of multiple readings of integrated doses, with good accuracy albeit only above a few Roentgens, inherent to CaF_2 of natural origin, should go a long way to meeting the objections of loss of information made to TLD, and this advantage impairs in no way whatsoever the accuracy and sensitivity of the normal thermoluminescence measurements.

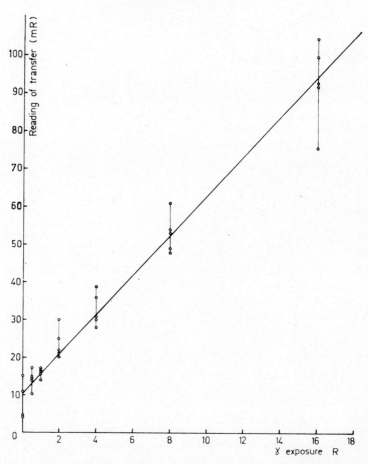

PNE 007 Dosimeter

LINEARITY OF TRANSFER IN THE
LOWER RANGE

FIGURE 18   Linearity of the U.V. light transfer for medium doses

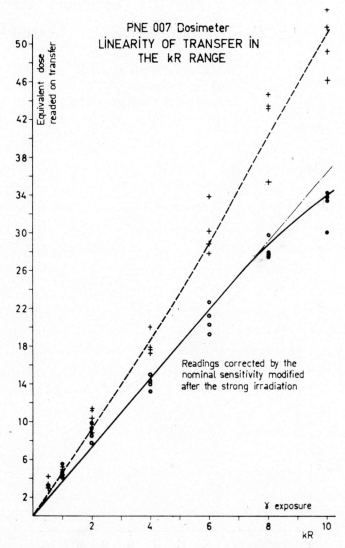

FIGURE 19   Linearity of the U.V. light transfer for large doses, showing the effect of increased sensitivity after a large dose

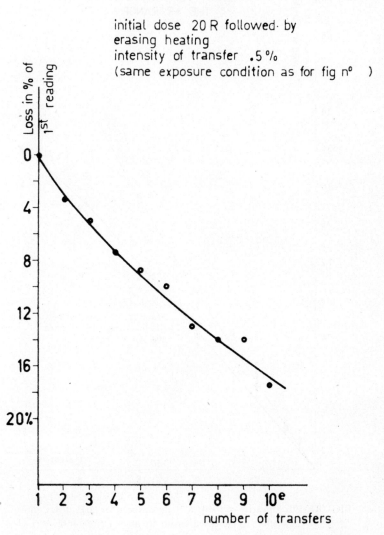

FIGURE 20   Loss of stored information for repetitive light transfers

References

1. C. Brooke and R. Schayes, "Recent developments in thermoluminescent dosimetry; extensions in the range of applications," *Solid State and Chemical Radiation Dosimetry in Medicine and Biology*, p. 31, I.A.E.A., Vienna (1967).
2. R. Schayes, C. Brooke, I. Kozlowitz, and M. Lheureux, "New developments in thermoluminescent dosimetry," *Health Physics* in press (1968).
3. J. R. Harvey, "Some applications of low-dose thermoluminescence measurements with calcium fluoride," *Luminescence Dosimetry* p. 331 – U.S.A.E.C. Conf. – 650637 (1967).
4. R. Schayes, C. Brooke, I. Kozlowitz, and M. Lheureux, Thermoluminescent properties of natural calcium fluoride; Luminescence Dosimetry p. 138 – U.S.A.E.C. Conf. – 650637 (1967).
5. S. G. Gorbics, "The emission spectra of various thermoluminescent materials" N.R.L. 6404 (1966).
6. J. R. Cameron, L. Dewerd, J. Wagner, C. Wilson, K. Doppke, and D. Zimmerman, "Non linearity of thermoluminescence as a function of dose for LiF (TLD-100)," *Solid State and Chemical Radiation Dosimetry in Medicine and Biology*" p. 77, I.A.E.A., Vienna (1967).

Film dosimetry and criticality dosimeters

R. BOULENGER and L. GHOOS

Contrôle — Radioprotection
c/o C.E.N. — Mol, Belgium

A   INTRODUCTION

The purpose of radiation dosimetry of personnel is to determine the doses absorbed by various critical organs of men professionally exposed to ionizing radiation sources.

In this way it will be possible:

— to compare these doses with the maximum permissible doses as determined by the I.C.R.P. and described in the national legal prescriptions.[1,2]

— to perform operational control in order to adapt the working methods and to improve the shielding dispositions and hence to decrease the doses to a minimum value.

— to provide indications which are required by the physician in charge of treatment in case of an accident.

The doses to be measured cover the whole range from doses comparable to the natural background up to fatal doses.

Doses due to the natural background are caused by cosmic rays and by the presence of non-negligible condensations of natural nuclides, e.g. from the uranium–radium and the thorium family. These doses are about 100 mr/year.

The maximum permissible doses allowed by the I.C.R.P. are:

— 3 rem/13 weeks and 5 rem/year for the blood-forming organs and the gonads.

— 15 rem/13 weeks and 60 rem/year for the extremities.

— 8 rem/13 weeks and 30 rem/year for skin, bone marrow and the thyroid gland.*

— 4 rem/13 weeks and 15 rem/year for the other organs.

To guide the medical diagnosis of the accidentally irradiated person, the dosimeters have to measure doses up to at least 1000 rad.

As the maximum permissible levels are different from one group of organs to the other, it is necessary, when dealing with high doses, to have means for estimating the doses at the various organs.

The absorbed doses may differ from one organ to the other:

— either due to the inhomogeneity of the irradiation: source close to the irradiated person, or a partially shielded source emitting a beam.

— either due to important absorption of less penetrating radiation.

— or due to inward build-up of dose following the multiple Compton collisions of photons with energies above some MeV.

Figure 1 (Ref. 3) shows this effect for γ- and x-irradiation. These curves have been calculated for water but are also valid for human tissue, the energy absorption coefficient being close to 2%. These curves show that the measurement of radiation at the human surface only is not sufficient for an adequate knowledge of the biological hazard.

---

* In the Euratom recommendations the thyroid gland is classified in the group of other organs: 4 rem/13 weeks and 15 rem/year.

Indeed, the ratio of the dose absorbed at the surface to the dose absorbed at 10 cm of depth is respectively:

500 for photons of 20 keV
20 for photons of 30 keV
2 for photons of 100 keV
±1 for photons of 200 keV to 10 MeV
0.25 for photons of 40 MeV
0.07 for photons of 100 MeV.

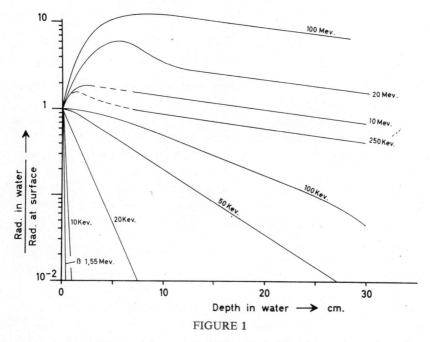

FIGURE 1

The number ±1 for photons from 200 keV to 10 MeV allows simplifications in many cases. When estimating the energy of photons it is nevertheless necessary to take into account not only the primary but also the secondary radiation of lower energy due to the multiple Compton collisions on the environment.

This secondary radiation may become very important in the case of a shield which is thick enough to protect personnel against direct radiation, but which does not enclose the source in a leaktight way and hence permits scattered radiation to reach the personnel.

43*

x-rays as used in diagnostics and therapy are produced by tubes powered by 30 to 200 kV. The radiation spectrum emitted by the electrons colliding in the anticathode ranges from 0 to the energy corresponding to the accelerating voltage: from 30 to 200 keV.

From the point of view of the continuous absorption spectrum, the useful energy, in the case of the normally used filters, is about half of the accelerating voltage: 15 to 100 keV. In addition to the continuous spectrum due to the colliding electrons, an emission line spectrum characteristic of the anticathode elements is recognized:

> copper   8   to 9 keV
> molybdenum 17.4 to 200 keV
> tungsten   58   to 69.2 keV

The tungsten anticathodes are mostly used for medical purposes. Other metals may be used for diffraction and fluorescence analysis.

The personnel dosimeters using x-ray generators should respond to energies of a few keV and should permit a rough spectrometry in order to estimate doses at different depths when the doses at the surface are higher than the doses permissible for the blood-forming organs and the gonads.

Betatrons are more frequently used in therapy. It is necessary to multiply the doses measured by the personnel dosimeters by a building factor related to the ratio of the doses at the blood-forming organs or the ovaries to the doses at the surfaces.

Furthermore, most dosimeters are worn at the chest. In the case of an inhomogeneous irradiation this may give rise to an erroneous estimation of dose.

When criticality accidents may arise, people are wearing belts provided with several neutron and gamma dosimeters in order to enable an estimation of the inhomogeneity of doses and the direction of the irradiation.

This practice could possibly be extrapolated to the use of x-rays: doses due to x-irradiations on a person's back can be underestimated or even not be detected at all by a dosimeter worn on the chest.

As many shielding windows do not offer enough attenuation it is very often recommended to provide a dosimeter at the forehead in order to control the doses at the eyes.

During manipulation of the β-emitting radionuclides without telemanipulators, the doses at the fingers should be measured: the filmdosimeters worn formerly for that purpose are now replaced by LiF-dosimeters.

The doses due to beta irradiations absorbed in human organisms, are limited to the skin and the organs at small depths, i.e. depths equal to the free range of the betas: a few cm of tissue. The protective layer for the eye is about 300 mg/cm². Figure 1 shows the variation of dose as a function of depth for betas of 1.5 MeV.

In practice two completely different situations have to be considered:

— daily control: the doses received are weak. The aim is to verify if doses are inferior to the imposed standards. The highest values which are communicated to the project leaders, should stimulate them to improve working conditions and shielding.

— hazardous irradiations yielding important doses; it is obviously of great interest for the irradiated persons to determine the doses with the highest possible precision and as completely as possible.[4]

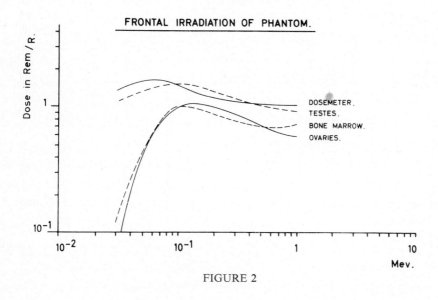

FIGURE 2

Figures 2 and 3 (from Jones, Ref. 5) refer to a homogeneous field of photons incident on a dummy exposed to a frontal irradiation or on a dummy irradiated while rotating on its vertical axis. The curves give the doses at the chest (dosimeter), bone marrow and gonads as a function of the energy of the incident radiation.

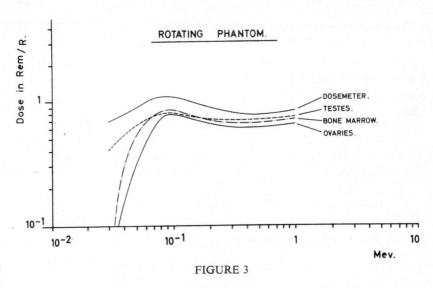

FIGURE 3

One observes that under these conditions the doses received by the dosi-meter are an upper limit. This will not be the case when the incident photons have an energy higher than a few MeV, which gives an important build-up or even when they have an energy below 100 keV but are incident at the back (Fig. 4).

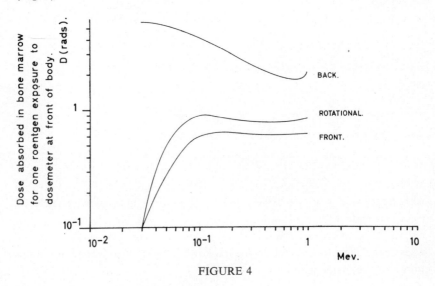

FIGURE 4

B DOSIMETRY BY PHOTOGRAPHIC FILMS

The use of photographic films as radiation detectors is obviously related to their use in radiography and autoradiography. Because of the high atomic number of silver and bromine compared with the atomic numbers of the elements in the air or in human tissues, the films will nevertheless show a much higher sensitivity to photons of lower energy (about 50 keV)—range of medical x-rays—than for photons with energy above 200 keV (Fig. 5).

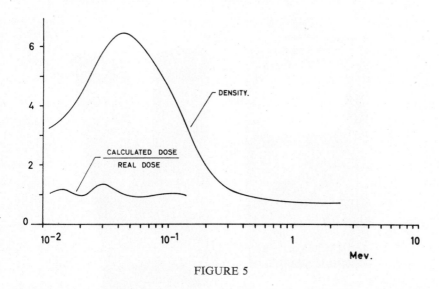

FIGURE 5

The measurement errors induced by this sensitivity variation could be eliminated either by absorbing shields or by fluorescent reinforcing shields. The latter ones have not been used in practical dosimetry since the reciprocity law is satisfied for the low intensities corresponding e.g. to incident dose rates lower than 10 mr/h.

Since the absorbing shield makes the films insensitive to photon energies below a given value, one uses different shields in order to differentiate photons of different energies, e.g. the beta radiation photons. By the use of shields exhibiting an (n, γ) reaction, thermal neutron may also be detected in this may.

On the other hand dosimetry of fast neutrons is performed by the use of nuclear emulsions. The dosimetry of intermediate neutrons has not yet been realized by dosimeters worn by personnel.

C DOSIMETRY BY FILMS C.E.N.—S.C.K.

To illustrate the principles mentioned above we will now give a description of the film dosimeter used in our laboratory (Fig. 6).

The holder is in polypropylene FG 41 Black 951 moulded by injection. This material has been chosen for its good mechanical properties and its opacity

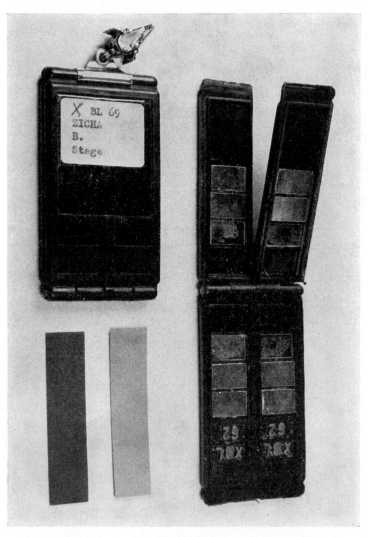

FIGURE 6

to light even in thin layers (100 mg/cm²); the films used are inserted in the holders without prior enveloping in a light absorbing paper, as is usually the case. The holder is built such that two film strips of 15 × 60 mm each can be independently reached. Both sides of the holder are symmetrically provided with pairs of filter shields. The holder is closed by means of a spring. Holes are provided for critically detectors. Lead figures and letters are put inside the holder, reproducing the exterior identification after being exposed to *x*-rays of 10 keV: only this part of the photographic film corresponding to the position of these identification marks is exposed during identification.

1 Characteristics of the film

Industrial radiography films Structurix D 10 and D 2 produced by Gevaert-Agfa are used.

The most sensitive film D 10 presents the following advantages: weak fog, remarkable sensitivity, no saturation effects in the range of densities from 0 to 7, low fading for a working period of 15 days in normal conditions.

The other low sensitive film D 2, has one emulsion whereas the D10 film has two emulsions and it is provided to extend the measurement range to very high doses: its capture factor is 60 times that of the Structurix D 10.

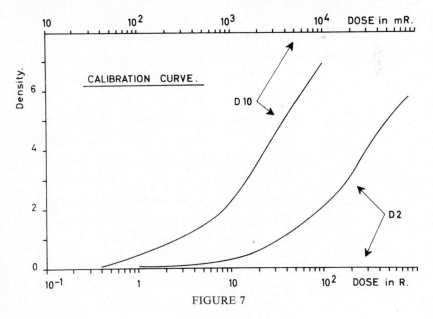

FIGURE 7

The characteristic curves of both films are shown in Fig. 7 for exposure to ^{60}Co radiations. These curves give the optical density as a function of the logarithm of dose. The optical density is the decimal logarithm of the ratio of transmitted to incident light intensity when the film is examined in a photometer.

For other energies, for other kinds of incident radiation, or for other filtering shields one obtains a family of density versus logarithm of dose curves and each of these curves is obtained by translation of another parallel to the horizontal.

Figure 8 the characteristic density curves as a function of dose for different energies of x-rays and beta rays, the film being protected by a

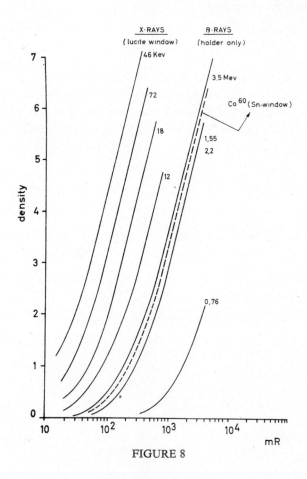

FIGURE 8

supplementary shield of lucite for the *x*-rays, and having no additional shield for beta rays.

2 Choice of the shielding windows

The holder is provided with four windows, three of which having an addional shield:

a) lead 220 mg/cm^2, tin 1100 mg/cm^2, aluminium 27 mg/cm^2

b) lead 220 mg/cm^2, cadmium 1100 mg/cm^2, aluminium 27 mg/cm^2

c) lucite 200 mg/cm^2

d) holder without additional shield 100 mg/cm^2.

Measurements of the optical density at each window allow successive determination of doses due to photons of energy above about 90 keV, to photons of energy below about 90 keV, to beta radiations and to thermal neutrons.

a *Dose due to photons with energy above 90 keV*

The shield composed of lead, tin and aluminium is used as a filter which allows the transmission of higher energy gamma or *x*-rays: the latter are almost not absorbed when passing through a thickness of water equivalent of that of the human body.

The sensitivity of the film under this window is not strictly independent of energy but the variations are negligible. The aluminium layer of 27 mg/cm^2 has been added to decrease the reinforcing effect, by emission of secondary electrons by the tin–lead shield, this effect being a function of energy.

The black paper, enveloping the film in other dosimeters, has a function similar to this aluminium layer.

b *Dose due to photons of energy below about 90 keV*

The measurement of electromagnetic radiation has to be extended to energies as low as 10 to 15 keV. The dose due to photons of energy below 90 keV is determined by means of the higher apparent dose received by the film under the lucite shield. As the film is much more sensitive to the low energies than to the energies of ^{60}Co radiation a correction factor which is a function of photon energy has to be applied to this supplement. In order to obtain a better determination of the energy of these photons, one may use the ratio of the higher apparent doses under the lucite window and under the bare window respectively.

Solid state dosimetry

By calibrating for these known energies the curves of Fig. 9 are obtained where the energy of photons is plotted on the horizontal axis. On the vertical axis we have plotted at the left the ratio of the higher apparent doses under the lucite shield to the one under the bare window. At the right side the correction factor which has to be applied for each energy has been plotted.

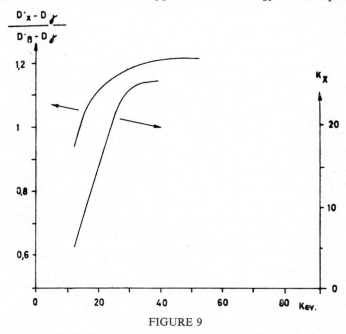

FIGURE 9

Such method can only be applied strictly when the dosimeter has been irradiated by one energy of photons below 90 keV and without exposure to beta irradiation.

In case this determination cannot be applied we use a mean correction factor equal to 25. The use of this factor brings about an underestimation of the dose for photons energies below 25 keV.

For *x*-rays having an energy below 10 keV, the absorption by the lucite window of 200 mg/cm^2 can be compared with the absorption by this window of beta rays having an energy of some MeV.

c   *Doses due to beta radiations*

The determination of doses due to beta rays is essentially based on the apparent dose supplement below the window without additional shield.

As mentioned in the previous section the x-rays of very low energies have an absorption comparable to the absorption of beta rays of some MeV. If the film dosimeters can be worn by personnel being possibly exposed to very low energy x-rays and beta rays, we recently added a filter having a thickness of 0.1 mm of copper covering one third of the base window's surface, a second third of this window being covered by 0.36 mm of aluminium. These filters offer equal absorption to beta rays while they act differently for low energy x-rays. Should there be any doubt, we have means for choosing the appropriate correction factor. During further calibration for x-rays, the dose behind the copper filter, compared to that behind the bare window, can give further information for determining the energy of the incident x-rays.

The thickness of the so-called bare window is 100 mg/cm^2 and the determination of doses is limited to energies higher than 0.7 MeV. The smallest detectable energy is far above 70 keV, i.e. the maximum energy stopped by the skin (7 mg/cm^2).

Nevertheless manipulation of beta ray emitters is usually done with sufficient protection to avoid significant doses to the skin due to betas of energy below 0.7 MeV.

In other cases a supplementary dosimeter is used based on LiF and protected by 7 mg/cm^2 of polyethylene.

The critical organ for betas is rather the crystalline lens of the eyes than the skin; the former is protected by about 300 mg/cm^2 soft tissue.

The characteristic density curves for beta rays of different maximum energies are given in Fig. 8 and they allow the determination of the correction factors.

These curves have been obtained by perpendicular irradiation of te-, dosimeters with the following sources: ^{106}Rh (3.5 MeV), ^{90}Sr (2.2 MeVh) ^{91}Y (1.55 MeV), ^{204}Tl (0.76 MeV).

d *Doses due to thermal neutrons*

Next to the lead-tin-aluminium filter another filter has been provided consisting of lead, cadmium, and aluminium which exhibits equivalent absorption for gamma and x-rays. Irradiation without any thermal neutrons, will yield equal densities behind both filters.

However, when the filter has been exposed to a thermal neutron flux, it will show a higher density behind the lead-cadmium-aluminium filter; this higher density is due to the photons emitted during the (n, γ) reaction in cadmium.

The apparent dose supplement in gammas has to be divided by 2.1 in order to give the thermal neutron dose expressed in rem.

In case of an important thermal neutron dose the capture photons may give rise to an increase of density of the film under the next filter and a correction factor must be applied to gamma dose determination.

3   Development and calibration

The films are developed and fixed following the general rules for Structurix radiographic films and after drying their densities are determined by means of a densitometer. Development is achieved in a climatized room in order to avoid temperature changes of the bath.

Each bath is prepared for simultaneous development or fixation of 220 films, some of them being the calibration films and the virgin film of the same emulsion. This has to be done in order to avoid the influence of variations of one bath to another due to temperature, duration or reduced action of the chemical agents.

The baths are not stirred since this results in an increased difference in density for films irradiated at equal doses. The films are sufficiently isolated in order to prevent reciprocal influence.

The calibration films have been irradiated with a ^{60}Co or a ^{226}Ra source to known doses. This calibration is performed in a wooden building and the distances from the source to the films are kept small with respect to the distances from the films to the ground in order to avoid as much as possible the influence of scattered radiation.

Measurement of these calibration films allows to plot the characteristic curves by which the determination of the doses received by the films developed simultaneously in the same bath is performed. Although these curves have practically always the same shape for the same type of film (i.e. one experimental point should in principle be sufficient for the plot) it is preferable to take a sufficient number of points into account to draw the curve.

As for dose determination, we use the densities measured under three windows (cadmium excluded), three curves are always drawn.

Calibration of the dosimeter for the different types of radiation has been carried out by SCK–CEN at Mol, by Physikalisch Technische Bundesanstalt at Brunswich (Germany) and by Radiological Protection Service at Sutton (England).

During 1964 the dosimeters have been submitted to different tests by the Health Physics of Euratom in different services for standard irradiations: following these tests improvements were performed at the dosimeter with regard to photons having energies between 30 keV and 3 MeV.

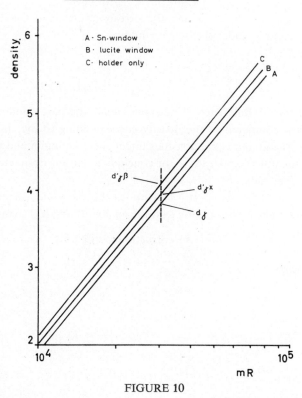

FIGURE 10

4   Determination of doses

a   *Single radiation*

i *Photons with energy higher than 90 keV*—If d_γ is the density of the film under the tin filter we deduce a dose D_γ using the calibration curve.

ii *Photons with energy below 90 keV*—If d_X is the density of the film under the lucite filter and d_β the density under the bare window, then D'_X and D'_β

are the corresponding doses taken from the characteristic curves drawn for the densities under the lucite and bare window respectively. The value of the ratio $\dfrac{D'_X}{D'_\beta}$ is a function of the energy of the incident electromagnetic radiation.

Knowing the value of this ratio, Fig. 8 allows to determine the effective energy of the incident radiation and the correction factor K_X which has to be applied.

On the other hand, a fictive dose D'_X corresponds to the density d_X, on the characteristic curve under the lucite window.

The real X-dose, is then

$$D_X = \frac{D'_X}{K_X}.$$

iii *Beta rays*—A difference of densities under the bare window and the lucite window compared to the density corresponding to the characteristic curve on one hand and equal densities under the aluminium and the copper window on the other hand leads to the conclusion that the dosimeter has been exposed to beta radiation.

We call d_β the density of the film under the bare window and D'_β the corresponding fictive dose on the calibration curve for ^{60}Co (bare window). The ratio $\dfrac{D'_X}{D'_\beta}$ allows to choose the correction factor which is a function of the beta ray energy

$$\frac{D'_X}{D'_\beta} > 0.7 \qquad\qquad K_\beta = 1$$

$$0.70 > \frac{D'_X}{D'_\beta} > 0.20 \qquad\qquad K_\beta = 1.5$$

$$0.20 > \frac{D'_X}{D'_\beta} \qquad\qquad K_\beta = 4.$$

The real β dose is then $D_\beta = D'_\beta \cdot K_\beta$

iv *Thermal neutrons*—We call d_{Cd} the density under the cadmium window. Using the calibration curve, corresponding to the tin filter (identical to the cobalt window curve) we find the corresponding fictive dose D'_{Cd}. The dose due to thermal neutrons is then

$$D_{th} = \frac{D'_{Cd}}{2.1}.$$

b *Multiple radiation*

When a dosimeter is exposed to different types of radiation; we have to take into account the reciprocal influence of each type of radiation on the density under the different windows.

  i *Mixture of photons with energy above 90 keV and beta rays*—Determination of the density under the tin window d_γ immediately yields the gamma dose D_γ. Corresponding to this dose D_γ on the characteristic calibration curves we obtain a density $d'_{\gamma\beta}$ under the bare window and $d'_{\gamma X}$ under the lucite window (Fig. 10).

The presence of beta rays increases the density under these windows and we obtain: $d_\beta > d'_{\gamma\beta}$ and $d_X > d'_{\gamma X}$.

The fictive dose corresponding to a density $d'_{\gamma\beta}$ equals D_γ. We call D'_β the dose corresponding to the density d_β on the calibration source ^{60}Co under the bare window.

The β dose equals $D_\beta = K_\beta(D'_\beta - D_\gamma)$.

K_β has been determined as for single beta radiation but by considering the ratio

$$\frac{D'_X - D_\gamma}{D'_\beta - D_\gamma},$$

where D'_X is the fictive dose corresponding to d'_X on the calibration curve ^{60}Co under the lucite window.

  ii *Mixture of electromagnetic energies having energies above and below 90 keV*—D_γ is again determined through d_γ.

The densities d_β and d_X are read under the respective windows and they yield the fictive dose D'_X and D'_β.

We determine the ratio

$$\frac{D'_X - D_\gamma}{D'_\beta - D_\gamma},$$

which is a function of the energy of the incident soft radiation.

The value of this ratio allows to determine the energy of the incident radiation (Fig. 9); the second curve of the figure gives the correction factor K_X which has to be applied to the fictive dose; the real dose equals

$$D_X = \frac{D'_X - D_\gamma}{K_X}.$$

D'_x has been determined on the calibration curve corresponding to the densities measured under the lucite window for a density d_x.

iii *Mixture of gamma rays and thermal neutrons*—By measuring the density under the tin window we determine the dose due to gamma rays as in the preceding cases. The density d_{Cd} under the cadmium shield is measured and we obtain $D_{\gamma Cd}$ on the calibration curve

$$D_{th} = \frac{D_{\gamma Cd} - D_\gamma}{2.1}.$$

iv *Mixture of gamma, X and beta rays, and thermal neutrons*—The interpretation method can be generalized. In the few cases where the dosimeter has been irradiated with photons of energy lower than 90 keV and with betas, the interpretation could give rise to erroneous results. In this case we intend to use an additional lithium fluoride dosimeter with a 100 mg/cm^2 shield.

5 Characteristics of the dosimeter

a *Gammas and hard X-rays*

The measurement of these types of radiation covers the energy range above 85 keV. The measurement range is from 10 mrad to 2000 rad with two regions

film D_{10} 10 mrad to 5 rad
film D_2 2 rad   to 2000 rad.

The relative error on the dose for an unknown radiation is about 25%.

b *Gammas and soft X-rays*

The measurement range for these energies depends on the energy of the incident radiation. For energies of about 40 keV where the film is most sensitive the following regions are recognized:

film D_{10} 1 mrad to 300 mrad
film D_2 100 mrad to 70 rad.

In the case of an exposure to a simple radiation with known energy, the measurement range can be increased by extending the calibration under the thicker lead–tin–aluminium window.

The relative error on the dose for an unknown radiation depends on the integrated dose: for lower doses (100 mrad) and for energies below 40 keV the error may amount to +100%, for higher doses at all energies (between 10 and 80 keV) the relative error is about 20%.

c Beta rays

The measurement of the beta ray absorption is delicate due to the important absorption of electrons by the holder itself and the important influence of the angle of incidence. It is however of main importance to detect the presence of beta rays.

The film D_{10} measures doses up to 7 rads while the film D_2 measures up to 2000 rads. The precision can be evaluated at some 50%.

d Thermal neutrons

The measurement range for thermal neutrons depends upon the gamma dose received: 5 mrem can already be measured with the D_{10} film while the film D_2 allows determination of doses up to 1000 rem.

In the absence of gamma rays the measurement range goes from 5 mrem to 2.5 rem for the film D_{10} and from 1 rem to 100 rem for the film D_2.

6 Use as criticality dosimeters

The holder of the film dosimeter can be completed with:

— sulphur for detection and measurement of the fission neutrons
— gold for the determination of thermal and epithermal neutrons,
— indium for quick identification of irradiated personnel
— a small LiF–teflon rod for measurement of the gamma dose.

a Characteristics of the different detectors

We will now briefly review the characteristics of the different detectors.

i *Sulphur*—The reaction $^{32}S\,(n, p)\,^{32}P$ with threshold at 2.8 MeV enables one to use sulphur as a detector for fission neutrons with a spectrum of the form

$$\phi(E)\,dE = 0.453\,e^{-E/0.965}\sinh{(2.29)^{1/2}} \cdot dE.$$

The mean cross section for these fission neutrons equals 0.065 barn and ^{32}P has a half-life of 14.2 days. 10.9 radiations per minute and per gramma

44*

correspond to one rad of fission neutrons and the beta rays emitted have an energy of 1.7 MeV.

ii *Gold*—The use of gold as a criticality detector is based on the reaction ^{197}Au (n, γ) ^{198}Au. The mean cross section for thermal neutrons equals 98.8 barns while for epithermal neutrons in a $1/E$ spectrum the resonance integral amounts to 1556 barns. The half life of ^{198}Au is 2.7 days and each desintegration gives rise to betas of 0.96 MeV for 99% and to gammas of 0.41 MeV for 100%. The number of desintegrations per minute, per gramme and per rad equals 1.47×10^5 for $1/E$ neutrons and 8.5×10^5 for thermal neutrons.

iii *Indium*—Indium has an isotopic abundance of 96% ^{115}In. The thermal neutron cross section for the reaction ^{115}In $(n\gamma)$ ^{116}In equals 150 barns while the resonance integral for the $1/E$ neutrons equals 2640 barns. The half life of ^{116}In equals 54 minutes.

These characteristics show its high sensitivity as a neutron detector. This high sensitivity allows its use as an exposure detector: its short half life is not a drawback since the exposed personnel can be selected within one hour after the accident.

iv *LiF–teflon*—The presence of teflon does not modify the excellent characteristics of LiF and its incorporation in our film dosimeters as a supplementary detector for gamma rays is fully justified.

Its response is practically independent of energy for beta, gamma and *x*-rays and the light materials which it is composed of, give it a response very near to that of human tissue. Used in the form of small rods having 6 mm of length and 1 mm of diameter, the ^{7}Li isotope (99.97%) permits determination of X and gamma doses higher than 1 r with a standard deviation of 3%.

b *Practical realization*

i—A platelet of 1 gram of precipitated pure sulphur is placed in the holder and is covered by an aluminium foil of 0.5 mm thickness. The β-activity of ^{32}P is measured after chemical separation with low β-chart counter with a background noise of 0.5 imp/min.

ii—The gold discs are mounted in the holder: in a piece of black lucite with thickness of 2 mm; two holes have been drilled with a diameter of 4.2 mm and a depth of 1.3 mm. In the first hole we put an aluminium holder with a golden plate having a thickness of 0.05 mm, a diameter of 3 mm and a weight of 6.8 mg. The cadmium holder put in the second hole also contains a golden disc with the same dimensions. The holders are closed with a lid of the corresponding material and at all sides the thickness is 0.5 mm.

The gamma activity of these discs is measured and their weight allows the determination of a dose of 1 rad in 15 minutes.

iii—The indium is glued at the interior of the film dosimeter holder. The same is done with the small LiF–teflon rod which first has been covered by a plastic protection.

Appendix   Determination of neutron dose in case of a criticality accident

The exact determination of the neutron dose implies the knowledge of the spectrum of the incident neutrons. This knowledge requires an important number of activation elements and dosimetry will be very complicated.

In order to allow a quick estimation of the dose soon after the accident, we choose a well known spectrum which is supposed to be a very close approach of the spectrum existing during a criticality accident.

The spectra which have been chosen, and which seem to be a very good approach, are:

—for fast neutrons: virgin fission spectrum

—for epithermal neutrons: $1/E$ spectrum between 0.12 eV and 1 MeV.

—for thermal neutrons: a Maxwellian distribution corresponding to a temperature of 20°C.

a Determination of the integrated neutron flux

i *Fast neutrons*—The integrated flux of fast neutrons equals

$$\phi t = \frac{A_s \times 32 \times 14 \times 8.64 \times 10^4}{0.603 \times 0.065 \times 0.693} = 1.425 \times 10^9 \, A_s \, \text{n/cm}^2 .$$

A_s is the sulphur activity in dps/g.

ii *Epithermal neutrons*—The integrated flux of epithermal neutrons equals:

$$\phi_{\text{epi}} t = \frac{A_{\text{epi}} \times 197 \times 2.7 \times 8.64 \times 10^4}{0.603 \times 1556 \times 0.693} \times \frac{1}{0.3} = 2.36 \times 10^5 A_{\text{epi}} \, \text{n/cm}^2 .$$

A_{epi} is the activity of the discs under cadmium in dps/g and the factor 0.3 is the resonance flux depression factor near a disc of gold having a thickness of 100 mg/cm².

iii *Thermal neutrons*—The integrated thermal neutron flux equals:

$$\phi_{th}t = \frac{A_{th} \times 197 \times 2.7 \times 8.6 \times 10^4}{0.603 \times 98.8 \times 0.693} \times \frac{1}{0.94} = 1.18 \times 10^6 \, A_{th} \, \text{n/cm}^2 \, .$$

A_{th} is the difference between the activity of gold under aluminium and under cadmium. The factor 0.94 is the thermal flux depression factor near a foil of gold having a thickness of 100 mg/cm^2.

b *Dose determination*

In order to convert neutron fluxes into dose values, the following conversion factors are to be applied:

for fast neutrons: 2.76×10^8 n/cm^2 per rad.
for epithermal neutrons: 2.81×10^9 n/cm^2 per rad
for thermal neutrons: 1.59×10^{10} n/cm^2 per rad.

This number of incident neutrons corresponds to the dose of one rad at the surface of the body, due to heavy charged particles. The dose of the thermal neutrons due to (n, γ) reactions in the hydrogen of the body has been accounted for by the gamma dosimeter.

References

1. Recommendation of the International Commission on Radiological Protection, Pergamon Press.
2. Report of the United Nations Scientific Comittee on the effect of atomic radiations, *Suppl.* **17** (A/3838) NY – Annex B IV pp. 59 (1958).
3. Considérations sur les problèmes de dosimétrie individuelle des radiations bêta, gamma et X. – H. Joffre, Symposium de Madrid, E.N.E.A.-O.C.E.D. (1963).
4. N. Parmentier, R. Boulenger, and G. Portal, "Problèmes de dosimétrie lors de l'accident du criticité survenu au rëacteur Vénus à Mol, en date du 30-12-65.
   I.R.P.A. – Rome 5-10 septembre 1966 (to be published by Pergamon Press).
5. Measurement of the dose absorbed in various organs, as a function of the external γ ray exposure. A. R. Jones, A.E.C.L. 2240 (1964).
6. Caractéristiques du nouveau dosimètre photographique développé au C.E.N. pour la dosimétrie individuelle.
   R. Boulenger—J. Delhove, CL 33 (1964). Les techniques de dosimétrie individuelle des radiations externes Symposium de Madrid 1963—E.N.E.A., O.E.C.D.-E.N.E.A. Symposium on Radiation Dose measurements. Their purpose, interpretation and required accuracy in radiological protection. Stockholm 12—16 June 1967. Emploi de films détecteurs pour la protection du personnel. A.I.E.A.—Vienna 1962—collection sécurité n° 8.

A survey of solid state dosimetry

JOHN R. CAMERON

*Departments of Radiology and Physics,
University of Wisconsin,
Madison, Wisconsin 53706*

INTRODUCTION

At the end of a two-week summer school dealing with solid state dosimetry, it is a difficult task to avoid repeating some of the material which was covered much more thoroughly by the earlier speakers. However, I believe there remain several areas to discuss. First, I would like to give more information relative to thermoluminescent dosimetry (TLD) and especially in regard to the characteristics of LiF used in TLD. Secondly, I would like to review briefly several of the solid state dosimetry systems which have not been discussed; that is, the *p–i–n* solid state detector, the organic scintillation detector, and dye systems.

CHARACTERISTICS OF LiF AS A DOSIMETER

At the present time, LiF (TLD-100)* is one of the important phosphors for measuring radiation using thermoluminescence. Because of this it seems worthwhile to spend a little more time discussing its characteristics. A typical glow curve is shown in Fig. 1. As has been mentioned earlier in this

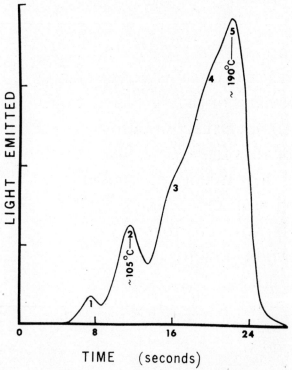

FIGURE 1   Typical glow curve of LiF (TLD-100) shortly after irradiating to 100 R. It had not received the 80° annealing

* Obtained from Harshaw Chemical Company, Cleveland, Ohio, U.S.A.

meeting, it suffers the disadvantage of having a more critical annealing procedure in order to reproduce its initial glow curve and sensitivity. This
annealing procedure is not complicated, but there are several aspects which
will now be outlined.

I. *Annealing at 400°C* for approximately one hour removes all of the TL
and also removes any sensitivity increase caused by the previous irradiation.
If the phosphor is embedded in teflon, it is not possible to give the 400°C
anneal because it would melt the teflon. However, the 400°C anneal can be
replaced by a longer annealing time of approximately $1\frac{1}{2}$ hours at 300°C.
After this annealing the samples should be cooled to room temperature, and
either II or III should be followed.

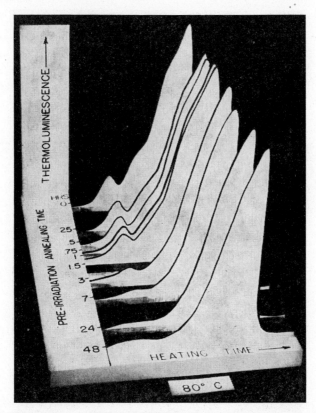

FIGURE 2 Effect of 80°C pre-irradiation annealing on the glow curve
of LiF (TLD-100). The samples were read about one hour after an exposure
of 100 R

II. *Annealing at 80°C* for approximately twenty-four hours greatly reduces the contribution of the low temperature peaks. (See Fig. 2). In the case of teflon-embedded LiF, the 80°C anneal appears to be more important than if powder or extruded LiF is used.[1]

III. *Annealing at 100°C* for 5–10 minutes after irradiation and before reading removes the low temperature peaks. This step may be used with or without II.

IV. *Annealing at 280°C* for one hour retains any sensitivity increase produced by previous irradiation. This annealing empties the main dosimetry traps but retains the increased sensitivity. More will be said about this subject in the next section.

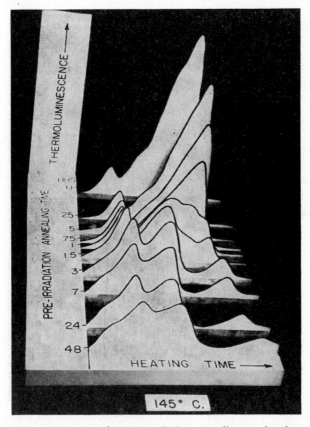

FIGURE 3   Effect of 145°C pre-irradiation annealing on the glow curve
of LiF (TLD-100)

V. *Annealing at 125° to 200°C* for a number of hours produces dramatic changes in the glow curves.[2] A typical example is shown in Fig. 3, where the phosphor has been annealed at 145°C for various periods of time, irradiated to 100 R, and the glow curve taken. Note the dramatic reduction in the higher temperature peaks.

Another unusual characteristic of LiF is its susceptibility to radiation damage.[3,4] LiF exhibits noticeable radiation damage at about 10^4 R; other TLD phosphors show little or no damage up to 10^6 R. The damage in LiF depends both upon whether the radiation is given in a single exposure or multiple exposures and also upon the quality of the radiation. However, this radiation damage does make possible the use of LiF as a dosimeter in the megarad region by measuring the amount of radiation damage. Care must be taken to calibrate the phosphor under the conditions being measured.

SUPRALINEARITY OF LiF

Figure 4 shows a typical TL *vs.* R curve for TLD-100. Figure 5 gives the TL/R *vs.* R curve for the same data. The increased sensitivity of LiF above 1,000 R seems especially puzzling. It appears to violate one of the common

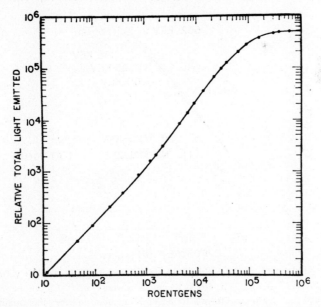

FIGURE 4 Integrated TL as a function of exposure for LiF (TLD-100)

experimental laws; that is, that one does not get something for nothing. Yet it is possible to increase the sensitivity of LiF (TLD-100) by about a factor of 6 following approximately 30,000 R of cesium-137 gamma radiation and one hour annealing at 280°C. Another type of LiF has shown sensitivity

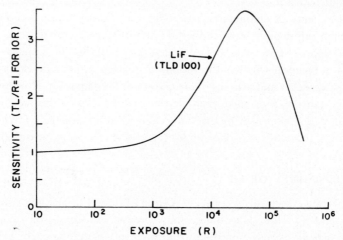

FIGURE 5   TL per roentgen as a function of exposure for LiF (TLD-100)

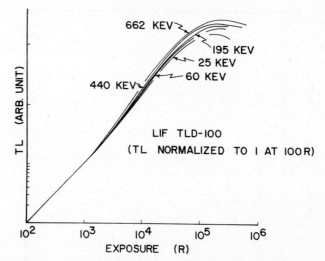

FIGURE 6   TL as a function of exposure for LiF (TLD-100) for various qualities of radiation. The 662 keV exposures were from ^{137}Cs gamma rays, the 440 keV quality was from a 1000 kVp X-ray unit, and the other qualities from a 250 kVp X-ray unit

increases of approximately 50.[5] In 1965 Naylor reported on the quality dependence of the supralinearity in LiF.[6] Naylor observed that the supralinearity was less for 130 keV radiation than for cobalt-60 γ-rays. We have further investigated this phenomenon, and a summary of our results for various qualities of x- and gamma radiation is shown in Fig. 6. In this case the usual energy dependence which appears at low keV has been removed by normalizing the TL per R to unity at approximately 100 R for all quali-

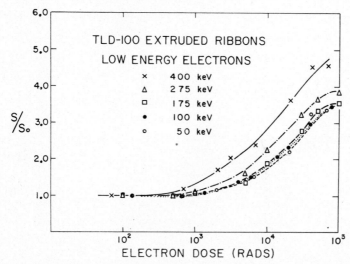

FIGURE 7 Sensitivity factors (S/S_0) of LiF (TLD-100) sensitized with low energy electrons as function of previous electron dose. S_0 is the TL response to 100 rads before any radiation and S is the TL response to 100 rads after the given electron dose and an annealing of one hour at 280°C

ties of radiation. Suntharalingam has recently investigated the phenomenon of supralinearity of LiF (TLD-100) in some detail.[7] He used a wide range of radiation qualities and monoenergetic electrons ranging from 50 keV to 33 MeV. Some of the results of his investigations are summarized in Fig. 7 and 8. His principal conclusions were: (1) The amount of supralinearity depends on the LET of the radiation, with low LET being the most effective for producing an increase of sensitivity, (2) The sensitivity increase is greater if measured by the height of the main dosimetry peak than if it is measured by the total integrated area under all of the glow peaks, (3) The sensitivity increase depended both upon the LET of the sensitizing radiation and also the LET of the testing radiation. A useful by-product of this investigation is the possibility of using this phenomenon as a method of determining the LET of unknown radiations, (4) The supralinearity was constant for all types of radiation having an LET less than that produced by cesium-137 gamma rays.

We first attributed the increased sensitivity to the creation of additional traps by the radiation.[5] Since the glow peak temperatures were the same for the sensitized phosphor as for the unsensitized phosphor, it seemed un-reasonable that we would be creating traps with identical physical charac-

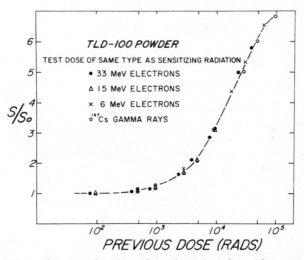

FIGURE 8 S/S_0 as a function of previous dose for various types of radiation. Low LET radiation produces approximately the same change in sensitivity (S/S_0) regardless of energy

teristics to those initially present; and this model was rejected. Our second model hypothesized the creation of recombination centers which were assum-ed to be initially in short supply. The TL spectra is assumed to be closely related to the characteristics of the recombination centers. However, when we measured the TL spectra before and after sensitization, they were found to be identical within experimental error. It seems unlikely we would create recombination centers that had the same energy levels as those originally present. Hence this model was also rejected.

Our present hypothesis is that the increased sensitivity is due to the pre-sence of a deep TL trap which has a higher cross-section for the capture of electrons during irradiation and thus will fill up first. After it has been filled at approximately 10,000 R, then the electrons produced during further ionization would have a greater probability of going to the traps which are observed in the normal glow curve. This hypothesis would suggest the presence of a TL trap at about 450 to 500°C which is not emptied at 280°C annealing but is emptied after an hour at 400°C. Investigations in our laboratory[8] showed that the stability of the increased sensitivity followed first order kinetics and could be fit to the Randall–Wilkins model.[9] Sensitized powder was annealed at various temperatures from 280 to 400°C for various periods of time, and it was found that the "sensitivity increase" decreased exponentially with time at each temperature. When the slopes of these decay curves were plotted *vs.* $1/T$ using the Randall–Wilkins model, the entity was found to have an activation energy of about 2 eV and a frequency factor of about 10^{12} sec^{-1}.

If the phosphor is sensitized by giving 30,000 R of cesium-137 gamma radiation, it is found that the increased sensitivity is not useful to measure low exposures because of the presence of background phosphorescence from a deep trap. A similar explanation may account for the supralinearity of lithium borate. In his paper, Schulman showed a curve demonstrating the increased sensitivity. In this case, annealing $Li_2B_4O_7$: Mn at 300°C for fifteen minutes retains the sensitivity, whereas annealing at 300°C for ninety minutes removes it. This would suggest the presence of a deep trap in the region of 350 to 400°C. Schulman also reported that when the phosphor is sensitized, it is not useful for low exposures because of phosphorescence from a deeper trap. Obviously, more research must be done on this subject.

In the above discussion no attempt was made to explain the LET dependence of the supralinearity. It appears that this is due to the finite number of traps available, and when high LET radiation is used, there is a considerable decrease in trapping efficiency because of the few traps available to a relatively large number of electrons. The analysis of the data by Suntharalingam may help clarify this point.[7]

USE OF TLD FOR INTERCOMPARISONS

Since the stored TL in LiF is stable for long periods of time, it has been used for intercomparison of radiation exposures between various laboratories.

The research groups at Memorial Hospital in New York and M. D. Anderson Hospital in Texas have used this successfully to compare the radiation doses from high energy x-ray and electron beams in the two institutions.[10] They used LiF powder for these experiments which has the drawback that it involves errors in measuring the mass of powder from which the TL is obtained. Despite this they were able to obtain standard deviations of the order of 2 % for a series of readings. The use of packaged TL dosimeters, such as the unit manufactured by M.B.L.E.*, might be more suitable for intercomparison purposes, since the amount of phosphor is essentially constant and the reproducibility should depend principally on the accuracy of the reading instrument. M.B.L.E. dosimeters use CaF_2 : natural as the TL phosphor, which does not show any decay of the stored energy in its main dosimetry peak. A preliminary study was made in co-operation with Mr. C. Brooke of M.B.L.E. and Mr. C. Wilson in our laboratory. The energy dependence of the dosimeters is not a problem if they are exposed to the same quality of radiation. For this purpose we chose cobalt-60 which is readily available in many laboratories. In the spring of 1967, Mr. Brooke mailed thirty of his standard dosimeters to us which he had previously calibrated in February and March and also recalibrated again in September after the experiment was completed. The calibration values for the various dosimeters are shown in Table I.

Note the small standard deviations for the calibrations. The calibration exposures in each case were 20 R, and the differences from this value were used to correct the experimental values. Groups of the dosimeters were exposed to known amounts of radiation in our laboratory over a one-month period. The exposure values were not known to M.B.L.E. although they knew that they were between 20 and 200 R. One unexposed dosimeter was included in each group. Table II shows the calculated exposures, the given exposures, and the percentage difference between these.

On the average the M.B.L.E. readings were only 0.75 % lower than the given exposures. Since the calibration of our cobalt unit is not known to better than to 2 %, this is surprisingly good agreement. This 0.75 % systematic difference has been removed from all readings in Table II, and the average deviation remaining is approximately 1.8 %. It should not be assumed that all of this error is due to the reading instrument, since some of it may be due to errors in the exposure. For example, dosimeters 1021 and 1047 were

---

* Manufacture Belge de Lampes et de Matèriel Electronique, Brussels, Belgium.

exposed at the same time to an assumed 40.1 R; and the two measured values are in good agreement but about 5% lower. It is quite possible that there was an error in exposure rather than in reading.

TABLE I   Calibration of M.B.L.E. dosimeters

Dos. Nr.	Response to a 20R exposure			
	Feb. 1967	March 1967	Sept. 1967	Mean value
1021	19.0	19.0	19.1	19.0
2	21.5	21.2	21.5	21.4
3	22.6	22.1	22.4	22.4
4	21.0	21.0	20.7	20.9
5	20.1	20.1	20.3	20.2
6	21.2	21.0	21.1	21.1
7	20.4	20.4	20.5	20.4
8	21.5	21.4	22.0	21.6
9	21.5	21.2	20.4	21.0
1030	20.8	20.4	20.9	20.7
1	21.6	21.4	21.1	21.4
2	21.6	21.0	20.7	21.1
3	18.4	18.6	17.9	18.3
4	22.1	21.9	22.3	22.1
5	19.6	19.6	19.6	19.6
6	20.4	20.2	20.7	20.4
7	20.0	19.7	19.7	19.8
8	18.4	18.5	18.5	18.5
9	21.0	20.7	20.8	20.8
1040	21.1	21.0	21.3	21.1
1	21.0	21.0	20.2	20.7
2	19.5	19.2	19.0	19.2
3	22.5	22.4	22.6	22.5
4	19.0	19.0	19.2	19.1
5	21.4	21.3	21.1	21.3
6	20.5	20.0	20.1	20.2
7	20.9	20.9	20.3	20.7
8	22.9	22.4	22.7	22.7
9	19.8	20.0	19.8	19.9
1050	21.6	21.4	21.4	21.5

It is quite likely that this accuracy can be improved and that other manu-facturers might have comparable accuracy for calibration purposes. We intend to make further studies during this coming year.

TABLE II   Results of M.B.L.E.-wisconsin intercomparison

Dosimeter Number	Given Exposure	Measured Value	Per cent Difference
1021	40.1	38.2	−4.5
2	0	0	—
3	189.9	195.4	+2.9
4	140.4	140.0	−0.3
5	90.3	91.2	+0.8
6	35.4	35.3	−0.3
7	184.0	188.4	+2.4
8	84.9	84.8	−0.1
9	0	0	—
1030	145.7	146.1	+0.3
1	134.8	132.0	−2.1
2	95.6	94.7	−0.9
3	195.6	191.4	−2.1
4	55.1	52.9	−4.0
5	0	0	—
6	49.5	49.4	−0.0
7	0	0	—
8	130.1	132.0	+1.5
9	80.6	81.6	+1.2
1040	179.6	183.4	+2.1
1	175.2	180.3	+2.9
2	25.4	26.2	+3.2
3	0	0	—
4	124.3	115.9	−3.5
5	74.9	74.6	−0.4
6	189.9	188.4	−0.8
7	40.1	38.3	−4.5
8	90.3	90.5	+0.2
9	140.4	141.0	−0.4
1050	0	0	—

FADING OF TL IN LiF

In 1964 Fowler *et al.* reported an unusual fading characteristic in various sources of LiF.[11] They reported a fading of 15 to 25 % in three weeks followed by some recovery in the following weeks. This unusual phenomenon was not observed in our studies. Because of the importance of the stability of the TL for dosimetry purposes, it was decided to do a co-operative ex-

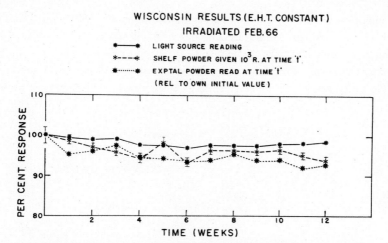

FIGURE 9 Wisconsin readings, photomultiplier voltage kept constant, data uncorrected for light standard changes. The solid line represents the light source reading, the dashed line the shelf powder and the dotted line the experimental powder

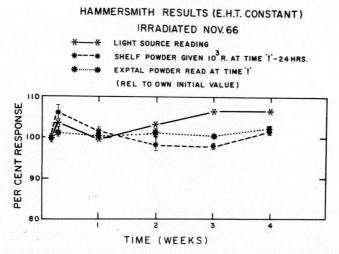

FIGURE 10 Hammersmith readings for same batch of LiF as in Fig. 9. Photomultiplier voltage kept constant, data uncorrected for light standard changes. The solid line represents the light source reading, the dashed line the shelf powder and the dotted line the experimental powder

45*

periment between Fowler's laboratory at Hammersmith Hospital, London, and our laboratories using the same batch of phosphor and the same technique.[12] A brief summary of the results are given in Figs. 9 and 10. It should be noted that the fading is less than 5 % in a twelve-week period. A summary of fading from various investigations is shown in Fig. 11. It would appear

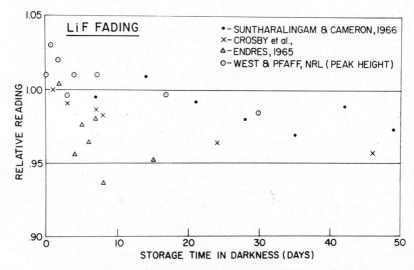

FIGURE 11   The results of different investigations on the fading characteristics of LiF. (Courtesy of F. H. Attix, NRL)

that the fading of the TL signal in LiF is not a serious problem for ordinary purposes. The explanation for the unusual fading and recovery reported by Fowler *et al.* is not known, but it is probably at least partly instrumental. There is also the possibility that they obtained some batches of powder which were not satisfactory. For the studies reported above,[12] they had replaced their photomultiplier tube and also kept their high voltage constant.

COMPARISON OF VARIOUS TLD PHOSPHORS

Table III summarizes the important dosimetry characteristics for the five TLD phosphors which are currently commercially available and are being used. This table will of course be out of date by the time of publication, but it will give the reader an idea of the diversity of the dosimetry material which is currently available.

TABLE III Characteristics of TLD phosphors

Characteristic	LiF	$Li_2B_4O_7$:Mn	CaF_2:Mn	CaF_2:nat	$CaSO_4$:Mn
Density (gm/cc)	2.64		3.18	3.18	2.61
Effective atomic no.	8.2	7.4	16.3	16.3	15.3
TL emission spectra (Å) range	3500–6000	5300–6300	4400–6000	3500–5000	4500–6000
maximum	4000	6050	5000	3800	5000
Temperature of main TL glow peak	195 °C	200 °C	260 °C	260 °C	110 °C
Efficiency at cobalt–60 (relative to LiF)	1.0	0.3	3	~23	~70
Energy response without added filter (30 keV/cobalt–60)	1.25	0.9	~13	~13	~10
Useful range	mR–10⁵ R	mR–10⁶ R	mR–3 × 10⁵ R	mR–10⁴ R	μR–10⁴ R
Fading	small <5%/12 wk	~10% in first month	~10% in first month	no detectable fading	50%–60% in the first 24 hrs
Light sensitivity	essentially none	essentially none	essentially none	yes	yes
Physical form	powder, extruded, Teflon-embedded, silicon-embedded, glass capillaries	powder, Teflon-embedded	powder, Teflon-embedded, hot-pressed chips, glass capillaries	special dosimeters	powder, Teflon-embedded

Although calcium sulfate suffers from a very rapid fading, it is still useful for certain applications because of its great sensitivity. It is possible to measure $5\,\mu R$ of ^{60}Co radiation using $CaSO_4$: Mn according to Mejdahl.[13]

In regard to lithium borate it is premature to predict its role in TLD, but at the moment it looks promising. It has an energy response which is quite good (see Fig. 12), and its sensitivity using a photomultiplier tube optimized for its longer wave length is comparable to that of LiF. At the present time, it is being produced commercially by at least two different concerns; and it

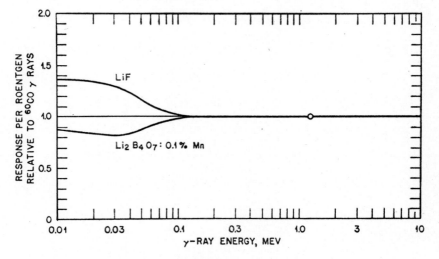

FIGURE 12   The theoretical response per roentgen as a function of photon energy showing a decrease in sensitivity at low keV for $Li_2B_4O_7$: Mn

appears that other recipes are being used in various laboratories. The usefulness of the phosphor will depend upon its availability with known characteristics at a reasonable cost. At the present time, it is not known how similar or reproducible the commercial products are. Since the production of lithium borate should be cheaper than LiF, it is hoped that the economics of TLD will be improved by its advent. It should be noted that at least one U.S. manufacturer* now claims to provide LiF at a low enough cost so that the samples may be discarded after use.

The lower limit of sensitivity for any of the systems will of course depend to a large extent upon the sensitivity of the detecting system. In addition, the

---

* Radiation Detection Company, Mountain View, California.

problem of comparing sensitivities from one phosphor to another is further complicated by the fact that for some phosphors it is conventional to use a peak reading technique, whereas for others the integration of the total TL is generally used. One should also keep in mind that the different spectral emission is going to cause variations in the sensitivities of the photomultiplier tube and thus also change the apparent sensitivity. In general, all TLD phosphors cover the range from milliroentgens to thousands of roentgens which is the region of greatest importance for health physics, radiobiology, and clinical applications of radiation.

The energy dependence of the various phosphors will also depend upon the shield surrounding the phosphor. The value given in the table is that for a phosphor with no shielding.

A SIMPLE TLD READER

There are at least 12 manufacturers of TLD reading equipment. (See Table IV).
We have tested all of the various units manufactured in the U.S. and find them all satisfactory for routine dosimetry purposes. I would assume that

TABLE 4   Manufacturers of TLD equipment

1. Amperex Electronic Corporation, Hicksville, L.I.N.Y. 11802.
2. Controls for Radiation Inc., 130 Alewife Brook Parkway, Cambridge, Mass. 02140.
3. Dynatron Electronics, St. Peter's Rd., Furze Platt, Maidenhead, Berks., England.
4. E. G. & G. Inc. (Edgerton, Germeshausen and Grier, Inc.), 130 Robin Hill Rd. Goleta, Calif. 93017.
5. EMI Electronic Ltd., Nucleonic Division, Hayes, Middlesex, England.
6. Harshaw Chemical Company, 1945 E. 97th St., Cleveland, Ohio 44106.
7. Madison Research & Development Laboratories, Inc., 7617 Donna Dr., Middleton, Wisc. 53562.
8. M.B.L.E. (Manufacture Belge de Lampes et de Matériel Electronique), Dosimetry Dept., 80 rue des Deux-Gares, Bruxelles 7, Belgium.
9. Radiation Detection Company, 385 Logue Ave., Mountain View, Calif. 94042.
10. Vakutronik Dresden, Dornbluthstrasse 14, 8021 Dresden, Deutsche Demokratische Republik.
11. Fa. Techn. Phys. Werkstaetten, Dr. Pychlan KG, Freiburg/Brsg., Loerracherstr. 7, Fed. Rep. of Germany.
12. Fa. Klemt, Elektr. Werkstaetten, D-8 Muenchen, Wotanstr. 68, Fed. Rep. of Germany.

the same is true of the European manufacturers. However, occasionally it is desirable to have equipment with more versatility and for a lower cost than that available commercially. We designed a simple reader which has the following characteristics:[14] (1) Simple and inexpensive to build, (2) Variable operating cycle and heating rate, (3) Able to accept a large variety of phosphor and sample sizes, and (4) Utilized standard laboratory auxillary components.

The reader is shown in Figs. 13 and 14. In Fig. 13 the device is shown in the position to load the sample, and in Fig. 14 it is shown in the reading

FIGURE 13   View of TLD reader in open position to permit placement of phosphor on heating pan

position. The long leading edge on the photomultiplier tube housing acts as a shutter while it is being slid over the sample. The somewhat unusual heating arrangement is shown in Fig. 15. A standard 150-watt projection bulb with a built-in mirror for focusing the light energy on the bottom of the thin, stainless steel heating element serves to raise the temperature in a nonuniform but reproducible manner up to approximately 400°C. A conventional "dimming control" is used to adjust the intensity of the light and thus the heating rate. The simple circuit for the reader is shown in

FIGURE 14 Photomultiplier tube in reading position. (Note that the view is from the opposite side shown in Fig. 13)

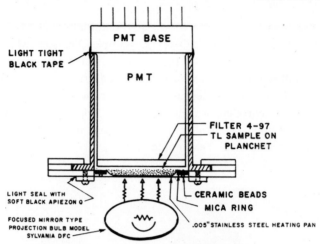

LIGHT TIGHT
BLACK TAPE

PMT BASE

PMT

FILTER 4-97
TL SAMPLE ON
PLANCHET

LIGHT SEAL WITH
SOFT BLACK APIEZON Q

CERAMIC BEADS
MICA RING

FOCUSED MIRROR TYPE
PROJECTION BULB MODEL
SYLVANIA DFC

.005"STAINLESS STEEL HEATING PAN

SECTION A-A SHOWING PMT HOUSING ALSO

FIGURE 15   Cross-sectional view through PMT in reading position to
show heating technique

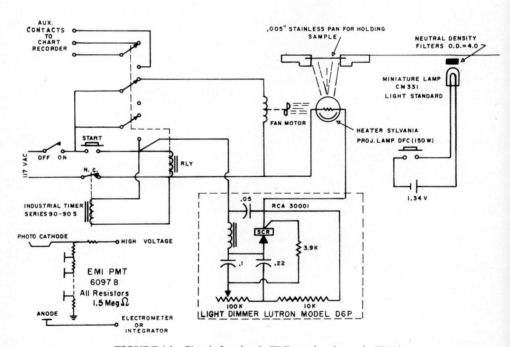

FIGURE 16   Circuit for simple TLD reader shown in Fig. 14

Fig. 16. This reader of course must be used with an auxillary high voltage supply and also some type of integrating or peak reading device such as an electrometer with a recording potentiometer. We have found the unit useful for teaching purposes and for investigations using large phosphor samples.

p–i–n SOLID STATE DETECTORS

The air ionization chamber was the first accurate technique for measuring ionizing radiation. Its importance is indicated by the fact that the definition for the roentgen as a unit of exposure is based on ionization in air. Ion chambers are still used extensively, but they often cannot be used in practical situations because of their large bulk. This problem can largely be overcome by using a solid ionization chamber rather than air. *pn* and *p–i–n* detectors

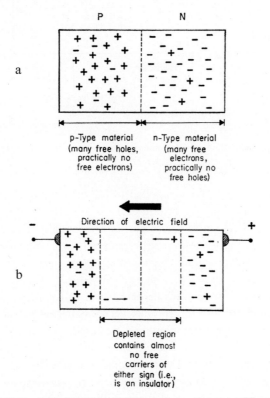

FIGURE 17   Schematic representation of a *pn* detector with and without an applied electric field (Courtesy of G. L. Miller, Reference 15)

are essentially solid ionization chambers whose density is approximately 1,800 times greater than air, thus permitting a great reduction in size. The basic operation of these detectors is shown in Fig. 17 and 18. Figure 17a shows the basic *pn* detector with positive charge carriers in one half and negative charge carriers in the other. When reverse bias is applied to this

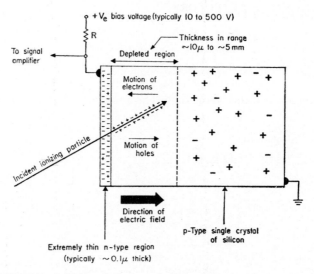

FIGURE 18   A lithium drifted *p–i–n* detector (Courtesy of G. L. Miller, Reference 15)

element, the positive carriers are pulled to the negative potential as shown in Fig. 17b; and the negative charge carriers are attracted to the positive potential, leaving a region in the center with essentially no charge carriers whose resistivity is that of the intrinsic material. If an ionizing event takes place in this charge-free region, the resulting charge carriers are attracted to the respective electrodes; and a pulse is produced whose magnitude is proportional to the ionization in the detector. The volume of a *pn* detector which is available for this purpose is very small, but it was discovered in 1958 that the sensitive area could be increased considerably by drifting lithium ions into the region which effectively increases the "intrinsic resistance" volume.[15] Figure 18 shows diagrammatically such a detector. These are often referred to as *p–i–n* detectors. It is now possible to have a thickness of the sensitive region of many millimeters which makes their use for gamma ray spectroscopy promising. *pn* and *p–i–n* detectors are basically rate devices, but it is possible to use them as integrating devices if the charge is collected during the time of exposure. More details on the principles and characteristics of these detectors is given in the chapter by Parker and Ref. 16 and 17.

SCINTILLATION DETECTORS

Normally scintillation detectors are not used for dosimetry purposes. The usual NaI(Tl) crystal used for gamma ray detection has a very pronounced energy dependence and is thus not very useful for dosimetry purposes.

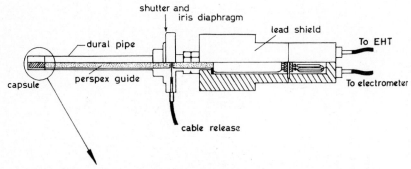

FIGURE 19   A plastic scintillation detector (Courtesy of F. O'Foghludha, Ref. 18)

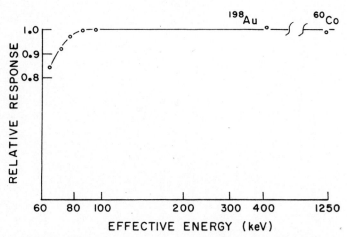

FIGURE 20   The energy dependence of a plastic scintillator as a function of X- or gamma ray energy (Courtesy of F. O'Foghludha)

TABLE V*   Coloration in plastics and dyes

UV absorption in plastics

Material	γ-ray exposure range (roentgens)	Maximum tested for rate-independence (R/sec)	Approximate precision ($\pm$%)	Post-irradiation change in optical density (24 hr) (%)	Comments	Reference
Polymethyl methacrylate	10^5–3×10^6	3×10^8	2	Rise $<5\%$	Peak at 2920 Å in certain commercial types. Useful	Boag *et al.* (1958); Boag (1963a, b)
Polyvinyl vinylidene	7×10^4–10^7	3×10^2	8	Rises over 100 days	Cannot be stabilized	Harris and Price (1961)
Polyvinyl chloride	5×10^5–6×10^6	?	10	Rises by factor of 2 over 3 days	Stabilized by annealing. Useful as thin film	Artandi and Stonehill (1958); Maul *et al.* (1961)
Polystyrene	10^6–2×10^8	?	2	50% fading in 4 days	Fading slight after 4 days. Mechanically good at very high doses	Fowler and Day (1955)
Polyethylene terephthalate	5×10^6–10^9	Exhibits rate dependence	5	No fading in 0.00025″ thickness	Rate dependence can be corrected for if times known	Boag *et al.* (1958); Ritz (1961)
Cellulose acetate	10^7–10^9	?	?	Small fading	—	Kügler and Scharmann (1959); Chapiro (1956)

Dyes in plastics, gels, etc.

Dye	Useful range (R)	Max dose rate	%	Stability	Remarks	Reference
Methylene blue in PVA	1–100 (?)	10^3 R/hr	?	—	Difficult to make	Oster and Broyde (1959)
Methylene blue in agar gel	5×10^2–5×10^4	?	?	—	Bubble N_2 to remove O_2-produced threshold	Day and Stein (1950)
Methyl yellow in CCl₄ and wax	5×10^2–4×10^3	?	?	—	Sensitive to UV and daylight	Potsaid and Irie (1961)
Tetrazolium blue in PVA	5×10^3–5×10^6	?	5	Stable	Useful	Taplin and Malin (1961)
Perspex Red 400	10^5–10^6	?	2	<5% fading	Useful, convenient	Day and Stein (1951) Whittaker (1963a, b)
Dyed cellophane	5×10^5–10^7	10^5 R/sec	10	Stable	Useful	Henley and Richman (1956)
Acid-base dye in PVC	5×10^5–10^7	?	5–10	?	Difficult to make	Henley and Miller (1951)
Dyes in porous glass	10^6–10^7	?	?	Stable	Further study needed	Brocklehurst (1959)

* From Fowler and Attix in Ref. 21.

However, the organic and plastic scintillator have a much more favorable energy response. Figure 19 shows the basic construction of a scintillation detector using a plastic phosphor.[18] The energy dependence of this phosphor is shown in Fig. 20. This type of detector is also basically a rate type, but it can be used as an integrating type by collecting the photomultiplier tube current for the period of interest. These devices have the advantage that they have a very large operating range, since they can be used in the pulse mode at very low dose rates and at high dose rates one can measure the photomultiplier tube current. It is also possible to reduce the light reaching the photomultiplier tube in order to further reduce the sensitivity.

DYE DOSIMETERS

In his paper, Schulman mentioned briefly dosimeter materials in which the radiation effect is basically permanent in nature although a small amount of fading may take place with time. The use of materials which change color following radiation has a long history. In fact, one of the early clinical dosimeters was based on this principle, and it was referred to as a pastille.[19] At the present time, there are many materials which exhibit a change in color due to radiation; and a summary of the characteristics of these materials is given in Table V.
You will notice that in general they are not very sensitive. One of the most sensitive of the systems is the methyl yellow in CCl_4 and wax. This material will respond to 500 R of x-rays, and it has proven useful in mapping radiation distributions for radiation therapy.[20]

The literature dealing with solid state dosimetry is now quite large, and besides the present volume the reader is referred to the new edition of *Radiation Dosimetry* by Attix *et al.*,[21] The proceedings of the International Conference on Luminescence Dosimetry[22] held in Stanford in 1965, and The Proceedings of a Symposium on Solid and Liquid State Dosimetry Applied to Biological and Medical Problems[23] held in Vienna in 1966. In addition to these general references, there are also a number of review articles.[24,25,26]

Much of the work on thermoluminescence dosimetry performed at the University of Wisconsin has been supported by U.S. Atomic Energy Commission Contract AT(11-1)-1105.

Bibliography

1. F. M. Lin, and J. R. Cameron, USAEC Rept. COO-1105-120 (1966).
2. D. W. Zimmerman, C. R. Rhyner, and J. R. Cameron: *Health Physics* **12**, 525 (1966).
3. M. J. Marrone and F. H. Attix, *Health Physics* **10**, 431 (1964).
4. K. P. Doppke and J. R. Cameron, AEC Rept. COO-1105-119 (1966).
5. J. R. Cameron, D. W. Zimmerman, and R. W. Bland, *Luminescence Dosimetry*, USAEC Rept. CONF-650637 (1965).
6. G. P. Naylor, *Phys. Med. Biol.* **10**, 564 (1965).
7. N. Suntharalingam, USAEC Rept. COO-1105-129 (1967).
8. C. R. Wilson, L. A. DeWerd, and J. R. Cameron, USAEC Rept. COO-1105-116 (1966).
9. J. T. Randall and M. H. F. Wilkins, *Proc. Roy. Soc. (London)* **A 184**, 366 and 390 (1945).
10. J. S. Laughlin, R. J. Shalek, J. Ovadia, and J. G. Holt, *Phys. Med. Biol.* **10**, 429 (1965).
11. J. F. Fowler, E. Shuttleworth, V. Svarcer, J. T. White, and C. J. Karzmark, *Nature* **207**, 997 (1965).
12. N. Suntharalingam, *et al.*, *Phys. Med. Biol.* **13**, 97 (1968).
13. J. Lippert and V. Mejdahl, *Luminescence Dosimetry*, USAEC Rept. CONF-650637 (1965).
14. J. Cameron, C. Vought, and M. Liss, USAEC Rept. COO-1105-133 (1967).
15. G. L. Miller, (1961) "The physics of semiconductor radiation detectors," *Brookhaven Lecture* Ser. No. 9 (BNL 699).
16. R. P. Parker and B. J. Morley, *Proc. Symp. Solid State and Chem. Rad. Dosimetry*, p. 167, IAEA, Vienna (1967).
17. R. P. Parker, *Proc. Symp. Solid State and Chem. Rad. Dosimetry*, p. 437, IAEA, Vienna (1967).
18. F. O'Foghludha, *Phys. Med. Biol.* **9**, 155 (1964).
19. F. W. Spiers, in *Radiation Dosimetry*, Spiers, F. W. and G. W. Reed, ed., Academic Press, New York (1964).
20. F. W. Lane, N. M. Johnson, and F. J. Bargoot, *Radiology* **82**, 827 (1964).
21. F. H. Attix and W. C. Roesch, Radiation Dosimetry, Second Edition, Vol. II, Academic Press, New York (1968).
22. F. H. Attix, ed. *Luminescence Dosimetry*, USAEC Rept. CONF-650637 (1965).
23. Proc. Symp. Solid State and Chem. Rad. Dosimetry in Medicine and Biology, IAEA, Vienna (1967).
24. J. H. Schulman, Prog. in Nuclear Energy Series, *Health Phys.* **1**, 150 (1959).
25. J. F. Fowler, *Phys. Med. Biol.* **8**, 1 (1963).
26. J. S. Laughlin, in *Radiation Dosimetry*, F. W. Spiers and G. W. Reed, ed., pp. 134–143, Academic Press, New York (1964).

Subject index